A HANDBOOK OF GENERAL EXPERIMENTAL PSYCHOLOGY

By

H. BANISTER

PHILIP BARD

W. B. CANNON

W. J. CROZIER

HALLOWELL DAVIS

J. G. DUSSER DE BARENNE

ALEXANDER FORBES

C. H. GRAHAM

H. HARTRIDGE

SELIG HECHT

HUDSON HOAGLAND

CLARK L. HULL

WALTER S. HUNTER

CARNEY LANDIS

K. S. LASHLEY

T. H. MORGAN

JOHN PAUL NAFE

EDWARD S. ROBINSON

CALVIN P. STONE

L. T. TROLAND

Edited by
CARL MURCHISON

PART I

ADJUSTIVE PROCESSES

NEW YORK / RUSSELL & RUSSELL

FIRST PUBLISHED IN 1934 BY

CLARK UNIVERSITY PRESS

REISSUED, 1969, BY RUSSELL & RUSSELL

A DIVISION OF ATHENEUM PUBLISHERS, INC.

BY ARRANGEMENT WITH CLARK UNIVERSITY PRESS

L. C. CATALOG CARD NO: 70-77679

PRINTED IN THE UNITED STATES OF AMERICA

PREFACE

Shortly after the publication in 1929 of *The Foundations of Experimental Psychology,* it became evident that it would be physically difficult to make single-volume revisions of that book. A choice had to be made between revising in several volumes or revising major subdivisions of the original book under separate titles. The latter choice was finally made and the first step in that direction was the publication of *A Handbook of Child Psychology.* The publication of this volume under the title, *A Handbook of General Experimental Psychology,* is the second step, and the complete enterprise will be consummated with the publication of *A Handbook of Social Psychology.*

Two or three of the chapters in this volume have not been greatly modified since their publication in *The Foundations of Experimental Psychology.* The explanation for this is that there has not been a great deal of new experimental material made available in the fields represented by these chapters. Several of the chapters have been entirely rewritten for this revision and several of the chapters are entirely new. The Editor is gratified to announce that Dr. Troland finished the revision of his chapter just a few weeks before his death.

There has not been any attempt to include chapters on the so-called higher mental processes. The explanation is that the divisions of the volume are vertical and not horizontal.

The Editor wishes to express his gratitude to the authors who have labored in this enterprise and to Dr. Luberta Harden, who has prepared the manuscripts for the printer and supervised the progress of the book through the press. The subject index has been made by Dr. Wallace Craig.

CARL MURCHISON

CLARK UNIVERSITY
WORCESTER, MASSACHUSETTS
JULY 17, 1934

174233

TABLE OF CONTENTS

PART I. ADJUSTIVE PROCESSES

PART I
ADJUSTIVE PROCESSES

CHAPTER 1

THE STUDY OF LIVING ORGANISMS

W. J. Crozier

Harvard University

AND

Hudson Hoagland

Clark University

"Scientific psychology is a part of physics, or the study of nature;
it is the record of how animals act. Literary psychology is the art
of imagining how they feel and think."
Santayana, Scepticism and Animal Faith

I

Introduction

The description and interpretation of the properties of living organisms encounter hazards more varied and insidious than those attending the scientific treatment of non-living objects. Even in the latter case, to be sure, description and interpretation are statements of properties of the observer and the theorist. By science one understands the unresting attempt to obtain a comprehensive, satisfying account of the universe and all that it contains; the essence of this account, as science, is that it must be based upon the fewest possible assumptions. Why such an attempt should be found satisfying presents a problem into which we need not now inquire. It has been most successfully pursued in the realm of physics. Until about 1800 physics had been concerned with the formulation of a conception of phenomena as they might be described in terms of "forces" acting between one body and another. More recently it has come to deal with ideas of a higher order of complexity, according to which the energy of a material system is regarded as controlled by the configuration and motion of the system; it is thus concerned notably with aspects of physical systems transcending any complete analysis of details. The parallel with the problem of biology is suggestive. From the examination of the properties of elementary aspects of conduct or behavior, it is probable that progress may be made toward the real understanding of more involved, more complexly integrated, features of organic action and control.

The biological system presented by a single individual, no less than that which may be conceived to be presented by any association or society of different individuals (Wheeler, 1928), is obviously not a "thing," a single event, but a system of *relations*. It is these relations which must be defined through investigation. To do this there is required a pro-

[3]

cedure which is essentially quantitative and mathematical in character. Quantitative treatment is not merely a matter of numbers and arithmetic. It is fundamentally and primarily concerned with relationships of functional dependence. This view is attractive because of its historical success in physics; it is also easily supported by appeal to ordinary sense. The common-sense process of defining units gives this view great force. "The most important step in the progress of every science is the measurement of quantities. Those whose curiosity is satisfied with observing what happens have occasionally done service by directing the attention of others to the phenomena they have seen but it is to those who endeavor to find out how much there is of anything that we owe all the great advances in our knowledge" (Maxwell, 1908). The measurement of quantities, which is necessary for the production of statements of functional dependence, implies units of measurement possessing definite dimensions, using "dimensions" in the sense of physics. The relationships between measured features of the performance of an organism and values of a known controlling variable supply the materials for statements of functional dependence. To be really satisfying and productive, these formulations must be rational, not merely empirical; the constants they contain must have a testable significance.

Everything which a living organism does, including, for example, the events of its development, might be termed an aspect of its "behavior"; such an attitude leads to vagueness, and the several attempts which have been made at the general discussion of the conduct of organisms on this basis have not been exactly fruitful. The employment of incompletely worked-out analogies between properties of non-living systems and of organic conduct, such as one frequently discovers in discussions of the "emergent" quality of organisms and of the configurationist modes of interpretation, is neither satisfying nor in any sense intrinsically productive. What is required is formulation of conduct in such a way as to permit measurable prediction of behavior. It is unfortunately true that many persons, no matter how intelligent, logically acute, and imaginatively alive they may be, are frequently paralyzed by the sight of a mathematical symbol. It has been the case in biology that the complexity of its phenomena has, on the whole, tended to encourage the emotional bias of this type of worker. It is sufficient to point out, however, that it appears to be an inescapable phase in the development of biology that there must ensue a long period of at first more or less unsuccessful attempts to obtain functional formulations of the properties of organisms before it will be worth while to discuss the question as to whether non-physical attributes must be assigned to them.

It is sometimes supposed that the changing viewpoint in modern physics, altering the conception of nineteenth-century mechanics, is unfavorable to those who have worked for a "mechanistic" interpretation of vital processes; the efficient reply is that the aim of mechanistic interpretation is to attain a basis for the common treatment of living and of non-living objects. The emotional rebellion at the thought that man may be a machine is largely based upon an inadequate conception of what a machine may be; nor does the development of now outworn notions about physical "machines" imply in any proper sense that these must be granted organic or quasi-biological properties. For this reason, one need not devote much time to the rather futile quarrel supported by those who stress the "non-mechanical," by implication non-mathematical, properties of organisms. The behavior of organisms presents from this standpoint what is unquestionably the most difficult of biological themes. This is in one sense its major attraction. If we consider for a moment the parallel provided by the state of theory dealing with facts of inheritance as it existed previous to 1900, and compare this with the solid, rational, theoretic structure of genetics which has been reared in the short time elapsing since then, on the basis of what is essentially a simple mathematical conception (Morgan, 1926) embodied in a theory of the gene which is in reality independent of any chromosomal or other crude mechanism, it is easily seen that there is abundant ground for encouragement.

Such advances are at bottom the result of a persisting tendency to extend to the most complex phenomena the general principle of the uniformity of nature and of the continuity of physical laws in space and time. The deduction of the composition and physical state in the interior of a distant star presents no more serious logical difficulty than does the interpretation of the behavior of an organism. In fact, there are certain instructive similarities. In the case of a distant star, the analysis must be made by indirect methods, since the material of which it is composed is not directly open to experimental handling. With an organism, the properties which may most concern us are more than likely to be obliterated as the result of any attempt at gross interference—again, the requisite analysis must proceed by somewhat indirect channels. Astrophysical deductions, the results of "boring into distant stars," can be checked by testing the consequences of the mathematical implications; as yet, no monumental failure has attended this procedure, which involves (again as in the case of an organism) descriptions of systems which are altering as a function of time. Similarly, the results of analysis of the conduct of organisms are also to be checked by examination of the mathematical implications of the treatment as they permit predictions open to test.

Historically, and perhaps largely owing to the association of academic philosophy with psychology, the development of such an attitude has been hampered by the impulse to work from a "general," all-inclusive, theoretical interpretation, before data making an interpretation possible have been obtained. To secure such data is a primary task of the experimental investigation of conduct. At one time it was supposed that this undertaking would proceed most easily on the basis of experiment with the allegedly simpler unicellular (better, non-cellular) forms, in which "elements" of conduct in general might be recognizable. But it is easily seen that the investigation of irritability and transmission ought to be most productive when one is able to deal with living structures in which these particular activities are available in the most unobscured, isolated, best-developed ways. It is upon the results of such investigations that it becomes possible to construct an increasingly more and more complete picture of the events which succeed one another in the chain of disturbances initiated in a sense-organ, transmitted over nervous or nerve-like pathways, entering into competition with other similar disturbances in the central nervous system of higher animals, and ultimately leading to the release of energy in muscles, glands of various kinds, and other effector parts. The attempt to obtain laws of *behavior*, however, which shall be descriptive of behavior as such, can probably not be obtained with sufficient completeness by that procedure. It is specifically with this problem that we shall be concerned, seeking to illustrate (1) the definition and interpretation of elements of organic performance through their relationships to magnitudes of known variables; (2) the examination of such typical formulations by synthesis of more complex situations, as a test of predictive power; and (3) the real significance of variability of performance.

II

ANALYSIS OF CONDUCT—SIMPLE TROPISMS

Elements of action in organic behavior which may submit to rational quantitative treatment were recognized by Loeb (1918) in the machine-like tropistic orientations of plants and animals. Since the anatomical basis for such actions is quite different in diverse organisms, but the behavior element dynamically identical, it is clear that the quantitative formulations arrived at refer to the *behavior*, and not to specific accidents of structure (such as the possession of a nervous system).

The primary assumption of the tropism doctrine is that, in instances properly regarded as falling under this description, the enforced movements resulting in orientation cease when the organism is equally affected upon its two symmetrical sides (Loeb, 1890, 1897, 1918). Such movements are regarded as forced because they are inevitable from the structure of the reacting organism and the presence of appropriate substances in its sense-organs (or in one or more areas serving as loci for excitation) symmetrically arranged. The term "forced movement" was at first introduced into such discussions from brain physiology (Loeb, 1918), but the wider understanding of the underlying notion more easily permits embracing relevant features of the behavior of plants and lower organisms, as well as those in certain higher animals, within the scope of a single interpretation. Dynamically, the circling motions of a dogfish forced to swim in spirals to the right when its left lower optic lobe has been removed are entirely comparable to the predominantly right-hand direction of swimming (Parker, 1914) in an uninjured dogfish with its left nasal sac plugged with cotton and in the presence of juices diffusing from crushed meat. The tonus of swimming muscles on one side has, in the first case, been lowered by interruption of nervous pathways, and on the heteronomous side reflexly increased; in the second case the difference in tonus has been brought about by continuous unilateral excitation.[1]

A quietly creeping meal-worm (larva of *Tenebrio*), or a diplopod such as *Spirobolus*, responds to the impress of unsymmetrical tensions on its musculature, as when the body is bent in an arc, by a prompt move-

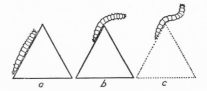

FIGURE 1

STEREOTROPIC ORIENTATION OF LARVAL *Tenebrio* (*a, b*, SUCCESSIVE POSITIONS) AND REFLEX HOMOSTROPHIC ORIENTATION RELEASED (AT *c*) WHEN SOURCE OF CONTACTS IS REMOVED
(From *J. Gen. Physiol.*)

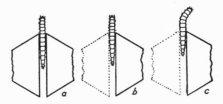

FIGURE 2

BALANCED ACTION OF EQUAL BILATERAL CONTACT SHOWN IN PURSUIT OF A STRAIGHT COURSE (*a*)
Removal of contact plate on one side (*b*) is immediately followed by stereotropic bending (*c*).
(From *J. Gen. Physiol.*)

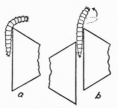

FIGURE 3

A LARVA IN STEREOTROPIC ORIENTATION TOWARD UNILATERAL CONTACT (*a*) RESPONDS BY LESSER STEREOTROPIC CURVATURE WHEN A LESS EXTENSIVE CONTACT IS INTRODUCED AT THE OTHER SIDE (*b*)
(From *J. Gen. Physiol.*)

---

[1] Cf. Loeb (1918), Kafka (1914), Hempelmann (1926), Oppenheimer and Pincussen (1925-27), and Rose (1929) for convenient bibliographic citations, and the detailed annual review in Köhler (1925 to date).

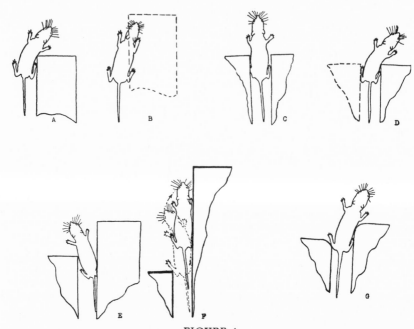

FIGURE 4

A. Stereotropic orientation of young rat or mouse at the corner of a box along one side of which it has been creeping.

B. A young rat or mouse has been creeping in contact with the side of a box (dashed outline); the removal of the box results in partial orientation toward that side.

C. A young rat or mouse creeping in a passage-way between two boxes, just wide enough to permit gentle contact on either side during the animal's swaying progression, is found to emerge from the passage-way without orientation. Equivalent bilateral stimulations prevent stereotropic turning.

D. An individual emerging from equal bilateral contacts with two boxes proceeds in a straight path, without orientation; but if one of the boxes be removed (dashed outline), it promptly orients toward the remaining one.

E. Contact at one side with the corner of a box may lead to orientation toward that side, apparently due, in part at least, to more intense tactile excitation than is provided by a continuous flat surface (or by smoothly rounded corners).

F. When such a corner is passed, orientation persists toward a continuing contact on the opposite side.

G. When blocks providing lateral contacts are of unequal extent, the young rat or mouse orients toward the side of more extensive contacts but does not completely turn the corner unless the difference in extent of the two blocks is more than half the length of the animal. This, the expected result from a tropistic standpoint, is obtained when the corners of the contact blocks are smoothly rounded.

(From *J. Gen. Physiol.*)

ment of the anterior end which, as with an earthworm similarly treated (Morgulis, 1910), results in the alignment of the axis of this end parallel to that of the posterior part (Moore, 1922-23; Crozier and Moore, 1922-23; Crozier, 1923-24*a*, 1923-24*b*). Contact with a lateral surface inhibits this response (Figure 1). The balanced action of equal zones of contact on either side results in the pursuit of a straight course (Figures 2 and 3). Similar effects are obtainable in other forms, for example, in young mice and rats (Figure 3); they illustrate the manner in which asymmetric excitation results in forced redistributions of tension in orienting structures, these differentials ceasing when excitation has become equalized on the two sides. Differences in structure from one kind of animal to another do not alter the fundamental character of the response.

The theory of the phototropic movements of insects considers the forced orientations under illumination as due to the effect of asymmetric sensory excitation upon the postures of opposed appendages (Holmes, 1905, 1916; Garrey, 1918-19; Kropp and Enzmann, 1933-34). It is not always clear to what extent the frequencies of phasic limb movements (Cole, 1922-23) and the postural influence upon effective lever action

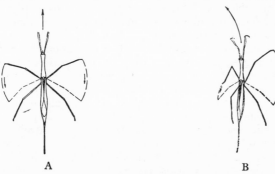

A   B

FIGURE 5

A. SHOWING POSITIONS OF THE LOCOMOTOR APPENDAGES IN A SWIMMING *Ranatra* FROM WHICH BOTH EYES HAVE BEEN REMOVED

The two limbs of a pair move synchronously and in phase. At the conclusion of the stroke (dashed lines) the legs are slightly more extended than at the beginning of the stroke (full lines); as the beat of the anterior legs is concluded, the posterior pair is moved to a position comparable to the initial position of the anterior limbs; thus the two pairs move in alternate phase.

B. ASYMMETRIC TONUS IN LEGS OF A SWIMMING *Ranatra* FROM WHICH ONE EYE (RIGHT) HAS BEEN REMOVED

The legs on the blind side assume positions comparable to those of the appendages of a completely de-eyed *Ranatra* (Figure 5, *A*). On the eye side the tonus of leg flexors is increased. This results in hydrostatic tilting of the whole body at rest. In swimming, the two legs of a pair move synchronously but the greater flexor tonus on the eye side is maintained throughout the execution of the swimming stroke, so that the extension of the left legs during the propulsive motion (arrows) is less than on the relatively atonic right side. The animal accordingly swims continuously in a circle toward the eye-bearing side.

(From *J. Gen. Physiol.*)

of the legs in progression have been separated as they are concerned in the turning movements (Mast, 1923, 1924; Baldi, 1922; Baldus, 1927). However, in sufficiently uncomplicated cases the rôle of posture is obvious. If one eye of the water scorpion *Ranatra* be removed (or covered), the insect under water continues for a long period to circle toward the remaining eye if it is illuminated from above. During creeping, in air or on vegetation under water, the opposite legs of each locomotor pair are used alternately, the diagonally opposite legs being in phase; but in swimming under water the legs of a morphological pair work synchronously, in phase, the two pairs alternating in the execution of the propulsive stroke. If both eyes have been covered or removed, and the animal put in a large cylindrical tank illuminated from a single source of light directly above, the *Ranatra* stays near the surface and moves irregularly. But if only one eye has been prevented from receiving excitation, the positively phototropic swimming, due to the greater extension of the legs upon the blind side, results in circus movements toward the side of the functional eye (Figures 4 and 5).

It should not be supposed that emphasis upon activities of this type seeks to imply that all the movements of organisms are tropistically regulated. A point which will bear restating is the distinction Loeb first drew between *phototropic* movements and responses to change of intensity of light (Loeb, 1918); the latter, for example, in the case of motile forms reacting negatively to increase of illumination, produces "shock reactions" and aggregation in relatively shaded areas—and has nothing to do with the phototropism, positive or negative, which they may also exhibit at the same time (Crozier and Arey, 1918; Arey, 1921). In many cases major features of the behavior of animals, involving actions of prime significance for their perpetuation, are obviously consistent with modes of tropistic response which experiment under controlled conditions may reveal, but it is also true that curious instances are encountered in which there exists superficially a striking exception to this state of affairs. The behavior of *Onchidium floridanum,* for example, exhibits a number of arresting features (Crozier and Arey, 1919-20; Arey, 1921). This is a small shell-less pulmonate which lives in holes and crevices of the limestone shore between tidal limits. Each inhabited cavity shelters, when the tide is in, a group of the mollusks. As low water approaches, and if the weather is fair, but only once in the twenty-four hours and only during daylight, the animals emerge one at a time from the "nest" and wander for limited distances over the algal carpet of the rocks, on which they feed. Before the tide rises again, the individuals emanating from any one nest simultaneously return to that nest. Certain possible factors in the control of this "homing" behavior have been considered. In the laboratory or on an artificial surface in the field *Onchidium floridanum* is negatively heliotropic. It also reacts definitely to quick reduction of the intensity of light. The tentacular eyes are of no significance for these responses, which are mediated by integumentary receptors. Yet the mollusks emerge from their crannies only in the daytime, and in their natural movements on the shore they are in no sense guided or directed by the light. It was possible to show that the phototropic responses are completely inhibited during the creeping of these animals upon the rocks immediately surrounding the specific home site. Removed to a new location, whether inhabited or not by other colonies of the same form, *Onchidium floridanum* is at the mercy of its heliotropic response and of its retractive response when shaded; it is thereby prevented from finding a new "home" before the tide rises, and becomes washed away. In Cuba, upon the other hand, another species of *Onchidium* has been found (Crozier and Navez, 1930) to occur only in shaded places, and is free from the necessity of returning to its specific home, although otherwise its behavior is similar; the natural movements of this form on the shore are entirely consistent with its negative heliotropism.

The fact that tropistic reactions may be modified through experience or experimental treatment does not at all alter their significance, remove their mechanical nature, or destroy their utility for analytical purposes when they are exhibited. The modification, or, as in the case of *Onchidium,* the suppression of such responses, presents merely an inviting opportunity to discover the molecular mechanisms whereby such modification may be produced. The chemical control of phototropic movements and of their positive and negative character (Loeb, 1918) remains to be developed as a means to this end. A quantitative treatment of tropistic behavior is essential if the understanding of conduct is to be furthered in this respect. By "quantitative" one does not imply simply that which has to do either with numbers of observations or of animals, nor yet merely numerical data which may be submitted to statistical treatment. One does imply the discussion of numerical data which may be accorded analysis in terms of intelligible theory; the "quantitative" has significance in the light of functional interrelationships which the analysis may reveal, and of the tests which it suggests.

From this standpoint the recognition and the characterization of a particular tropism and its modifications in a specified organism is scarcely an exciting end in its own right. The tropism in question may become, however, a powerful instrument of analysis under suitable conditions. If it can be shown, for example, that in controlled circumstances the direction of movement of given animals may be predictably determined even when more than one orienting force is at work, we then have a means (as yet in an elementary state of development) whereby a real test of theories of oriented movement may be applied. Illustrations of this will be given. Moreover, this general procedure may be employed to obtain information about central nervous states and conditions not otherwise approachable; the mechanism whereby the central nervous system of a given animal functions in the integration and adjustment of the effects of competing modes of excitation, originating in different peripheral areas, must be undertaken by some such method.

If the tropistic behavior of animals is in any real degree that of orienting machines, it must be possible to deal with such problems as the following: Knowing the orienting efficiency of light of a particular composition, from a single source, it should be possible to predict the form and amount of the orientation when lights from two similar sources play upon the animal. The question is but deceptively simple, yet in certain essentials it can be answered. The answer is based chiefly upon the single assumption of the tropism concept, namely, that forced orientation ceases when equivalence of bilaterial excitation is attained; it involves quantitative knowledge of the connection between light intensity and orienting efficiency, with certain implicit assumptions (which can be tested) regarding the central nervous interplay between excitations of different peripheral origins.

In the negatively phototropic slug *Limax maximus* the eyes are the effective photoreceptors. With illumination from above, a dark-adapted *Limax* from which one eye has been removed circles continuously toward the non-stimulated side. The circling posture is continuously maintained until photic adaptation supervenes. The posture of the body is due to differences in the maintained tensions of the muscles of the two sides of the body-wall. The tension difference is maintained only under illumination, and disappears in darkness. With care to insure absence of air currents, odorous stimulation, and the like, and with proper selection of phototropic individuals, a measure of the orienting posture is easily secured. The experiment is particularly significant because the muscular mechanisms for creeping and for turning are structurally distinct in such gastropods (Arey, 1921; Crozier and Navez, 1930), although the two are nervously interrelated in such a way that faster progression (controlled by the release of pedal waves) is correlated with less effective turning. The two mechanisms can be separated in an analytical way through their relations to temperature (Crozier and Federighi, 1924-25a, 1924-25c) and in other ways. With comparable speeds of progression, the phototropic effect is measured by the ratio *degrees turned per centimeter of path*, which describes the slug's posture.

While it might seem to be a matter of simple common sense, it is nevertheless necessary to emphasize that for such experiments selection of individual animals is just as necessary as control of light intensity and of temperature. A confusion unquestionably exists as to the objective of such experiments; it seems to be supposed at times that the purpose is to examine a random lot of individuals of a particular sort and to note whether they are phototropic. This kind of inquiry can result, at best, in statements to the effect that under such-and-such conditions *x per cent* of the organisms were seen to respond, which tells us precisely nothing about the character or the measurable attributes of the response when it is exhibited. At the moment we are concerned to discover the relation between light intensity and orienting effect in phototropic *Limax*, and non-reactive individuals [such as are easily produced at will by certain experimental treatments (Crozier and Libby, 1924-25)] are of no interest.

It turns out that the circus-movement effect, expressed as the amount of turning per unit length of path, is directly proportional to the logarithm of the light intensity, over a fairly wide range (Figures 6, 6*a,* and 7). This kind of relation is often labeled "Weber's law," apparently with the thought that it is thereby explained. The status of the Weber-Fechner formulation in relation to photic excitation has been adequately treated by Hecht (1918-19, 1919-20*a*, 1919-20*b*, 1922-23, 1923-24, 1924-25); certain more general considerations will be referred to subsequently. It is important to realize that such empirical relationships may be useful, where formulations of greater theoretic implication are clumsy or unmanageable. There are other methods whereby the orienting power of light from a single source can be expressed (Wolf and Crozier, 1927-

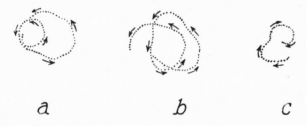

$$a \qquad\qquad b \qquad\qquad c$$

FIGURE 6

TYPICAL PHOTOTROPIC CIRCUS MOVEMENT TRAILS OF *Limax*
(From *J. Gen. Physiol.*)

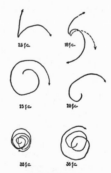

FIGURE 6*a*

CIRCUS MOVEMENT TRAILS OF YOUNG RATS WITH ONE EYE (THE RIGHT)
REMOVED, THE EYELIDS OF THE OTHER NOT YET PARTED

Illumination from a single source, vertically above the center of the creeping stage. Intensities of illumination (foot candles) measured photometrically at the creeping stage. Scale 1:10. These trails are typical. The amplitude of the orientation movement increases with the intensity of the light. This is in part due to the fact that the animal creeps little but turns constantly. The records were obtained by following the positions of a marked spot at shoulder level on the animal's back as seen against a system of coordinates in white lines upon a black cloth covering the creeping stage.
(From *J. Gen. Physiol.*)

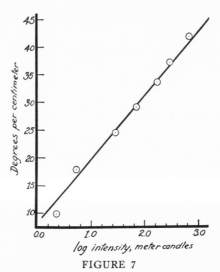

FIGURE 7

DATA FROM EXPERIMENTS BY CROZIER AND COLE ON THE CIRCUS MOVEMENTS
OF THE SLUG *Limax*

One eye-bearing tentacle has been amputated; illumination is from directly above;
the measure of circling posture is given by *angular deflection per unit length
of path;* mean values of this quantity are plotted against corresponding values
of log I, where I is the intensity of illumination at the photoreceptive surface of
the remaining tentacle.   Light-adaptation being slow, the circling movement should
continue for some time, which is the fact; and the tropistic effect should be
independent of the animal's position, inasmuch as only one eye is functioning.
The effect is expressed as a difference in tension reflexly established on the two
sides of the body, continuously maintained during continuous excitation.   This
postural effect is proportional in magnitude, over the range of illuminations
used, to log I.

28; Crozier and Wolf, 1927-28; Yagi, 1927-28), but their explanation
involves additional considerations.   In general, however, they lead to
two forms of relation in different cases: The orienting power is directly
proportional to the light intensity or, more commonly, to its logarithm.
Both relations are consistent with elementary photochemistry and with
the fact that for the production of a given threshold (measured) photosensory effect with light of a given intensity the Roscoe-Bunsen law (or
Talbot's law) is adequately obeyed (Loeb, 1918; Hecht, 1919-20a, 1919-
20b; Northrop and Loeb, 1922-23).

When circus-movement effects are studied under proper conditions
(Cole, 1922-23; Crozier and Federighi, 1924-25a, 1924-25c), the illumination of the organism does not change during orientation, and the
resulting data should permit one to predict the form of the resulting
pathway when a phototropic organism is illuminated from one side.   In
a number of cases in which it has been attempted to investigate circus
movements on a horizontal surface with horizontal illumination it has

been recorded that a phototropic animal with one eye covered at first performs circus movements in creeping toward the light, but that after successive trials it may come to creep directly toward the light. It has been suggested that this phenomenon simulates learning and might be due to the gradual elimination of motions tending to carry the animal away from the light, and thus to a kind of psychic effect connected with repeated excursions toward the light. It has been shown, however, that under these conditions there intervenes a simple photic adaptation bringing about a lessened effectiveness of the excitation upon the functional eye (Crozier and Pincus, 1926-27b; Clark, 1928). The case is sometimes complicated by the kind of effect which has led to von Buddenbrock's (1917, 1918, 1933) conception of *Lichtkompassbewegung,* namely, that since a positively phototropic caterpillar may approach a small source of light in its own plane along a *spiral* path even, with one or more turnings about the light, it is really responding in such a way as to put its body axis at a constant angle to the light rays reaching it from moment to moment. This behavior has been examined by Crozier and Stier in larvae of *Malacosoma* (tent-caterpillars). A path such as von Buddenbrock requires would be a logarithmic spiral, which has well-known simple properties. The actual paths do not exhibit these properties. Therefore the *Lichtkompass* effect need not be invoked in such cases, and, indeed, is no explanation. The spiral paths are, in fact, due to the simultaneous exhibition of two separately identifiable modes of response. The orienting effect of the light increases the tonus of longitudinal muscles on the illuminated side, and the bending of the caterpillar's body so produced evokes the body-straightening movements which constitute the homostrophic reflex (Morgulis, 1910; Moore, 1922-23, 1923-24; Crozier and Moore, 1922-23; Crozier, 1923-24a, 1923-24b). The animal consequently proceeds under the simultaneous influence of two directive vectors—one, increasingly preponderant with closer approach to the light, directed to the light and varying as the inverse square of the distance (or its logarithm); the other, leading by itself to tangential motion with constant speed, is expressible as of constant magnitude. The actual path represents a continuous adjustment between these two forces, and trails of the kind found are easily obtained by graphical construction on the assumption that they are the efficient controlling elements; and the equations of such loci have been obtained.

It is sometimes voiced as a reproach that the simplification involved in quantitative experimentation requires "unnatural conditions"—whatever "unnatural" may be supposed to mean. An instructive instance is supplied by the phototropic circus movements of *Limax.* Experiments over a range of temperature show that in the performance of circus movements under light of constant intensity two chief factors are involved—the rate of creeping and the amplitude of turning. The structural basis for each is distinct, but the two are functionally interrelated. Within a zone of temperatures in the immediate neighborhood of 16°-15°C., which probably would be commonly accepted as "normal" for this animal, the

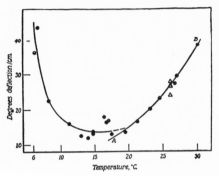

FIGURE 8

THE RATIO, *Degrees Deflection*: *Cm. Length of Path,* IN CIRCUS MOVEMENTS
OF *Limax* UNDER CONSTANT VERTICAL ILLUMINATION, AS A
FUNCTION OF TEMPERATURE

Several independent determinations shown as triangles.   The curve *A-B* is a
theoretical one, such that μ=16,800.
(From *J. Gen. Physiol.*)

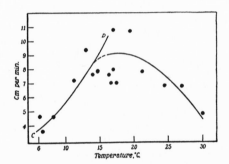

FIGURE 9

THE RATE OF CREEPING OF *Limax* DURING CIRCUS MOVEMENTS UNDER CONSTANT
ILLUMINATION AT DIFFERENT TEMPERATURES
(From *J. Gen. Physiol.*)

response is distinctly more variable, quantitatively, than at temperatures
either higher or lower.   Above 16° the amount of turning increases
with rise of temperature, while below 15° the reverse is true (Figures 8
and 9).   In this region of "normal" temperature conditions, the balance
between (1) the tendency to release pedal waves, which result in progression, and (2) the turning tendency is close to a critical point (for related
phenomena involving discontinuities in the effects of temperature, cf.
Crozier, 1924-25*a*, 1924-25*b*).   Slight circumstances may thus determine
in particular instances which of the two effects is dominant—hence statistical variation in the amplitude of turning per unit length of path.   At
higher temperatures the turning mechanism is in control, and the slug

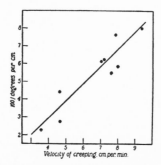

FIGURE 10

At temperatures up to about 15° the reciprocal of the amplitude of turning movements is directly proportional to the velocity of creeping of *Limax* when showing
circus movements under constant illumination.
(From *J. Gen. Physiol.*)

creeps only so fast as the central mechanism having to do with differential
bilateral tonus will permit. At lower temperatures the amount of
turning is limited and controlled by the speed of creeping, to which it
is inversely proportional (Figure 10). The "control" of creeping by
the central nervous determination of differential tonus in the musculature
of the body is demonstrated by the results of treatment with strychnine
(Crozier and Federighi, 1924-25c), which suppresses the phototropism.

Under "natural" conditions, consequently, certain kinds of variability
in response may be fairly conceived to result from the fact of delicate
dynamic adjustment among processes which (in effect) compete for control of the animal's mechanisms of movement. The perhaps curious
principle ensues that, for real understanding of the determination
of conduct and the identification of its elements, it is in many cases practically essential to place the organism under distinctly "abnormal" conditions such as are favorable to the unhampered expression of separate
elements of the usual nexus.

The primary difficulty in such studies is, of course, the essential requirement that the integrity of the organism shall not be violated. The very
thing which we desire to learn about depends upon the absence of destructive interference; we must not employ such treatments as may provoke
irreversible changes. There remain, free from such objection, certain
additional avenues of approach. Taken singly and in combination, we
have a right to expect that these may assist in the way desired. There
is first the modification of the temperature of the organism and the consideration of the relations between temperature and the frequencies or
velocities of measurable activities. It happens that these relations "make
sense" in terms of elementary physical theory, and the ways in which
they can be modified experimentally (Crozier and Stier, 1924-25a)
already yield suggestive conclusions (Crozier, 1923, 1923-24b; Crozier
and Federighi, 1923; Hoagland, 1927). The process of excitation by

light (Hecht, 1918-19, 1919-20a, 1919-20b, 1922-23, 1923-24, 1924-25, 1926-27) permits similar treatment. The methods of genetics, combined with such procedures, make possible to a degree the unification of the experimental objects as fairly comparable individuals, and in a few cases (where enough is known of the genetic behavior) even permit the making-up, at will, of individuals possessing particular characteristics required for specific purposes. Genetic analysis also permits a very profound testing of the reality of formulations of functional dependence (Crozier and Pincus, 1931-32a, 1931-32b, 1931-32c, 1931-32d).

When in a given compound field of illumination it is possible to account precisely for the amount of orientation exhibited by a phototropic organism, certain constants remain in the equations. It is tempting to regard these as in part "threshold" constants, and as such perhaps relating to the mechanism of central nervous adjustments between competing excitations. In an organism exposed to two sources of stimulation the resultant movements may be determined by the summation or by the balance of the respective excitations; with other suitable conditions the movement may be decided by one of the two excitations to the complete exclusion of the effects of the other. Such a "decision" may be taken to represent an elementary act of central nervous adjustment, and, given rational units in which to express the effects of the two sources of excitation when acting singly, its nature may be investigated by measuring its quantitative modification under controlled conditions. There should be procurable, in this way, a means of approach to central nervous functions which might hope to effect a rationalization of their nature (Crozier, 1923-24a, 1923-24b, 1924-25a, 1924-25b, 1924a, 1924b, 1925-28, 1926-27b, 1928; Crozier and Pincus, 1926-27c; Crozier and Stier, 1927-28). In this respect the quantitative description of tropistic orientation can become a potent analytic device.

In the examination of phototropism it is found possible to account for orientation under the influence of two beams of light on the basis of a single assumption derived from experience with a single source of illumination. The fact that quantitative theory can here be tested by experiment only under certain simple conditions is due not to a failure of the analysis but to mathematical intricacies attending even the process of orientation in a non-living machine. The problem of orientation with *three* sources of light is practically unsolvable, merely as an exercise in mathematics. The quantitative description of photic orientation under conditions which exclude mechanical interference can be carried out with some success (Crozier, 1925-28; Mitchell and Crozier, 1927-28). Consider a negatively phototropic animal on a horizontal surface, illuminated by two point-sources of light (Figure 11). The X-axis of a system of reference coordinates passes through the lights, the Y-axis bisects the distance between them. The animal at any moment has its anterior end A at a point (x, y), and the coordinates of the lights L' and L'' are respectively $(-a, o)$ and (a, o). Then the distances AL' and AL'' are $m^2 = (x+a)^2 + y^2$ and $n^2 = (x-a)^2 + y^2$. The dimensions of the

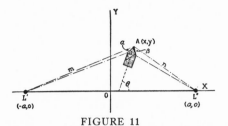

FIGURE 11

PHOTONEGATIVE ORGANISM AT A (x, y) ORIENTED BY POINT-SOURCES
OF LIGHT L' AND L''

(From *J. Gen. Physiol.*)

photoreceptors are safely assumed small in relation to m and n. The lights L' and L'' have luminous intensities P' and P'' candles respectively. Orientation should be accomplished and maintained when the photochemical effects on the two photoreceptive surfaces are equal. This is the *only* assumption of the tropism doctrine, and it turns out to be sufficient. Taking first the case in which the organism is attached to the substratum, but able to orient, the position of orientation is defined by the positive angle θ which its axis makes with the X-axis connecting the lights, and it may be shown that the necessary relation between θ and the other quantities concerned is:

$$\tan \theta = \frac{P'n^3 \left[\tan h \ (a+x)+y\right] + P'' \ m^3 \left[\tan h \ (a-x) + y\right]}{P'n^3 \left[a+x-y \tan h\right] - P''m^3 \left[a-x-y \tan h\right]},$$

where $h =$ the angle between a photoreceptive surface and the axis of orientation; for an ideal organism which is *positively* phototropic similar equations are obtainable which differ only in detail. The formula given (and simpler expressions of it easily deduced for various cases) holds equally well whether the primary photosensory effect is proportional to the intensity of the light I or to log I. With negatively phototropic organisms illuminated by beams of parallel rays opposed at 180°, the equation reduces to

$$\tan \theta_1 = \tan h \ \frac{I' + I''}{I' - I''} \ ;$$

with beams crossing at an angle of 90°,

$$\tan \theta_2 = \frac{(I' + I'') \ (1 + \tan h)}{(I' - I'') \ (1 - \tan h)}$$

[cf. Crozier (1925-28), where these equations are directly deduced, but with $H/2 = h$, $\theta = 90° - \theta_1$ for the first case, $\theta = \theta_2 - 45°$ for the second]. When the light rays are parallel, there is no necessity for restricting forward movement in testing the equations.

These equations can be tested by a number of series of measurements. In some forms, as the larva of the blow-fly, the functional angle h is constant. With other forms it is zero, and in such forms the fact that $h = 0$ can be directly checked by failure to obtain orientation with lights opposed at 180°. A further check is given by the known facts of orientation (e.g., in experiments due to Buder, 1917-19) for forms in which $h = 0$, namely, various protista swimming in a helical ("spiral") path, and in which beams of light are used which cross at an oblique angle. In this case, from the general formula one obtains $\tan \phi = \dfrac{\sin \psi}{I'/I'' + \cos \psi}$, where ϕ is the angle of the path of oriented movement with the axis of one of the two beams, and ψ is the angle between the beams. The agreement with experiment is extremely good.

The angle h is not constant, however, in all cases. If photokinetic excitation results in "random" movements of the head, the frequency, speed, and amplitude of such movements should influence the calculated value of h, and this should be a function of the total intensity of excitation; h would be expected to decrease in proportion either to $(I_1 + I_2)$ or to $\log I_1 I_2$. In young rats (before the eyelids have parted) this is its behavior (Figures 12 and 13) (Crozier, 1925-28; Crozier and Pincus, 1926). In other forms h increases with low total intensities of illumination, due to the suppression of random motions resulting from other kinds of excitation, and then passes through a maximum as the highest intensities provoke increasing "random" movements of the head. It is to be noted that there is obtainable in this way a *measure* of "random" movements and a key to their interpretation.

When these considerations are applied to the case of a moving animal in a field illuminated by two point-sources of light in the same horizontal plane, further complications arise. To distinguish this situation from that

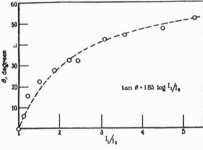

FIGURE 12

The empirical formula $\tan \theta = K I_1/I_2$ gives an approximate description of the variation in angle of orientation of young rats illuminated by opposed beams as dependent upon I_1 and I_2 and may be used in order to obtain a graphical representation of the results.

(From *J. Gen. Physiol.*)

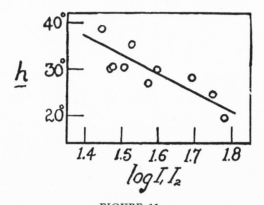

FIGURE 13

VALUES OF h COMPUTED FROM EXPERIMENTS WITH YOUNG RATS
$h = -K \log I_1 I_2 + C$ (see text)
(From *J. Gen. Physiol.*)

already treated we may speak of orientation of a *sessile* form as presenting a problem of orientation *in situ;* the orientation of a motile form in beams of parallel rays is, of course, dynamically identical with this; the phototropic progression of a motile organism may be termed orientation *in transitu* (Mitchell and Crozier, 1927-28). Here, the path of the animal from any point in the illuminated field depends upon the direction in which it is moving when subjected to the lights at that point. Differential photochemical effects in the two photoreceptors affect the rate at which the slope of the path varies with time (or with respect to distance covered, if the velocity of creeping be sensibly constant). The change of slope is $d\theta/dt$, but we cannot at once decide whether in such an instance the rate of turning depends upon the *difference* between the excitations on the two sides, or upon their *ratio*; and in either case there may be a direct or a logarithmic relation between excitation and the luminous flux. If the rate of creeping is very small, we have (from the general formula already given):

$$\frac{dy}{dx} = \frac{P'n^3 \left[(a+x) \tan h+y\right] + P''m^3 \left[(a-x) \tan h-y\right]}{P'n^3 \left[a+x-y \tan h\right] - P''m^3 \left[a-x-y \tan h\right]}.$$

Since m and n are complicated functions of x, y, and a, the expression is practically unsolvable as a differential equation, although it can be tested by several modes of approximation (cf. Figure 14).

The elementary conditions for movement oriented by light have been reviewed in order to bring out the basis for a particular conclusion. Regarded simply as the orientation of a machine with bilaterally disposed photoreceptors (the symmetry may be dynamical, as in helical-swimming protista, rather than of an obvious structural sort), the description of

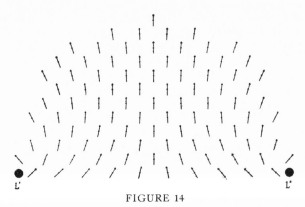

FIGURE 14

ARROWS SHOW THE VALUES OF θ FOR A PHOTO-NEGATIVE ORGANISM AT DIFFERENT POINTS IN THE FIELD

The point-sources of light L' and L'' are equal in luminous intensity and for calculation tan $h = 0.9$.

(From *J. Gen. Physiol.*)

phototropic movement is seen to present a very fair degree of complexity. This becomes apparent at once if we seek to predict the character and extent of orientation when more than one source of light is acting, on the basis of what is known concerning phototropism in the simplest kinds of situations. Inability to deal quantitatively with the measurable aspects of the orientation of organisms in complex fields of illumination, therefore, is not to be taken gratuitously as evidence either of incomplete understanding of the case, or, on the other hand, as indicating supra-mechanical influence at work within the organism. In an elementary way the kinds of complexity revealed by the present discussion serve to demonstrate concretely the justification for quantitative investigation under the most rigidly simplified conditions attainable, to which testable formulations can be applied.

It is not always true that the simplest conditions will be found in the most obvious place. An especially clear instance is found among galvanotropic phenomena. In the case of annelids (Moore, 1922-23) and certain other metazoans, the interpretation of galvanotropic orientation turns upon the necessary and sufficient assumption that the current serves to excite definite groups of nerve-cell bodies. This is consistent with the mode of action of strychnine, which produces a relatively specific reversal of inhibition in response to peripheral excitation, and also reverses the mode of galvanotropic response. These effects seem to have considerable generality (Crozier, 1926-27*b*; Fries, 1927-28). It is of interest that galvanotropic movements were early reported as occurring in the roots of plants and subsequently examined in various animals. It turns out (Navez, 1926-27) that the "galvanotropic" curvatures of roots, which because of their slowness and the definite manner of their exhibition might be useful for quantitative investigation of the mechanism of stimulation in a structurally simple system, are, however, artifacts due to chemical products of polarization at the electrodes ordinarily used: The "galvanotropism" of the roots disappears if the electrodes are made non-polarizable.

III

COMPOUND TROPISMS AND FUNCTIONAL GENETICS

The compounding of tropistic modes of behavior has been relatively little studied quantitatively, partly because the necessary preliminary descriptions have only begun to be available. The balancing of phototropic and stereotropic excitations, for instances in which it is possible to show that the stereotropic effect obeys the laws of compounding already indicated for phototropism (Crozier and Moore, 1922-23; Crozier, 1923-24a; 1923-24b; 1926-27b), provides one illustration. Thus with *Tenebrio* larvae it is possible to obtain, from measurements of the intensities of lights of different wave-lengths required to counterbalance stereotropic adherence to a glass surface, a picture of the absorption of light by the photoreceptive organs of this insect (Figure 15). By compounding the

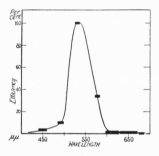

FIGURE 15

Measurements were made of the intensity of lights of different wave-lengths (obtained by filters of known transmissions) required to force creeping *Tenebrio* larvae to orient away from a vertical glass plate with which they otherwise maintained stereotropic contact. The light passed normally through the plate. Reciprocals of these intensities (i.e., the efficiencies) measure the proportionate absorption by the photoreceptive system at these wave-lengths. The maximum of effectiveness is sharply localized. (Each observation is given as a bar, of which the width includes the zone comprising the wave-lengths embracing two-thirds of the energy transmission of each filter.)
(From *J. Gen. Physiol.*)

effects of galvanic and photic fields mutually perpendicular, it is possible (Crozier and Stier, 1927-28) to find for each of several intensities of light a current density which forces orientation of marine planarians (*Leptoplana*) at exactly 45° to the axis of either field. The galvanic excitation must then be equal, in its differential tonus effect, to the photic. Since the latter is practically proportional to log I, we expect and find the current density (for 45° orientation) to be a rectilinear function of log *I*.   The organism behaves, in this case, not as if the compound situation involves properties peculiarly its own but as it should if responding to each kind of excitation separately; the effect is purely additive.   Moreover, one

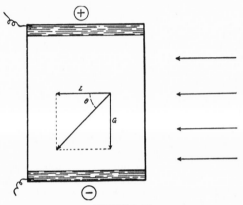

FIGURE 16

DIAGRAM OF EXPERIMENTAL TROUGH FOR ESTABLISHMENT OF CONSTANT ELECTRIC
CURRENT GIVING RISE TO THE GALVANOTROPIC VECTOR, *G*

Light from the right side (arrows) ʒ responsible for the phototropic orienting vector, *L*.   The galvanotropic effect (*G*) is equivalent to the phototropic when the resultant path of the planarian makes an angle $\theta = 45$ degrees.
(From *J. Gen. Physiol.*)

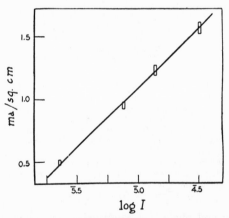

FIGURE 17

The current density in milliamperes per sq. cm. is directly proportional to the logarithm of the relative intensity of the light for orientation at 45° to the path under either mode of stimulation alone.   The observations are plotted as bars centered on the mean current densities and having a vertical height equal to twice the probable error.
(From *J. Gen. Physiol.*)

secures a measure of the galvanic excitation in energy units even without knowing how much current goes through the organism; and, since the excitation is found proportional to the current density, one has direct proof that the current probably stimulates by moving ions.

This type of procedure may be pursued further by following the consequences of compounding the influences of photic and gravitational orienting effects. To do so requires a formulation of gravitationally controlled orientations, which may incidentally be used to illustrate additional means whereby the significance of descriptive equations may be tested. We shall confine attention to geotropic movements carried out upon a substratum, neglecting the problem of orientation in space (Kühn, 1919).

A negatively geotropic animal, such as a tent-caterpillar, orients upward upon an inclined plane; but, in the absence of interfering modes of stimulation (i.e., under non-stimulating weak red light), it does not creep "straight upward" unless the surface upon which it moves is nearly vertical. The upward orientation ceases at an angle θ with the intersection between the creeping plane and the horizontal (Figure 18). At various

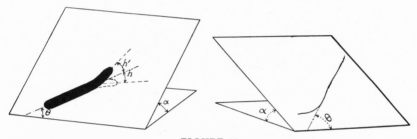

FIGURE 18

ILLUSTRATING THE DEFINITION OF THE ANGLES, a AND θ, INVOLVED IN THE DESCRIPTION
OF GEOTROPIC ORIENTATION OF *Malacosoma* LARVAE

The traced line of progression of the caterpillar, when creeping is started with the axis of the body horizontal, comes to make a definite angle θ on the inclined plane. In many instances the path is more complicated. The effect of the lateral movements of the anterior end ("head angle" $h+h'$) is discussed in the text.
(From *J. Gen. Physiol.*)

inclinations of the surface (a) it is found that the average value of θ (or the geometric mean) is a definite function of a, such that, purely as an empirical relationship which has useful properties, $\theta = K \log \sin a$.

If we seek to obtain the reason for this effect, the progression movements must be examined. It is to be noticed that the anterior end (head and thorax) of the caterpillar swings from side to side during locomotion. The possibility of a control of the angle θ is therefore given if we assume that orientation ceases when the difference between the pull of the weight of the anterior end of the body (freed from the substratum at the execution of each lateral swing) in the "up" position and in the "down" position is reduced to a threshold magnitude. Since the active component of gravity, in the plane of progression, is obviously proportional to sin a, this assumption is expressed by the equation

$$K \Delta \sin a \, [\Delta \cos (\theta - h) - \Delta \cos (\theta + h')] = -\text{const.},$$

where h and h' are the mean angles between the axis of the anterior swung portion of the body with the main axis, in the "up" and the "down" positions respectively. There are means of showing that h and h' are statistically equal. The equation at once reduces to

$$(\sin a) \ (\sin h) \ (\sin \theta) = -K'.$$

If h be sensibly constant, and independent of θ (in the average),

$$(\sin a) \ (\sin \theta) = -K''.$$

If a be constant, θ must vary inversely with h. By means of trails upon smoked paper, permitting measurement of the lateral excursions of the head, the latter assumption can be tested and is easily verified. When a large number of trails are studied (about 3000) this variable cancels out, and we should find sin θ inversely proportional to sin a (Figure 19).

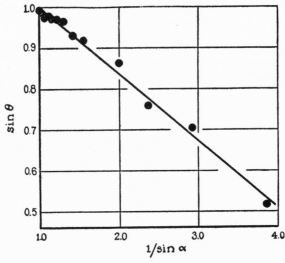

FIGURE 19
$$\sin \theta = -K \, / \sin a + C$$
(From *J. Gen. Physiol.*)

This expectation is thoroughly realized in the experimental results. The case is of interest in several ways. The "head angle" (Figure 18) is similar to that previously involved in the discussion of phototropism and is essentially a dynamic thing rather than directly a matter of structural symmetry. These facts can be compared with the geotropic orientation of such an organism as the slug *Agriolimax* (Wolf, 1926-27), where a

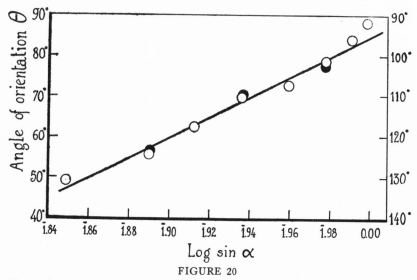

FIGURE 20

The angle of geotropic orientation (θ) of the slug *Agriolimax* is directly proportional to log sin α, where α is the angle of inclination of the creeping plane. The solid circles are from measurements made at inclinations greater than 90° (i.e., the animal hanging from the under surface of the plane).

structural angle of the required sort is readily perceptible; in this case also the formula just given is definitely obeyed (Figure 20). As an empirical relationship, it is in addition found that the mean orientation angle (θ) is very nearly a straight-line function of log sin α.

It is to be recognized that such formulae describe *positions* of orientation, and only indirectly have to do with questions of the *intensity* of stimulation. This should be sufficient in itself to prevent one from regarding the logarithmic formulation as an example of the Weber-Fechner rule. While it is impossible to convert the simple logarithmic formula into the trigonometric one, the former retains a definite utility in connections in which the trigonometric expression is unmanageable. Moreover, as will be indicated, it is possible to obtain some insight into its real meaning.

The first experiments looking toward this type of formulation were made with young mammals, rats and mice (Crozier and Pincus, 1926-27a, 1926-27b, 1926-27c, 1926-27e, 1927-28; Pincus, 1926-27; Crozier and Oxnard, 1927-28; Keeler, 1927-28). They require special attention to the state of the animals, their care and handling, and to the conditions of the tests. Since the results are open to a particular kind of mathematical treatment, it is important to realize that the results of this treatment can be checked in several independent ways. The conditions of creeping in young rats change rapidly with age during the time within which it is possible to make tests having the desired significance, hence it is necessary to average results from a number of individuals.   The observations involve determining the relationship between the angle θ, already defined, and the inclination of the surface (a).   Individual litters are selected from lines of rats long inbred by brother-sister or other close mating.   This insures genetic uniformity among individuals and can be demonstrated to be a necessary precaution.   Small litters are chosen so that all the rats may be vigorous creepers; this also is necessary.   At the age of 12 to 14 days, before the eyes have opened, such individuals, with very rare temporary exceptions in the stocks we have employed, orient upward upon a surface tilted at 15° to 20° to the horizontal or greater.   In a ventilated dark room where the temperature is 22° to 25°, observation is possible either under non-stimulating red light of low intensity or (in darkness) by means of markings with luminous paint.   Accurate record is made of the paths pursued.   At any one inclination the probable error of the mean θ is quite small, if due attention is given to the selection of the litters at the start and to their intermittent replacement with the mothers for feeding.   Just preceding the opening of the eyes the variability of behavior is definitely increased; this is seen also in mice.   Low intensities of white light, before

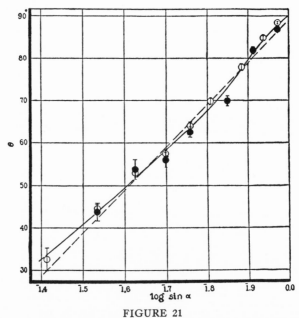

FIGURE 21

Showing the agreement in the relation between amplitude of negatively geotropic orientation θ and log sin a, where a is the angle between plane of creeping and the horizontal, in two series of tests with young rats (*R. norvegicus,* line *K*) made 15 months apart.   The height of the vertical bars = 2 P.E.   For certain purposes the relation may be regarded as effectively rectilinear, though in reality it is sigmoid.

(From *J. Gen. Physiol.*)

or after the opening of the eyes, render it very difficult to secure uniform orientations. This effect cannot be obviated by surgical removal of the eyes, which enhances irregularity of creeping and accentuates pauses; in these animals, as appears to be the general rule, geotropic orientation is evident only *during* progression; the consequence of removal of the eyes is undoubtedly comparable to that seen in certain fishes (Crozier, 1918a). The desired test can, however, be made in another way, using a gene which prevents the development of the retinal rods; mice carrying this gene are blind and can be used for the geotropism experiments in daylight (Keeler, 1927-28).

As a sufficient approximation, θ is found nearly proportional to log sin a (Figure 21). The graph is more exactly a long-drawn S, however, as every series of experiments has shown. The logarithmic fitting is sufficient, none the less, for certain purposes. More exactly, considering the way in which the weight of the body is carried by the legs, it is possible to show that cos θ would be expected to decline in proportion to sin a (Figure 22). This expectation is obeyed. The constants in the resulting

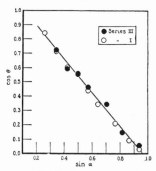

FIGURE 22

THE AGREEMENT OF TWO INDEPENDENT SERIES IN TERMS OF A RECTILINEAR CONNECTION BETWEEN COS θ AND SIN a
(From *J. Gen. Physiol.*)

equations are recoverable in new tests with rats of the same stock during successive generations (Crozier and Pincus, 1927-28, 1931-32a, 1931-32b, 1931-32c, 1931-32d). The data from such experiments can be submitted to a variety of independent tests, which can be only very briefly referred to here. The *speed* of upward progression obeys the same rules as θ (Pincus, 1926-27) (Figure 23); from this fact computations can be made as to the rate of doing work when the body is lifted, as a function of a. The effect upon θ of adding weights, attached to the root of the tail, which is predicted in the subsequent derivation of the relation $\Delta \cos \theta / \Delta \sin a = -$const., is also found experimentally (Crozier and Pincus, 1926-27e; Pincus, 1926-27) (Figure 24). The *variability* of θ at successive magnitudes of a shows that the measurements contain within themselves an automatic check upon their real significance; this will be discussed more

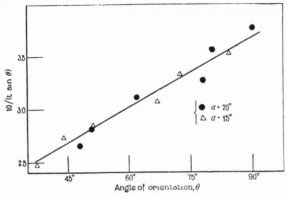

FIGURE 23

THE RATE OF CREEPING OF YOUNG RATS WITH ATTACHED WEIGHTS AT TWO ANGLES
OF INCLINATION (15° AND 20°) PLOTTED AGAINST THE OBSERVED ANGLES
OF ORIENTATION AT THESE ANGLES OF INCLINATION
(From *J. Gen. Physiol.*)

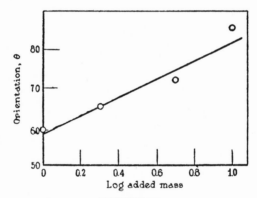

FIGURE 24

SHOWING THAT THE ANGLE OF UPWARD ORIENTATION IS PROPORTIONAL TO THE
LOGARITHM OF THE MASS ADDED TO THE TAIL OF THE RAT WHEN THE
INCLINATION OF THE CREEPING PLANE IS CONSTANT
(From *J. Gen. Physiol.*)

fully in a later section. If θ is determined by a in the manner indicated, increasing sin a should *decrease* the variability of θ according to the same rule as that by which θ itself increases. This is due to the fact that increasing geotropic excitation not only involves a greater amplitude of response but proportionately cuts down the effects due to unavoidable sources of stimulation not directly concerned with the experiment. We find, in fact, that the statistical measure of the variability of θ decreases in direct proportion to log sin a. Moreover, if this conception be sound, the apparent *rate* of this decrease should depend directly upon the number of individuals involved (the total number of observations of θ being the same in each case). A litter of two individuals, indeed, gives one-half the rate of decreasing C.V. θ as log sin a increases, as is shown by a comparable one of four individuals (Figure 25).

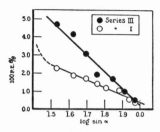

FIGURE 25

The variability of θ, expressed by P.E. θ as a percentage of the mean (the number of variates being 40 in each case), declines directly as log sin a increases. The rate of the decline is directly proportional to the number of individuals concerned: in Series I, 2 individuals; in Series III, 4; the slopes of the lines being in the ratio 1:2:1.
(From *J. Gen. Physiol.*)

Mathematical formulations of geotropic orientation thus far presented are either such as may have a usable meaning, or else they must be the happy results of a species of accident in some way due to the averaging of observations. If the latter were true, then it is scarcely conceivable that animals creeping in quite different ways, in which the possible manner of support of the body upon an inclined surface is completely different, should provide specifically different empirical relationships between θ and a or obey diverse rational equations. The beetle *Tetraopes tetraopthalmus* has been studied in this connection. The body is in contact with the supporting surface at the tips of the legs and at the posterior end of the abdomen; θ is found proportional to sin a directly, *not* to log sin a. The complete formulation for this case is difficult and need not here be considered further. Essentially, the magnitude of θ is determined by the fact that the leg muscles not only support the downward pull of the mass of the body but are also subject to a torque due to the twisting movement of the abdomen, the center of gravity being posterior to the point of origin of the legs. This interpretation is readily controlled by the attachment of additional loads (wax) to different parts of the beetle's body. When a mass of wax is attached to the abdomen, θ is increased. If it is attached to the anterior end of the body, θ is *decreased,* although the total load carried has been augmented, because the torque due to the abdomen is reduced. Again, with these insects, it is possible to perform the converse experiment and to *reduce* the load carried, and at the same time the torque on the legs, by amputating the abdomen. If our understanding of the situation is sound, θ should then be decreased, which is in fact the case.

These instances, and a number of others, can thus be understood as manifestations of geotropism which depend upon the distribution of the pull of the organism's mass upon the supporting musculature. The particular situation in any given form [adult rats (Upton and Stavsky, 1932), kittens (Stavsky, 1932, 1933), chick (Hoagland, 1929), fiddler crab (Kropp and Crozier, 1928-29), and others] will depend upon the morphology of the organism. The analysis does not exclude the involvement of statocyst function in geotropism, but leaves to be demonstrated just what this function may be in specific instances (Arey and Crozier, 1919, 1921; Cole, 1925-28; Crozier and Federighi, 1924-25b). Related to this matter is the failure to obtain clean-cut relationships between θ and α in the case of certain slowly moving marine and fresh-water gastropods; but this point cannot be developed at present (cf. Jäger, 1932), nor can the very attractive questions arising when geotropic orientation is reversed. Two groups of facts should be mentioned, however, as concerned in the demonstration that the pull of the mass of the body of a snail or slug upon its parietal and columellar muscles is a determining factor in geotropic

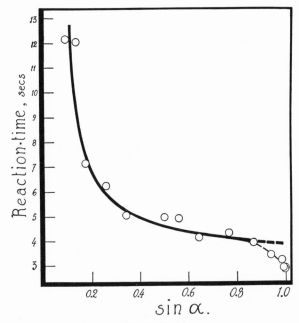

FIGURE 26

A snail (*Helix*) creeps straight upward upon a surface inclined at $\alpha°$ to the horizontal. When this plate is rotated smoothly but quickly in its own plane, the snail orients to a new upwardly directed path. The reaction-time, measured from the point of mid-rotation of the plane, decreases systematically as sin α increases. The latent period for geotropic response is thus a function of the magnitude of the exciting component of gravity.

response. When a snail such as *Helix* is creeping straight upward ($\theta =$ 90°) on a sloping surface which can be rotated in its own plane, rotation through 90° is followed by orientation of the snail after a definite latent period. This latent period is a function of the active gravitational component, such that reciprocal of (*latent period minus a constant*) is directly proportional to the sine of the angle of slope of the surface; the velocity of the effects underlying gravitational excitation is thus determined by the gravitational pull (Figure 26). On a vertical surface the latent period for reaction, after 90° displacement of the axis of a creeping snail such as *Liguus,* is systematically decreased by the addition of weights, is increased if the experiment is made under water, and decreases again (under water) if additional weights are carried (Crozier and Navez, 1930). The orientation of fiddler crabs may be taken as a particular illustration of the fact that the empirical and the rational formulae applicable for mechanically diverse instances of geotropic orientation cannot be regarded as "accidents," and that, in consequence, the muscle-tension theory of the limitation of orientation is not merely adequate but necessary. *Uca* creeps not straight forward but sideways. In the dark, Kropp and Crozier (1928-29) found θ very closely proportional to sin a directly. If this is due to the attainment of mechanical stability, and thus to the release of a certain class of tensions on the legs, θ should be altered if the center of gravity is shifted. It happens that nature has performed the experiment. The large claw of the male fiddler may be carried "up" or "down" as the animal creeps sideways on an inclined plane. In the former case, θ should be less at each value of a, and this is the fact. Removal of the claw abolishes the asymmetry, which does not appear in the symmetrical females (Figure 27).

Two facts have been referred to which it is necessary to bring into con-

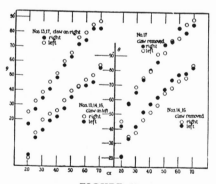

FIGURE 27

Mean orientation angles to right and to left for 2♂♂ *Uca* (13, 17) with large claw on the right side, and for 3 (10, 14, 16) with the large claw on the left, demonstrating lower θ's when creeping is toward the side carrying the large chela. This relationship is obliterated when the large claw is removed.
(From *J. Gen. Physiol.*)

junction in dealing with a final aspect of this geotropic orientation. One is that, in the case of the rats with which we will have most to do, the graph of θ vs. log sin a is *almost* a straight line, but, in reality, a long-drawn S. The other is the necessity for genetic uniformity in the test material. The latter is proved by the fact that whereas the same values of the constants in the equations, and indeed identical curves, are repeatedly obtained with individuals from the same stock, it is nevertheless an easy matter to obtain separate stocks, of known different genetic history, and distinct species, for which the curves are different (Figure 28). Con-

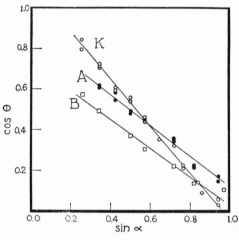

FIGURE 28

Data from several series of observations with young rats of race K, of race A, and of race B demonstrate the consistent differences with which the upward orientations (θ) on a surface of slope a adhere to the formulation cos $\theta = a$—b sin a, where a and b are constants. (It will not do to fix the straight lines and determine the constants a and b for the purpose of obtaining Figure 29 by differentiation, because the departures of the observations from rectilinearity are systematic and significant, and it is these departures which in part determine the essential characteristics of Figure 29.)

sistent performance within an inbred line of animals must be due to homogeneity of inheritance, though it does not follow that it should be easy to work out its actual basis. Yet the experimentation undertaken on this basis has shown that it is possible to learn something about it and at the same time to obtain a neat justification of the initial treatment of the data.

Behind such attempts there persists a general problem, which has been more or less ignored as a problem. It has to do with the question as to the degree with which the behavior of an organism can legitimately be given mathematical formulation in an equation. The consistency of observations can, of course, be weighted by statistical methods, but this is not primarily the point. In other cases the general mode of treatment, the kind of interpretation provided, can be tested by deduction of the forms of hitherto untested but contingent relationships, subsequently studied in a quantitative way. But this does not completely answer the requirement, because not infrequently a question remains as to the biological "reality" of the assumptions employed in the original formulations. This difficulty is in part an emotional one and is often justified. Of the two types of formulation consciously employed, that which is purely statistical is unsatisfying, since the constants it provides are dimensionless and arbitrary; expressions derived from physical theory have the enormous advantage that the character of their contained constants immediately gives basis for concrete experimental tests. Without such tests these equations may also remain arbitrary. If the organic significance of the constants is the objective of inquiry, it becomes necessary to justify in some independent way the specific equation chosen to express the initial results, or at least the mode of representation adopted for them.

The proof of the physical adequacy of a given mathematical formulation for events, behavior, in an organism seems to necessitate demonstration that its constants have a "real" biological basis. It is easy to object that biological transactions are "too variable" to warrant such an undertaking, but there is ground for rejecting this view. It can also be objected, with greater cogency, that for any smooth relationship between two variables a large number of different formulations might be devised. This difficulty is avoided, however, if we confine attention to the attempt to show that the *difference* between two magnitudes of a dimensionally identical constant is biologically a real difference.

A "biologically real difference" would be one which, for example, behaves in a definite, unitary way when subjected to manipulation of a purely biological sort. It must then be conceded a molecular substratum. A unitary effect in inheritance, exhibiting allelomorphic relationships with other similar units, is an example of such reality. For our further purposes, however, it is necessary to consider a "unitary effect in inheritance" as not precisely a *gene,* as the concept supporting this term is customarily used, but to consider it as a unit of inheritance having the dimensions of "amount or degree or organic expression *per unit of some (specified) controlling variable."*

In our several genetically stabilized lines of young rats the extent of upward orientation on an inclined surface is a function of the slope of the surface. The form of this function is the same in the several races, but the numerical values of the respective constants are characteristic for each race. Figure 28 contains data from successive series of measurements with rats of lines K and A. (Details of the procedure and of the statistical weights of the mean orientation angles are given in the original reports.) In terms of the formulation previously given, $\Delta \cos \theta / \Delta \sin a = $ —const., in each case, where $\theta = $ orientation angle on the surface inclined at $a°$ to the horizontal. But the intercept constants and the slope factor are clearly different for the two lines. The graph for A is as if rotated about a mid-point of that for K. With an additional race, labeled B, we find that the slope $\Delta \cos \theta / \Delta \sin a$ is sensibly the same as for race A, but that the threshold intercept is higher. There are thus two kinds of differences recognizable.

Every series of these measurements shows that the relationship of θ to log sin a is to be described as a long-drawn S. (It happens that lines A, K, and B give a straight-line relation between cos θ and sin a over the whole working range of sin a. In other genetically uniform groups of rats, different parts of the sin a range give lines of different slopes. The reason for this becomes obvious in the later treatment of the data.) The relation $\Delta \cos \theta / \Delta \sin a = $ —const. was arrived at by considering that stable orientation on the inclined surface is achieved when the tension excitations due to the pull of the animal's weight are the same, within a threshold difference, on the legs of the two sides of the body. In this event the extent of upward turning is a direct proportional measure of the total amount of stimulation per (large) unit of time.

The total excitation of the tension receptors must be regarded as involving, over a gross interval of time (1) the total array of these receptors with thresholds below a certain value, which is a function of the stretching force, and (2) the frequency of change of tension, which is essential for stimulation. The latter, it is to be presumed, is determined chiefly by the frequency with which steps are taken and should thus be proportional to the speed of progression. It has been shown that the speed of progression is a straight-line function of log sin a (Figure 23). Hence the differential, $\Delta \theta / \Delta \log \sin a$, when plotted as a function of the stretching force (sin a), should give a picture of the distribution of effective thresholds among the available tension receptors in terms of the exciting component of gravity. For lines A and K these distributions are given in Figure 29. They are clearly resolvable in each case into three distinct

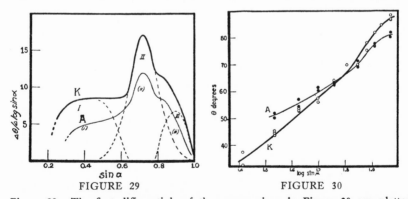

FIGURE 29   FIGURE 30

Figure 29. The first differentials of the curves given in Figure 30 are plotted against sin a, to obtain a picture of the array of thresholds among tension receptors concerned in the geotropic orientation. The curves are clearly composite, and resolvable into three portions in each case.

Figure 30. The amount of upward orientation, in degrees (θ), is related to log sin a, where a is the slope, by a sigmoid curve; data from races K and A.

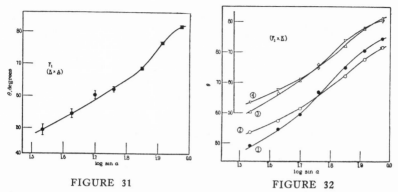

FIGURE 31   FIGURE 32

Figure 31. θ *vs.* log sin a for the F_1 progeny $(K \times A)$; points are plotted as bars with height $= 2 \times$ P.E.

Figure 32. θ *vs.* log sin a for the four groups of individuals segregated in the back-cross progeny $(F_1 \times K)$; 1 should be like the grand-parental K; 3 should have its low-a end like that for 1, its mid-portion like that of 2; 2 should resemble closely, except at $a = 55°$-$70°$, the grand-parental A, or more closely the (i, ii, III) segregates in the back-cross $(F_1 \times A)$, with which its curve is indeed identical; 4 should show a lower portion of its curve like that in the curve for 2, its later portion like that in the curve for 1. In other words, as regards the slopes of these curves, considering each curve divided into two parts on either side of $a = 35°$, we should find all possible combinations of low and high slopes—high slope below 35° combined with either high or low slope above 35° (up to $a = 55°$), and reciprocally. It is clear that these combinations are indeed found.

groups of sensory elements. The only real difference between these curves has to do with magnitudes of the respective ordinates, which are in constant ratio throughout.

In the case of race B the three components of the array of receptors are again apparent, but the distribution curve for each one is broadened; the modes, however, occur at the same points on the sin a scale. In other races slightly different complications are apparent.

Each of the two presumptive elements in excitation, (1) number of receptor elements according to their respective thresholds and (2) frequency of excitation, has been tested separately. By means of tests in which small masses of metal are attached to the animal's back in one or another of several positions, it has been possible to show that the several "groups of sense-organs" may be selectively influenced by the added load (Crozier and Pincus, 1927-28, 1931-32*a*, 1931-32*b*). On the other hand, the frequency of stepping in geotropic progression can be increased, without altering the load carried, by intraperitoneal injection of adrenin (Crozier and Pincus, 1932-33*a*); in this case the distortions of the θ-a curve are similar to those induced by the presence of added loads. Redistributions of gravitationally induced tensions may also be brought about by attaching a balloon to a geotropically orienting animal (Elliott and Stavsky, 1933), with results predictable on the basis of the present considerations.

Since individuals from diverse pure lines show consistent performances which differ from line to line, it is possible to institute a genetic test of the biological reality of the formulations of geotropic response in the case of these rats. Such experiments have been made involving the cross-breeding of lines K and A and also the cross-breeding of races A and B. Individuals of the F_1 generation produced by crossing lines K and A give a curve relating θ to a which exhibits a lower segment identical with that for the A parents (Parts I and II of the curve in Figure 29) and an upper segment similar to that for the K parent (cf. Figure 31).

A sufficient genetic test of the "reality" of the constants in the formulae descriptively connecting the response a with the exciting component of gravity should thus be obtained by the study of individuals produced in the back-cross generations (F_1 x A) and (F_1 x K). In the first case the individuals should yield curves all of one kind except that in one half of them the terminal slopes of the curve of θ vs. log sin a should be steeper than with the other half. This is found to be true, although the differences sought are small. In the other back-cross, however, we look for four phenotypic groups of individuals, respectively showing: $I, II; i, II; I, ii; i, ii$. In the numbers of cases tested, these four classes are clearly recognizable, by several independent criteria, and occur with equal frequencies. A summary of data is given in Figure 32. A corresponding genetic analysis has been made of the cross of races A x B, where in F_1 there is complete dominance of the B properties.

It is clearly not the amount of the response (θ) which is subject to hereditary transmission, but the way in which this response changes as a function of its inciting condition. Without such formulation, the real nature of the differences between lines A, K, and B in the respects which here concern us could not be recognized, let alone analyzed. It should be mentioned that the statistical significance of the differences relied upon for the analysis is fully protected through the demonstration that the variability of the responses is subject to exactly the same rules as those which connect the amount of response (θ) with the gravitationally exciting component (sin a) (cf. Crozier and Pincus, 1927-28, 1931-32a).

The fact that the case investigated is complex, in the sense that three pairs of "factors" have been distinguished, points the way to certain attractive theoretical possibilities. The problem initially raised had to do with the possibility of demonstrating that the difference between numerical values of a dimensionally identical constant describing the homologous behavior of two different groups, genetically stabilized, of the same kind of organism, may have a "real" significance. The facts summarized show that the required demonstration seems to have been obtained and that the specific values of the slope constants obtained in the examination of the races K, A, and B are recoverable in a genetically rational scheme after two generations of cross-breeding. It is to be presumed that in the great majority of cases the possibility of demonstrating a genetic basis for behavioral characteristics and mental attributes will depend almost entirely upon securing statements of the manner in which expressions of these properties are related to magnitudes of controllable variables. The cases which have been summarily reviewed here show how it is possible to deal with "multiple factor" and "blending" phenomena which must play a large part in the determination of complex features of organic deportment.

IV

VARIABILITY

The responses of an organism are not invariable to the degree usually seen in the activities of simple, well-built machines. This has often served as an excuse, if not indeed as an apology, for loose experimentation concerning the conduct of animals, including that of man, and for obscure thinking in the discussion of experimental results.

Two quite different modes of regarding this variableness are of practical consequence: (1) We may consider that variation, "unpredictableness," is a category of phenomena exhibited by organic systems, presumably originating either as a result of the devastating complexity of such systems or as due to the participating interest of whatever god or devil one's private system of vitalistic "causation" may chance to be entertaining at the moment. In any event, it is indefensible to rely upon the physical principle of micro-indeterminism, although some have succumbed to the temptation. (2) In a quite different way we may seek to classify variableness in the general sense, attempting to recognize types and modes of its expression. It is quite apparent that a diversity of sorts of happenings have been loosely grouped under the general notion of variableness and unpredictability; certain aspects of such classifications are referred to in several examples which may be cited (Crozier and Federighi, 1924-25a, 1924-25b, 1924-25c; Crozier, 1928; Crozier and Pincus, 1926-27a, 1926-27b, 1926, 1926-27c, 1926-27d, 1926-27e, 1927-28).

Distinctions must be made between phenomena of mere difference, of variation, and of variability; by *variability* we understand "ability to vary," and it is implied that the property of the organism in question which exhibits variation will have this variation in performance limited, or incited by the circumstances arousing the performance or the conditions under which it takes place. It follows that the nature of *variability* can be understood if we secure expressions of its relationship to relevant circumstances and conditions. In other words, we should obtain indices of the variation as a function of some significant measurable attribute of the system or situation which concerns us; this will provide a measure of the "ability to vary." Despite its very elementary appearance, the conception of *variability* based upon variation expressed as a function of some independent variable has been little used. In the majority of cases, writers dealing with "variability of behavior" have been content to record differences in behavior and to draw some obscure comfort from the fact that differences exist "under the same conditions." One excludes those multitudinous recorded instances in which some measurable feature of conduct has been shown to be *modifiable* because the changes properly so described comprise a clearly separable assemblage of problems and are not adequately cited as instances of variability. The distinction is illustrated by phenomena of photic excitation. With successive stimulations by constant increase of intensity of light, the reaction-time in the case of such forms as *Ciona* (Hecht, 1919-20a) undergoes progressive orderly change; the modification of amplitude of response with *continuous* excitation by constant light is of an entirely comparable sort (Wolf and Crozier, 1927-28; Crozier and Wolf, 1927-28, 1928-29). In each instance the change can be understood completely as due to sensory adjustment, in terms of a simple photochemical system which embraces also the phenomena of dark-adaption (Hecht, 1919-20a, 1919-20b, 1926-27; Crozier, 1915; Crozier and Wolf, 1928-29). These are cases in which the energy change external to the organism, the "stimulus," or, more correctly, the *stimulating agency*, is obviously constant, yet the response of the organism is not the same; but its changes are not satisfactorily accounted for by mere reference to "variation," or "modification," because it is the precise form of the orderly change, as a function of time, which assumes significance. Without analysis, for which exact experimentation is necessary, it would be easy to speak of "higher behavior," "learning," or similar effects. Dodge (1927) has discussed variability of response in human beings, giving essentially descriptions of the fact that the same individual is not always alike in response to "the same stimulus." Dodge urges study of "progressive modifications of response"—but these modifications (of reaction-time) are not treated as functions even of psychologically or biologically significant "time"; and the assumption that the "stimulus" is the same because the same change in the intensity factor of some form of energy external to the organism has been employed as a means of excitation is palpably exposed to the possibility of serious error. The fact that the *variation* in response, at any one period of time, is described statistically does not enable us to discuss parameters of the variation as a function either of the conditions of excitation or of any change in the organism. Yet it is this type of procedure, namely, the mere recording of differences (qualitative merely, or between averages), with or without functional characterization of variation about average values of "response," which has usually been employed in the investigation of variability. The methods of correlation do not supply what is needed, since they do not provide means of expressing variation as a function of some independent variable but merely state in terms of pure number the degree of association between mean values of co-varying attributes.

To describe the *variability* of a response, then, it should be necessary to characterize not the mean value of the response as a function of something else, but the variation as such a function. The variability of response might then be found to be far from lawless. The importance of such findings would be considerable. Upholders of the view that behavior is essentially unpredictable, that is, not directly a function of knowable conditions, inevitably trade upon the margin of variation supposed to be typical of organisms as contrasted with machines. If variability can be shown not to be lawless, the supposed logical foundation for this type of obscurantism disappears.

Moment-to-moment changes in the behavior of animals have practical consequence in at least two ways: (1) They frequently interfere with or complicate attempts to analyze the mechanics of irritability and response by way of quantitative tests of relations between excitation and reaction. They raise serious problems in connection with the attempt to decide whether one has selected the suitable theory (equation) to account for experimental results. As a source of such trouble, intrinsic variability has usually been regarded as an inescapable nuisance, perhaps justifying superficial control of external variables; but, since "errors of observation" may influence end results in a multiplicative way and *not* by a principle of exclusive limitation, this view is, practically, unjustified. (2) On the other hand, it may be possible to utilize this variability, provided it can be expressed in quantitative terms. In the illustration of the basic notion employed we must for the present be content to rely upon relatively crude statistical methods, because the existing data do not justify the labor inseparable from the execution of certain obvious refinements. This in no way restricts the generality of the conception. It is unfortunately necessary to point out that the data of psychophysics as yet supply very scanty material for the purpose—although it is in this field that such data might be most expected to be found.

The practicable characterization of the variability apparent in the responses of different individuals of the same general sort, under external conditions physically similar throughout, may be based upon one of several considerations, applicable in different instances. We might deal with the standard deviations of the measurements, or with the relative standard deviations of the measurements (as percentages of the means), or, again, with the absolute ranges of scatter of the data. Presumably every case must be examined on its merits, to permit decision as to whether "errors of observation" predominate in the variability of the data or in variation of an intrinsic sort. In general, it can be foreseen that it is desirable to obtain measurements upon the *same individuals* at each of a number of values of the experimentally controllable variable, thus keeping the foci of origin of variation the same as to number and as to kind. It is also clear that the numbers of measurements made should likewise be uniform, else the computed statistics will not have equal weights. If in any series of measurements such as we might desire to use there are present two different sorts of "variation," respectively those for which uncontrollable "errors" are directly responsible and, on the other hand, those for which the inner variability of the organism is the cause, the disentangling of the two will depend upon keeping the numbers of observations constant at each value of the chosen independent variable.

Without treating in detail the methods whereby such observations have been obtained, we take as illustration data from experiments already cited on the geotropic orientation of young rats. Each series of measurements involved the recording of a certain fixed number of orientation angles exhibited by each individual in a given homogeneous lot of young rats, under standardized conditions, at each of a number of inclinations of a surface on which creeping occurred.

The variation of the measured orientation decreased as the extent of upward turning became greater. The interpretation proposed turned upon the assumptions (1) that upward orientation involved an adjustment of the axis of the body such that the pull of the mass of the body on the legs induced tension excitations during progression which at the definitely oriented position became equivalent (i.e., sensorially equal, within a threshold difference) on the two sides of the body, and (2) that increasing the effective pull of gravity, proportional to sin a, involved greater total excitation (measured therefore by the angle θ), and at the same time proportionately interfered with the disorienting or otherwise competing effects of other sources of excitation. If in any one series of measurements the variation of response is due to a set of conditions, statistically uniform at different values of sin a, which may exert minor influences upon the angles of orientation, and if the several individuals used are strictly comparable, and if the foregoing assumptions (1) and (2) are valid (particularly 2), then the variation of response (θ) should be proportional, at each value of sin a, to the ratio V/θ, where V is the integrated influence of the minor orienting "errors" (including errors of recording and measuring the orientations). The scatter of the observations should thus be reduced as sin a is increased; this is the case (Figure 33). The remaining assumptions can be tested by ascertaining if σ_θ/θ is influenced in the same way by increasing sin a as is the extent of orientation (θ) itself (Crozier and Pincus, 1926-27a, 1931-32a–1932-33b, etc.). σ_θ/θ turns out to decline rectilinearly as log sin a increases, or (more exactly) as θ increases (Figures 34 and 35). Since

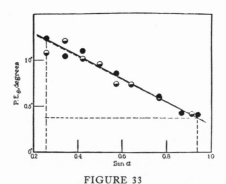

FIGURE 33

P.E.$_\theta$ vs. LOG SIN a, SERIES II AND III

For each of these series, $N = 4$, $n = 20$. The two sets of data are in close agreement.

in any one series of observations the number of observations made on each (n) is the same at all values of a, the fact that the distribution of θ is skewed (Crozier and Pincus, 1927-28) at each magnitude of a is in no sense a disadvantage. If it were necessary to correct for skewness,

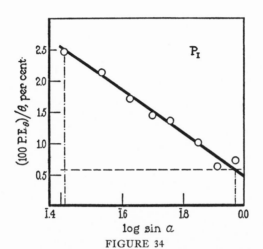

FIGURE 34

THE RELATIVE VARIABILITY OF THE GEOTROPIC ORIENTATION ($P.E._\theta/\theta$) DECLINES RECTILINEARLY AS LOG SIN a IS INCREASED
Series I

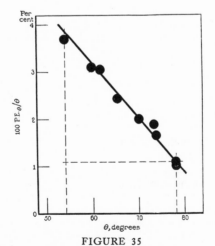

FIGURE 35

THE RELATIVE VARIATION OF PERFORMANCE AS RELATED TO THE MAGNITUDE OF THE RESPONSE, FOR YOUNG RATS OF RACE A INJECTED WITH ADRENALIN
The variation number (V.N.$_\theta$) is 3.64, the total relative variation, 127 units.

this could be done (1) by recognizing the logarithmic nature of the skewness, or (2) by dealing with the symmetrical frequency distributions of cos θ.

As a qualitative proof of the legitimacy of the view thus far developed it may be pointed out that when *inhomogeneous* groups of individuals are purposely used the formulation fails in a predictable way (Crozier and Pincus, 1927-28); moreover, when different individuals are used at different values the slope θ the relationship of σ_θ/θ to log sin a is no longer so exact, though it remains roughly proportional (Wolf, 1926-27; Kropp and Crozier, 1928-29). Quantitative proof is obtained in another way.

In Figure 35 there is representation of a series of measurements of this kind. In such a graph the area under the fitted line, between the working limits of the observations, measures the total "variation" of the observations. It is clearly composed of two parts. The lower portion is that uninfluenced by the increase of sin a and includes errors of observations and of recording, if these enter significantly. With trained observers and with observations taken within a limited interval (but in such a way as to avoid fatigue effects), this area should be constant in any one series of the kind earlier specified. The upper section of the total is that part of the total variation which is subject to control according to the magnitudes of the independent variable concerned in the experiments, namely, by log sin a.

An important feature of these relationships is the finding that for cases in which there is a discontinuous relationship between performance and magnitudes of controlled variable the indices of variation (if the experiments have been adequately performed) permit one to detect the discontinuity by independent means (Figure 36 gives one example).

We have elsewhere pointed out (Crozier and Pincus, 1927-28) that the comparison of two groups of individuals as regards *amounts of response* cannot, in general, be made merely by comparing their responses at *one* value of the intensity of excitation. For analogous reasons, in the present connection it is to be stressed that relative variability of response cannot be examined by contrasting *variation* of response in two individuals or groups, with a single value of the controlling variable, unless it is demonstrated that the variation as measured contains no element which is not modified by the variable in question. These considerations are important when one seeks to compare the intrinsic variability of performance characteristic of two individuals or of two homogeneous groups. It is necessary to investigate both the total observable variation of performance and the manner of dependence of the variation upon the chosen experimental variable (Crozier and Pincus, 1932-33a, 1932-33b); otherwise, conclusions totally erroneous may result. This may be illustrated by means of experiments designed to test the constitutional character of the variation of performance in the geotropic orientation of young rats. The injection of adrenin (Crozier and Pincus, 1932-33a) distorts the curve connecting θ with a, but when the total

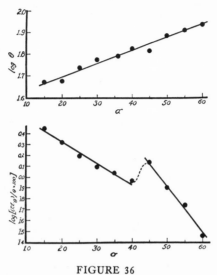

FIGURE 36

DATA FROM EXPERIMENTS ON GEOTROPIC ORIENTATION OF YOUNG GUINEA PIGS

The method of support upon the inclined surface (a = slope) differs from that in rats, the body being free above the surface. Empirically, log θ *vs.* a gives in this case a nearly straight line. The cusp evident at a=45° is real, however, and is correlated with an easily observable change in the method of progression at slopes above this magnitude. Its reality is made evident when the variability function is considered. In the lower graph the logarithm of the relative *variation* of θ (n here = 80) is plotted against a; the unmistakable discontinuity is apparent at $a = 45°$, marking the transition to a new set of conditions at greater slopes which affect both θ and its variations as functions of the slope.

(From Upton, 1929-30)

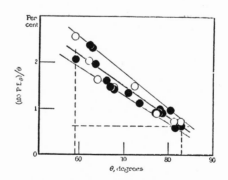

FIGURE 37

THE RELATIVE VARIATION OF ORIENTATION IS THE SAME FOR ADULTS OF RACE A, AT EQUAL MAGNITUDES OF PERFORMANCE, WITH ADRENIN INJECTION (OPEN CIRCLES) OR WITHOUT

variability of performance is examined it is found to be quite unaffected; if variation at constant slope of surface were to be the criterion, it would have to be concluded that the variation of performance had been increased by the action of the drug (cf. Figure 37).

Data from certain additional sources—from the study of judgment of lifted weights, for example—can be analyzed in these terms. Among a number of further instances it is worth while to choose several in which the variation of "reaction" of performance is independent of the condition of the performance itself. In any particular case it may remain a problem as to whether the standard deviation or the *relative* variation (σ/mean) is the proper measure of variation, and this must be decided by additional evidence and in part by the nature of the inquiry it is desired to make. Lashley (1915) found that with increasing skill developed in successive equal practice periods the range of scatter of archery "shots" decreases but that the relative variation remained practically constant (the same number of shots being made in each period). In such cases it is tempting to conclude that the mechanism of variability is one which is independent of that governing the change in accuracy due to experience. Similar conditions appear in certain other data relating to learning, memorizing, and forgetting. In the early excitements connected with the popularization of biometry a similar problem arose as to the proper index of variations in the measurements of organisms (cf. Duncker, 1900), namely, the question as to whether (1) the standard deviation of a character, or (2) the ratio between this statistic and the mean (or median) of the character is a proper index of its absolute variability. Verschaeffelt (1894) assumed the second of these alternatives, and Davenport (cf. Brewster, 1897), Pearson (1897), and others also assumed the relation between σ and the average for a character to be similar to that between the errors of measurement by successive applications of a foot-rule and the length measured. Duncker (1900) believed that there is no relation whatever between the average magnitude and the variability of a character, since in his view the causes of variation are to be considered essentially different from the factors determining total size. The argument included the notion that homologous characters in allied forms ought to show similar indices of variability but not necessarily equal average values. Certain series of measurements (as of rostral spines in *Palaemonetes*) show variation in a way supporting this view. In general, a *coefficient of variation* of the order of 5 to 10 *per cent* is found for continuously varying biological characters; for seriations of integral variates C.V. tends to be larger, and more irregular, while σ is relatively more constant. The problem assumes a slightly different form, however, when the intention is to investigate variation as a function of some controllable quantity external to the organism. We can illustrate this briefly by means of data drawn from studies on the relations between temperature and the speeds or frequencies of certain processes in organisms.

We choose data of this sort because it again shows a way in which variation of performance, instead of remaining a handicap, can be made to prove something in a useful way. This requires experimentation with the utmost care for the control of all recognizable external sources of difference in the mean values of the measured quantities, other than provided by the single variable one uses for the investigation. The control of this one variable, temperature, must be as exact as possible. Where the temperature of the organism differs from that of the surrounding medium it must be measured by special means. Into the technical side of such operations we need not go. If the frequency of the heart beats be measured, let us say, in caterpillars of the same stock, at each of a good number of temperatures, over a range of temperature within which change of temperature produces no irreversible effects, there is found a definite and smooth relationship between temperature and frequency. The observations are secured in such a way that the time is always measured for 10 beats of the pulsating vessel. A well-known law, with adequate theoretical underpinning, relates the velocities of chemical reactions proceeding at measurable speeds to temperature. It states that the velocity constant is proportional to the exponential of $-\mu/RT$, where R is the gas constant, T is the temperature on the Kelvin scale, and μ is a quantity having the dimensions of "energy of activation" of the molecules whose activation governs the rate of the process. It happens that the same equation applies to the biological situation. The problem then arises, does the quantity μ have, in such instances, a *specific* significance? It is possible to suggest a good many reasons why it might not have any specific significance. Protoplasm is colloidal; temperature influences its viscosity; and the like. Such suggestions are more in the nature of apologies for avoidance of rigorous experimentation, however, than anything else, and appear to be pretty certainly based upon misconceptions of the rôle of viscosity and diffusion in microscopic systems, because it would then still remain mysterious why relations of the type illustrated in Figure 38 are in fact the rule (with indeed but few exceptions). We are not at the moment concerned with this problem of the possible specific significance of magnitudes of the constant μ in biological systems, which the evidence, however, clearly supports, but with the method of using the variability of the measurements. The plot in Figure 38 shows that the "time for ten movements" is not absolutely constant. Neither does it vary at random. On a logarithmic plot of the function

$$1/\text{time for 10 movements} = A e^{-\mu/RT} + \text{const.,}$$

this is, in terms of the physicochemical theory previously mentioned, the observations tend to lie strictly in a band with parallel edges. The latitude of variation is then such that the highest frequencies of movement are a constant times greater than the lowest frequencies (Crozier and Stier, 1924-25a). This means that the latitude of variation is a constant percentage of the mean frequency *and is independent of the temperature.* Since the latitude of variation in such experiments is far outside the

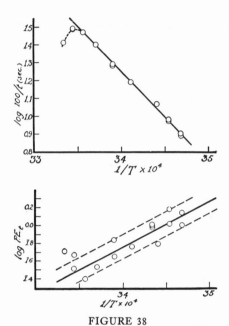

FIGURE 38

To Illustrate Certain Features of Variability of Performance in a Living System

A typical example of the relation between the frequency of breathing movements and (internal) temperature in a young mouse. The points on the upper curve are averages of 40 readings each. Log *frequency* declines rectilinearly with increase $1/T$, where T is the temperature Kelvin. The log of the probable error of the mean *time* for 10 *movements* increases in the same manner. Hence the relative variation of the mean frequency (or time for a constant number of movements) is independent of the temperature. A temperature of 25°C. is "critical" for the mice of this particular strain. This is shown both by a decline in frequency of movements and by the concurrent increase in variation.

(Data from experiments by Dr. G. Pincus.)

limits of any possible "errors of measurement," and certainly represents *organic* variation, this means that the physical condition of the milieu in which the frequency of movement is determined is not significantly altered as a function of temperature. More generally, the temperature coefficients of the various processes determining the apparent value of μ must be the same, which is highly unlikely if there be more than one such process. The *variability* of the frequency, as a function of temperature, is zero, or indistinguishably close thereto (Crozier, 1924-25*b*, etc.). One is thus allowed to conclude that change of temperature (within specified limits) does not alter in any relevant way the physical properties of the system in which there takes place the process determining the expression of the mean frequency of movement as a function of temperature.

With regard to a variety of instances involving measurements of excitation and response, these methods have now given very interesting checks upon the worth of the observations (cf. Hoagland and Crozier, 1931-32; Wolf and Crozier, 1932-33; Wolf, 1932-33, etc.). The results speak powerfully in support of the view that the variation of behavior of living organisms is neither random nor lawless—and that its character may be quantitatively predicted.

V

TROPISTIC ANALYSIS OF RECEPTIVE MECHANISMS

Under certain conditions it is possible to account quantitatively for elementary manifestations of geotropic and of phototropic orientation. It is desirable to exhibit in a summary way specific applications of the analyses. These consist, in a sense, in testing one's ability to predict quantitative features of response in situations such that both phototropic and geotropic orientation are in evidence. Conceivably, this sort of inquiry might ultimately be pushed to include the nomographic repre-

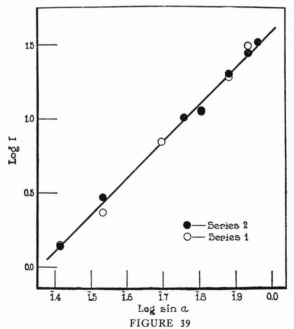

FIGURE 39

The intensity of light required to inhibit geotropic orientation of young rats varies with the inclination of the creeping surface in such a way that $\Delta \log I / \Delta \log \sin \alpha$ is constant. For Series 1 each point is the mean of 15 determinations; for Series 2 of 20 determinations.

(From *J. Gen. Physiol.*)

sentation of determined conduct when such variables as gravity, light intensity and wave-length, galvanic current, temperature, oxygen tension, time, and other conditions can be controlled. Thus far, the data do not exist for such an extension, and the simpler instances about to be mentioned are, from an experimental standpoint, difficult enough.

With young rats it was possible to expect (Crozier, 1926-27c), from previous acquaintance with the geotropic orientation and phototropic orientation (in the case of animals with unopened eyes), that the intensity of light required to effect a definite phototropic counterbalancing of the geotropic orienting influence should be a power function of the sine of the angle of inclination of the creeping plane (Figure 39). It was also possible on the same basis to account for the changing variability of the measured values of I as a was increased. It is of interest to deal at greater length with a case where time enters as an additional variable. This will illustrate the general problem of orientation in compound fields and also the way in which the results of this procedure lend themselves to a more penetrating treatment of mechanisms of excitation. The experiments involve the effect of phototropic excitation upon the direction of gravitationally oriented creeping of the slug *Agriolimax*. The operative problem first consists in securing a measure of the orienting effect of light, with the gravitation influence held constant. In darkness a negatively geotropic *Agriolimax* upon a vertical surface creeps straight upward. When light (horizontal rays) falls upon one side of the animal, previously dark-adapted, it continues to creep upward but at the same time away from the light, the path departing from the vertical by an angle β (Figure 40). Time enters as a variable, since photic adaptation is fast. While it would be preferable in some respects to measure at each chosen moment the intensity of light necessary to produce a constant deviation of the path from the vertical, it has been easier to measure the deviation itself as a function of time (Figure 41) (cf.

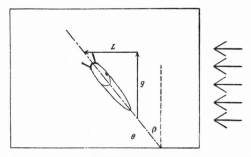

FIGURE 40

Orientation of negatively geotropic and negatively phototropic *Agriolimax* on a vertical plate with light from the right—to indicate terminology of the phototropic (L) and geotropic (g) vectors, the angle of orientation (θ) and its complement (β).

(From *J. Gen. Physiol.*)

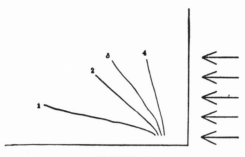

FIGURE 41

SUCCESSIVE TRAILS MADE BY INITIALLY DARK-ADAPTED *Agriolimax* ON A VERTICAL
PLATE, LIGHT FROM THE RIGHT, AT INTERVALS OF 1 MINUTE (MID-POINTS)
This gives the form of the records as available for analysis; actually the trails all
began at the same point.

(From *J. Gen. Physiol.*)

Wolf and Crozier, 1927-28). Two forces are apparent in such experiments. The light leads to photonegative orientation, and the geotropic stimulus forces the slug to creep upward. If, during exposure, the test light is removed, orientation is at once upward. If, on the other hand, the inclination of the creeping plane is decreased, orientation is more completely away from the light. Therefore the path actually followed depends upon the effects of concurrent continuous stimulations of the two kinds. The geotropic stimulus may be regarded as constant. Then the angle β depends on the relation $\tan \beta = L/g$, where L is the phototropic vector. We may assume that at any moment the photic irritability is proportional to an amount of photosensitive material S, only very slowly produced by the processes underlying dark-adaptation, and that the photolysis of S adheres to the kinetics of a first-order reaction (Hecht, 1922-23, 1923-24, 1924-25). This means that over any short interval the decomposition products formed from S, which are responsible for excitation, will be proportional to S_t and thus to $S_o e^{-Kt}$, when S_o is the amount of S at complete dark-adaption. Inserting this relation in the previous equation, $\tan \beta$ should be proportional to e^{-Kt}, and $\log \tan \beta$ should be directly proportional to $-t$ (Figure 42). Moreover, the rate coefficient of light-adaptation, K in the preceding expression, would be expected to be practically proportional to the logarithm of the intensity of the light used to produce adaptation. Both of these expectations are verified. They are further checked by the orientation effect with forms only very slowly adapting to light (cf. Yagi, 1927-28), as in *Limax*, even where the vectors g and L are not at right angles (Figure 43).

Since β decreases with time, it might be suspected that the slug "learns" to overcome the effect of the light. This would suppose that the concomitance of geotropic and phototropic excitations produces, cen-

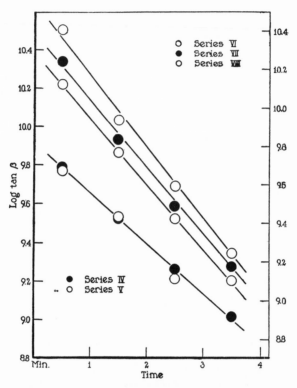

FIGURE 42

THE COURSE OF LIGHT-ADAPTATION IN FIVE SERIES OF EXPERIMENTS, AT TWO DIFFER-
ENT INTENSITIES: FOR SERIES IV, V, 16.32 F.C.; FOR SERIES
VI TO VIII, 73.69 F.C.

(From *J. Gen. Physiol.*)

trally, a "block" for photic impulses (or else, enhances the geotropic
effect). This would be interesting in itself, if verifiable, since the process clearly obeys a definite law. The alternative interpretation is that
the photic adaptation is direct, and occurs in the eye. By means of
experiments in which the animal creeps on the vertical plane only during
the brief interval required to measure β, the exposure to light being
continuous, it was shown (Crozier and Wolf, 1927-28) that the measurable adaptation does not depend upon the simultaneous competitive action
of the geotropic stimulation (Figure 44); it must therefore be regarded
as located in the eye.

The notion that excitation by light is a photochemical matter and that
the maintenance of photic reactivity and its recovery after exhausion may
be in some fashion connected with a reversible photochemical receptor
system seems to have been held in a very general form since Hering.

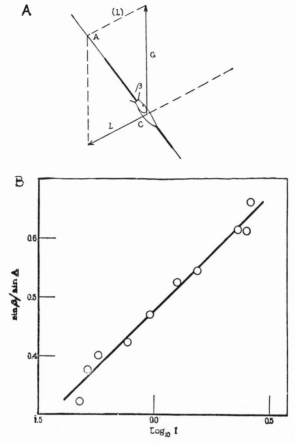

FIGURE 43

A. A slug (*Limax*), previously dark-adapted, is creeping on a vertical plate of ground glass which has been moistened. It is illuminated at an angle from one side by light from a small condensed-filament lamp. To avoid effects of the observer's breathing currents, the path of the slug is observed from the other side of the plate. At the point C the slug is under the influence of an orienting field containing two significant vectors: a gravitational vector G, which is assumed constant; and a photic vector L, of magnitude assumed proportional to log I. I is *measured* at C, with a photometer giving illumination in foot candles. The direction of progression is given by the heavy line. Then if the assumptions are valid

$$L = K \log I = \left(\frac{G}{\sin A}\right) \times (\sin \beta);$$

or,

$$\frac{K' \sin \beta}{\sin A} = \log I.$$

B. The plot in Figure B shows that the equation is satisfactorily obeyed. The residual variation is about the same at all points (*ca.* ± 4.0°).

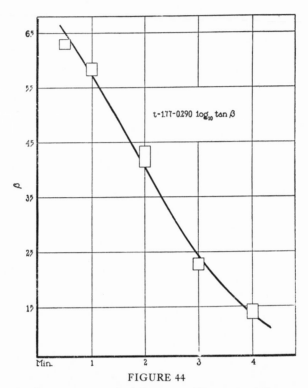

$$t - 1.77 - 0.290 \log_{10} \tan \beta$$

FIGURE 44

THE ANGLE OF ORIENTATION OF *Agriolimax*, THE DEPARTURE (β) FROM A VERTICAL
PATH UPON A VERTICAL PLANE AS FORCED BY THE PHOTOTROPIC EFFECT OF
LIGHT FROM ONE SIDE, AFTER INCREASING PERIODS OF EXPOSURE
TO ILLUMINATION OF 29.4 F.C.

The slugs were creeping upon a *horizontal* surface except during the half minute
required to obtain the orientation trail. The observations are plotted as bars
centered on the means, with height = 2 P.E. The curve is that of the equation
$$\text{time} = 1.77 - 0.290 \log_{10} \tan \beta,$$
and the agreement with the observations shows that, as previously found (Wolf
and Crozier, 1927-28), log tan β decreases linearly with time.

(From *J. Gen. Physiol.*)

Growing knowledge of the chemical effects of light made it attractive to
translate such ideas into photochemical terms. An early attempt to treat
the question precisely and specifically, but with some important deficiencies, was made by Müller (1896). To explain the simultaneous exhibition of capacity to react to a sharp decrease in light intensity and also
to be excited to phototropic movements by the continuous action of light,
as seen in the integument of certain holothurians, it was suggested that
the same photochemical system, if part of a reversible reaction of a certain
kind, might be conceived to serve for both modes of stimulation (Crozier,

1915). Hecht has been able to achieve the step-by-step proof, in a very satisfying manner, that a particular type of reversible photochemical system underlies photic excitation in such forms as *Mya, Ciona, Pholas,* and in the human eye. A major property of the underlying mechanism is adequately expressed (Hecht, 1918-19, 1922-23) in the following paradigm, where S represents primary photosensitive substance, P and A two of the products of its photolysis

$$S \underset{\text{dark}}{\overset{\text{light}}{\rightleftarrows}} P + A.$$

The system is reversible, and with time, under continuous constant illumination, there is established a stationary state ("equilibrium"). The "dark" process, of which the kinetics serve to describe the course of dark-adaptation, is definitely bimolecular (Hecht, 1926-27), with high temperature characteristic; the "light" reaction is of first order, and negligibly influenced by temperature (Hecht, 1919-20a).

These relationships have been established most elaborately by means of experiments with organisms in which the speed of response following the delivery of a measurable quantity of light gives data necessary for the quantitative treatment, and in which light-adaptation is rapid and photic excitation therefore necessarily discontinuous. To carry over such considerations to the analysis of continuous excitation, as in phototropic stimulation, it has been necessary to find phototropic organisms in which the rate of light-adaptation is measurable, neither inconveniently rapid nor too slow. The photic adaptation of *Agriolimax* has been followed by causing the phototropic influence of the light to work against the "brake" provided by a vectorially constant excitation of a different kind, namely, that due to gravity, acting at right angles to the phototropic vector. The function of such a "brake" in contributing to the significance of the measured orientations has been discussed previously in relation to circus movements (Crozier and Federighi, 1924-25a). Data necessary for treatment of the light-adaptation are obtained from measurements of the resultant angles of orientation as related to time and to intensity (Wolf and Crozier, 1927-28). Such measurements are possible because the rate of light-adaptation, especially at temperatures in the neighborhood of 15° or slightly above, is so much faster than that of dark-adaptation, as adequate tests showed. It was easily established that the rate of light-adaptation is very little influenced, if at all perceptibly, by temperature; and that its course follows that of a first-order reaction in which the "velocity constant" is a linear function of the logarithms of the light intensity, as already indicated. These phenomena therefore parallel, in an exact manner, the properties of the "light" reaction already discussed.

The interpretation of dark-adaptation during phototropic excitation requires measurements of the photic excitability at successive intervals following exclusion of light from individuals previously light-adapted. To reduce the probability of adventitious errors of estimation the experiments were made at a temperature high enough to bring the time for practically complete dark-adaptation down to a little over one hour. At about 12°, the time required may be as long as three to four hours; at 20.5°-22°, the temperature prevailing throughout the present experiments, the time is less than half of this. Since light-adaptation, *as measured by the power to influence geotropic creeping on a vertical surface,* is effectively complete

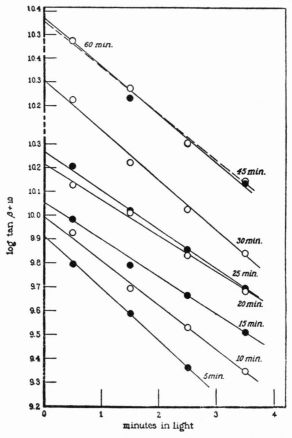

FIGURE 45

The angle (β) of orientation of *Agriolimax* away from the vertical path on a perpendicular plate, as enforced by exposure to horizontal light of 29.4 f.c. on the right side, at successive minutes during exposure, following increasing residence in darkness (5 to 60 minutes) of slugs initially light-adapted. Time of exposure plotted against log tan β gives graphs sensibly rectilinear. The intercepts of these graphs on the ordinate axis give a means of estimating the photic excitability at the very first moment of exposure to light (see text). (The ordinate axis has been shifted vertically for "30 min." and for "45 min." and "60 min." to obviate overlapping.)

(From *J. Gen. Physiol.*)

within about five minutes, as a rule, with high intensities, the experiments must take the form of establishing curves of light-adaptation as affected by known preceding periods in darkness. From such data it is required to deduce the ideal photic excitability at the last moment in darkness, before the exposure has begun, or in other words the kinetics of the "dark" reaction.

The simplest assumptions which serve to explain the data are the following: We suppose that the excitation at any moment is proportional to $-ds/dt$. The intercepts on the $\log_{10} \tan \beta$ axis at zero time of exposure to the light (Figure 45) give measures of $-ds/dt$ at the first instant of exposure (Figure 46). The ratio $\tan \beta_0 / \tan \beta_t$, labeled R, where β_0 is the

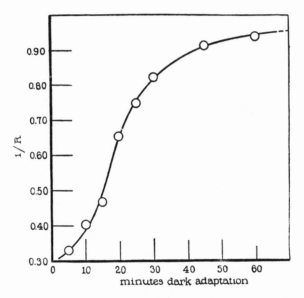

FIGURE 46

The "dark" restitution of S through a second-order reaction with positive auto-catalysis would require that the photic excitability, $-ds/dt$, or its proportionate equivalent, $1/R$, should exhibit a maximum velocity of change when (S_t) has been brought to a little less than $2/3$ (S_∞); I/R should therefore pass through an inflection point when $1/R = $ a little less than 0.67—; the inflection is found at $1/R = 0.64$.

(From *J. Gen. Physiol.*)

intercept angle for fully dark-adapted slugs, permits one to manipulate the resulting equations with somewhat greater ease. At different levels of dark-adaptation the formation of sensitive material must be taken into account. Various simpler hypotheses do not agree with the facts so far obtained, and the "dark" reaction in question has to be taken as a second-order reaction with positive autocatalysis. The differential equation for such a process is:

$$\frac{ds}{dt} = [K' + K_2 (S_0—x)]x^2,$$

where S_0 = concentration of S at complete dark-adaptation, x = concentration of P or A, and K' and K_2 are velocity constants. It is usually sufficient to neglect the constant K', which in most autocatalytic systems appears to be very small. The photolysis of S requires $—ds/dt = K_1 (S_0 —x)$. When both processes go on together,

$$—ds/dt = K_1S_0 — K_1x — K_2S_0x^2 + K_2x^3.$$

The integral equation to which this gives rise is superficially formidable, but a variety of simple consequences at once derive from it and are found to correspond with directly ascertained experimental data:

$$-t = \frac{1}{K_1—K_2S_0{}^2} \cdot \frac{1}{2} \log \frac{K_1S_t{}^2}{S_0{}^2(K_1—K_2S_0+2K_2S_0S_t—2KS_t{}^2)} + \frac{K_2S_0}{\sqrt{K_1K_2}} \tan h^{-1} \frac{K_2(S_0—S_t)}{\sqrt{K_1K_2}} \Bigg\}.$$

For example, the second derivative of this expression gives the way in which the ratio R should change with time of dark-adaptation; it should be found that $1/R$, plotted against time, is a sigmoid curve with an inflection point occurring when the dark reaction is just a little less than 0.67 completed. The experimental value is 0.64 (Figure 46). The rate of

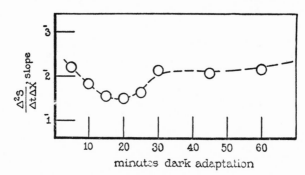

FIGURE 47

The second-order "dark" formation of S requires that the rate of light-adaptation, i.e., change of $—ds/dt$ should be a *minimum* when ds/dt is increasing most rapidly. The minimum found shows precise agreement with this requirement.

(From *J. Gen. Physiol.*)

light-adaptation at different levels of dark-adaptation, the *slope* of each line in Figure 47, is given by

$$-\frac{d^2s}{dt\,dx} = K_1 - 2K_2S_0x + 3Kx^2,$$

and this must pass through a minimum value at a period of dark-adaptation corresponding to the point at which the curve $1/R$ is inflected. This is true experimentally. Moreover, for early stages of light-adaptation, at any level of dark-adaptation, as in the present measurements, log tan β (i.e., log S) should be almost linearly related to $-t$, since K_2 is known to be much less than K_1. Other deductions might be mentioned, but enough has been said to indicate the way in which the results of compounding tropistic effects can be employed, in this case, as a test of the tropism concept and for the development of its utility.

VI

CHEMICAL PACE-MAKERS AND BEHAVIOR

To illustrate the functional analysis of complex behavior by the use of an equation with dimensionally significant variables and constants we may consider the effects of temperature on living systems. Events occurring in living systems are known to be affected markedly by temperature. The rates and frequencies of occurrence of a great diversity of vital processes are fitted by the sort of equation describing the relation between temperature and measured rates of chemical reactions, and the descriptive constants have the proper order of magnitude.

The range of temperature over which most organisms exist is small, roughly from 0 to 40°C. for poikilothermous animals (38±3° for most birds and for mammals). Higher vertebrates have developed complex nervous and chemical mechanisms which maintain constancy of body temperature. Among these animals, except for periods during early development and in hibernation, changes of a few degrees in body temperature may produce irreversible chemical changes which result in death.

The relation between temperature and equilibrium states in chemical systems, rates of reactions, and the nature of resulting end-products, has been examined in considerable detail for numerous homogeneous and heterogeneous inorganic and organic systems. The theory of the relationship has been most completely worked out for reactions occurring in the gas phase. Temperature proves to be an especially convenient physical variable because of its comparative ease of control and the high degree of accuracy of methods available for its measurement. The influence of temperature on the rates of the vast majority of chemical reactions is quite marked. The rate is usually doubled or trebled for a rise of temperature of 10°C., within the temperature range ordinarily considered. In the case of reactions in solution, which are the most important ones from the standpoint of biochemistry, other variable factors, besides the temperature, which may determine the apparent velocity of reaction are the amount of undecomposed reactants, the amount of products formed by the reaction, diffusion effects, the surface distributions of catalyst and substrate, and the concentration of the dissolved catalyst. A catalyst is a substance which accelerates a reaction as a function of its concentration, but which is found at the conclusion of the reaction to be present in the same concentration as at the start. It is probable that in solutions all chemical reactions with measurable velocities are catalyzed. Very minute traces of catalyst are usually effective.

Studies of chemical reaction velocities have given information of great significance concerning mechanisms of the reactions. In the simplest cases, under constant conditions, rates of chemical reactions are found to be proportional to the concentrations of the reactants as required by the law of mass action. According to this law the first conditions for a reaction between molecules A and B is that they shall be in contact. The probability that a molecule of A shall be in a given position at a given time is proportional to the number of molecules of A, or the concentration of A, in the reacting system. Similarly for molecules of the species B. The probability that a molecule of A shall meet a molecule of B is equal to the products of the two probabilities that A and B shall individually be present in the same space at the same time. If a and b are respectively the concentrations of A and B this product is ab. The probability that m molecules of A will meet n molecules of B is proportional to $a^m b^n$. The rate of the reaction at constant temperature will, therefore, be

$$\frac{da}{dt} = \frac{db}{dt} = k\, a^m b^n,$$

where k is the velocity constant of the reaction with the dimensions of reciprocal time, i.e., a rate. The velocity constant is an important means of characterizing a reaction when extraneous variables are effectively controlled.

In complicated systems involving several serial reactions of the form

$$A \xrightarrow{k_1} \quad B \xrightarrow{k_2} \quad C \xrightarrow{k_3} D$$

one specific velocity constant may characterize the formation of the final substance D. This is true if one of the reactions in the series is very slow compared to the others. The velocity for the formation of D will approximately depend upon the slowest link in the series so that the smallest of the three velocity constants may characterize the sequence,

$$A \xrightarrow{k_{min.}} D.$$

This fact has led to the notion of the "master" reaction as the slowest reaction in a series of irreversible processes. The conception of the controlling master reaction has proved useful in interpreting a number of physiological events. Robertson (1923), and more recently Crozier (1926-

$27a$), have used it in formulating the chemical kinetics underlying the control of the growth of organisms. We shall consider applications of the conception of controlling master reactions to certain specific problems of animal behavior. It should be noted that the conception of the master reaction depends only upon the relative rates of the linked irreversible processes, i.e., the relative magnitudes of velocity constants, without hypothesizing any particular mechanism of the reaction, and without assumptions as to the means whereby the successive steps in the chain of events are interconnected.

Let us consider how the velocity constant is related to the fundamental properties of reacting molecules and to the temperature. In the case of reversible chemical systems of the general form

$$A + B \overset{k_1}{\underset{k_2}{\rightleftarrows}} C + D,$$

at constant temperature, again designating concentrations of the respective substances by the small letters a, b, c, d, we have

$$k_1\, a.b = k_2\, c.d$$

and

$$K = \frac{k_1}{k_2} = \frac{c.d}{a.b},$$

where K is the equilibrium constant for the reversible system.

This equilibrium constant Van't Hoff showed to change with temperature according to the equation

$$\frac{d \ln K}{dT} = \frac{\Delta H}{RT^2}$$

where T is the absolute temperature, R is the gas constant, $\ln K$ is the natural logarithm (to the base e) of the equilibrium constant, and ΔH is the heat of the reaction.

Arrhenius in 1889 pointed out that

$$\Delta H = \mu_1 - \mu_2$$

where μ_1 and μ_2 are the respective heats of reaction of the forward and back reactions. Since each of the individual velocity constants, k_1 and k_2, varies empirically with temperature, according to the same equation as that describing the behavior of equilibrium constants we have,

$$\frac{d \ln k_1}{dT} = \frac{\mu_1}{RT^2} \qquad \frac{d \ln k_2}{dT} = \frac{\mu_2}{RT^2}$$

Integration of the general Arrhenius equation, in this form, yields

$$k = e^{-\mu/RT} + C,$$

where e is the base of natural logarithms and k is a velocity constant.

Arrhenius was led to the conclusion that μ is essentially an energy of activation, that is, the amount of energy which must be absorbed by a mol of substance in order to make it react. Subsequent workers in recent years have shown this assumption to be justified. Colliding molecules do not react unless they have received a threshold increment of energy over and above the average, either in the form of radiant (thermal) energy from the environment, or as kinetic energy of collision, or from their own internal degrees of freedom (Tolman, 1927; Rice, 1923; Hinshelwood, 1929). (Cf. also Taylor, 1931.) This "critical thermal increment" or liminal activating energy is a characteristic of the reacting molecular species.

Catalysts, which include enzymes, are believed, in general, to facilitate chemical reactions by forming intermediate compounds with the substrates. These compounds are considered to require a much lower threshold energy of activation than the substrates alone so that they decompose readily into the catalyst and other decomposition products. This may be illustrated by a quotation from Hinshelwood (1929).

> Suppose the reaction A B $\rightarrow$ A $+$ B is accelerated by a homogeneous catalyst which forms a complex with the molecule A B. The reaction would be accelerated if the molecular compound A B.C had a much lower energy of activation for the change A B.C $\rightarrow$ A $+$ B $+$ C than the molecule A B had for the simple decomposition.
> "Let the energy of activation of the simple reaction be E_1 and that of the catalysed reaction be (E_1-e_1). Now at equal concentrations the complexes will decompose more rapidly than the molecules in the ratio $\dfrac{e^{-(E_1-e_1)/RT}}{e^{-E_1/RT}}$ which equals $e^{e_1/RT}$."

Since e_1 in the above discussion is the molecular energy of activation of the catalyst we might expect that different substrates catalyzed by the same substance, other conditions being equal, would yield the same critical thermal increment, e_1, or μ, of the Arrhenius equation. There is some evidence that this is true, and more is being accumulated. A value of $\mu = 16,000\pm$ calories has been found, for example, from data upon iron catalysis in connection with aerobic respiratory oxidations in cells and in charcoal respiratory models containing traces of iron. The value of $\mu = 11,000\pm$ calories has been found in connection with hydroxyl ion catalysis. $\mu = 20,000\pm$ calories appears to be associated with many reactions catalyzed by hydrogen ion (Rice, 1923).

In recent years the Arrhenius equation has been extensively applied to biological systems. Most of this work has been done since 1923 by Crozier and workers in his laboratory. Various poikilothermous organisms (those which do not possess temperature-controlling mechanisms) have been placed in accurate thermostats (cf. Crozier and Stier 1932-33) and aspects of their behavior have been studied between temperatures of from 0 to 40°C. The phenomena examined have been diverse and include, among others, frequencies of heart rates (Crozier and Federighi, 1924-25d), respiratory movements (Crozier and Stier, 1924-25a, 1924-25b), the beating of cilia (Crozier, 1924-25a), growth (Crozier, 1926-27a), rates of segmentation of eggs (Crozier, 1924-25a), sensory reaction-times of organisms (Hecht, 1926-27), the production of CO_2, and the utiliza- of oxygen by plant and animal tissues (Tang, 1931-32; Crozier, 1924-25a), the frequency of chirping of crickets (Crozier 1924-25a), and the release of pedal movements from the central nervous systems of ants (Crozier 1924-25a). For a discussion of this work see especially Crozier (1924-25a, 1924-25b), also Stier (1932-33). The rates, or frequencies, of these processes are found to obey the Arrhenius equation, which may be written most conveniently in the form

$$ ln \frac{k_2}{k_1} = \mu/R \left(\frac{1}{T_1} - \frac{1}{T_2} \right) $$

where k_1 and k_2 are rates of physiological activities, frequencies, etc., as- sumed to be directly proportional to the velocity constants of underlying chemical reactions at the absolute temperatures T_1 and T_2, R is the gas constant and μ is the critical thermal increment or *temperature characteris- tic* (Crozier, 1924-25a).

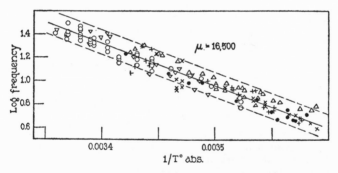

FIGURE 48

<small>The Frequency (100 Divided by Time for 10 Movements) of Rhythmic Opercu- lar Movements in Six Goldfish (Different Symbols) at Different Tempera- tures, When the Pectoral Fins Are Not Obviously Moving
The four most divergent points are single observations; the majority of the others, averages of four or more closely concordant readings. The critical increment is 16,500 calories. (The observations pertaining to one individual [black circles] are divided by 1.34.)
(From *J. Gen. Physiol.*)</small>

Figure 48 shows a typical Arrhenius equation plot of the frequency of opercular breathing movements of goldfish as a function of temperature. The value of $\mu = 16,500$ calories implies the central release of respiratory discharges at a frequency directly proportional to the speed of a continuous oxidative process in the cells, possibly catalyzed by iron. Figure 49 shows the effect of temperature on the rate of chirping of crickets. The value of $\mu = 12,200$ calories. The figure implies the central release of the chirping activity at a frequency directly proportional to the speed of a specific chemical reaction in the central nervous system.

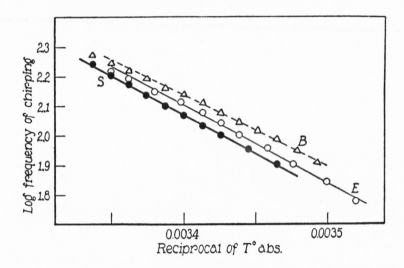

FIGURE 49

THE RATE OF CHIRPING OF THE TREE CRICKET *Œcanthus* AS A FUNCTION OF
TEMPERATURE

B—data from Bessey and Bessey (1898); *E*—data from Edes (1899); *S*—data
from Shull (1907); the last series is probably the most significant. The observations were all made in the field.
(From *J. Gen. Physiol.*)

The equation describes the data for a wide variety of vital processes, and
the magnitudes of μ have been found to be highly significant in that they
are not scattered at random but are found to be grouped in definite modes.
The multimodal frequency distribution curves of temperature characteristics implies the existence of a limited number of catalytic substances involved in the control of master reactions determining rates of a wide
variety of physiological processes, including the emission of repetitive discharges of impulses from nerve centers. The values of μ for all known
observations clearly exhibit modes at 8, 11, 12, 16, 18, 20, 22, 24, and 32
thousand calories (Crozier 1925-26).

The slowest of a series of consecutive reactions involved in the production of a physiological response is called the "master" reaction. If
among hundreds of such reactions in living systems there are a few commonly recurring ones which are slow with respect to the others we might
expect to find these few acting as pace-makers for a great variety of different events in photoplasmic systems. This actually seems to be the
case, the nine above modes for μ values having been obtained from 286
different physiological processes.

Many processes are found to give different values of μ on either side of a critical temperature. This has been interpreted as indicating the existence of two or more consecutive dependent reactions of the form

$$A \xrightarrow{k_1} B \xrightarrow{k_2} C,$$

in which the velocity constants k_1 and k_2 are not affected to the same degree by temperature so that on one side of a critical temperature $k_1 > k_2$ while on the other side of this temperature $k_2 > k_1$. In such systems we have seen that the slower of the two reactions (i.e., the one with the smaller velocity constant) is the "master" reaction or pace-maker for the system. The analytical significance of these critical temperatures, from the standpoint of biochemistry, along with certain deviations from the Arrhenius equation encountered in some processes has been discussed elsewhere (Crozier, 1924-25b). For a consideration of the rôle of successive irreversible processes in the maintenance of steady states in protoplasm see Osterhout (1922).

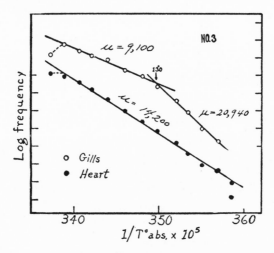

FIGURE 50

TYPICAL OBSERVATIONS ON FREQUENCY OF HEART BEAT AND OF RESPIRATORY MOVE-
MENTS MADE SIMULTANEOUSLY BY TWO OBSERVERS FROM TWO
EXPERIMENTS WITH *Daphnia* OVER A WIDE
RANGE OF TEMPERATURE
Open circles refer to "gill" movements, solid circles to heart beat.
(From *J. Gen. Physiol.*)

Figure 50 shows the effect of temperature on the heart beat and gill movements of *Daphnia* (Stier and Wolf, 1932-33). Two temperature characteristics for gill movements are in evidence on either side of the critical temperature of 13°C. Figure 51 illustrates the effect of temperature on the frequency of nerve impulses discharged from "spontaneously" active

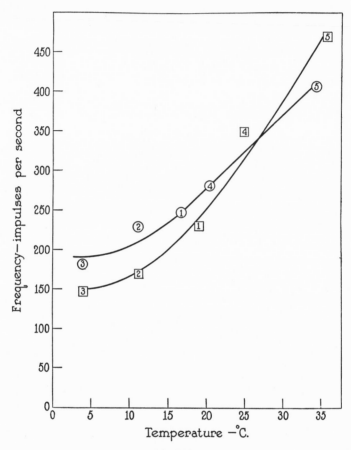

FIGURE 51

FREQUENCY OF NERVE IMPULSES FROM "SPONTANEOUS" ACTIVE LATERAL-LINE
RECEPTORS OF CATFISH AS A FUNCTION OF TEMPERATURE

The number of the experimental points indicates the order in which they were
determined.

(From *J. Gen. Physiol.*)

lateral-line receptors of catfish (Hoagland, 1932-33*b*). The nerve was
at constant temperature; the temperature of the receptors was varied.
Figure 52 is an Arrhenius equation plot of this type of nerve-impulse discharge. The impulses appear to be released at frequencies determined by
the rate of continuous underlying reactions in the receptor cells.

As we have seen, an equation of the same general form as the Arrhenius
equation was earlier proposed by Van't Hoff to account for the effect of
temperature on reversible chemical systems. This equation substitutes

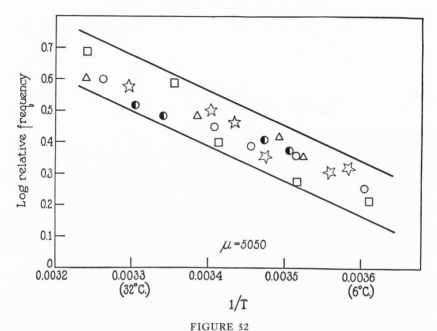

FIGURE 52

PLOT OF TEMPERATURE VS. FREQUENCY ACCORDING TO THE ARRHENIUS EQUATION
(From *J. Gen. Physiol.*)

equilibrium constants for the velocity constants of the Arrhenius equation. The equilibrium constants, since they are each ratios of the velocity constants of the reversible reactions, do not give diagnostically significant values of μ. The value of the thermal constant for the reversible system (generally called Q or ΔH) is here essentially equivalent to the algebraic sum of the critical thermal increments for the forward and back reactions. The fact that most biochemical reactions involve essentially dynamic steady states produced by successive irreversible processes instead of thermodynamic equilibria renders the temperature characteristics of greater significance in protoplasmic systems, since the thermal constants may frequently be simple energies of activation of catalysts, as is suggested by the recurring modal values of μ for different processes.

The molecular significance of μ has been strikingly demonstrated by some experiments of Pincus (1930-31), who tested the inheritance of temperature characteristics determined for the respiratory movements of very young mice of highly inbred strains and their crossed progeny. By using mice only a few days old, before the development of their temperature regulatory mechanisms, it was possible to obtain μ values over the range of 15 to 25°C. Various highly inbred strains were used. Young mice of one strain gave consistently $\mu = 24,000\pm$ calories or, less frequently 28,000± calories for frequencies of respiratory movements. Those of another inbred strain gave values of 34,000±, or, less frequently, 14,-000± calories. The F_1 hybrids of these two strains and the back-cross generations to either parent strain "exhibited only those four values exhibited in the parent strain and none other. One may therefore speak of the inheritance of the value of the constant μ."

This kind of analysis of events occurring in living systems indicates that an individual cyclic activity such as the heart beat, respiratory movements, and rhythmic release of impulses from nerve centers is, in general, controlled by a specific master chemical reaction (probably the slowest reaction in the consecutive processes which result in the performance). A variety of evidence, aside from temperature considerations, supports this point of view.[2] The work of Sherrington and his collaborators (1932) has occounted for phenomena of reflex excitation, inhibition, occlusion, facilitation, and after-discharge in reflex centers in terms of excitatory and inhibitory states which may sum algebraically, essentially as specific chemical entities, facilitating or inhibiting the passage of impulses across synapses. Adrian (1928, 1932) and others have shown great differences in the abilities of receptors to discharge nerve impulses in response to constant stimulation. Superficial tactile receptors adapt very rapidly, giving only a few impulses in response to a constantly applied pressure (Adrian, Cattell, and Hoagland, 1931; Cattell and Hoagland, 1931; Hoagland, 1932-33c, 1934-35); muscle spindles adapt much more slowly, initiating impulses in their nerve fibers for a minute or more during a constant tension on the muscle (Matthews, 1931a, 1931b). Hoagland (1932-33b) found that the lateral-line receptors in certain fishes are normally in a state of constant excitation, discharging impulses over the lateral-line nerve fibers spontaneously at definite frequencies. The spontaneously discharging lateral-line receptors seem to be end-organs which essentially show no adaptation. It is as if normal metabolic processes occurring in these receptors were capable of maintaining an excitatory state such that nerve impulses are initiated at a frequency determined by this excitatory process. The pattern of frequencies from the receptors under varying conditions gives evidence for believing that the frequency of the discharge depends upon the velocity of a continuous chemical process within the receptors (Hoagland, 1933-34). Figures 51 and 52 describe the effect of temperature on this process.

---

[2] It should be cautioned that the same value of μ is not necessarily always found for the same physiological function. That is to say, for example, there is no particular μ generally characteristic of heart rates alone. There are, however, certain values which hold for heart rates fairly constantly among related species of animals. This in no way invalidates the theoretical significance of the temperature characteristic for physiological analysis (cf. Crozier and Stier, 1927-28). Protoplasm is essentially complex and with a number of potential master reactions to control a phenomenon it is not surprising that different reactions may serve in this capacity in different organisms or even in the same organism at different times under stress of variable internal conditions.

A somewhat similar state of affairs appears to be maintained in the respiratory centers of animals; Adrian (1931) has shown that the brainstem of the goldfish, when removed from the body, undergoes rhythmic and "spontaneous" changes of potential at a frequency corresponding to the normal opercular breathing rhythm (cf. Figure 53 and also Figure 50).

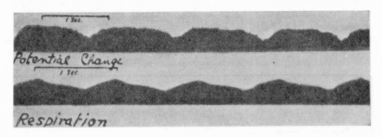

FIGURE 53

RHYTHMIC POTENTIAL CHANGES IN THE ISOLATED BRAIN-STEM OF THE GOLDFISH COMPARED WITH RECORD OF GILL MOVEMENTS IN AN INTACT FISH

From Adrian (1932, p. 82), by permission of the University of Pennsylvania Press.

Adrian (1931) has also shown that the thoracic and abdominal ganglia of the beetle *Dytiscus marginalis* periodically show variations in potential independently of afferent control. The electrical variations produce corresponding bursts of impulses from nerves connected with the ganglia. A similar rhythmicity of the respiratory center of mammals and its fundamental independence of afferent control have been demonstrated by Bronk and Ferguson (1933). Prosser (1934) has recorded repetitive, rhythmic discharges of nerve impulses (probably proprioceptive in nature) from ganglia of the crayfish. These impulses appear not to be initiated by afferent stimuli or by injury. For other references to studies of spontaneous activity in the central nervous system cf. Hoagland and Perkins (1934-35).

Lillie (1929) made a model of a receptor with its attached nerve fiber from the well-known iron-wire, nitric-acid system. By covering a part of the wire with glass tubing he so limited the diffusion of acid, and hence the recovery process on the glass-sheathed wire, that continuous oxidation of the iron took place within the tube. This continuous action was found to set up rhythmic discharges of impulses over the acid-immersed wire outside of the tube as fast as it recovered from the refractory period following each impulse.

Parker (1932) has presented a variety of evidence for believing that substances excreted at nerve endings are responsible for the excitation of effector organs.

We may consider the application of temperature analysis to certain problems of psychological interest, and begin with the problem of estimating time. It is frequently possible to waken oneself within a few minutes of a time decided upon before going to sleep (Brush, 1930). Experiments in-

volving the wakening of sleeping subjects and having them guess the time
have shown an accuracy of ±15 minutes (Boring and Boring, 1917).
These facts, along with our normal waking estimations of duration, call
for a timing process of considerable accuracy. It has been suggested that
the pulse or the respiration may serve as a clock which becomes correlated
with our conventional time scale, but evidence for this is unconvincing.
[For an experimental approach to this problem see Goudriaan (1921).]

A more likely basis for a subjective time scale would appear to be not an
overt form of highly variable motor activity, such as the pulse or respiratory movements, but rather a chemical clock, perhaps associated with the

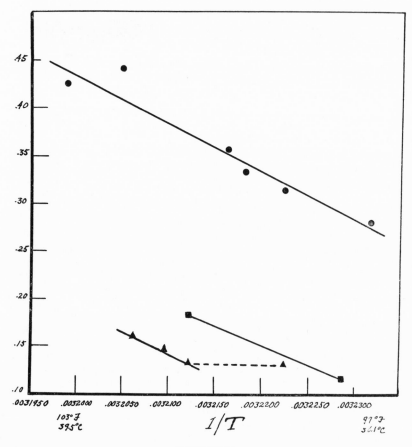

FIGURE 54

PLOT ACCORDING TO THE ARRHENIUS EQUATION OF ESTIMATIONS OF DURATION AS A
FUNCTION OF THE INTERNAL BODY TEMPERATURE

Three experiments on different subjects are indicated. For discussion see text.
(From *J. Gen. Psychol.*)

continuous respiration of cortical nervous tissue. With this hypothesis in mind, Hoagland (1933) determined the effect of internal body temperatures on judgments of short durations. Two experiments on influenza patients suffering from fever are plotted according to the Arrhenius equation in Figure 54. In this same figure are recorded results obtained from a normal person whose internal temperature was raised several degrees by diathermy treatment (the curve represented by triangles). The subjects were naïve concerning the nature of the experiment and were asked simply to count sixty to themselves at a rate of what they believed to be one per second. The maximum range of temperature obtained was only 3.2°C., and usually this is not great enough to show deviations from the Arrhenius equation if such exist, but the very large logarithmic ordinate employed in

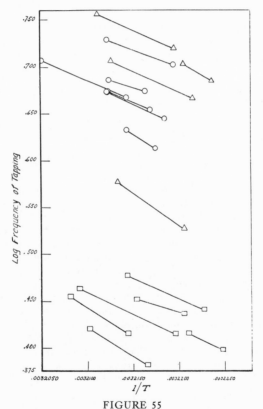

FIGURE 55

PLOT SIMILAR TO FIGURE 54 OF DATA OBTAINED BY FRANÇOIS (1927) IN WHICH A DIFFERENT EXPERIMENTAL PROCEDURE WAS EMPLOYED FROM THAT USED IN OBTAINING THE DATA OF FIGURE 54

(For discussion see text.)

(From *J. Gen. Psychol.*)

Figure 54 would accentuate deviations. The line represented by solid circles covers the range of 3.2°C. and appears to be substantially straight, yielding a value of $\mu = 24,000$ calories.

Unfortunately only two points, indicated by squares, were obtained from a second influenza patient. If it is assumed, however, that the Arrhenius equation describes the data and the points are connected by a straight line, the slope is found to give a value of $\mu = 24,000$ calories, as do the slopes of the three last points to be taken using diathermy technique for the third subject.

In 1927 François considered the relation of body temperature to temporal judgments. The principal procedure used consisted in having subjects tap out instructed rhythms at what they believed to be a constant rate. The rhythms were recorded on a kymograph drum. The subjects were given diathermy treatment and their temperatures were elevated roughly a degree and the tapping was repeated under identical instructions. All the subjects in some sixteen experiments showed consistently faster tapping at the elevated temperatures. Assuming that the Arrhenius equation describes his data, Figure 55 is a plot in which the same large coordinates are used as in Figure 54. The open circles, triangles, and squares represent three different subjects. Each of François' sixteen experiments (on three subjects) involving the tapping of rhythms is represented by two points and their connecting line. The slopes are fairly constant, although the absolute rates, as determined by the ordinates, vary considerably, not only for different subjects but for different experiments with the same individual. The subject indicated by the squares shows uniformly aster rhythms of tapping than either of the others, but the effect of temperature on the rhythms is similar to that in the others. The person indicated by triangles shows large variation in his absolute judgments of time from day to day; it is as if his physiological clock were capable of fluctuations in speed over gross intervals of time. The unique chemical nature of the "clock" is indicated, however, by the constancy of the effect of temperature as indicated by the slopes of the lines.

Figure 56 shows a combined plot of the data of Figures 54 and 55, made by tracing each curve of Figures 54 and 55 in such a way that, while the same abscissas were used, the differences in the absolute values of the ordinates are eliminated. The composite plot yields $\mu = 24,000$ calories. These results definitely imply the existence of a unitary chemical process serving as a basis for the subjective time scale, a process probably irreversible in nature and perhaps catalyzed in a specific way, since the critical increment of 24,000 calories is one of the modal groups characteristic of irreversible kinetics in living systems.[3]

---

[3]According to a wide variety of evidence (cf. especially Osterhout, 1922) steady states in living systems are maintained dynamically by sequences of irreversible reactions. Thermodynamic equilibria play a very subsidiary rôle. The good fit of the Arrhenius equation to biological data and the multimodal distribution of μ values for many processes suggest that we are primarily concerned with irreversible reactions (cf. citations in the bibliographies of the papers on temperature effects).

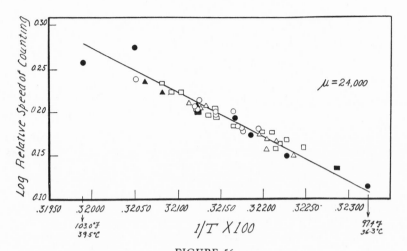

FIGURE 56

COMPOSITE PLOT OF DATA OF FIGURES 54 AND 55 SHOWING SIMILARITIES OF SLOPES
(AND HENCE μ VALUES) FOR ALL OF THE EXPERIMENTS
(For discussion see text.)
(From *J. Gen. Psychol.*)

Much of psychological experimentation on the estimation of time has
been concerned with the study of effects of various forms of sensory and
sensorimotor activity on the judgments of relatively short intervals [for
a recent review of this work see Weber (1933)]. The work indicates
clearly that sensorimotor activity shortens the estimations of short intervals to a degree roughly proportional to its extent (cf. Axel, 1925; Gulliksen, 1927). This experimental literature is entirely consistent with
the hypothesis of a chemical master reaction in the nervous system furnishing its possessor with a subjective time scale. Various changes in the immediate internal environment of the chemical clock may modify its velocity.
Such changes may be those of temperature or variations in the activity of
sensory and motor areas of the brain acting to accelerate or to inhibit the
continuous chemical mechanism. A good example of an effect of just this
kind is illustrated by the activity of the respiratory center. As we have
seen, the excised brain-stem of the goldfish emits rhythmical fluctuations
of electrical potential at exactly the frequency of normal resting opercular
breathing rhythms of intact fishes (Adrian and Buytendijk, 1931).
These variations in potential produce synchronous bursts of efferent impulses to the respiratory musculature. Crozier and Stier (1924-25b)
earlier showed that the opercular rhythm of goldfish obeys the Arrhenius
equation when they plotted the logarithm of the frequency of opercular
beats as a function of the reciprocal of the absolute temperature (cf. Figure 48). A temperature characteristic of 16,500 calories was obtained,
which indicates that the rhythms are probably produced within the cen-

ter by a continuous respiratory, oxidative process catalyzed by iron. Measurements of the metabolism of goldfish as a function of temperature have been made by Ege and Krogh (1914). They found that the velocity of oxygen consumption also yields a μ of 16,500 calories.

The respiratory center is known to be very sensitive to changes of hydrogen ion (or CO_2) concentration in its tissues, even very slight decreases in the normal pH, such as are produced by mild muscular exercise, accelerating respiratory movements (cf. Gesell, 1925). It is not unreasonable to suppose that chemical changes locally produced in the brain by excited groups of neurons would decrease the velocity of our hypothetical "clock," making time appear to pass more rapidly when we are active. This effect, here inhibitory, might be especially apparent when the activity involves extensive excitation of higher levels of the central nervous system. Increases in the frequency of the opercular beats of goldfish have been accounted for by Crozier and Stier (1925-26) in a way similar to this. To quote from their paper:

> The nature of the variation of the frequency of opercular movements at constant temperature, requires brief consideration. The pertinent facts are these: the latitude of variation tends to be a well defined constant fraction of the mean frequency, at each temperature; the incidence of pectoral (fin) movements accelerates the opercular rhythm but there is a clear indication that the central discharge controlling the movements is thereby merely pitched at a new level, —for the critical increment is sensibly the same; a similar result is obtained under moderate starvation. . . . . A full theory of these effects awaits further testing but it is believed that they permit the assumption of definite views regarding the mechanism of variability of central nervous processes. If it be supposed that the reactions controlling discharge from the respiratory center are specifically synaptic in locus, the effective mass of a governing catalyst might be varied according to the influx of nerve impulses from other parts of the central nervous system. Changes of this kind would abruptly alter the frequency of the observed activity without changing the critical increment.

The critical increment, or temperature characteristic, of opercular rhythms may, however, be altered in goldfish. Crozier and Stier (1925-26) accomplished this by exposing fishes previously ascertained to yield a μ of 16,500 calories to a temperature of 25° C. for three hours in water with an oxygen content of about three cc. per liter. A new increment of 8,300 calories was then obtained which lasted for some hours after the treatment, indicating a temporary shift in the catalytic mechanism of the master reaction controlling respiration.

Figure 57 illustrates the possible effect of central nervous activity involved in the production of fin movements on the absolute rate of the reaction determining opercular breathing. The absolute frequency of breathing of a fish supporting itself in mid-water is greater than when the fish is at rest, but the value of μ is the same regardless of the movements. The typical effect of the motor activity (fin movements) of fish in accelerating the master reaction controlling respiratory movements offers a striking parallel with the possible control of our

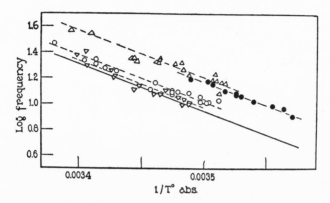

FIGURE 57

THE FREQUENCY OF OPERCULAR MOVEMENTS IN GOLDFISH AT DIFFERENT TEMPERA-
TURES WHEN THE FISH ARE POISED IN MID-WATER WITH
PECTORAL FINS MOVING RHYTHMICALLY

The frequency of opercular movements in goldfish poised in mid-water with pectoral fins moving rhythmically is higher at each temperature than in animals with
motionless pectorals (Figure 48); but the critical increment is unchanged. The
solid line is drawn in the same position as in Figure 48. The plotted points are
averages. The amount of the frequency increase varies with the individual
considered (different symbols).

(From *J. Gen. Physiol.*)

hypothetical chemical clock by sensorimotor activity. The similarities
between Figures 54, 55, and 56 and Figures 48 and 57 are self-evident
and can best be interpreted on the assumption that specific chemical
mechanisms release in one case the rhythms of counting and, in the
other case, the fishes' respiratory movements. The rhythms in both
cases are subject to a similar type of modification by sensorimotor
activity.

In both Hoagland's experiments and those of François, sensorimotor
conditions were relatively constant corresponding to a "resting condition" in one case, or tapping "filled" time in the other. Axel (1925)
has shown that these two temporal "fillers" are essentially equivalent.
Fluctuations in estimates from day to day by the same subject in his
absolute estimates of time occurred in the experiments, and this is to
be expected since many possible internal variables could be controlled
only roughly. The constancy of the value of $\mu = 24,000$ calories,
however, indicates that a unitary chemical mechanism is probably basically
determining the judgments. The fact that this value of μ is characteristic of a number of vital processes (cf. Crozier, 1925-26) suggests
that the chemical mechanism basically involves an irreversible process,
catalyzed by a specific agent, as yet unidentified, but common to many
protoplasmic systems. The value of $\mu = 24,000\pm$ calories has been
obtained in some ten or a dozen cases. It is usually found to be associ-

ated with cell respiration. For example, Tang (1931-32) finds $\mu =$ 24,000 calories for the production of CO_2 by germinating seeds of *Lupinus albus.* Oxygen consumption in these tissues yields $\mu = 16,600$ calories. Crozier and Stier (1925-26), using data of Pütter on the oxygen consumption of leeches, find $\mu = 24,000$ calories when the oxygen tension is only 130± mm. Hg. At higher oxygen tensions (400± mm. Hg) a value of $\mu = 7,900$ was obtained, indicating the existence of two possible catalytic master reactions either of which may control the rate of oxygen uptake depending on the oxygen tension. Observations by Stier on the heart beat of the garter snake as a function of temperature were found to yield $\mu = 23,500$ calories (Crozier, 1925-26).

Since physiological time passes more rapidly at higher temperatures, while physical time continues at a constant rate, we should expect time to appear to pass more slowly during a fever than when at rest. This appears to be a common experience.

The experiments on the estimation of time have dealt only with short durations. It is possible that other mechanisms of a cyclic nature are involved in estimates of longer intervals. Boring and Boring (1917) found a variety of possible cues used by subjects who were awakened during the night and asked to estimate the time. Conscious internal cues such as restlessness, fatigue, "clearness of consciousness," and sensations involved in excretory and digestive functions apparently served as a basis for the time judgments. These are processes of a complex physiological nature, but are essentially rhythmically recurrent, and may, therefore, serve as clocks. Evidence exists which supports the idea that cyclic periods of alternate rest and quiescence in mammals, i.e., periods of "spontaneous" activity, are controlled by specific master chemical reactions which serve to regulate the periods (Stier, 1930).

Excretory and digestive cycles which furnished the basis of temporal judgment of some of the subjects in the experiments of Boring and Boring may be regarded basically as "spontaneous" activities as this term is used by Stier. Temperature characteristics for such cycles in very young poikilothermous mammals indicate that they may be dependent upon specifically catalyzed master chemical reactions different from those previously discussed (Stier, 1930). These facts lend support to the notion that reactions may be involved in the estimation of long durations which may be different from the reaction indicated in this paper (corresponding to $\mu = 24,000$ calories) which serve as a basis for judging short temporal intervals. [Cf. also Carrel (1931) for a discussion of the physiological basis of psychological time of the order of a life-span.]

That the pulse rhythm is not involved in the estimation of short intervals has been demonstrated (Hoagland and Perkins, 1934-35). Studies of many clinical records of patients treated with hyperpyrexia (general diathermy) at the Worcester State Hospital yield a μ value of 29,400 calories for the effect of temperature on the pulse frequency. This indicates a different chemical pace-making mechanism from that involved in time judgments (24,000 calories).

The temperature analysis may be applied to the problem of learning (Hoagland, 1931). From work on learning and conditioning, despite obvious difficulties inherent in diverse forms of measurement, workers have obtained a certain generalized learning curve. This is characteristically S-shaped or sigmoid when one plots the amount learned as ordinate against the number of experimental repetitions of the learning act as abscissa. The sigmoid relation appears, provided that the organism begins the experiments in an unconditioned state with respect to the act to be learned, and provided that the task is one not too readily mastered.

The sigmoid shape of the learning curve and the approximately hyperbolic nature of the curve of forgetting led Robertson (1909) to suggest that learning might depend on the accumulation, through a first-order autocatalyzed chemical reaction, of a facilitating substance somewhere in the reflex arcs, and that forgetting might depend upon the washing-away of this substance from a colloidal matrix. His hypothesis for a molecular basis of conditioning is superficially somewhat similar to Sherrington's proposal of excitatory and inhibitory substances to account for the phenomena of spinal reflexes. In the absence of direct experimental evidence, however, the mere shapes of the learning and forgetting curves can have little specific diagnostic significance, owing to a variety of possible theoretical alternatives. In a discussion of the theoretical basis for certain sigmoid curves, Hoagland (1930) pointed out some of these alternatives and tentatively suggested, in the case of learning, that the sigmoid nature of the relation might just as well be due to the fact that the curve is essentially an integral distribution curve for thresholds of activations of central nervous units, repetition of the conditioning bringing into play more and more of these units. Such an hypothesis is consistent with Lashley's interpretations of his experiments, that the degree of retention of maze habits in rats is directly proportional to the amount of cortex or number of neurons left intact after extirpation rather than to specific localization within the remaining tissue.

Primarily with a view to testing Robertson's hypothesis Hoagland (1931) measured a learning process in ants as a function of temperature. Common carpenter ants, *Camponotus herculeanus,* were chosen because of their availability, hardiness, genetic homogeneity, and educability. The animals were taught, one at a time, to escape from a very simple maze placed in an accurate thermostat. Both the length of time and the number of trials required for the ant to learn to pass from one compartment through an aperture to another when air charged with peppermint oil was passed through the apparatus served as indices of learning. A vibratory stimulus applied to the "maze" was also used to drive the ant from one compartment to the other. The behavior was independent of the nature of the driving stimulus. The stimulus was always stopped when the ant passed the partition separating the two chambers. At the beginning of the experiment an ant would usually take a minute or more to find the hole and escape. At the end of the experiment, determined by a fixed arbitrary number of successive adequate solutions, the ant would go through the hole in a few seconds without showing random behavior. The variability of the response, as determined by the mean probable errors of the times required for solution, was found to parallel closely the time measure of learning and served as a check on the analysis.

One hundred and ninety-two ants were each taught the maze once at various fixed temperature intervals of from 15° to 29.4° C. Figure 58 shows the effect of temperature on the mean rates of learning

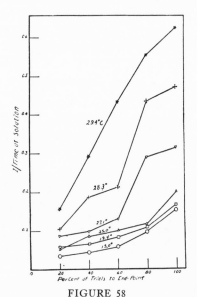

FIGURE 58

PLOT OF TOTAL SPEED OF SOLUTION AS A FUNCTION OF THE PERCENTAGE LEARNED FOR SIX DIFFERENT TEMPERATURES

(From *J. Gen. Psychol.*)

(measured by 1/time of solution) for 130 ants of one colony. Speed of creeping of ants also varies with temperature (cf. Crozier, 1924-25a). Since it is safe to assume that very little learning has taken place during the first 20 per cent of the trials, we may eliminate the speed-of-creeping factor *per se* by starting all our curves from zero rate of learning and 20 per cent of trials-to-end-point on the abscissa. Figure 59 shows the effect of temperature on learning after making this correction. It is clear that learning is not much affected by temperature from 15° to 25° C., but that a marked acceleration in the rate of learn-

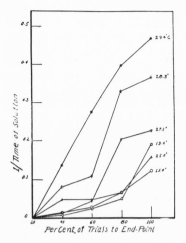

FIGURE 59

PLOT SHOWING SPEED OF "LEARNING" AS A FUNCTION OF THE PERCENTAGE OF LEARN-
ING ACCOMPLISHED FOR SIX DIFFERENT TEMPERATURES

The reduction to a zero origin, by subtracting the speeds for the first 20 per cent
of the trials in which learning is assumed to be negligible, eliminates, in this plot,
the effect of temperature on the speed of running.

(From *J. Gen. Psychol.*)

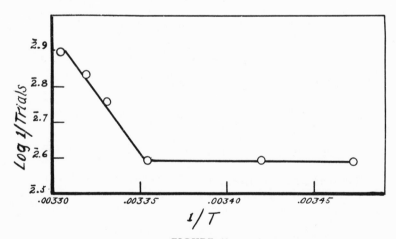

FIGURE 60

PLOT OF THE LOGARITHM OF "RATE OF LEARNING AS A FUNCTION OF TEMPERATURE
ACCORDING TO THE ARRHENIUS EQUATION

The value of μ for the range of 25° to 29.4° is 7,300 calories.

(From *J. Gen. Psychol.*)

ing occurs between 25° and 29.4° C., the ants progressively becoming veritable geniuses within this range.

This is even better illustrated by the Arrhenius equation plot of Figure 60, which shows the logarithm of the reciprocal of the number of trials to reach a fixed arbitrary end point of learning plotted against the reciprocals of the absolute temperatures. The data are means for 130 individuals. The value of μ between 25° and 29.4° is 7,300 calories. This short temperature range combined with the variation of the data does not permit us to say with certainty that the Arrhenius equation describes the data, but, assuming that it does, the value of $\mu =$ 7,300 calories can at present have little significance as a "catalyst indicator." About all that can be said is that the value is suggestive of chemical facilitation of learning above 25° C., which may involve the depositions of excitatory synaptic substances facilitating the learning response. The lack of effect of temperature on learning below 25° C. might be expected if learning here were determined by certain purely physical factors such as diffusion or molecular effects of a physical nature. On the other hand, a similar lack of temperature effect might occur if the facilitation depended upon equilibrium in a system with a low heat of reaction, or in other ways upon opposing effects oppositely influenced by temperature.

The result sheds little light on Robertson's hypothesis, but the experiments have been described to illustrate a suggestive approach to the learning problem. It is possible that an extensive and systematic examination of learning and conditioning as a function of temperature in many poikilothermous animals might yield information about the chemical mechanisms underlying this important aspect of central nervous integration.

VII

General Physiology and the Weber-Fechner Law

Another good illustration of the differences between a purely empirical formulation and a theoretically significant one is furnished by a consideration of the Weber-Fechner law.

Weber's law states that $\dfrac{\Delta I}{I}$ is a constant, where I is the magnitude of the stimulus and ΔI is an increment of the stimulus such that $I + \Delta I$ can just be distinguished as greater than I. This law is a very rough approximation and appears to hold for mid-range intensities in a number of sense modalities.

Fechner extended the generalization by the process of integrating the function $dS = k \dfrac{dI}{I}$ and obtained the relation

$$S = k \log I + C,$$

where S is the magnitude of sensation measured on a sensory scale. The validity of an integration of this type has often been called in question, since if sensory scales appear to be composed of discontinuous magnitudes the specific "just-noticeable differences" make integration illegitimate. The integrated form of Weber's law has, however, been found also to hold empirically over mid-regions of sensory intensity scales.

While many workers from Fechner on have speculated as to the basis of the logarithmic relation between stimulus and sensation, little theoretical advancement was made until the work of Hecht on photoreception. Many workers have been content (and still are content) to see whether the law describes their experimental data and to state the limits of its applicability without ever questioning the relevance or meaning of the so-called law.

Since Hecht's work is familiar (cf. Chapter 14 of this book), we need only briefly summarize his treatment of the Weber-Fechner law (cf. also Hoagland, 1930). Hecht, working with vertebrate eyes, and Hecht and Wolf, studying compound insect eyes, have accounted quantitatively for the data of visual acuity and intensity discrimination in vision on the assumption that intensity thresholds for the rods and cones in vertebrate eyes and for ommatidia in bees' eyes follow statistical distribution curves. On this basis Hecht showed that empirical sigmoid curves relating visual acuity to the logarithm of the light intensity are identical with the sum of the integral distribution curves for the thresholds of activation of the receptor units. The sigmoid curves are described by the equation for the steady state of a reversible chemical system of the form

$$S \underset{\underset{k_2}{\text{dark}}}{\overset{\overset{k_1}{\text{light}}}{\underset{\leftarrow}{\rightarrow}}} P + A.$$

The equation for the steady state is $KI = \dfrac{x^2}{a-x}$, where I is the light intensity, x is the fraction of S changed to P and A at photic equilibrium, a is the initial concentration of S, and K is the equilibrium constant for the system (i.e., $K = \dfrac{k_1}{k_2}$).

The curve relating intensity discrimination to the logarithm of the light intensity is also sigmoid and identical with that describing visual acuity as a function of the logarithm of the light intensity. Hecht points out that this indicates a linear relation between the number of functioning units and the concentration, x, of the product of photolysis.

We see, therefore, that the apparent logarithmic Weber-Fechner law in vision is merely a by-product of the fact that the sigmoid curves for acuity and intensity discrimination are approximately linear in the mid-range of light intensities on a semi-log plot. The curve is actually nowhere really logarithmic, as may be seen from the above equation. As long as the equation relating stimulus and sensory intensity were regarded as simply empirically logarithmic, the Weber-Fechner approximation tended to cloud, rather than to clarify, the essential underlying mechanism.

An analysis similar to that just described and dealt with at some length in this chapter is that of Crozier and Pincus (1929-30a, 1929-30b) in connection with proprioception. They examined the geotropic orientation of young rats of inbred strains and found a pseudo-linear relation between θ, the angle of orientation of the rats in the plane, and the logarithm of sin a, where a is the angle of the slope of the plane. Since sin a is the gravitational component acting in the plane on the rat, and since θ is a measure of the total excitation producing the response, this might appear to be an instance of the Weber-Fechner law. Crozier and Pincus have shown, however, that the semi-log relation is not strictly linear but is a long-drawn-out sigmoid curve. This curve is an integral distribution curve for thresholds of activation of tension receptors on the two sides of the rat's body. By considering that the animals orient upward in the plane until the tensions of muscles on the two sides of the body are equal (within a threshold difference), and by taking into consideration the mechanics of progression, Crozier and Pincus obtained a numerical measure of the number of excited stretch receptors. As we have seen, this measure is expressed as $\dfrac{\Delta\theta}{\Delta \log \sin a}$. A plot of this expression against the gravitational component sin a gives differential distribution curves for three specific groups of tension receptors involved in the orientation. The relation between θ and log sin a is the resultant of the summation of three integral population curves for thresholds of activation of tension receptors. Here again the logarithmic Weber-Fechner law appears to be only a crude approximation to the range covered by the integral curves of distribution of thresholds of activation of the groups of tension receptors.

Hoagland (1930) analyzed data of Adrian and Zotterman on myotatic reflexes relating frequency of afferent impulses, electrically recorded, as a function of the logarithm of the tension. With preparations containing many end-organs, sigmoid curves were obtained. Sigmoid curves were also obtained from data of Adrian and Zotterman relating frequency of nerve-impulse discharge to the logarithm of pressure applied to toe pads of cats. Since Adrian (1928) has shown that a direct relation exists between frequency of nerve impulses and sensory intensity these examples are of especial interest. Presumably the sigmoid curves describe thresholds of activation of the receptors. The empirical logarithmic Weber-Fechner law, literally considered, would not indicate this.

Work involving electrical recording of nerve impulses from single receptors as a function of the intensity of the stimulus has shown that a wide range of intensities may be mediated by a single receptor unit (cf. Adrian, 1928, 1932; Hartline and Graham, 1932; Matthews, 1931a;

Hoagland, 1932-33*a*, 1932-33*b*). Matthews (1931*a*) has recently shown that the frequency of response of a single muscle receptor is directly proportional to the logarithm of the tension applied to the muscle. Here the Weber-Fechner law holds in its original form for the single muscle spindle over the entire range of frequencies that it can mediate, but since we probably never consciously sense the activity of a single receptor unit it is unlikely that this fact is relevant to the problems of psychophysics. Where many receptors are involved the sigmoid relation describing thresholds of activation of the units, as discussed above, is found. Hartline and Graham have recently shown that the frequency of response from a single fiber of the optic nerve of *Limulus*, when a single ommatidium is illuminated at different intensities, is neither logarithmic nor sigmoid.

The above considerations indicate that the Weber-Fechner law is merely a crude approximation for intermediate stimulus intensities to integral distribution curves for thresholds of activation of visual, pressure, and proprioceptors. Care should be taken, however, in the extension of this generalization to all sense modalities since other factors may be involved. Thermal reception in the case of fish seems to follow a very different law. For this reason it might be desirable to consider this case in some detail.

Hoagland (1932-33*b*) analyzed the frequencies of nerve impulses discharged from the lateral-line receptors of fishes as a function of the number of units contributing to the discharge. Records of nerve impulses from the lateral-line nerves of catfish and trout show that the lateral-line sense-organs are in a state of continuous activity producing a massive discharge of impulses (Hoagland, 1932-33*a*). The lateral-line organs are conspicuously marked in most fishes by a row of pores along the side. The pores lead into a lymph-filled canal in the skin in which occur groups of receptor cells at intervals between the pores. The receptors, called neuromasts, are supplied by a sensory branch of the vagus nerve which runs a course parallel to the canal and sends out branches to innervate the groups of neuromasts.

The spontaneous, continuous discharge of nerve impulses from the receptors is found to be modified during the direct application of pressure on the skin over the canal, by ripples in the water bathing the trunk, by irregular currents of water, and by the *concave* bending of the fish's trunk. The asynchronous discharge becomes phasic when the vibrations of tuning forks are transmitted to the water. The frequency of the response is constant for a wide range of tuning forks, and it appears, therefore, as behavior experiments of Parker and Van Heusen (1917) had already indicated, that the receptors act as a very crude ear which can respond to a range of tones without being able to analyze them.

Temperature modifies the frequency of the spontaneous discharge (Figures 51 and 52). From this and a variety of other evidence (cf.

Hoagland, 1932-33*a*), the receptors may be regarded as functioning as thermal receptors as well as functioning as mechanoreceptors.[4]

For recording purposes the lateral-line nerve is exposed under the skin just behind the head. It may then be cut cephalad, leaving it in connection with some 30-35 neuromast groups (in catfish *Ameiurus nebulosus*) along the flank. Each group contains several hundred receptor cells supplied by ten to twenty nerve fibers, the number of fibers supplying the groups decreasing from head to tail. If one now progressively slices through the lateral-line system at intervals, one may obtain responses from as many functioning receptor groups as one chooses by simply counting the pores between the slice and the region of initial incisions where the nerve

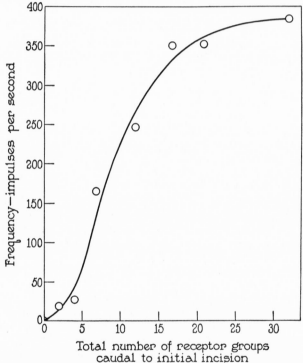

FIGURE 61

RELATION BETWEEN FREQUENCY OF NERVE-IMPULSE DISCHARGE AND NUMBER OF
CONTRIBUTORY LATERAL-LINE RECEPTOR GROUPS
(From *J. Gen. Physiol.*)

---

[4]Mr. Morton Rubin (unpublished results) has recently studied at Clark University the behavior of a number of species of fish to rapidly rising temperatures. He has found definite responses to occur at certain specific water temperatures. When the lateral-line nerves are cut these responses no longer occur. Control fish operated on but without cutting the lateral-line nerves behave as do the normal fish.

leaves the body to go to the electrodes. From the oscillograph records of action potential it is possible to count the frequency of "spontaneous" impulses as a function of the number of active receptor groups. The sigmoid relation shown in Figure 61 is a typical record of such an experiment with a catfish. This curve may be regarded as an integral distribution curve for the frequencies contributed by each group along the flank. Figure 62 is the differential curve made by plotting the tangents to the curve of Figure 61. This curve, therefore, describes the contributions of the individual groups to the response.

From Figure 62 it is clear that there is a diminution in discharge of impulses from the tenth group beyond the operation back to the place of

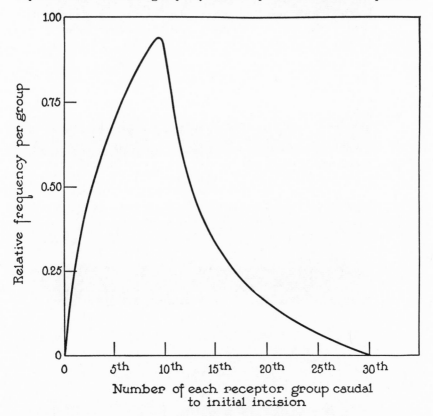

FIGURE 62

THE DIFFERENTIAL CURVE DERIVED FROM FIGURE 61 MADE BY PLOTTING THE SLOPE OF THAT CURVE AGAINST THE NUMBER OF RECEPTOR GROUPS

The curve shows the relative contribution made by each receptor group to the total response.

(From *J. Gen. Physiol.*)

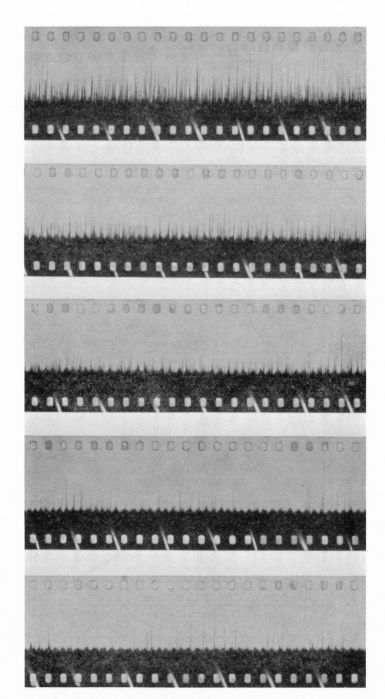

FIGURE 63

SAMPLE PHOTOGRAPHIC RECORDS OF THE RESPONES FOR VARYING NUMBERS OF
RECEPTOR GROUPS

These are samples of the data actually used in determining the curve of Figure 61.
a—responses from 32 receptor groups. *b*—responses from 17 receptor groups.
c—responses from 7 receptor groups. *d* and *e* show responses from only two or
three active fibers. Since there are from ten to twenty fibers supplying each of
the more cephalad receptor groups, it is clear that most of these fibers are inactive.
Reasons for this inactivity are discussed.

(From *J. Gen. Physiol.*)

emergence of the nerve. This decreased activity along the line of receptor groups has been shown to be produced probably by the effects of spread of injury from the initial operation involved in freeing the nerve. These injury effects, most intense near the operation, progressively diminish in their inhibitory effects to about the ninth or tenth neuromast group. From, roughly, the tenth group, back to the tail, the frequency contributed by each receptor group is seen in Figure 62 to decline progressively. The most probable reason for this decline is that increasingly fewer nerve fibers supply the more posterior receptor groups and contribute to the response. Figure 63 shows a series of typical oscillograph records used in making Figures 61 and 62. The spiked lines are nerve impulses; the heights of the spikes are directly proportional to the axon action potentials. The frequency is seen to decline with the removal of receptor groups. Each receptor group contains several hundred receptor cells and is supplied, especially towards the head, by from ten to twenty nerve fibers, decreasing to about half of this number towards the tail. Figure 63, *e,* shows the response from only two receptor groups within roughly a centimeter of the region of exit of the nerve to the electrodes. In this figure only two nerve fibers are active, as indicated by the fact that the all-or-nothing potentials of the impulses are grouped within one of two magnitudes. Since anatomically some 15± fibers innervate each of the two groups, it is clear that most of these are inactive.

This analysis shows how the surgical removal of functional units may produce curves similar to those produced by the functional removal of receptor units in other sense modalities when the intensity of the activating stimulus falls below their thresholds of activation.

The responses of the lateral-line receptors also furnish an interesting application of the variability analysis, examples of which have been described in another part of this chapter. This may be illustrated as follows: Figure 63, *e,* shows the spontaneous response of two fibers of a lateral-line nerve. If one studies the responses from one or two receptor groups by chilling the receptors, it is possible to get preparations showing the activity of only a single nerve fiber since certain of the receptors have temperature thresholds below which they are no longer spontaneously active. The response of the single unit (cf. Figure 63, *e*) generally occurs in rhythms of five to ten impulses at frequencies of thirty to fifty per second separated by silent periods of several tenths of a second. This fluctuating activity produces considerable variation in frequencies counted in successive tenths of a second's interval when only a few fibers are active.

With many active fibers the variation declines since silent periods of some fibers are coincident with active periods of others, thus smoothing out the response (cf. Figure 63, *a* and *b*). A plot, therefore, of the percentage variability expressed as

$$\frac{\text{Probable error of mean frequency}}{\text{Mean frequency for 15 tenth-second intervals}}$$

against the number of active receptor units may be made. Figure 64 shows

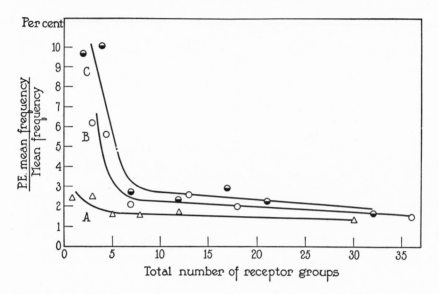

FIGURE 64

PLOT OF RELATIVE VARIATION AGAINST THE TOTAL NUMBER OF RECEPTOR GROUPS
The significance of the curves is discussed in the text.
(From *J. Gen. Physiol.*)

the results of three experiments on lateral-line responses from three cat-fish. Curve *C* shows the maximum variability. This curve corresponds to the experiment illustrated in Figures 62 and 63 where there is a marked decline in activity of sense-organs near the region of operation. Curve *A* of Figure 64 illustrates a second experiment in which is shown a minimal amount of variation throughout, while curve *B* for a third experiment shows an intermediate amount of variability for receptors near the place of operation. The oscillograph records from which curve *A* was made show that quite a number of receptors were active near the operation in this experiment—the spread of injury was slight. The nerve-impulse records used in making curve *B* clearly show an intermediate density of discharge for receptors near the region of emergence of the nerve as compared to the records used in the experiments for curves *A* and *C*. The variability analysis in this case offers, therefore, a sensitive index of the spread of injury effects along the line of receptors.

If temperature produces a decline in the number of functional receptor units in terms of their thresholds of activation, we might expect to get curves similar to those of Figure 64 by plotting the variability of response against the temperature. Figure 65 is such a plot for four experiments with catfish. Here lowering the temperature evidently inactivates units. This is apparent in some experiments to a greater extent than in others.

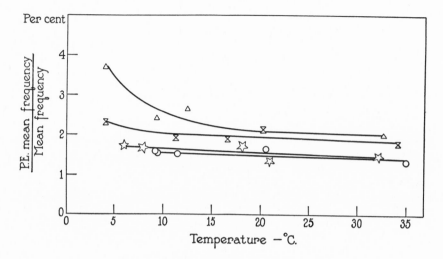

FIGURE 65
RELATIVE VARIABILITY AS A FUNCTION OF TEMPERATURE
(From *J. Gen. Physiol.*)

Lowering the temperature has also been shown to cause a decline in the frequency of discharge of impulses from the individual units. From an inspection of the nerve-impulse records of the four experiments described by the data of Figure 65 it is clear that the large variability of frequency at low temperatures, for the experiment indicated by triangles in Figure 65, is due to a reason similar to that for the large variability of frequencies recorded in curve *B* and especially curve *C* of Figure 64, namely, the activity of only two or three nerve fibers firing asynchronously. In Figure 64 inhibitory effects due to surgical manipulation produced a progressive spread of inactivation from the region of the operation which reduced the spontaneous response of the first seven receptor groups to that of only two or three fibers which were active, despite the fact that some 150 fibers supplied these groups. In the experiment indicated by triangles in Figure 65 the lowered temperature (around 5°C.) produced inactivation of all but two or three fibers out of the total of some five hundred fibers supplying the thirty-two intact receptor groups caudal to the exit of the nerve. The experiments indicated by stars and circles in Figure 65, while showing a reduced response with temperature (cf. Figure 51), produced this response primarily by the reduction of frequency of impulses from active units. Some six or more fibers were still active as judged by the all-or-nothing potential spikes on the oscillograph records at the low temperatures.

Let us return to a consideration of the Weber-Fechner law. Figure 51 describes the frequency of nerve impulses as a function of the temperature of the receptors. Here we have to do with an exception to the Weber-

Fechner law, both in the traditional logarithmic sense, and also in terms of the notion of a simple frequency distribution curve of receptor thresholds. The Arrhenius equation describes the data (Figure 52) and this in its simplest form may be expressed as

$$f = e^{-c/T}$$

where c is a constant equal to μ/R, and f is the frequency assumed to be directly proportional to the velocity of the stimulating chemical reaction in the receptor cells [for a consideration of the chemical basis of the spontaneous activity cf. Hoagland (1933-34)]. Here, in the case of the fishes' thermal receptors, the law describing the relation between stimulus and frequency of nerve-impulse response, the frequency believed in other sense modalities to be directly proportional to sensory intensities, is clearly not the logarithmic Weber-Fechner law but the Arrhenius equation. The decline in the velocity of the chemical determinant of the frequency may, as we have seen, decrease the frequency either in individual units or by silencing units below temperature thresholds. The case is an interesting example of an exception to the Weber-Fechner law which illustrates the need of regarding the stimulus-response relation in each case specifically rather than attempting to apply a general empirical equation which may merely serve to mask underlying determinants.

VIII

"Spontaneous" Activity

An aspect of complex behavior exhibited by intact organisms is that of "spontaneous activity," i.e., movements which appear to arise as a result of changes entirely within the organism, as far as can be told. In general, the so-called "random movements" tend to be related by writers to the natural or normal exploratory wanderings (so-called) of many organisms, the occurrence of which seems to be understood as accentuated or accelerated when the organism is stimulated.

The theory of random movements as often stated implies a hopelessly haphazard relation between stimulation and activation of motor organs such as should vitiate any possibility of regularity and predicability in the conduct of animals. It is easily seen that the doctrine of "physiological states" is intimately connected with the random-movement doctrine. The appeal to such states, in themselves uncharacterized, easily leads to unfortunate mysticism.

The manner in which behavior in a field of excitation might be governed or limited through the exhibition of spontaneous movements can best be studied after the exclusion of extraneous stimulation. In general, it is found that after such exclusion gross bodily movements still occur which apparently in no way depend upon peripheral excitation and in some cases may even occur whether external excitation is deliberately applied or not.

If it should prove that, basically, such movements occur in a manner simulating the automatic spontaneity exhibited by a contracting heart or a pulsating jellyfish, it scarcely remains possible to regard such movements as lawless or in any proper sense "random," or as supporting arguments in favor of "free-will" control.

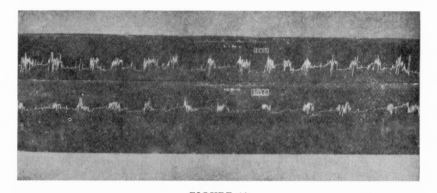

FIGURE 66

RECORDS OF SPONTANEOUS ACTIVITY OF A YOUNG MOUSE (TWO DAYS OLD) AT TWO
TEMPERATURES OF THE BODY, SHOWING REGULARITY IN OCCURRENCE
OF PERIODS OF ACTIVE MOVEMENT
(See text.)

Experiments of Stier (1930), previously cited in connection with considerations of the effect of temperature on estimations of time, illustrate an interesting approach to the problem of spontaneous activity. Stier used white mice under two days of age, before the development of their temperature-regulating mechanisms. When extraneous excitation in the environment of the mouse was eliminated, random movements still occurred but not haphazardly. Figure 66 illustrates the surging periods of activity with alternate rest periods of a young mouse at 22.1 and 20.2°C.

The average frequencies of bursts of activity were found to vary according to the Arrhenius equation, yielding a value of $\mu = 25,300$ calories. The durations of intervals of quiescence and of activity were also found to change as a function of temperature; when their reciprocals were plotted according to the Arrhenius equation, the value of $\mu = 13,200$ was obtained for activity, and $\mu = 30,900$ for quiescence. Stier suggested as a working hypothesis that these different values indicate that at least two processes are responsible for control of activity and of quiescence in the young mice. It was assumed that activity results when the concentration of a substance A is maintained above a threshold level. Quiescence begins when A is reduced below this level, the velocity of the formation and removal being controlled by chemical changes.

Mice forty to ninety days of age show the same cyclic occurrence of periods of activity as exhibited by the two-day-old mice. Variation from an assumed basic cycle was found to occur in multiples of 15 minutes for activity and in steps of 24 minutes for periods of quiescence.

Evidence, first presented by Loeb (1909) and recently developed by other workers, is reviewed in Stier's paper and shows that movements of an intact animal are often correlated with vigorous "hunger contractions" of its empty stomach. The mechanism controlling the spontaneous locomotor activity may, therefore, have for its "center" the gastro-intestinal tract, since movements of the empty stomach are correlated with the incidence of bodily activity.

A somewhat different kind of approach to the problem of spontaneous activity has recently been presented by Skinner (1933a), who studied the distance run by adult rats placed inside a running-wheel. The method of recording yielded a continuous distance-time graph of the behavior. Skinner found that the behavior of rats may be divided into two parts—an active part and a quiescent part. If any extensive activity was prohibited during part of a day, the remaining part showed a greater density of activity per unit time. When the period of confinement was made sufficiently long, the resulting active period assumed certain continuous properties. In addition the effect of conditioned hunger cycles on the running-behavior was studied, as well as the effect of friction on the rate of running. Throughout, the so-called "random" activity was found to be quantifiable and predictable in terms of the experimental setting.

The contrast between quiescence and movement is seen in an extreme form, but of nevertheless widespread occurrence, in the phenomenon of tonic immobility or "death feigning."

Reflex assumption of a motionless state, often supposed to simulate death and hence commonly referred to as "death feigning," is well known to be exhibited by a great variety of animals. Many unsuitable names have been applied to this condition. We shall speak of it as tonic immobility. In its typical manifestations this tonic immobility is to be distinguished sharply from mere cessation of neuromuscular activities; those cases with which we shall deal are characterized by a continuous (but, in at least some instances, plastic) tonic contracture of the muscles of the body and especially of the appendages. The phenomenon is developed to a notable degree among arthropods. A number of writers have discussed its natural history and to some extent its structural basis. Rabaud (1919) has recently given an extensive account of reflex immobilization among arthropods, and Mangold (1920) has prepared a digest of most of the older observations upon the general subject (cf. also Andova, 1929). The contributions have usually dwelt at length upon the supposed utility or otherwise of "death feigning," and Mangold, in particular, in connection with suggestions by a number of earlier writers, has attempted to erect a terminological scheme whereby "simulation of death" may be brought into relation with hypnosis, catalepsis, and analogous states characterized by the cessation of spontaneous movements (cf. also Piéron, 1913).

Singularly little attention has been given to the physiological analysis of tonic immobility. This is the more surprising because the phenomena of immobilization would seem to give opportunity, as we shall attempt to show, for convenient inquiry as to the sorts of forces and processes operative in a central nervous functional activity having sensible duration. These have been tested by means of experiments with the terrestrial isopod ("sowbug") *Oniscus asellus* Linn (Crozier and Federighi, 1923). With various arthropods, and in an amphibian, it has been noticed that the duration of an act of reflex immobility is influenced by the temperature. Such influence was found by Holmes (1906), the Severins (1911), Polimanti (1911), Szymanski (1912), Löhner (1919), and Grasse (1922). No attempt was made by any of these observers to determine the actual form of the relation to temperature.

The length of an act of immobility initiated by appropriate stimulation of an insect or crustacean is in reality determined by the duration of a sustained condition in the central nervous system. It is easily shown that in a variety of hexapods and isopods, with which the experiments were concerned, the animal gives other well-defined reflexes without emergence from the specific immobile state. With *Ranatra,* in particular, several striking proofs are obtained of the reciprocal innervation of the appendages and of the orientations of their central connections.

Nevertheless, as Rabaud has insisted, in each organism there are certain peripheral loci, stimulation of which at once arouses an immobile specimen at the will of the experimenter.

The duration of successive acts of immobility is rhythmic. In isopods and lizards at least, and probably also in such mammals as the guinea pig, the rhythm does not exist as a general metabolic rhythm on which the observations are, so to speak, superimposed. It is initiated by the first stimulation of a series. Once initiated, however, a cycle rises to a maximum of possible duration, then falls to practically zero duration, independently of further excitations. This is proved by results of tests in which various known intervals elapse between acts of immobilization and by tests in which the animal is aroused to normal activity before its spontaneous "emergence," then re-immobilized.

The stimulus evoking tonic reflex immobility thus serves apparently to release a system of events, possibly synaptic in location, which determines at any moment the duration of a then-initiated control of motor elements by suitable stimulation. The nature of this fundamental cycle, of quite appreciable duration, is deducible from the form of the cycle of successive immobilizations.

If suitably stimulated following spontaneous emergence from induced immobility, the isopod again becomes immobile, but for a longer time; tests of this sort show a periodic rise to a certain maximum duration. The amount of this maximum duration is determined chiefly by the temperature. At 6° the maximum duration is 270 sec.; at 29°, 23 sec. The cycle of immobility is not the reflection of a general metabolic cycle but is determined by a central nervous process initiated by the first stimulations of the series of trials.

An analysis of the relation of temperature to the processes underlying the duration of reflex immobility involves comparison of the durations at different temperatures but at corresponding stages of the cycle. Between 5° and 16° the maxima lie upon one exponential curve with respect to temperature; above 16°, and continuing to 30°, the maxima lie upon an intersecting exponential curve of lesser slope. The exponential relation of duration to temperature makes it likely that the duration is determined by an amount of substance produced in a chemical system rather than that the maxima in the duration curves are to be considered points of minimum "speeds of emergence" from the immobile state. The curves are in fact fitted by Arrhenius' equation $1/\text{time} = e^{-\frac{\mu}{Rt}} + \text{const.}$ with $\mu = 24,000$ for the range 5°-16°, $\mu = 9,200$ for 16°-30°. These values of μ are within the range characteristic for chemical processes. More precise analysis of these relations is possible upon the basis of detailed consideration of the kinetics of the assumed underlying processes.

It appears, then, that the duration of an act of reflex immobility may be determined by a condition similar to synaptic transmissivity, continuously maintained for the duration of the act, and itself proportional to the amount of a substance formed by and broken down in two catenary processes having different temperature coefficients.

The durations of successive periods of induced tonic immobility in the lizard *Anolis carolinensis* were examined by Hoagland (1927-28) as a function of temperature. The durations of the immobile periods were found to vary rhythmically in most cases. The reciprocal of the duration of the rhythm, i.e., the rate of change of the process underlying the rhythms, when plotted as a function of temperature according to the Arrhenius equation, shows distributions of points in two straight-line groups. One of these groups or bands of points extends throughout the entire temperature range with a temperature characteristic of approximately $\mu = 31,000$ calories, and the other covers the range of 20° to 35°C. with μ equal to approximately 9,000.

These results are interpreted by assuming the release, through reflex stimulation, of hormonal substances, one effective between 5° and 35°C., and the other effective between 20° and 35°C. These substances are assumed to act as selective inhibitors of impulses from so-called "higher centers," allowing impulses from tonic centers to pass to the muscles. In some experiments a progressive lengthening in successively induced periods of immobility was observed. The logarithm of the frequency of recovery when plotted against time in most of these cases (i.e., except for a few in which irregularities occurred) gave a linear function of negative slope which was substantially unaffected by temperature. In these cases it is assumed that a diffusion process is controlling the amount of available *A* substance.

Injections of small amounts of adrenalin above a threshold value are found to prolong the durations of tonic immobility of *Anolis* by an amount which is a logarithmic function of the "dose." It is possible that internally secreted adrenalin, above a threshold amount, may be involved in the maintenance of tonic immobility. This effect of injected adrenalin in prolonging the rhythms of successively induced periods of tonic immobility in guinea pigs has also been found by Upton (unpublished results).

In the present chapter we have sought to illustrate by selected examples the application of certain rational mathematical formulations to a variety of problems of animal behavior. Such procedures often involve the use of equations which cut sharply across conventional departmental classifications of subject-matter, for example, the application of the Arrhenius equation with its theoretical foundation in molecular kinetics to the traditional psychological problem of time judgments. The fact that an exponential curve describes the effect of temperature on time judgments, while perhaps empirically interesting, gains considerably more significance when it is found that not just any one of a variety of exponential curves describes the data but that the data are satisfied by that exponential curve having the form of the Arrhenius equation and in which the value of the temperature characteristic is specific and identical with that found for a variety of cellular metabolic processes.

While it seems desirable to use rational equations of this sort, provided their hypothetical bases can be tested experimentally, we do not wish to underestimate the desirability of empirical descriptive laws of behavior despite the fact that they may not imply physiological mechanisms. Certain kinds of behavior problems can often be approached, at least initially, only in this way.

Skinner has recently published papers dealing with the conceptions of "drive" and "reflex strength," in which empirical equations are presented describing very precisely various stimulus-response aspects of the conduct of white rats. In a historical résumé of the reflex concept, Skinner (1931) points out that the essential characteristic of a reflex is a correlation between measurable aspects of the stimulus and response, without regard to inferred mechanisms such as the reflex arc with its implied synaptic properties. The reflex is essentially defined by the equation

$$R = f (S)$$

where R is a response and S is a stimulus.

In the case of spinal reflexes, for example, variations in the stimulus may produce variations in such aspects of the response as latency, after-discharge, and threshold (i.e., for values below a given value of S, $R = 0$). With repetition of the reflex, a third variable may be introduced in the above equation so that we may write

$$R = f (S, A)$$

where A may be either time or the number of elicitations at a given rate. This variable may be a measure of reflex fatigue or of reflex strength and the relations may be described without recourse to inferred physiological mechanisms. The introduction of the variable A in the above equation may produce alterations of the ratio of R to S for a variety of reflex attributes.

According to Skinner, "reflex strength" expresses in a very general way the state of a given correlation at a given time with respect to many of its characteristics. The reflex he regards as essentially an empirical law relating stimulus to response.

This generalized conception of the reflex is experimentally amplified by experiments performed by Skinner (1932a, 1932b) on the rate of eating of white rats. A standard food was so arranged that a rat could obtain it, one pellet at a time (without other restraints), from a presentation machine. The rat's behavior was recorded automatically. Figure 67 shows a typical "eating" curve in which the number of pieces of food eaten is plotted against the time. The curve is described by the equation for a parabola,

$$N = k\ t^n$$

where N equals amount of food eaten at time t, counted from the beginning of the experimental period, and k and n are constants. This curve is taken as a measure of the strength of the eating reflex, or of the chain

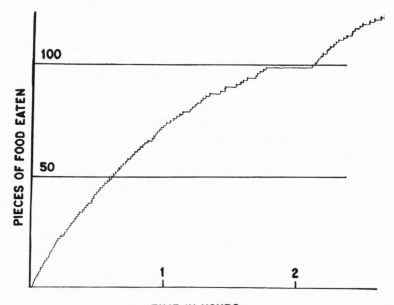

TIME IN HOURS

FIGURE 67

KYMOGRAPH RECORD OF THE EATING BEHAVIOR OF A WHITE RAT

At each elevation of the writing point the rat ate a pellet of food of standard size. The rate of eating is given by the slope of the line and can be seen to decrease regularly throughout the period of 2 1/2 hours. The curve is described by the equation $N = Kt^n$, where N is the number of pieces eaten at time t, and K and n are constants.

(From *J. Gen. Psychol.*)

of reflexes which result in eating: its meaning is, as a first approximation, that the rate of eating at any moment (dN/dt) is directly proportional to N and inversely proportional to the elapsed time. When the presentation of food was interrupted for a period the rats later ate more rapidly, as is illustrated by Figure 68. If the normal curve prior to the interruption is taken as a measure of the reflex strength, clearly the increased rate of feeding following the delay period in Figure 68 serves as a quantitative description of the "drive" resulting from the forced delay.

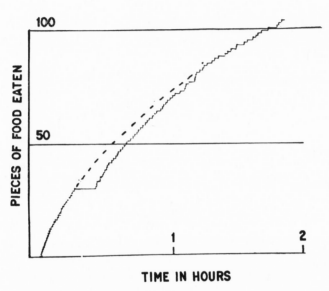

TIME IN HOURS

FIGURE 68

KYMOGRAPH RECORD OF THE EATING BEHAVIOR OF A RAT UPON THE THIRD OCCASION
WHEN THE SUPPLY OF FOOD IS CUT OFF FOR TEN MINUTES
(For discussion see text.)
(From *J. Gen. Psychol.*)

Skinner (1933*b*) has recently studied the process of discrimination in terms of this operational conception of reflexes. "Technically the establishment of a discrimination consists in the continued reinforcement of one reflex and the concurrent extinction of another, where the two stimuli possess properties in common, but also differ in some significant respect. The two processes cannot go on independently and the problem of discrimination arises because of their mutual interference." Relations are presented which indicate the nature of the interference in connection with the "eating reflex" and test similarities of properties of the two processes involved in discrimination.

IX

CONCLUDING REMARKS

"Simplicity" of experimental conditions means control of experimental conditions. It does not necessarily mean that the organism must not be surrounded with apparatus; it does often imply that the undisturbed intact organism should be studied. Simplification of conditions through control may make possible fruitful distinctions between phenomena of (1) *difference,* (2) *variation,* and (3) *variability* in the investigation of conduct, which unquestionably have been confused. This requires the biological uniformity of individuals, measurements from which are to be averaged. The essence of the notion of *variability* is found in the conception of variation (or response or performance) as a function of some controlling variable; otherwise, no proper *measure* of variability is obtainable. With suitably chosen conditions it is possible to separate the total variation over a range of fixed values of an independent variable governing the behavior in question into two parts, one of them modifiable according to the magnitudes of the governing intensity of excitation. In measurements of the geotropic orientation of young rats the variability of the measured orientations can be expressed in this way as a number which is independent of the size of the sample (within the limits used), and is characteristic for the stabilized strains employed in the experiments. In such cases it is no longer possible to speak of a lawless variation or unpredictableness of behavior.

When attention is given to the formulation of oriented movements, these are found to be machine-like in the sense that the conditions for stable position are easily interpreted in a physical way. The statement of such conditions involves a mathematical expression of functional dependence, which ceases to be arbitrary when its contained constants can be shown to correspond to a biological reality. In at least one case it has been shown that they remain "constants" when subjected to the purely biological manipulation involved in a breeding test. In other instances they provide clues for further analysis. On the basis of such formulations it has been possible to account quantitatively for the conduct of tested organisms in compound fields involving competition of excitations and change with time. It may be at least serviceably provocative to suggest that in this way a measure can be had of certain adjustor properties of the central nervous system. At least, it can be foreseen that through the difficult but attractive synthesis òf more complex situations there is good likelihood of arriving at some measure of understanding of what animals do.

In the present chapter we have also applied concepts of general physiology to certain traditional problems of psychology, such as the time "sense," learning, and the Weber-Fechner law. The attempt has been made to approach, by means of rational formulations in contrast to purely empirical descriptions, basic mechanisms involved in the determination of these events.

BIBLIOGRAPHY

Sufficient introduction to the literature of animal conduct, with especial emphasis upon the analyzable behavior of invertebrates and lower vertebrates, is given in a number of works containing extensive bibliographies:

ADRIAN, E. D. 1928. The basis of sensation: the action of the sense organs. London: Christophers; New York: Norton. Pp. 122.

————. 1932. The mechanism of nervous action: electrical studies of the neurone. *(The Eldridge Reeves Johnson Foundation Lectures.)* London: Oxford Univ. Press; Philadelphia: Univ. Pa. Press. Pp. x+103.

ARRHENIUS, S. 1915. Quantitative laws in biological chemistry. London: Bell. Pp. vii+163.

CLAPARÈDE, E. 1913. Tierpsychologie. In Vol. 9 of *Handwörterbuch der Naturwissenschaften,* ed. by E. Korschelt, G. Linck, *et al.* Jena: Fischer. Pp. 1187-1204.

CREED, R. S., DENNY-BROWN, D., ECCLES, J. C., LIDDELL, E. G. T., & SHERRINGTON, C. S. 1932. Reflex activity of the spinal cord. Oxford: Clarendon Press. Pp. vii+183.

DANIELS, F. 1928. Mathematical preparation for physical chemistry. New York & London: McGraw-Hill. Pp. x+308.

HEMPELMANN, F. 1926. Tierpsychologie vom Standpunkte des Biologen. Leipzig: Akad. Verlagsgesellsch. Pp. viii+676.

HERTER, K. 1925. Tastsinn, Stromungssinn und Temperatursinn der Tiere und die diesen Sinnen zugeordneten Reaktionen. *(Zoöl. Bausteine,* Vol. 1.) Berlin: Gebr. Borntraeger. Pp. iv+182.

HINSHELWOOD, C. N. 1929. The kinetics of chemical change in gaseous systems. (2nd ed.) London: Oxford Univ. Press. Pp. 266.

HITCHCOCK, F. L., & ROBINSON, C. S. 1923. Differential equations in applied chemistry. New York: Wiley. Pp. vi+110.

HOLMES, S. J. 1916. Studies in animal behavior. Boston: Badger. Pp. 266.

JENNINGS, H. S. 1906. Behavior of lower organisms. New York: Columbia Univ. Press. Pp. viii+366.

KAFKA, G. 1914. Einführung in die Tierpsychologie auf experimenteller und ethnologischer Grundlage. Vol. 1. Leipzig: Barth. Pp. xii+593.

————. 1922. Tierpsychologie. In Vol. 1, Pt. 1 of *Handbuch der vergleichenden Psychologie,* ed. by G. Kafka. Munich: Reinhardt. Pp. viii+526.

KÖHLER, O. 1925—. Sinnesphysiologie der Tiere. (Uebersichtsreferat.) *Jahresber. ü. d. ges. Physiol.*

————. 1928. Untersuchungsmethoden der allgemeinen Reizphysiologie und der Verhaltensforschung an Tieren. In Vol. 2 of *Methodik der wissenschaftlichen Biologie,* ed. by T. Péterfi. Berlin: Springer. Pp. 845-925.

KÜHN, A. 1919. Die Orientierung der Tiere im Raum. Jena: Fischer. Pp. iv+71.

————. 1926. Phototropismus und Phototaxis der Tiere. In Vol. 12, Pt. 2 of *Handbuch der normalen und pathologischen Physiologie,* ed. by A. Bethe, G. v. Bergmann, G. Embden, and A. Ellinger. Berlin: Springer. Pp. x+742.

LOEB, J. 1900. Physiology of the brain. New York & London: Putnam's. Pp. x+309.

————. 1906. Dynamics of living matter. New York: Macmillan. Pp. xi+233.

————. 1913. Die Tropismen. In Vol. 4 of *Handbuch der vergleichenden Physiologie,* ed. by H. Winterstein. Jena: Fischer.

————— 1916. The organism as a whole. New York & London: Putnam's. Pp. x+379.

—————. 1918. Tropisms, forced movements, and animal conduct. Philadelphia & London: Lippincott. Pp. 209.

MAXWELL, J. C. 1908. Theory of heat. (10th ed.) London: Longmans, Green. Pp. 348.

MAXWELL, S. S. 1923. Labyrinth and equilibrium. *(Monog. on Exper. Biol.)* Philadelphia & London: Lippincott. Pp. 163.

MICHAELIS, L. 1927. Einführung in die Mathematik. (3rd ed.) Berlin: Springer. Pp. vi+313.

MORGAN, T. H. 1926. The theory of the gene. New Haven, Conn.: Yale Univ. Press. Pp. xvi+343.

OSTERHOUT, W. J. V. 1922. Injury, recovery, and death, in relation to conductivity and permeability. *(Monog. on Exper. Biol.)* Philadelphia & London: Lippincott. Pp. 259.

PARKER, G. H. 1919. The elementary nervous system. Philadelphia & London: Lippincott. Pp. 229.

—————. 1932. Humoral agents in nervous activity. Cambridge, England: Univ. Press. Pp. x+79.

RICE, F. O. 1928. The mechanism of homogeneous organic reactions from the physical-chemical standpoint. New York: Chem. Catalog Co. Pp. 3-217.

ROBERTSON, T. B. 1923. The chemical basis of growth and senescence. Philadelphia: Lippincott. Pp. viii+389.

TAYLOR, H. S. [Ed.] 1931. Treatise on physical chemistry. Vol. 2. (2nd ed.) New York: Van Nostrand. Pp. 901-1766.

THOMPSON, S. P. 1919. Calculus made easy. London: Macmillan. (2nd ed.) 1927. Pp. x+301.

TOLMAN, R. C. 1927. Statistical mechanics, with applications to physics and chemistry. *(Amer. Chem. Soc. Monog. Ser.)* New York: Chem. Catalog Co. Pp. 334.

WALTHER, A. 1928. Einführung in die mathematische Behandlung naturwissenschaftlicher Fragen: Part 1. Berlin: Springer. Pp. vii+220.

WATSON, J. B. 1914. Behavior: an introduction to comparative psychology. New York: Holt. Pp. xii+439.

WHEELER, W. M. 1928. The social insects. New York: Harcourt, Brace. Pp. xviii+378.

Papers and books here listed have reference to specific points raised in the text; attention has been given chiefly to recent articles.

ADRIAN, E. D., & BUYTENDIJK, J. F. F. 1931. Potential changes in the isolated brain stem of the goldfish. *J. Physiol.*, **71**, 121-135.

ADRIAN, E. D., CATTELL, McK., & HOAGLAND, H. 1931. Sensory discharges in single cutaneous nerve fibres. *J. Physiol.*, **72**, 377-391.

ANDOVA, A. 1929. Thantose des grossen Rosskäfers *Geotrupes stercorarius* L. *Zsch. f. Morphol. u. Oekol.*, **13**, 722-744.

AREY, L. B., & CROZIER, W. J. 1918. The 'homing habits' of the pulmonate mollusk *Onchidium*. *Proc. Nat. Acad. Sci.*, **4**, 319-321.

—————. 1919. The sensory responses of *Chiton*. *J. Exper. Zoöl.*, **29**, 157-260.

—————. 1921. Natural history of *Onchidium*. *J. Exper. Zoöl.*, **32**, 443-502.

AXEL, R. 1925. Estimation of time. *Arch. Psychol.*, **12**, No. 74. Pp. 77.

BALDI, E. 1922. Studi sulla fisiologia del sistema nervoso negli insetti: II. Richerche sui movimenti nei coleotteri. *J. Exper. Zoöl.*, **36**, 211-288.

BALDUS, K. 1927. Untersuchungen zur Analyse der Zwangsbewegungen der Insekten. *Zsch. f. vergl. Physiol.*, **6**, 99-149.

BANCROFT, F. W. 1913. Heliotropism, differential sensibility and galvanotropism in Euglena. *J. Exper. Zoöl.*, **15**, 383-428.

BORING, L. D., & BORING, E. G. 1917. Temporal judgment after sleep. In *Studies in psychology: Titchener commemorative volume.* Worcester, Mass.: Wilson. Pp. 255-279.

BOYSEN-JENSEN, P. 1910. Ueber die Leitung des phototropischen Reizes in Avenakeimphlanzen. *Ber. d. dtsch. bot. Gesellsch.*, **28**, 118.

—————. 1913. Ueber die Leitung des phototropischen Reizes in der Avenakoleoptile. *Ber. d. dtsch. bot. Gesellsch.*, **31**, 559.

BRONK, D. W., & FERGUSON, L. K. 1933. The nervous regulation of the respiratory movements of intercostal muscles. *Amer. J. Physiol.*, **105**, 13.

BRUSH, E. N. 1930. Observations on the temporal judgment during sleep. *Amer. J. Psychol.*, **42**, 408-411.

BUDDENBROCK, W. v. 1917. Die Lichtkompassbewegung bei Insekten. *Sitzber. d. Heidelberg. Akad. d. Wiss., math.-naturwiss. Kl.*, Abt. B, Abh. 7. Pp. 25.

—————. 1918. Die vermutliche Lösung der Halterenfrage. *Sitzber. d. Heidelberg. Akad. d. Wiss., math.-naturwiss. Kl.*, Abt. B, Abh. 7. Pp. iii+10.

BUDDENBROCK, W. v., & SCHULZ, E. 1933. Beiträge zur Kenntnis der Lichtkompassbewegung und der Adaptation des Insektenauges. *Zoöl. Jahrb., Abt. d. Physiol.*, **52**, 513-536.

CARREL, A. 1931. Physiological time. *Science*, **74**, 618-621.

CASTLE, E. S. 1928-29. Dark adaptation and the light-growth response of *Phycomyces*. *J. Gen. Physiol.*, **12**, 391-400.

CATTELL, McK., & HOAGLAND, H. 1931. Responses of tactile receptors to intermittent stimulation. *J. Physiol.*, **72**, 392-404.

CLARK, L. B. 1928. Adaptation versus experience as an explanation of modification in certain types of behavior (circus movements in Notonecta). *J. Exper. Zoöl.*, **51**, 37-50.

COLE, W. H. 1922-23. Circus movements of *Limulus* and the tropism theory. *J. Gen. Physiol.*, **5**, 417-426.

—————. 1925-28. Geotropism and muscle tension in *Helix*. *J. Gen. Physiol.*, **8**, 253-263.

CROZIER, W. J. 1914. The orientation of a holuthurian by light. *Amer. J. Physiol.*, **36**, 8-20.

—————. 1915. The sensory reactions of *Holuthuria surinamensis* Ludwig. *Zool. Jahrb., Abt. f. Zool. u. Physiol.*, **35**, 233-297.

—————. 1917. The behavior of holuthurians in balanced illumination. *Amer. J. Physiol.*, **43**, 510-513.

—————. 1918a. On tactile response of the de-eyed hamlet *(Epinephelus striatus)*. *J. Comp. Neur.*, **29**, 163-175.

—————. 1918b. Assortive mating in a nudibranch, *Chromodoris zebra* Heilprin. *J. Exper. Zoöl.*, **27**, 247-292.

—————. 1918-19. On the control of the response to shading in the branchiae of *Chromodoris*. *J. Gen. Physiol.*, **1**, 585-591.

—————. 1923. Reflex immobility and the central nervous system. *Proc. Soc. Exper. Biol. & Med.*, **21**, 55-57.

—————. 1923-24a. On stereotropism in *Tenebrio* larvae. *J. Gen. Physiol.*, **6**, 531-539.

—————. 1923-24b. Wave length of light and photic inhibition of stereotropism in *Tenebrio* larvae. *J. Gen. Physiol.*, **6**, 647-652.

————. 1924a. Biological researches relating to the nervous system. *Carnegie Instit. Yrbk.*, No. 23, 227-229.

————. 1924b. On the possibility of identifying chemical processes in living matter. *Proc. Nat. Acad. Sci.*, **10**, 461-464.

————. 1924-25a. On the critical thermal increment for the locomotion of a diplopod. *J. Gen. Physiol.*, **7**, 123-136.

————. 1924-25b. On biological oxidations as a function of temperature. *J. Gen. Physiol.*, **7**, 189-216.

————. 1925-26. The distribution of temperature characteristics for biological processes; critical increments for heart rates. *J. Gen. Physiol.*, **9**, 531-546.

————. 1925-28. The orientation of animals by opposed beams of light. *J. Gen. Physiol.*, **8**, 671-684.

————. 1926-27a. On curves of growth especially in relation to temperature. *J. Gen. Physiol.*, **10**, 53-73.

————. 1926-27b. Galvanotropism and "reversal of inhibition" by strychnine. *J. Gen. Physiol.*, **10**, 395-406.

————. 1927-28. On the geotropic orientation of young mammals. *J. Gen. Physiol.*, **11**, 789-802.

————. 1928. Tropisms. *J. Gen. Psychol.*, **1**, 213-238.

CROZIER, W. J., & AREY, L. B. 1918. On the significance of the reaction to shading in Chiton. *Amer. J. Physiol.*, **46**, 487-492.

————. 1919. Sensory reaction of *Chromodoris zebra*. *J. Exper. Zoöl.*, **29**, 261-310.

————. 1919-20. The heliotropism of *Onchidium:* a problem in the analysis of animal conduct. *J. Gen. Physiol.*, **2**, 107-112.

CROZIER, W. J., & COLE, W. H. 1923. Circus movements and heliotropism. *Anat. Rec.*, **24**, 362.

CROZIER, W. J., & FEDERIGHI, H. 1923. On the character of central nervous processes. *Proc. Soc. Exper. Biol. & Med.*, **21**, 55-57.

————. 1924-25a. Phototropic circus movements of *Limax* as affected by temperature. *J. Gen. Physiol.*, **7**, 151-169.

————. 1924-25b. The phototropic mechanism in *Ranatra*. *J. Gen. Physiol.*, **7**, 217-221.

————. 1924-25c. Suppression of phototropic circus movements of *Limax* by strychnine. *J. Gen. Physiol.*, **7**, 221-224.

————. 1924-25d. Temperature characteristics for heart rhythm of the silkworm. *J. Gen. Physiol.*, **7**, 565-579.

CROZIER, W. J., & LIBBY, R. L. 1924-25. Temporary abolition of phototropism in *Limax* after feeding. *J. Gen. Physiol.*, **7**, 421-427.

CROZIER, W. J., & MANGELSDORF, A. F. 1923-24. A note on the relative photosensory effect of polarized light. *J. Gen. Physiol.*, **6**, 703-709.

CROZIER, W. J., & MOORE, A. R. 1922-23. Homostrophic reflex and stereotropism in diplopods. *J. Gen. Physiol.*, **5**, 597-604.

CROZIER, W. J., & NAVEZ, A. E. 1930. Geotropic orientation of gastropods. *J. Gen. Psychol.*, **3**, 3-37.

CROZIER, W. J., & OXNARD, T. T. 1927-28. Geotropic orientation of young mice. *J. Gen. Physiol.*, **11**, 141-146.

CROZIER, W. J., & PINCUS, G. 1926. Tropisms of mammals. *Proc. Nat. Acad. Sci.*, **12**, 612-616.

————. 1926-27a. Stereotropism in rats and mice. *J. Gen. Physiol.*, **10**, 195-203.

————. 1926-27*b*. The geotropic conduct of young rats. *J. Gen. Physiol.*, **10**, 257-269.

————. 1926-27*c*. Phototropism in young rats. *J. Gen. Physiol.*, **10**, 404-417.

————. 1926-27*d*. On the equilibration of geotropic and phototropic excitations in the rat. *J. Gen. Physiol.*, **10**, 419-424.

————. 1926-27*e*. Geotropic orientation of young rats. *J. Gen. Physiol.*, **10**, 519-524.

————. 1927-28. On the geotropic orientation of young mammals. *J. Gen. Physiol.*, **11**, 789-802.

————. 1929-30*a*. Analysis of the geotropic orientation of young rats: I. *J. Gen. Physiol.*, **13**, 57-80

————. 1929-30*b*. Analysis of the geotropic orientation of young rats: II. *J. Gen. Physiol.*, **13**, 81-120.

————. 1931-32*a*. Analysis of the geotropic orientation of young rats: III. *J. Gen. Physiol.*, **15**, 201-241.

————. 1931-32*b*. Analysis of the geotropic orientation of young rats: IV. *J. Gen. Physiol.*, **15**, 243-256.

————. 1931-32*c*. Analysis of the geotropic orientation of young rats: V. *J. Gen. Physiol.*, **15**, 421-426.

————. 1931-32*d*. Analysis of the geotropic orientation of young rats: VI. *J. Gen. Physiol.*, **15**, 437-462.

————. 1932-33*a*. Analysis of the geotropic orientation of young rats: VII. *J. Gen. Physiol.*, **16**, 801-813.

————. 1932-33*b*. Analysis of the geotropic orientation of young rats: VIII. *J. Gen. Physiol.*, **16**, 883-893.

CROZIER, W. J., & STIER, T. J. B. 1924-25*a*. Critical thermal increments for rhythmic respiratory movements of insects. *J. Gen. Physiol.*, **7**, 429-447.

————. 1924-25*b*. Critical thermal increments for opercular breathing rhythm in goldfish. *J. Gen. Physiol.*, **7**, 699-704.

————. 1925-26. On the modification of temperature characteristics. *J. Gen. Physiol.*, **9**, 547-559.

————. 1927-28. The measurement of galvanotropic excitation. *J. Gen. Physiol.*, **11**, 283-288.

————. 1932-33. Thermostat for lower temperatures. *J. Gen. Physiol.*, **16**, 757-766.

CROZIER, W. J., & WOLF, E. 1927-28. On the place of photic adaptation. *J. Gen. Physiol.*, **11**, 289-295.

————. 1928-29. Dark adaptation in *Agriolimax*. *J. Gen. Physiol.*, **12**, 83-109.

DODGE, R. 1927. Elementary conditions of human variability. New York: Columbia Univ. Press. Pp. 107.

DOLLEY, W. L., JR. 1916. Reactions to light in *Vanessa antiopa* with special reference to circus-movements. *J. Exper. Zöol.*, **20**, 357-420.

EGE, R., & KROGH, A. 1914. On the relation between the temperature and the respiratory exchange in fishes. *Int. Rev. d. ges. Hydrobiol. u. Hydrograph.*, **7**, 48-55.

ELLIOTT, M. H., & STAVSKY, W. H. 1933. The effect of an upward stress upon the geotropic orientation of young guinea pigs. *J. Gen. Psychol.*, **9**, 216-220.

FRANÇOIS, M. 1927. Contribution à l'étude du sens du temps. La température interne, comme facteur de variation de l'appréciation subjective des durées. *Année psychol.*, **28**, 186-204.

FRIES, E. F. B. 1927-28. Drug action in galvanotropic responses. *J. Gen. Physiol.*, **11**, 507-513.

GARREY, W. E. 1918-19. Light and the muscle tonus of insects. The heliotropic mechanism. *J. Gen. Physiol.,* 1, 101-125.

GESELL, R. 1925. The chemical regulation of respiration. *Physiol. Revs.,* 5, 551-595.

GOUDRIAAN, J. C. 1921. Le rhythm psychique dans ses rapports avec les fréquences cardiaques et respiratoires. *Arch. néerl. de physiol.,* 6, 77-110.

GULLIKSEN, H. 1927. The influence of occupation upon the perception of time. *J. Exper. Psychol.,* 10, 59-92.

HARTLINE, H. K. 1923-24. Influence of light of very low intensity on phototropic reactions of animals. *J. Gen. Physiol.,* 6, 137-152.

HARTLINE, H. K., & GRAHAM, C. H. 1932. Nerve impulses from single receptors in the eye. *J. Cell. & Comp. Physiol.,* 5, 277-295.

HECHT, S. 1918-19. Sensory equilibrium and dark adaptation in *Mya arenaria. J. Gen. Physiol.,* 1, 545-558.

————. 1919-20a. The photochemical nature of the photosensory process. *J. Gen. Physiol.,* 2, 229-246.

————. 1919-20b. Intensity and the process of photoreception. *J. Gen. Physiol.,* 2, 337-342.

————. 1922-23. Sensory adaptation and the stationary state. *J. Gen. Physiol.,* 5, 555-579.

————. 1923-24. Intensity discrimination and the stationary state. *J. Gen. Physiol.,* 6, 355-373.

————. 1924-25. The visual discrimination of intensity and the Weber-Fechner law. *J. Gen. Physiol.,* 7, 235-267.

————. 1926-27. The kinetics of dark adaptation. *J. Gen. Physiol.,* 10, 781-809.

HOAGLAND, H. 1927. Quantitative aspects of tonic immobility in vertebrates. *Proc. Nat. Acad. Sci.,* 13, 838-843.

————. 1927-28. The mechanism of tonic immobility in vertebrates. *J. Gen. Physiol.,* 11, 715-741.

————. 1928. The mechanism of tonic immobility ("animal hypnosis"). *J. Gen. Psychol.,* 1, 426-447.

————. 1929. Geotropic orientation of chicks. *J. Gen. Psychol.,* 2, 187-198.

————. 1930. The Weber-Fechner law and the all-or-none theory. *J. Gen. Psychol.,* 3, 351-373.

————. 1931. A study of the physiology of learning in ants. *J. Gen. Psychol.,* 5, 21-41.

————. 1932-33a. Electrical responses from lateral-line nerves of fishes: I. *J. Gen. Physiol.,* 16, 695-714.

————. 1932-33b. Quantitative analysis of responses from lateral-line nerves of fishes: II. *J. Gen. Physiol.,* 16, 715-731.

————. 1932-33c. Quantitative aspects of cutaneous sensory adaptation: I. *J. Gen. Physiol.,* 16, 911-923.

————. 1933. The physiological control of judgments of duration: evidence for a chemical clock. *J. Gen. Psychol.,* 9, 267-287.

————. 1933-34. Electrical responses from the lateral-line nerves of fishes: IV. The repetitive discharge. *J. Gen. Physiol.,* 17, 195-209.

————. 1934-35. Adaptation of cutaneous tactile receptors: II. *J. Gen. Physiol.,* 18 (in press).

HOAGLAND, H., & CROZIER, W. J. 1931-32. Geotropic excitation in *Helix. J. Gen. Physiol.,* 15, 15-28.

HOAGLAND, H., & PERKINS, C. T. 1934-35. Some temperature characteristics in man. *J. Gen. Physiol.,* 18 (in press).

HOLMES, S. J. 1905. The reactions of *Ranatra* to light. *J. Comp. Neur. & Psychol.,* **15**, 305-349.

JÄGER, H. 1932. Untersuchungen über die geotaktischen Reaktionen verschiedener Evertebraten auf schiefer Ebene. *Zöol. Jahrb., Abt. f. Physiol.,* **51**, 289-320.

JENNINGS, H. S. 1905*a*. Contribution to the study of the behavior of lower organisms. (*Publ. Carnegie Instit.,* No. 16.) Washington, D. C.: Carnegie Instit. Pp. 256.

―――. 1905*b*. Modifiability in behavior: I. Behavior of the sea anemones. *J. Exper. Zöol.,* **2**, 447-485.

―――. 1906. Modifiability in behavior: II. Factors determining direction and character of movement in the earthworm. *J. Exper. Zöol.,* **3**, 435-455.

JUST, E. 1926. Untersuchungen zur Frage der Gültigkeit des Resultantengesetzes. *Verhandl. dtsch. zool. Gesell.*

KEELER, C. E. 1927-28. The geotropic reaction of rodless mice in light and in darkness. *J. Gen. Physiol.,* **11**, 361-368.

KROPP, B., & CROZIER, W. J. 1928-29. Geotropic orientation in arthropods: III. The fiddler crab *Uca. J. Gen. Physiol.,* **12**, 111-122.

KROPP, B., & ENZMANN, E. V. 1933-34. Photic stimulation and leg movements in the crayfish. *J. Gen. Physiol.,* **16**, 905-910.

LASHLEY, K. S. 1915. The acquisition of skill in archery. *Carnegie Publ.,* **7**, No. 211, 107-128.

LILLIE, R. S. 1929-30. Resemblances between the electromotor variations of rhythmically reacting living and non-living systems. *J. Gen. Physiol.,* **13**, 1-11.

LOEB, J. 1890. Der Heliotropismus der Thiere und seine Übereinstimmung mit dem Heliotropismus der Pflanzen. Würzburg: Hertz. Pp. iv+118.

―――. 1897. Zur Theorie der physiologischen Licht- und Schwerkraftwirkungen. *Pflüg. Arch. f. d. ges. Physiol.,* **54**, 81-107.

―――. 1905. Studies in general physiology. 2 vols. Chicago: Univ. Chicago Press. Pp. x+782.

―――. 1912. The mechanistic conception of life. Chicago: Univ. Chicago Press. Pp. 232.

―――. 1918. Tropisms, forced movements, and animal conduct. Philadelphia & London: Lippincott. Pp. 209.

LOEB, J., & EWALD, W. F. 1914. Ueber die Gültigkeit des Bunsen-Roscoeschen Gesetzes für die heliotropische Erscheinung bei Tieren. *Zentbl. f. Physiol.,* **27**, 1165.

MANGOLD, E. 1920. *Ergeb. d. Physiol.,* **18**, 79-117.

MAST, S. O. 1911. Light and the behavior of organisms. New York: Wiley; London: Chapman & Hall. Pp. 410.

―――. 1923. Photic orientation in insects with special reference to the drone-fly, *Eristalis tenax,* and the robber-fly, *Erax refibarbis. Amer. J. Physiol.,* **38**, 109-205.

―――. 1924. The process of orientation in the robber-fly, *Proctacanthus philadelphicus. Amer. J. Physiol.,* **68**, 262-279.

―――. 1926. Reaction to light in *Volvox,* with special reference to the process of orientation. *Zsch. f. vergl. Physiol.,* **4**, 637-658.

MATTHEWS, B. H. C. 1931*a*. The response of a single end-organ. *J. Physiol.,* **71**, 64-110.

―――. 1931*b*. The response of a muscle spindle during active contraction of a muscle. *J. Physiol.,* **72**, 153-174.

MAXWELL, J. C. 1908. Theory of heat. (10th ed.) London: Longmans, Green. Pp. 348.

MINNICH, D. E. 1919. The photic reactions of the honey-bee, *Apismellifera* L. *J. Exper. Zöol.*, **29**, 343-425.

MITCHELL, W. H., JR., & CROZIER, W. J. 1927-28. Photic orientation by two point-sources of light. *J. Gen. Physiol.*, **11**, 563-583.

MOORE, A. R. 1916. The mechanism of orientation in *Gonium*. *J. Exper. Zöol.*, **21**, 431-432.

————. 1919-20. Stereotropism as a function of neuromuscular organization. *J. Gen. Physiol.*, **2**, 319-324.

————. 1922-23. Muscle tension and reflexes in the earthworm. *J. Gen. Physiol.*, **5**, 327-333.

————. 1923-24. *Proc. Soc. Exper. Biol. & Med.*, **21**, 365.

MORGAN, T. H. 1926. The theory of the gene. New Haven, Conn.: Yale Univ. Press. Pp. xvi+343.

MORGULIS, S. 1910. The movements of the earthworm: a study of a neglected factor. *J. Comp. Neur. & Psychol.*, **20**, 615-624.

MÜLLER, A. 1925. Ueber Lichtreaktionen von Landasseln. *Zsch. f. vergl. Physiol.*, **3**, 113-144.

MÜLLER, H. 1924. Die Lichtreaktionen von *Julus fallax* und *Polydesmus complanatus*. *Zool. Jahrb., Abt. f. allg. Zool. u. Physiol.*, **40**, 399-487.

NAVEZ, A. E. 1926-27. "Galvanotropism" of roots. *J. Gen. Physiol.*, **10**, 551-558.

NORTHROP, J. H., & LOEB, J. 1922-23. The photochemical basis of animal heliotropism. *J. Gen. Physiol.*, **5**, 581-597.

OPPENHEIMER, C., & PINCUSSEN, L. 1925-27. Tabulae biologicae. Berlin: Junk. Pp. vi+522; viii+567; vi+829.

OSTEROUT, W. J. V. 1931. Physiological studies of single plant cells. *Biol. Revs.*, **6**, 369-411.

PAAL, A. 1914. Ueber phototropische Reizlietungen. *Ber. ü. d. dtsch. bot. Gesellsch.*, **32**, 499.

PARKER, G. H. 1914. The directive influence of the sense of smell in the dogfish. *Bull. U. S. Bur. Fisheries, **33**, 63-68.

————. 1920. The elementary nervous system. Philadelphia & London: Lippincott. Pp. 229.

PARKER, G. H., & VAN HEUSEN, A. P. 1917. The reception of mechanical stimuli by the skin, lateral-line organs, and ears in fishes, especially in *Amiurus*. *Amer. J. Physiol.*, **44**, 463-489.

PATTEN, B. M. 1914. A quantitative determination of orienting reaction in the blowfly larva (*Calliphora erythrocephala* Meigen). *J. Exper. Zöol.*, **17**, 213-280.

————. 1918-19. Photoreactions of partially blinded whip-tail scorpions. *J. Gen. Physiol.*, **1**, 435-458.

PIÉRON, H. 1913. Le problème physiologique du sommeil. Paris: Masson. Pp. xv+520.

PINCUS, G. 1926-27. Geotropic creeping of young rats. *J. Gen. Physiol.*, **10**, 525-532.

————. 1930-31. On the temperature characteristics from frequency of breathing movements in inbred strains of mice and in their hybrid offspring: I. *J. Gen. Physiol.*, **14**, 421-444.

PROSSER, C. L. 1934. Action potentials in the nervous system of the crayfish: I. Spontaneous impulses. *J. Cell. & Comp. Physiol.*, **4**, 185-209.

RABAUD, E. 1919. L'immobilisation réflexe et l'activité normal des arthropodes. *Bull. biol. de France et Belge*, **53**, 1-149.

RICE, F. O. 1923. *J. Amer. Chem. Soc.*, **45**, 2808.

RICHTER, C. P. 1927. Animal behavior and internal drives. *Quar. Rev. Biol.*, **2**, 307-343.

ROBERTSON, T. B. 1909. A biochemical conception of memory and sensation. *Monist*, **19**, 367-386.

ROSE, M. 1929. La question des tropismes. Paris: Presses universitaires de France. Pp. 469.

SKINNER, B. F. 1931. The concept of the reflex in the description of behavior. *J. Gen. Psychol.*, **5**, 427-458.

————. 1932a. Drive and reflex strength: I. *J. Gen. Psychol.*, **6**, 22-37.

————. 1932b. Drive and reflex strength: II. *J. Gen. Psychol.*, **6**, 38-48.

————. 1933a. The measurement of "spontaneous activity." *J. Gen. Psychol.*, **9**, 3-23.

————. 1933b. The rate of establishment of a discrimination. *J. Gen. Psychol.*, **9**, 302-350.

STARK, P. 1921. Studien über traumatotrope und haptotrope Reizleitungsvorgänge mit besonderer Berücksichtigung der Reizübertragung auf fremde Arten und Gattungen. *Jahrb. f. wiss. Bot.*, **60**, 67.

STARK, P., & DRESCHEL, O. 1922. Phototropische Reizleitungsvorgänge bei Unterbrechung des organischen Zusammenhangs. *Jahrb. f. wiss. Bot.*, **61**, 339.

STAVSKY, W. H. 1932. The geotropic conduct of young kittens. *J. Gen. Psychol.*, **6**, 441-446.

————. 1933. The geotropic conduct of young kittens: II. *J. Gen. Psychol.*, **9**, 452-455.

STIER, T. J. B. 1925-26. Reversal of phototropism in *Diemyctylus viridescens*. *J. Gen. Physiol.*, **9**, 521-523.

————. 1930. "Spontaneous activity" of mice. *J. Gen. Psychol.*, **4**, 67-101.

————. 1932-33. The rate of oxygen utilization by yeast as a function of temperature. *J. Gen. Physiol.*, **16**, 815-840.

STIER, T. J. B., & WOLF, E. 1932-33. On temperature characteristics for different processes in the same organism. *J. Gen. Physiol.*, **16**, 367-374.

TALIAFERRO, W. H. 1920. Reactions to light in *Planaria maculata*. *J. Exper. Zoöl.*, **31**, 59-116.

TANG, P. S. 1931-32. Temperature characteristics for the production of CO_2 by germinating seeds of *Lupinus albus*. *J. Gen. Physiol.*, **15**, 87-96.

TORREY, H. B., & HAYS, G. P. 1914. The rôle of random movements in the orientation of *Porcellio scaber* to light. *J. Anim. Behav.*, **4**, 110-120.

UPTON, M. 1929-30. The geotropic conduct of young guinea pigs. *J. Gen. Physiol.*, **13**, 647-655.

UPTON, M., & STAVSKY, W. H. 1932. The geotropic conduct of adult rats. *J. Gen. Psychol.*, **6**, 3-21.

WEBER, A. O. 1933. Estimation of time. *Psychol. Bull.*, **30**, 233-252.

WEISS, P. 1925. Tierisches Verhalten als "Systemreaktion." *Biologia generalis*, **1**.

WHEELER, W. M. 1911. The ant-colony as an organism. *J. Morph.*, **22**, 307-325.

————. 1923. Social life among the insects. New York: Harcourt, Brace. Pp. vii+375.

————. 1928. The social insects. New York: Harcourt, Brace. Pp. xviii+378.

WOLF, E. 1925. Physiologische Untersuchungen über das Umdrehen der Seesterne und Schlangensterne. *Zsch. f. vergl. Physiol.*, **3**.

————. 1926-27. Geotropism of *Agriolimax*. *J. Gen. Physiol.*, **10**, 757-765.

————. 1932-33. The visual intensity discrimination of the honey bee. *J. Gen. Physiol.*, **16**, 407-422.

WOLF, E., & CROZIER, W. J. 1927-28. Orientation in compound fields of excitation; photic adaptation in phototropism. *J. Gen. Physiol.*, **11**, 7-24.

————. 1932-33. The variability of intensity discrimination by the honey bee in relation to visual acuity. *J. Gen. Physiol.*, **16**, 787-793.

YAGI, N. 1927-28. Phototropism of *Dixippus morosus*. *J. Gen. Physiol.*, **11**, 297-300.

CHAPTER 2

THE MECHANISM AND LAWS OF HEREDITY

T. H. MORGAN

California Institute of Technology

If newly acquired habits of an individual should cause corresponding structural and psychic changes in its offspring, heredity would become a branch of animal psychology. The slogan that instincts are inherited habits has, it is true, at times held the attention of philosophers, and even of scientists of the old school. Lamarck, the acknowledged founder of the doctrine of the inheritance of acquired characters, brought forward no sufficient evidence in support of his views, since the cases he cites by way of illustration—the giraffe's long neck as a result of stretching, the toe membranes of wading birds from spreading the toes in mud, etc.—are largely figments of the imagination. In fact, the idea itself did not originate with Lamarck, but is a very ancient one. A belief in such transmission is found in the folklore of many peoples, and Lamarck's "evidence" is indeed as naïve as that of these stories and myths. It is, I think, largely because Lamarck relied on argument rather than objective proof that his theory failed to be accepted widely by physiologists trained in the more exact methods of science and found its adherents largely amongst artists, amateurs, paleontologists, psychologists, and zoölogists not addicted to the rigors of experimental science.

Herbert Spencer (1866, 1890, 1893a, 1893b, 1893c), at the end of the last century, carried the message to a large audience, ready to believe but not over-informed as to the difficulties inherent in the problem. Spencer brought forward no new evidence but exploited to full advantage certain theoretical situations. Perhaps his most characteristic argument relates to the discrimination of the sense of touch in different parts of the human body. A study of the topography of this function shows, he claimed, that this sense is most refined wherever the skin is most exposed to contact with the outside world—on the lips, fingertips, etc.—and decreases in proportion to the distance from the extremities in question. The discrimination rests on the distribution of touch-buds, but Spencer failed to show that these would develop more abundantly in an individual where contact is most frequent, and more abundantly in the offspring of the individual in question. Here, as in all such cases, the real point at issue is assumed on the basis of circumstantial evidence and the biological difficulties ignored. Moreover, when the theory does not strictly apply, imaginary possibilities are introduced; and where it is the simplest solution, no actual evidence is supplied to establish it, but its plausibility is urged as sufficient argument for its validity.

Hering in 1870 pointed out similarities between memory and heredity and, because of a striking but superficial resemblance, attempted to

109

identify one with the other. The argument, like others of its kind, ignores the actualities in the two situations. These differences have become greater as our information in the two fields has become more specific. Samuel Butler (1878, 1882), better known as a romantic novelist and writer than as a scientist, wrote vehemently in behalf of the identification of memory with heredity, undaunted by the difficulty of attempting to explain the better-known phenomena of heredity by an appeal to the less well-understood processes of memory. Somewhat similar attempts in later years have been made by Ward (1913), Semon (1905*a*, 1905*b*, 1907, 1911, 1912), and Eldridge (1925), not to mention less ambitious attempts by others.

More serious consideration must be given to the experimental evidence recently brought forward by Griffith (1922) and later reviewed by Detlefsen (1923, 1925), also to the elaborate experiment of McDougall (1927) on the inherited effect of training of white rats.

Griffith's experiments with continuous rotation appear to furnish a case of inheritance of specific disequilibration. Adult rats were rotated in pens for long periods, some in a clockwise and others in a counter-clockwise direction. Several weeks after removal some of the rats developed a peculiar twist of the head and a permanent nystagmus in direct relation to the direction of rotation, etc. Griffith also reported the appearance of disequilibration in the descendants of these rats, and, what is more important, in the earlier oral reports by Detlefsen and in Griffith's report there was stated to be a high correlation between the right or left reaction of the treated parents and that of their offspring. Later observations by Casamajor, Detlefsen (1923), and McCordock and Congdon (1924) have shown that disequilibrated rats occasionally appear without previous rotation. These rats give the same physiological reaction that the rotated rats exhibit. There is more than a suspicion that the reaction is due to defects or disease in one of the ears. Detlefsen has also called forth the same reaction by injuring one labyrinth. It seems, therefore, not improbable that the rotation caused similar injuries, but this still will not explain the reported correlation between parent and offspring in Griffith's experiment. The not-infrequent occurrence, however, of disequilibrated rats that have not been rotated cannot but jeopardize the results of Griffith's experiments, even though he found no such disequilibration in the brothers and sisters of his treated stock or in their descendants. The experiment calls for careful repetition in the light of this evidence on rats that have been made as nearly homozygous as possible beforehand, and also for careful scrutiny as to possible infection or indirect transmission of a diseased condition of the ears.

McDougall's experiments in which white rats were dropped in a tank of water and given a choice of routes for escape with or without punishment seem to him to show that the results of training are in some degree inherited. The earlier work, the results of which were reported in 1927, has been continued and the outcome reported in 1930. In the first report the statement that, since the rats had long been inbred, the stock was thoroughly homogeneous is offset by another statement that there were "very large individual differences between the animals in respect of the rate at which they master their tasks." In another connection McDougall points out that some of the rats and their descendants showed a tendency to go to the right (or left). This would lead a geneticist to question the suitability of this or closely related stock for this particular purpose. It is disturbing, to say the least, to meet with the statement that "there is some indication that the transmission of effects of training follows a law of segregation reminiscent of Mendel's law, the effects being transmitted to some individuals and not at all to others." Such statements are too vague to mean much, if anything. The earlier experiments were carried through thirteen generations, the later through ten generations more (fourteenth to twenty-third generations), and the results showed a further increase in facility of learning. The average number of errors per rat in the fourteenth generation was 80; in the twenty-third generation it was only 25. The number of errors of the best rate in the fourteenth generation was 42, and of the worst rat, 102. In the twenty-third generation the best rat committed only 3 errors and the worst, 71. These figures, taken in connection with the progressive changes throughout all the series, leave little doubt that a change of some kind had taken place. The results are also compared with those obtained in a new set of experiments on untrained parents from the original stock and on their offspring. Moreover, in the new generation of these rats a reversed selection was made on five rats, using rats that were inferior in respect to their rate of learning. There were eighteen offspring trained. The worst half of the offspring were inbred, and twelve of their offspring (WC₅) were tested. There was evidence that an improvement had taken place despite that fact that the two preceding generations had been selected against, etc. "This seems to imply that the Lamarckian transmission of acquired facility overcomes the opposed influence of adverse selection."

Taking the figures at their face value, there seems to have been a distinct improvement in the successive generations of trained rats. To a geneticist the results bear all the earmarks of some kind of selection's taking place despite the conscientious attempt of the experimenter to avoid it. There are genetic methods by which selection can be eliminated, but this would require a more critical procedure than has been applied. The reverse selection on which McDougall lays so much emphasis is quite inadequate to cover the situation, although, if carried out under genetic control, it might be expected to give significant results. But if, as McDougall says, "the vague possibility of some 'telepathic' influence from me to the rat must be regarded seriously," the problem is quite outside the range of genetic science. In the absence of published data to indicate how long after training the young of the next litter were born, a serious question arises as to whether the effects of the training may or may not be lost. Is habit formation an irreversible process? If a new habit can be "formed" in fifteen days, how much, one asks, may be lost after several months? Does the "loss" or "disuse" occur also in the germ-cells of the individual, or does the registration once made there last forever?

Physiologists can show a small but no less distinguished list of advocates of the doctrine. The experiments of Brown-Séquard on guinea pigs have been for a long time in the literature, but owing to the conflicting and largely negative evidence that has resulted from attempts to repeat his experiment his case has slowly drifted into the background. Romanes (1892, 1895, 1897) has discussed this evidence at length, and more recently it has been considered by several other observers.

Brown-Séquard (1869, 1870-71a, 1870-71b, 1872, 1880, 1882, 1892, 1893) reported the appearance of epilepsy in the off-spring of parents that had been made epileptic by an injury to the spinal cord or to the sciatic nerve. He also reported partial closure of the eyes in animals born of parents showing a similar state of the eyelids after sectioning of the superior cervical ganglion. Exophthalmia appeared in the off-spring of parents in which injury to the restiform body had produced a protrusion of the eyeball. Absence of some of the toes occurred in the offspring of animals whose parents had eaten off some of their toes, or in which the toes had been affected after cutting the sciatic nerve. These and a few other observations seem to relate to cases of specific inheritance. Brown-Séquard states that he had never observed similar defects in guinea pigs not operated upon. Many attempts to confirm these results have been made. A few cases of partial confirmation have been reported, as well as failures. Weismann's attempt to explain away the results as due to direct infection of the offspring by the parent will not account for the reported specific nature of the transmission. The most serious criticism of Brown-Séquard's results is the sporadic occurrence of the reported transmission, the absence of data to show the frequency of failure to transmit, and the failure to use pedigreed material known to be free from inherited defects of the kind reported. In the case of epilepsy the nature of the disease (?) is problematical. The suggestion that it may appear in animals weakened by treatment or otherwise has been regarded as plausible. Whether the offspring of animals which have been made epileptic produce weaker offspring is not known. The absence of information on these and other conditions is a serious obstacle to the acceptance of Brown-Séquard's conclusions. Other experimenters have in recent years reported the appearance of defects in the offspring of guinea pigs whose parents have been injured, but it appears that these facts may be more simply explained as due to direct injuries to the germ-cells. Until such an explanation of Brown-Séquard's experiments can be shown not to hold, his results cannot be regarded as establishing his claims of somatic induction of specific defects.

A few years ago Pavlov startled the scientific world by a report of experiments made with mice. He stated that conditioned reflexes, established by the sound of a bell as a call for food, were transmitted to the offspring. Expectation hung for several years in the balance, for the great reputation of Pavlov called for serious consideration of his very positive statements based supposedly on exact experiments. Others who had already worked in the same field (MacDowell, 1919, 1921, 1923; Vicari, 1924; and Tolman, 1924) had seen no such effects where they should have been even more in evidence did they occur, since these workers dealt with the histories of individual cases and in one instance with homogeneous material. It now appears that some error had crept into Pavlov's experiments, since he has sponsored their withdrawal.

Zoölogists, too, can supply a long list of devoted adherents to the theory of the inheritance of acquired characters, and, while Weismann's attack in 1886 convinced almost everyone that more care was required in weighing the reported evidence, nevertheless there have not been lacking serious attempts to rehabilitate the theory on the grounds of new evidence.

We may pass over the views of the paleontologists, who could not possibly from the nature of their material supply the necessary critical evidence, for, however convinced they are that the course of evolution has been along lines of adaptation to environmental needs in a mechanical sense, they cannot be expected to disprove the possibility that such adaptations might have come about in other ways.

Zoölogists who have argued the question on general grounds, as did Darwin, and later Delage, Pauly (1905), Semon (1905a, 1905b, 1907, 1911, 1912), Cunningham (1892, 1895, 1896, 1900), and others, have supplied no really critical evidence. On the other hand, the experimental work of several other zoölogists has kept the discussion alive. Kammerer's (1911, 1924) numerous reports of extensive series of experiments, claiming to establish the transmission of artificially induced structural changes and physiological activities, have been under fire from the beginning. The experiments were ingeniously planned, and, taken at their face value, appeared over-abundantly to establish his contention. To demonstrate his claims, careful and unselected data are called for that have quantitative measurements to support them. In the absence of such data, the expressed conviction of the author that such effects do occur introduces a personal equation that may well color the facts as reported. When his experiments have been repeated by others (Herbst, 1919), with more attention to detail, they have failed to confirm his claims, and have made it clear that in his haste to establish his principles he has often neglected facts that vitiate the evidence. His final and most heralded result on the thumb pad of the midwife toad has been shown, in one crucial case at least, to have been fraudulent, the responsibility for which Kammerer repudiated before his tragic death.

Guyer and Smith (1918, 1920) reported a few cases in which eye defects in rabbits, induced *in utero,* reappeared in a few of the descendants. Later a more specific result was obtained by Guyer (1922a, 1923) by injuring the lens with a needle. Again, eye defects were found in a few of the offspring. In criticism of this evidence it should be pointed out that the effects were at best sporadic and not beyond the possibility that they were due to defective germ-plasm in the stock used—the controls not being sufficient protection against this possibility. Guyer has been careful to guard against this contingency and has never made extravagant claims as to the certainty of the results' being due to transmission. In more recent years several repetitions of the experiments (Huxley and Carr-Saunders, 1924; Findlay, 1924; and others) have failed to confirm Guyer's results, and others (von Hipple; von Szily, 1924; Hochstetter; and Koyanagi) have reported eye defects in rabbits that occasionally crop up often enough to make the material suspect.

Certain moths have been reported to develop a black strain in certain factory districts in England. Harrison has made some experiments with these moths by putting into the food of the caterpillars some of the ingredients that might be supposed to have fallen on the larvae from factory smoke and to have caused the observed changes. The caterpillars so treated produced moths. A very few of the eggs of these moths gave melanic individuals and this character was transmitted to their offspring as a Mendelian character. In his earlier reports Harrison explained this as due to the inheritance of an acquired character in the conventional sense. A closer scrutiny of the evidence, however, does not support this conclusion, since it becomes evident that the result can be explained, and better explained, I think, as the result of a direct action on the germ-cells Interpreted in this way, the body cells have not changed the germ-cells, at first indifferent, into their own likeness, so to speak, but a change took place in the preceding generation in some of the germ-cells that was transmitted both to the body cells and to the germ-cells of the black individuals. In other words, there was a direct action of the environment producing a mutation in one or more germ-cells and not "somatic induction." Dürken's (1923) experiment purporting to show the inherited influence of light on pupae of a butterfly can be accounted for by the selection of individuals more or less sensitive to light from a mixed population.

That germ-cells may be affected by the environment has been shown by recent work on the effects of radium and X-rays (Little and Bagg, 1924; Muller, 1927a, 1927b, 1928, 1930). The action of radium in producing irregularities in the distribution of chromosomes and parts of chromosomes had already been demonstrated by the earlier work of Hertwig (1905, 1923), Packard (1893, 1894), Mohr (1919), and several others. Apparently in line with this evidence is that obtained by Stockard (1893) and Stockard and Papanicolaou (1916, 1918) on guinea pigs. The results were at first obscured by the fact that the lenses of the eyes of the adult guinea pig that had received alcohol treatment were made opaque. The offspring occasionally showed defects, and amongst these were eye defects of various kinds. Stockard is inclined to interpret the results as due to the direct effects of the alcohol on the germ-cells of the treated individuals.

An impartial survey of all this evidence cannot fail, I think, to give the impression that the many attempts to obtain crucial evidence that somatically acquired characters produce specific changes of the same kind in the germ-cells have failed. If such effects are transmitted, and especially if these are pre-eminently adaptive ones, there is every reason to suppose that evidence of such transmission should be obtainable—in fact should be abundantly apparent to anyone making careful observations. There is lack of care in experimentation and of acumen in reasoning from the evidence manifest in most of the reported results. To suggest that the influence may not be felt unless extended over many, or an indefinite number of generations, removes the problem from the field of experimental science. The situation is even worse when behavior patterns are considered, for all such adaptive reactions are highly complex, involving intricate nerve and muscle adjustments. It is, I venture to think, beyond the imaginative capacity of biologists, familiar with what is best known today in embryonic development and in genetics, to suggest any rational process by which such complexities could be carried over *as a whole* from the body cells to the germ-cells. If, then, the alliance between psychology and genetics is not likely to be established along this line, it remains to discover whether the present status of heredity points to other possible relations that may exist between these two branches of science.

Mendelian Heredity

In the meantime, while argument and counter-argument have continued without apparently bringing any relief or real support to the Larmarckians, there has been remarkable progress in several other fields that must have an important influence on all questions concerning heredity. I refer to the study of the egg, its fertilization and development, to the results of cytological work bearing on the nature of the chromosomes, and to the extraordinary series of events that occur at the time of the maturation of the germ-cells. These discoveries have become such an integral part of the modern theory of heredity that to ignore them through prejudice or ignorance would be tantamount to a disregard of the most accurate information that is known relating to the mechanism of heredity. The details of this cytological work will be found in numerous texts now available. Only the most general conclusions need be stated here.

The evidence from genetics has shown that the chromosomes are the bearers of the hereditary elements. Each species of animal and plant has a definite number of chromosomes of characteristic size. There are two chromosomes of each kind in all the body cells as well as in the young germ-cells. The members of each pair are, in homogeneous races, identical in their hereditary elements, but in the hybrid, or heterozygous individual, one member of a pair may differ from the other in one or more elements or genes. The cells are double-barreled or duplex with respect to their hereditary elements. The different pairs of chromosomes carry different sets of elements.

The genetic evidence further indicates that the hereditary elements, the genes, lie in a linear order in the chromosomes—like beads on a string—or at least the facts can be explained on this assumption, the genes themselves being too small to be visible. The serial order of the genes is maintained throughout all successive divisions of the cell and from one

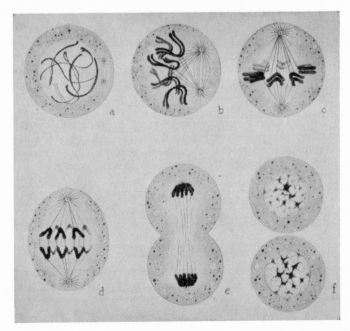

FIGURE 1

DIAGRAM ILLUSTRATING CELL DIVISION

The chromosomes are represented as black threads (*a*), or bent rods which become connected with protoplasmic threads (*b*). Each chromosome splits lengthwise (*c*), and the halves or daughter chromosomes pass to opposite poles (*d, e*), where they subsequently become vacuolated to form the resting nuclei of the two daughter cells (*f*).

generation to the next. This is made possible by the way the chromosomes divide at each cell division. Each chromosome splits lengthwise into daughter threads, exactly equivalent (Figure 1). Since all the cells of the body contain the duplex set of genes, we must regard every cell, no matter how it is differentiated, as carrying the entire equipment of hereditary elements. In other words, the different cells of the body, no matter what their function, are looked upon as containing all the elements. It is difficult to furnish complete proof of the last statement, but since there is a great deal of direct evidence supporting it, and none opposed, it seems not unreasonable to make this somewhat broad generalization.

The implications in this statement are significant, for they mean that the embryonic development—the extensive processes of specialization or differentiation in the cells derived from the fertilized egg—cannot be explained, as Roux and Weismann once supposed, by the sorting-out of the hereditary elements of the chromosomes, but must be explained on either of two hypotheses: first, that different genes begin to function at different stages of development; or, second, that the initial differences lie in the cytoplasm. In fact, the evidence at hand indicates that the initiation of differentiation of some of the important characters begins in the egg before the chromosomes are separated.

If differentiation of the parts of the individual is a property of the protoplasm of the egg and embryo, why, it may be asked, is not the protoplasm the real bearer of heredity? The answer is that there is today explicit evidence showing that the behavior of the cytoplasm is determined in the last analysis by the composition of the chromosomes. The determination may take place before development begins or at later stages. The evidence supporting this assumption will be given later, after the facts of Mendelian inheritance have been reviewed.

The Chromosome Mechanism of Heredity

Mendel's (1865) two laws of heredity were deduced from numerical data derived from crosses of two individuals that differed in one or more characters. Since the types selected for crossing were sharply separable for one or more striking characters, these characters came later to be spoken of as unit characters.

Mendel assumed that each one of the contrasted characters is due to an element or unit in the germ-plasm responsible for that character, and that these units separate from each other in the eggs and pollen of the hybrid.

In the early days of Mendelism—at the beginning of this century—the idea prevailed in certain quarters that each element in the germ-cells produces in the individual one particular character. Needless confusion soon arose from the identification of the germinal unit with the unit character. The identification was misleading when it was attempted to show that the fluctuations in the character arose from similar fluctuations in the germinal unit. If this erroneous idea had gained headway it would have gone far to undo the all-important clue that Mendel's discovery had furnished as an explanation of heredity.

There is abundant evidence at the present time to prove that the germinal units or genes may, and generally do, affect more than one of the characters of the individual, and that these effects are present whenever a specific gene is present. As a rule the *most conspicuous* amongst these effects is designated as the character whose heredity we study. It would be equally possible in most cases to follow one of the minor characters. The outcome would be the same.

The idea that each character is the product of a single gene is in a sense correct, but only in so far as the presence of a particular gene is determinative for a given character. The genes are only differentials. But the same gene may affect many other characters; in fact, it might be said that a change in a pair of genes (or in one only if it is dominant) might affect every single character of the individual, but, since we cannot identify all of its effects, there is little to be gained in pressing this point.

In fact, there are good and sufficient reasons to infer that some characters are not affected at all by certain specific genes, since "the principle of all or none" seems to be a rather general property of differentiation.

Conversely, if the genes frequently have such far-reaching influences as just suggested, it would seem to follow that a great many and perhaps all the genes are contributory agents to every character of the individual. The individual would be the effect of all of its genes in every part. It is not necessary at present to carry this statement too far, but it agrees with what embryonic development teaches with clarity, namely, that each organ passes through a series of changes before reaching its goal, and most organs are also composites of several or many kinds of tissues whose differentiation has taken place along different lines. The human eye, for example, comes in part from the forebrain, in part from the ectoderm of the side of the head. Mesenchyme and mesoderm contribute to it, and blood vessels are also pushed into the interior of the mass. Therefore, when we contrast in heredity blue and brown eyes, we are describing a single difference dependent on the presence or absence of brown pigment granules in the iris (in which the two kinds of eyes differ), yet there remain numbers of characters that the eyes have in common. Here we pick out only a pair of contrasted conditions, but it may be pointed out that the same pair of genes that leads to a failure in the development of brown pigment may have other effects in other parts of the body—in the nervous system or in the skin, for instance—that we have not yet identified. In any case the eye is found to be a complex of tissues to whose development a host of genes may be contributory.

For present purposes, however, the important fact is that we can ascribe this effect on the eye color to a particular chromosome and in similar cases locate the gene in a limited region of a chromosome. In order to show in general how this has been possible, it will be necessary to describe how the mechanism that is implied but not expressed in Mendel's laws is due to the behavior of chromosomes as wholes, and how later work has enabled us to locate, within the chromosome chain of genes, the particular gene that produces certain effects.

Just before the final stages in the ripening of the germ-cells (egg and sperm) an extraordinary event takes place. In each cell the chromosomes come together in pairs. Each pair consists of one maternally derived and one paternally derived chromosome. This is illustrated in Figure 2, *a,* where the maternal chromosomes are black and the paternal white.

At the time of conjugation, the chromosomes stretch out as thin threads —possibly a line of genes. They come together in pairs throughout their length and then shorten to form rods which are often bent.

The nuclear wall next disappears. The condensed chromosomes then pass onto a spindle that has meanwhile developed in the protoplasm (Figure 2, *b*). Here they come to lie in a flat plate at the equator of the spindle. The members of each pair then pass to opposite poles (Figure 2, *c, d*). Around each set a new membrane develops.

Each daughter cell now contains one of each kind of chromosome. The

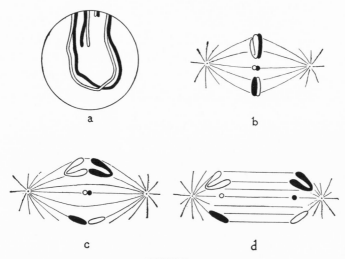

FIGURE 2

DIAGRAM TO ILLUSTRATE CONJUGATION AND REDUCTION OF THE CHROMOSOMES

In (a) pairs of chromosomes in the form of thin threads are coming together (conjugation). In (b) they have shortened and occupy the equator of the "spindle." In (c) one member of each pair is passing to one pole and its mate to the opposite pole of the spindle. In (d) they have reached the pole. Cell division then taking place, two cells result each with the half number of chromosomes. The second maturation division is not shown here.

original number is reduced to half in each daughter cell, and, since at the time of separation the maternal and paternal members of the different pairs are distributed at random, the half number may be made up both of maternal and paternal chromosomes, but each cell always has one member of each pair.

After a short resting period (in the sperm-cells at least) another division phase sets in. Here each chromosome is split throughout its length, as in ordinary division, and the halves pass to daughter cells. Each cell still has the half number of chromosomes which now pass again into the nuclear resting phase. Out of these cells the mature germ-cells are produced—eggs and spermatozoa.

The generalized description just given covers the essential facts, but in detail the changes differ in the ripening of eggs and sperm-cells. The sperm-cell follows closely the above scheme (Figure 3). Four spermatozoa are produced by two divisions of the original mother cell. Each sperm carries half the total number of chromosomes. The egg cell also divides twice (Figure 4), but in animals one of the products of the division is extremely small—invisible to the unaided eye. It is called a polar body. Two such bodies are "given off" by two miotic divisions that are exactly comparable to those in the sperm except for size. The first polar body generally divides again. The three polar bodies and the egg are compara-

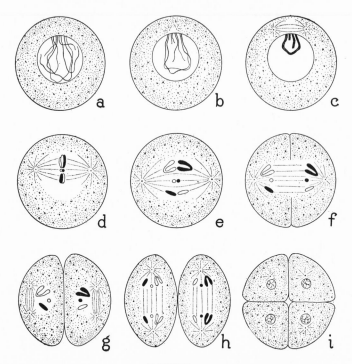

FIGURE 3

DIAGRAM TO ILLUSTRATE THE TWO MATURATION DIVISIONS OF A SPERM
MOTHER CELL

In the upper line (*a, b, c*) conjugation is shown. In the second line (*d, e, f*) the reduction at the first division is taking place. In the third line (*g, h, i*) the second or equatorial division is taking place in each of the two cells. In the latter division each chromosome splits lengthwise as in ordinary cell division.

ble to the four spermatozoa, but the egg alone is capable of further development. Since the first division of the chromosomes reduces the number in the egg as it does in the spermatozoa, there will be as many kinds of eggs as there are kinds of spermatozoa.

Fertilization of the eggs, each by a single sperm, leads to the union of the nucleus of the egg with that of the sperm to form a new nucleus containing the sum of the two sets of chromosomes, or the total number (Figure 5). Each divides lengthwise at every subsequent division of the segmenting egg, and, in consequence, every cell of the body comes to contain the duplex number.

The application of the chromosome mechanism to Mendel's laws may be illustrated by the following example, in which symbols for the genes will first be given (Figure 6) and then (Figure 8) chromosomes substituted for the letters. Mendel crossed a pea from a race breeding true to tallness

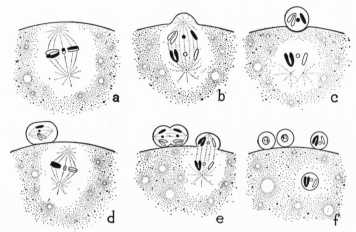

FIGURE 4

DIAGRAM TO ILLUSTRATE THE TWO MATURATION DIVISIONS OF THE EGG

In the upper line (a, b, c) the reduction division is taking place. The first polar body is given off (c). In the second line (d, e, f) the second or equatorial division is taking place, each chromosome splitting lengthwise. A second polar body is given off (e, f), and at the same time the first polar body divides.

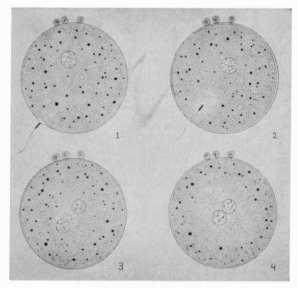

FIGURE 5

DIAGRAM TO ILLUSTRATE THE FERTILIZING OF THE EGG BY A SINGLE SPERM WHICH BRINGS IN THE SPERM NUCLEUS

The two nuclei fuse to form the segmentation nucleus which will have the total number of chromosomes.

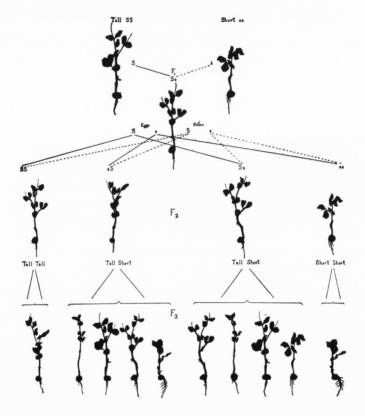

FIGURE 6

DIAGRAM TO ILLUSTRATE A CROSS BETWEEN TALL AND SHORT EDIBLE PEAS

The small letter *s* stands for the short-producing gene. The large letter *S* for the normal allelomorph or tall. The offspring or "hybrid" (F₁ *Ss*) is tall. It produces two kinds of eggs and two kinds of germ-cells or gametes, viz., *S* and *s*. Self-fertilization gives three kinds of offspring (F₂) in the ratio of 1:2:1, viz.: tall tall, tall short, and short short. The first and last breed true as shown in F₃.

to a pea from a short race (Figure 6). The genes for tallness may be designated by the letters *SS*. The ripe egg will contain one of them, *S*. Similarly in the other race (*ss*) each pollen grain will contain one gene for short, *s*. After crossing, the fertilized egg will contain this pair of genes, *Ss*—one for tall and one for short. The hybrid that develops from the egg will contain the same pair in all of its cells.

The fact that the hybrid itself is tall means that, when both are present, the tall gene produces its full effect, and is said to be dominant or to dominate.

When in the hybrid the germ-cells ripen, the genes in question, tall and

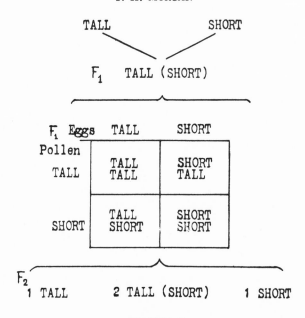

FIGURE 7

DIAGRAM TO ILLUSTRATE THE FERTILIZATION OF THE TWO KINDS OF EGGS, TALL AND SHORT, OF THE HYBRID (F₁) BY THE TWO KINDS OF POLLEN GRAINS, GIVING THE RATIO 1:2:1 IN F₂

short, will separate, and each germ-cell will come to contain one or the other (Figure 6). The garden pea is hermaphroditic or bisexual. Eggs and pollen develop on the same plant. Half of the eggs of the hybrid will, when maturation is completed, contain the short-producing, and half will contain the long-producing, gene. The same is true for the pollen. Chance fertilization of any egg by any pollen grain will give four classes of individuals in the ratio of 1:2:1 (Figure 7).

One class will be pure for tall, since it contains both of the tall-producing genes. It will breed as true to this character as did the original tall parent, even though one of its grandparents was short.

Two classes will be hybrid. They contain one tall-producing and one short-producing gene. If self-fertilized they will behave like the hybrid parent (F_1), and give again a ratio of 1:2:1.

The remaining class will be short, since it contains the two short-producing genes. It will breed true to this character, even though its parents were tall (Figure 6).

If, instead of representing the elements (genes) for tall and short by letters, they are represented by a pair of chromosomes, the outcome (Figure 8) is the same as that just described. In this diagram the chromosomes which carry the genes for tall are represented by black rods, the homologous chromosomes, which carry the genes for short, are represented by

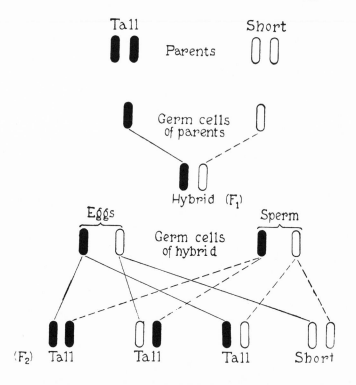

FIGURE 8

DIAGRAM ILLUSTRATING HOW A PAIR OF CHROMOSOMES BEHAVES IN THE CROSS
BETWEEN A TALL AND A SHORT PEA

The black rods are each supposed to carry the gene for tall, the white rods the
one for short.

white rods. The hybrid has one of each kind. These, separating at maturation of the germ-cells, give two kinds of reduced eggs and two kinds of
reduced pollen cells. Chance fertilization of any egg by any pollen
grain gives the 1:2:1 ratio.

This example shows how the chromosomes supply the mechanism for
Mendel's first law, that may be called the law of segregation, which
means that in the hybrid the contrasted elements are segregated into different germ-cells.

There is an adequate test of Mendel's first law by means of a back-
cross. If, in the last case, the eggs of the F_1 hybrid were artificially fertilized, not by its own pollen but by pollen from a race of short peas, the
expectation on the theory would be for half the offspring to be tall, half
short, because, on the theory, the hybrid produces two kinds of germ-cells
—tall and short—in equal numbers, and the germ-cells of the short peas
are recessive and all short-producing. The offspring should then be hybrid

(i.e., tall) and short in equal numbers. The results confirm the expectations. Many other tests are possible and have all been made in other Mendelian crosses. They confirm Mendel's theory.

When two independent pairs of characters enter into the same cross, the elements of each pair being carried by a different pair of chromosomes, each pair follows the first law, but, since each pair segregates independently, there will be four kinds of germ-cells that give by recombination in the second generation 16 classes. These fall into four groups in the ratio of 9:3:3:1. For example, if a pea that is tall and has purple flowers is crossed to a short pea with white flowers (Figure 9), the first generation peas are all tall and purple, since these two characters dominate. When the chromosome pairs are segregated in the hybrids, there will be four and only four assortments (germ-cells) possible, as shown in Figure 9.

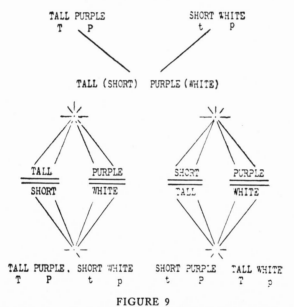

FIGURE 9

DIAGRAM ILLUSTRATING A CROSS BETWEEN TALL PURPLE AND SHORT WHITE PEAS

The two spindles in the lower part of the diagram show how the independent assortment of the two pairs leads to the formation of four kinds of germ-cells (*TP, tp, tP, Tp*).

These are tall purple, tall white, short purple, short white, in equal numbers. If, when the hybrid is self-fertilized, the meeting of any one of the four kinds of pollen grains with any one of the four kinds of eggs is a chance event (which means that there is no selective fertilization), the 16 possible unions result that are shown in the next diagram (Figure 10). When the characters shown by the individuals are classified according to dominance, there are present nine with two dominants, three with one, and

EGGS

	Tall purple	Tall white	Dwarf purple	Dwarf white
Tall purple	Tall purple Tall purple (9)	Tall white Tall purple (9)	Dwarf purple Tall purple (9)	Dwarf white Tall purple (9)
Tall white	Tall purple Tall white (9)	Tall white Tall white (3a)	Dwarf purple Tall white (9)	Dwarf white Tall white (3a)
Dwarf purple	Tall purple Dwarf purple (9)	Tall white Dwarf purple (9)	Dwarf purple Dwarf purple (3b)	Dwarf white Dwarf purple (3b)
Dwarf white	Tall purple Dwarf white (9)	Tall white Dwarf white (3a)	Dwarf purple Dwarf white (3b)	Dwarf white Dwarf white (1)

Pollen

FIGURE 10

DIAGRAM ILLUSTRATING THE 16 CLASSES OF F_2 INDIVIDUALS RESULTING FROM A CROSS BETWEEN TALL PURPLE AND SHORT WHITE PEAS

These 16 classes fall into four groups as determined by the presence of two or one or no dominant gene, giving the $9:3:3:1$ ratio.

three with the other dominant, and one with neither dominant, the so-called double recessive.

The outcome in the second generation from a cross involving two pairs of genes is the same regardless as to whether both dominants went in from one side and both recessives from the other side (as above) or whether a dominant of one pair and a recessive from the other pair go in together. Independent assortment of the pairs leads in both cases to the same kinds of germ-cells in the hybrid.

On the other hand, as will be shown later, the result would be expected to be different, as it is in fact, if two (or more) pairs of genes should be in the same chromosome pair. Mendel did not meet with cases of this kind although several are known today in garden peas and a great many such cases in other types.

When three or more independent pairs of characters are present in a cross, the principles involved are the same—there will be, of course, more classes in the second generation.

Mendel regarded one member of a pair of characters as completely dominant over the other member. Many such cases are at present known, but there are many other cases in which dominance is not complete, and the character in the hybrid lies somewhere between those of its parents. Nevertheless, by suitable tests it has been amply shown that the segregation of the genes in the hybrid is as accurate and clean-cut as in the former cases.

One of the difficulties that has come up as our information has broadened relates to situations where modifiers of characters are present. The simplest cases of this sort are those where specific genes exist that intensify or, conversely, dilute the character in question. In extreme cases a modifier may completely suppress the expression of another character. The occurrence of such genes is an ever-present anxiety to the geneticist, but suitable methods are known by which modifiers can themselves be studied as are other Mendelian characters.

More difficult to handle are multiple-factor cases in which the development of a character is the direct result of more than one kind of gene—all, taken together, adding to or subtracting from a given measurement. Height in man or in corn is an example. The height of a man may be due to length of legs or body or neck or of all taken together or to what is known as hybrid vigor. Height in man may be due to the time at which sexual maturity is reached or to the activity of glands of internal secretion, etc. Different genetic factors may bring about these changes. Hence no one or even a few factors suffice to explain the result, and, since their effects may overlap, the analysis is made difficult. In such cases the usual resort is to employ statistical methods, but the interest of the geneticist lies in the detection of the specific genes involved. As long as a given result is the outcome of different, unknown, genetic factors, the statistical treatment may serve as a temporary expedient. When the genetic analysis can be made, it clears up the situation by resolving it into the specific agencies producing a complex result.

So far the chromosomes have been considered as wholes, but during the last fifteen years evidence has been obtained that proves that at one stage in their cycle there may occur interchanges between the members of each pair. In so far as this takes place, Mendel's second law no longer covers the facts. The new procedure enables us, none the less, to treat the problems of heredity that arise with the same exactness as applies to Mendel's laws. This phenomenon is known as crossing over.

An example will serve to illustrate crossing over. There is a mutant race of the vinegar fly *Drosophila* that has black wings. It gives, when crossed to the wild fly that has gray wings, three grays to one black in the second generation. There is another mutant race that has vestiges of wings. The wings of the wild type may be called long. Vestigial crossed to long gives three longs to one vestigial in the second generation. In other words, the two mutant characters are recessive, and when each alone is present in a cross it gives the Mendelian ratio 3:1 in F_2, and in a back-cross a 1:1 ratio.

Now, if a fly that is *both* black and vestigial is crossed to one that is gray and long, the offspring (F_1) are gray and long. If the F_1 females are mated to double-recessive, black, vestigial males of stock, the next generation gives:

Gray	Black	Gray	Black
long	vestigial	vestigial	long
41.5	41.5	8.5	8.5

Since the black vestigial male used in the back-cross carried only recessive genes, the result reveals the kinds and proportions of the germ-cells of the hybrid female (F_1). The result means that 41.5% of her germ-cells contained the two recessive genes that went in from one parent and 41.5% of the germ-cells contained the two dominant genes that went in from the other parent. We speak of these genes as linked together to the extent shown by the figures. In addition there are two other classes of germ-cells that are, so to speak, interchanges between the combinations that went in together. These classes are called cross-overs and constitute 17% of all the F_2 flies.

If we suppose that black (b) and vestigial (v) are carried by the same chromosome and that gray (B) and long (V) are carried by the homologous chromosome of the other parent, then, as shown in Figure 11,

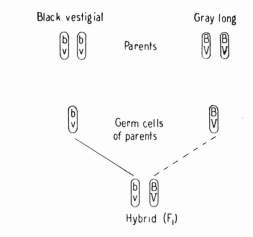

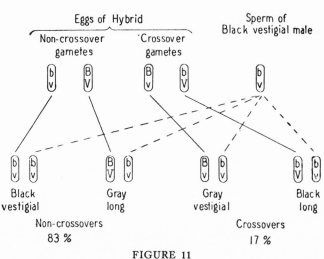

FIGURE 11

DIAGRAM ILLUSTRATING CROSSING OVER BETWEEN MEMBERS OF A CHROMOSOME PAIR OF THE HYBRID FROM A CROSS BETWEEN A BLACK VESTIGIAL AND A GRAY LONG FLY

The gene for black is b, and for gray B; that for vestigial is small v, and that for long wings is large V.

the two chromosomes are segregated in the F_1 female into different cells. If nothing further had happened, there would be only two kinds of germ-cells (*bv* and *BV*), 50% of each kind, but, as the results show, there are only about 42% of each of these.   In addition there are two other kinds of egg cells that can be accounted for if a reciprocal interchange has taken place between the two chromosomes in question.   This may be represented in a diagram by the two chromosomes overlapping at points between the Mendelian pairs (Figure 12).   If the chromosomes fuse at the point of

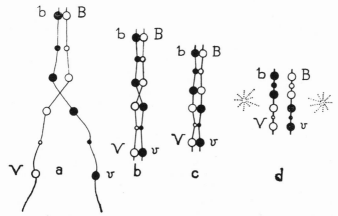

FIGURE 12

DIAGRAM ILLUSTRATING CROSSING OVER BETWEEN A PAIR OF CHROMOSOMES, ONE (BLACK DOTS) CARRYING THE GENES FOR BLACK (*b*) AND VESTIGIAL (*v*), THE OTHER FOR GRAY (*B*) AND LONG (*V*)

In (*a*) these two chromosomes overlap before coming together as in (*b*). In (*c*) they are represented as having come together. The two lines of genes on each side of the plane of union have now united each into a single line.

crossing (between the pairs) and the four ends reunite on each side of the crossing, the two resulting chromosomes will be *bV* and *Bv* respectively. It is to be noted that the interchange has involved large pieces of the chromosomes, but each will still contain its complete number of genes in the same sequence as before.   As the numerical results show, the interchange takes place in only 17% of the original germ-cells.

There is another important relation that the work on crossing over has revealed.   The outcome is in principle the same whether the two recessives enter from one side and the two dominants from the other, as in the case above, or whether a recessive and a dominant enter together.   The classes themselves in F_2 will, of course, be different.   Thus, if black and long had entered together from one individual and gray and vestigial from the other, the second generation of flies (F_2) from a back-cross gives:

NON–CROSS-OVERS		CROSS-OVERS	
Black long	Gray vestigial	Black vestigial	Gray long
41.5	41.5	8.5	8.5

Again it is evident that the combinations that went in together stay together (linkage) more often than they interchange (cross over) and that the ratios of the different classes are the same as in the other combination. In other words, the result does not depend on the nature of the combinations that enter together but on the chromosomes as wholes. This relation has been found to hold for all cases studied.

In the example given above, the two characters involve the same organs —the wings. This means nothing in itself, for an example might equally well have been chosen in which one pair of characters involved one organ and the other a different one—a wing and an eye, for instance. In fact, the genetic work has shown that the order of the genes in the chromosomes bears no relation whatsoever to the principal effect produced by them in the individual. In this connection it is worth while to recall that since each gene may affect several different parts at the same time, and that we select only the major one for purposes of classification, there is no *a priori* reason to expect that the structure of the chromosome would or need have any corresponding relation to the structure of the individual.

The study of many pairs of genes in the same chromosome has shown that for any two pairs studied together a definite amount of crossing over takes place. Of course this varies somewhat in each case when the environments are different. Temperature may have an effect; the presence of other genes even seems in some cases to have an effect. If, as happens in extreme cases, the order of the genes becomes changed in a part of a chromosome, the effect on crossing over is marked in the region affected when one chromosome of the pair has the genes in normal sequence and its mate in the reverse. We can see, in a way, why this should happen, because the like loci no longer lie opposite each other. If crossing over does take place, the resulting chromosomes will lack one or the other set of genes that are normally present, and in their absence the fly dies sooner or later.

Crossing over may be approximately the same in both sexes, but it may also be different. In extreme cases, such as *Drosophila,* there is no crossing over in the male.

It has been possible to determine the relative position of the genes in the chromosomes by taking advantage of crossing over. If we assume that, in general, crossing over is as likely to occur at one level as at any other, it follows that the nearer together two pairs of genes lie, the less the chance that crossing over will occur between them. Also, the farther apart they lie, the greater this chance. If, then, we interpret the numerical results of crossing over as distance between the genes, we get a value for their position.

After getting the "distance" apart of two pairs, we proceed with a third pair and locate it in relation to the first two pairs. Proceeding in like manner, we can locate all of the genes in any linked series, i.e., in any one chromosome. In this way charts of the chromosomes have been constructed. By arbitrarily taking one end of a series as a reference point, calling it zero, numerical, serial distances or numbers can be assigned to all the other genes of that chromosome. Such a chart enables one to calculate for any new gene in a given group its relation to all the other genes in the group, after determining its crossing-over value with any other two known genes. The charts would, then, justify themselves even if the argument on which they are based were not sound, because, like Mendel's laws themselves, the charts enable us to handle genetic results on a numerical or quantitative basis.

Human Inheritance and Psychology

The modern theory of heredity touches, at many points, questions relating to human psychology, even though the inheritance of acquired behavior patterns is not one of them. Man, it is true, furnishes very poor genetic material, because the output of a given pair is too meager to furnish a characteristic sample, and, when it comes to psychological traits, so called, the diagnosis is sometimes uncertain, and a collection of materials from different matings is often too heterogeneous for accurate analysis.

In so far as structure is concerned, there can be no doubt that human characters follow Mendel's laws. There is, of course, every *a priori* expectation that this should be so, for in his physical characters man is like other mammals. To the extent that types of behavior are direct expressions of the gross physical characters, we might anticipate that the same laws would be found to hold, but it would be unsafe to press too far this anticipation, because man is almost unique amongst animals in his extraordinary capacity to learn. His prolonged childhood gives an opportunity to impress upon him the traditions, customs, beliefs, and prejudices of his race. Even if there were several or very many inherited backgrounds or reaction systems, it would remain to be shown to what extent these might be obliterated or expanded by training. This is a question of paramount importance for the bearing of genetics on psychology. Before attempting to discuss it, I shall bring forward some illustrations of the inheritance of typical human physical characters, since their acceptance or rejection must supply the validity for any further profitable discussion of the more complex subject of psychological traits.

The most familiar and oft-quoted case is that of brown versus blue eyes. A brown-eyed man, with an ancestry of brown eyes only, marries a blue-eyed woman. All the children have brown eyes. If two individuals that have had this origin should mate, they will, on the average, have three brown-eyed children to one blue. One such (F_1) pair would not have enough children to make the ratio statistically valid, but when data from enough such material are collected, it is found that there is an approach to a 3:1 ratio. There are, it is true, a few apparent discrepancies that have been reported. Some of them may be due to illegitimate children or to differences in classifying the eye colors, for there are other iris colors, and their relation to brown is not understood. There are also cases where the brown is present only as a fleck. One step more and it might not be recognizable. With all due allowance for these exceptions, there is no reasonable doubt that brown and not-brown (blue) are a contrasted pair of genes.

The brachydactyl or short-fingered hand (and foot) furnishes a striking dominant character. One segment of the fingers is absent. The character breeds true to type without intergrades, and at present is known only in a hybrid condition. Whether the double dominant is lethal is not known. The individuals of the strain, having recessive or normal hands, breed true, i.e., never give brachydactyl offspring, and this is entirely consistent with the behavior of the normal hand as a Mendelian recessive in contrast with the dominant brachydactyl hand.

There are also several other structural characters in man, nearly all of which would be called malformations, that are simple cases of Mendelian inheritance, and there are many others that have not, as yet, been proved to be the effect of a single pair of genes. The medical literature contains a very large number of pedigrees showing the recurrence in successive generations of one or another bodily defect. Taken collectively they form an impressive mass of evidence showing that defective germ-plasm is constantly cropping out in man. It may seem surprising that such defects have not become more widely distributed, but in some cases the individuals may be selected against or be less productive, which would tend to eliminate the character. On the other hand, when recessive, the gene might be carried in the heterozygote for some time beneath the surface, and become more or less spread in this way. Even then its distribution would tend to be limited. Perhaps more significant might be its proximity (linkage) to other genes that do or do not count in the viability of the individual.

When two such heterozygous individuals meet, one-fourth of their offspring would show the recessive character, even though none of the progenitors had shown it for several generations. If such a defect-producing gene should happen to lie in a chromosome carrying a gene especially advantageous to the propagation of the individual it might be carried much further in the general population, but again the character would appear only when two individuals carrying the gene came together. Under such circumstances it would be practically impossible to eliminate the gene. Such a population would be condemned to produce defectives. This might continue indefinitely, provided the advantageous gene more than compensated for the loss.

Most races are mixtures, in different proportions, of four blood types that may be represented in Mendelian terms by AB, Ab, aB, ab—that is, as combinations of two pairs of genes. The data are also covered by the assumption of three allelomorphic genes, A, B, R, giving the four groups AB, AA (and AR), BB (and BR), and RR. In some respects the one formulation fits the data better, in other respects the other. In either case the evidence is sufficient to show that the differences are discontinuous and follow Mendel's principle of segregation. In passing, it may be noted that, so far as is known, no other subsidiary differences, either physiological or psychological, are associated with these blood types. No one of them has any known advantage over the others. The relative proportions in which they are found are probably due to racial mixtures.

The ground under our feet is less sure when we come to consider the effects of glandular disturbances either in body or mind, for, while the evidence of a close relation exists in a physiological sense, the support is very weak when we examine the case for inheritance. Cretinism is perhaps the best example. It is due to a deficiency in thyroid. The effects can be counteracted—if not too prolonged—by the administration of thyroid extract. The malady was supposed to be endemic in certain parts of the world, and is believed to be due to insufficient iodine in the food. Since in such localities only a small percentage of individuals are cretins, the question arises whether they are genetically different from the other members of the community in the sense that they are more sensitive, or less resistant, hence more easily affected by lack of iodine, or whether some environmental difference has caught a few individuals unprepared. The cretin is a physiological type accompanied by distinct psychological deficiencies. If, as stated to be the case, the mind may, after treatment, become normal, it follows either that the brain may develop to the normal stage after treatment, or that its functioning is restored with a sufficiency of thyroid secretion.

It has become popular in recent years to classify human beings, supposedly normal, according to the activity of the glands of internal secretion. One extremist calls them the "glands of personality" and tries to recognize a thyroid type, a pituitary type, and an adrenal type, which recalls the old-fashioned division of mankind into bilious and lymphatic, nervous and sanguine temperaments. Other classifiers speak of the athletic, the asthenic, and the pyknic, and ascribe to them associated peculiarities of physique and temperament. These crude efforts lend themselves to literary extravagances. Scientifically their interest rests on the more or less plausible assumption that the endocrines do play a rôle in the development of the individual and have some part in molding both physical characters and psychological traits. There are, however, several considerations that should make us pause before accepting this evidence at its face value. First, it is probable that some of the observed results are the outcome of the combined action of several or many endocrine and hormone factors. To presuppose that the classified types are due to the preponderance of one alone of these endocrines ignores the recognized compensatory properties of these glands about which very little is known but enough to put us on our guard. Second, the effects are supposed to wax and wane in response to environmental influences that affect the glands in question. Here again we are ignorant as to how significant are the supposedly inherited differences in the functional activity of the glands, and how important are the secondary influences of the individual's personal history. Finally, practically nothing is accurately known as to the rôle of inheritance in transmitting supposedly different types. It may be freely conceded that we may expect to find by further observation and experiment that there are quantitative and qualitative differences in the glandular make-up of individuals and that these follow the same laws of inheritance as do other bodily characters, but *at present* this anticipation furnishes a very insecure basis for the extravagances of popular writers on these topics.

There are other human types that are supposed to be inherited, but the evidence for which is unsatisfactory. There are individuals who are subnormal in regard to their capacity to learn certain technical subjects or conventions that "normal" persons can be taught. The "deficient" types are sometimes collectively called feebleminded and sometimes classified as idiots, imbeciles, morons. There are no certain physical stigmata that characterize the imbecile or moron. Their mental development is vaguely compared with that of a child of 1-2, 3-7, 8-12 years old. It is not known whether there is only one defective type of this sort, or several, or many. If only one, and if it is recessive, it should give, when inbred, offspring like itself; but if there are different types, two imbeciles would give normal offspring in the first generation. If the condition is due to several genes, the expectation is more complex. The pedigrees are by no means consistent or convincing. There is more than a suspicion that in some cases the disorder is the result of syphilitic infection at or after birth, and possibly in other cases to infantile disease or infection, or to physical disorders of one or another kind.

The same and other possibilities apply also to the higher "grades" of defectives. Under the circumstances one may hesitate before accepting some of the far-reaching programs for eliminating these defective strains from the human germ-plasm, especially when it is realized that these, to be effective in a reasonable time, entail celibacy on all the suspected kin.

The same criticism may be made of the way in which criminality and other anti-social types have been handled as literary material for popular consumption. It is needless to point out perhaps that most of this sort of propaganda is at present outside the range of genetics even when carried on by students of genetics.

There are a few pedigrees that seem to indicate that certain types of insanity are hereditary. One type, Huntington's chorea, is probably the best authenticated case, both because it is a dominant trait and appears in each generation in individuals who have passed middle age, and also because the disease is so rare that its reappearance in successive generations in the same stock could not be due to mere chance. But even here the diagnosis is sometimes uncertain, and the same criticism applies *a fortiori* to several of the other forms of insanity. In fact, in some cases at least, the type of outbreak or expression shown by individuals is so different that it is by no means certain that it is traceable to what is generally spoken of as an unstable heredity or neurotic basis. The latter expression is obviously too vague to permit more than plausible guessing, which in the hands of enthusiasts is more likely to bring genetics into disrepute than it is to lead to an increase in human understanding.

It is needless to go over the many other cases of human defective types that, on the basis of rather meager pedigree charts, are claimed as cases of heredity. Taken as a whole they are interesting and convincing to the extent that hereditary factors are probably responsible for many of the defective and pathological structural characters found in the human races. In fact, all the books that deal with inheritance in man cannot fail to give the impression that nearly all of our definite information about human inheritance concerns malformations, diseases, mental defects, and trivial characters of several sorts.   When we look for the other side of the picture, the heredity of beneficial traits, we usually meet with more eloquence than evidence.   The difficulty here seems to be due partly to the absence of any type that may be called the normal.   Without a standard for comparison the treatment becomes vague.   Moreover, in human society as it exists at present it is not easy to decide that one physical type is better adapted than another, and, when it comes to deciding which emotional and intelligent types are better or worse, the situation becomes far too complex to handle with any probability of success.   The socially "successful" individual may be more a creature of his family influence and training and social opportunities than of any inherited psychical advantage over his fellows.

Under the circumstances one resort has been to apply biometrical methods to these complicated problems.   Francis Galton (1883, 1889, 1892, 1897, 1901, 1905), in his famous studies on the heredity of human traits, initiated biologists into the statistical treatment of problems of heredity.[1]   His books on *Hereditary Genius* and on *Natural Inheritance* are the recognized masterpieces in the literature of the subject.

In originality, in broad-mindedness, in moderation of statement, Galton's work stands out above all others of his time.   He recognized the limitations of his methods, and he saw far more clearly than others the complexities of the problems.   His recognition of the significance of discontinuous inheritance was far in advance of his time and an important step forward in the Darwinian field—or at least would have been so had not his statements been forgotten by his followers.   Galton dealt with mixed populations and attempted by statistical treatment of the materials to deduce certain laws or principles of heredity.   This method of approach has advantages when it is impossible to disentangle the many factors that enter into the result, but it may be misleading and admittedly fails to furnish the specific solution of the problem.

According to Galton: "The two parents between them contribute *on the average* one-half of each inherited faculty, each of them contributing one-quarter of it.   The four grandparents contribute between them one-quarter, or each of them one-sixteenth, and so on—the sum of the series, $1/2+1/4+1/8+1/16+$etc. being equal to 1."   Pearson later gave slightly different values for the average contribution from each generation, and Yule formulated the law as follows: "The mean character of the offspring can be calculated with the more exactness, the more extensive our knowledge of the corresponding characters of the ancestry."   When a complex character such as the height of a man supplies the raw data, the

---

[1]Quetelet had earlier utilized such methods in the measurements of human stature.

results for each generation correspond approximately with the Galton formula. Today, in the light of Johannsen's (1903) work on the sizes and weights of beans, we get further insight into the relations that lead to the expression of the kind of data that are behind Galton's law. Populations are sometimes mixed, that is, made up of individuals that have different genes that affect the same character. Furthermore, the same character, size, for example, may be also influenced by environmental factors that are not inherited. In consequence, the expression of the character is only in part determined by its genes—hence its measurements are not an exact index of what the individual received from its parents or transmits to its offspring. The error may be so great as entirely to vitiate conclusions that attempt to deduce from such data the fundamental principles of heredity. In so far as the environmental factors are constant and cancel out in each generation, certain correlations between generations may be made manifest, but the exact laws of heredity that give such correlated results cannot be brought to light by this procedure. Selection in such a mixed population will in time sort out the genetically pure lines of which it is composed. The reversion toward mediocrity, one of Galton's best-known contributions, finds a specific explanation in those relations that Johannsen's work brings to light.

An example will serve to illustrate the difference in the treatment of a specific case when Galton's and Mendel's procedures are followed. Galton collected data on the inheritance of eye color in man and formulated conclusions as to the inheritance of brown and blue eyes. He clearly recognized the discontinuity in the contrasted eye colors and compared it with the blended type of inheritance shown by stature. Students of Mendelian heredity have also reached conclusions from the same and from similar data on eye color. The Mendelian formula states that when a brown-eyed individual that has come from a brown- and blue-eyed parent is mated to a blue-eyed individual, half the offspring will be brown- and half blue-eyed. It furnishes an hypothesis as to why this numerical ratio holds, viz.: that the brown and blue elements in the hybrid parent separate in the hybrid, and half of the germ-cells contain one element, half the other. The result does not depend on the number of brown-eyed ancestors behind one of the parents or the number of blue-eyed ancestors of the other. Here we are dealing with a specific event for which a simple hypothesis suffices. Moreover, this hypothesis, when checked up in numerous ways, gives consistent results.

If we attempt to handle the same situation by means of Galton's formula, it becomes obvious that it fails if applied to individual cases. For example, the blues extracted, in the case given above, breed true to blue. The fact that one parent had brown eyes does not enter into the result. It is true that Galton's law does not pretend to apply to single cases but states only the statistical expectation for all the offspring in a mixed population of browns and blues. Nevertheless, if it is the laws of heredity that are sought for, it is clear that Mendel's procedure is the more profitable course to pursue.

The preceding statements are not intended to imply that statistical methods of study are not of value to genetics where the theory of probability is involved, for even in Mendelian studies certain problems can be advantageously checked by recognized mathematical applications.

IDENTICAL TWINS

The most convincing evidence of the far-reaching influence of heredity in man is derived from a study of identical twins. There are, as generally recognized, two kinds of human twins, fraternal twins and identical twins. Identical twins are always of the same sex, and, as the name implies, are extremely alike in their physical traits. On the other hand, fraternal twins are no more alike physically than any other two children of the same parentage, even though born at the same time and reared under similar conditions. Fraternal twins (ordinary twins) may both be girls or both boys, or a boy and a girl.

Twin births occur about once in a hundred times. This includes both identical and fraternal twins. Certain families produce a much higher percentage of twins, and this propensity seems to be transmitted both through the father and mother to later generations. Taking all twins together, the exception *on chance alone* for like pairs of twins and for unlike pairs of twins would be $1♀♀ : 2♀♂ : 1♂♂$, or two twins of like sex to two of unlike sex. But, in fact, the actual numbers in one tabulation are $234,497♀♀ : 264,098♀♂ : 219,312♂♂$, or nearly 1 : 1 : 1. This means that the occurrence of identical twins is more frequent than generally supposed, since more twins of the same sex occur than chance alone calls for. It is estimated that about 1/4 to 1/5 of all twins must be identical to fulfill the requirements of these data.

The resemblance of identical twins to each other extends to the most minute details of their physical make-up. This resemblance persists throughout life, even when the persons have lived apart and under different conditions. The resemblance is, of course, generally enhanced by dressing the twins in the same way, but, while this may tend to hide any differences that they show, their similarity is entirely borne out by physical measurements.

The two most significant characteristics of identical twins, their sex and their resemblance to each other, can be accounted for by the modern theory of heredity based on certain known facts about chromosomes. In man, as in other mammals and also in several other large groups, the female has two X chromosomes and the male one X. According to a few observers the male has also a Y chromosome; according to a few others there is no Y in the male. We are familiar in other animals with situations paralleling both of these conditions. The genetic relation would be the same as long as the presence of the Y chromosome does not interfere with the effects of genes carried by the X chromosome. In *Drosophila* this holds, and, since in man the inheritance of the few sex-linked characters that are known shows no influence of the Y chromosome, we may safely assume that if present it behaves as does the Y in *Drosophila*.

This mechanism insures approximately equal numbers of males and females; since each egg, after extrusion of the polar bodies, carries one X, it will, when fertilized by an X-bearing sperm, give rise to a female (XX), and, when fertilized by a Y-bearing sperm, to a male (X or XY). The important consideration, for present purposes, is that the sex of the individual is determined at the time of fertilization of the egg. If, then, identical twins come from a single egg fertilized by one sperm—the normal rule—both individuals should always be of the same sex.

There is circumstantial evidence that in man identical twins do come from one egg. It is known in many cases that identical twins are enclosed in a common embryonic envelope, the chorionic membrane. Fraternal twins are never so enclosed, but each has its separate chorion. There is corroborative evidence of another sort. In the South American armadillo, Azara reported on hearsay, and J. Hering in 1885 confirmed the fact, that all the young of one pregnancy are of the same sex. Fernandez (1909) and Newman and Patterson (1909) substantiated the essential facts, the latter for the North American species, and gave further evidence concerning the origin of these armadillo embryos. The latter especially have published conclusive evidence that all the embryos of one birth develop from a single egg.

The explanation of the physical resemblance of twins rests on the following evidence: Two individuals derived from the same egg have the same chromosomes, and, since the chromosomes are the bearers of the hereditary characters, the two individuals should be alike except in so far as the environment affects these characters. The prenatal environment of man is the uterus, which for twins would seem to give as nearly homogeneous surroundings as possible, but that its effects are of secondary importance is shown by the fact that fraternal twins may at birth be physically quite different.

The environment of twins after birth may be similar, or, if they are separated, quite different, yet the fact that identical twins remain throughout life about as similar as at birth points to the overwhelming influence of the inheritance of physical traits.

Why two embryos occasionally develop from a single fertile egg is not understood, even though by artificial treatment twinning can sometimes be brought about in other vertebrates. Several years ago it was supposed that an explanation had been found. In certain animals, sea-urchins, Amphioxus, salamanders, etc., two embryos can be produced from one egg by separating the two cells of the two-cell stage. The eggs of mammals divide into two parts. This stage has not been seen for the human ovum, but there can be no doubt that it follows the same course as do the eggs of other mammals.

Despite this experimental evidence it seems more probable that twinning in man may come about in the same way as it does in the armadillo, where it has been definitely shown by Newman and Patterson that the doubling first appears later than the two-cell stage. In the armadillo the primordium of the four embryos is laid down at four equidistant points of the young blastoderm. The cause of this duplication is, as I have said, not known. It seems improbable that it is due to the partial separation of the first four cells, although this has not been disproved. Therefore, if a property of this sort, whatever its origin, exists in one mammal, it seems better, for the present at least, to refer the occasional human twinning to the same source.

In other vertebrates also, in fish, reptiles, and birds, more than one embryo may begin to develop in a single egg. These are often united in various combinations—two heads, two heads and bodies, etc. In man, too, similar united embryos have been frequently reported. These are in all cases identical twins—diplopagi. Their occurrence is a further argument for the view that separated identical twins come from a single egg.

The chromosome mechanism also helps us to understand why fraternal twins are different from one another. Without going too much into detail, I may state that the explanation rests in part on the way in which the chromosomes are redistributed after they have paired at the ripening stage. The members of each pair are distributed at random to the daughter cells at the maturation divisions of the germ-cells. Half of the chromosomes have come from one parent and half from the other parent. If those from one parent carry different hereditary elements from those from the other parent, we can calculate how many combinations of chromosomes are possible.

Let us suppose that a species has only two chromosomes, one pair. Each mature egg and sperm gets one or the other. If one of them is different from the other in some hereditary unit, call one chromosome A, the other a, then each ripe germ-cell (each egg and each sperm) will contain one or the other, and when they are recombined again at fertilization in F_2 there will be three kinds of recombinations, or $AA+Aa+aa$, in the ratio of $1:2:1$.

In a species with *two pairs* or four chromosomes (each pair having one or more differences), there will be nine classes. Man has 48 chromosomes, which gives 282,429,536,481 possible kinds of individuals on the assumption that there are differences in the units of each pair. This is not a very improbable assumption since man is a most extraordinary mixture of many kinds of characters.

The chances, then, of any two individuals' (coming from different eggs and sperms) being identical would be more than one in a billion. Of course, there would actually be many individuals more or less alike for a large number of hereditary units, and this fits in with what we see in our fellow-men—some of them do look alike even when they have a different parentage. Moreover, in general, we should expect *on the average* that members of the same family would more often resemble each other than they do other groups, and this too is true.

If, then, as a result of free assortment, the number of different kinds of human beings is very large, the number may be very much larger if crossing over takes place between members of the same pair of chromosomes.

Crossing over is known to occur in other animals and in plants. In the female *Drosophila* it occurs in about 57% of the gametes for the sex chromosome, and considerably more for the two other large pairs. In man there are no certain cases of interchanges of this kind, but this probably means that as yet there are no recorded cases where two pairs of characters are known to be in the same linkage group. Our lack of information is due partly to the relatively small number of cases in man where the inheritance is definitely known, and partly to the large number of chromosomes resulting in the dispersion of human characters amongst them. Furthermore, the number of offspring from a pair is generally too small to give sufficient information and, as stated before, the diagnosis is often too uncertain when more than single matings are brought together.

The question is often asked why, if unit characters are discontinuous in inheritance, we do not easily recognize such characters in man, the details of whose physiognomy and bodily structure serve as the basis for our ability to distinguish individuals from each other. There are many reasons why we cannot often pick out such characters. A number of mutant characters are known to overlap the "normal" and may grade by invisible degrees into each other in their expression, even though the genes segregate as cleanly as in more typical cases. The hybrid form or heterozygous character is in many cases intermediate between the dominant and recessive characters and may overlap one or the other. Specific modifiers may increase the difficulty. It frequently happens that many factors affect the same organ, and until they can be isolated and studied apart their presence obscures the results. In other animals and plants they can be isolated by suitable matings, but in man this has not been feasible. Again, the same genes may occur in several forms (allelomorphs), each one producing a slightly different effect and any two of them combined, an intermediate effect. Until they are isolated by suitable tests, the identification of the corresponding characters is difficult. It has been suggested that the difference in the brown hair of man is such a case. It requires, then, in most cases of mixed material, more information than we now possess for human traits to discover the unit characters. This kind of work can better be done on forms whose breeding is under experimental control.

The Rôle of Nature and Nurture in Human Behavior

Confronted with the evidence from identical twins showing that heredity controls the physical characters of man down to the most minute details, the student of psychological human traits may ask to what extent this conclusion applies to his problems. We face the fact that man is almost unique amongst animals in his extraordinary ability to learn. His prolonged childhood gives an opportunity to impress upon him the particular associations to which he has been subjected. Are these extraneous influences powerful enough to submerge whatever differences may be inherited by each individual? The difficulties of reaching a decision are at present almost insuperable. There are students of heredity—extremists—who insist that all differences in behavior are due to inheritance, i.e., to the kind of reaction system that the genetic constitution supplies. There are others who are equally positive that our behavior is due entirely, or almost so, to our upbringing—the environment of the child, i.e., his early experiences, his training, education, or his imitative capacities. Most psychologists, I suppose, and certainly most geneticists who have given serious thought to this situation will stand somewhere between these extremes.

The older procedure of assigning innate individual psychological differences to constitutional backgrounds, in the sense of being inborn, has been seriously questioned. The inspirational source of such a point of view does not recommend itself as a scientific method of getting reliable data. The wide differences of opinion, for example, as to how many "instincts" are common to all human beings—not to mention individual variants of these—has not led to a satisfactory outcome and has raised the question as to whether this is not clever dialectic rather than modern science.

The position taken by extremists on the other side, of whom Watson is perhaps the outstanding example, has also raised doubts and questions in the minds of the students of heredity. The experimental approach that Watson insists upon makes a strong appeal as a procedure that will help to some extent to determine how much is due to individual training. The further question as to what extent the evidence relating to physical individual differences supports or does not support the contention that, to the same degree, individual differences in human behavior have the same innate or inherited or congenital background remains unanswered. The problem is difficult for two reasons: first, because crucial evidence is almost entirely lacking; and, second, because there is sufficient evidence, I think, to show that many traits of human conduct are acquired only through association. The point at issue is, then, even if constitutional differences are admitted, whether and how far they may be completely modified by the establishment of associations, conditioned reflexes, etc., in early life.

The discussion of the problem is full of pitfalls and there is the widest possible divergence of predilections and prejudices that make an independent attitude well-nigh impossible. One approach is through a consideration of the influence of those hereditary physical differences that seem to have a significant influence on the behavior of the individual. For example, the effects of internal secretions are generally conceded to be a case in point. As already stated, their excessive presence or absence at any time may be a factor in the kind of reactions shown by the individual that may become thereby reinforced and later habitual. If there are inherited differences in the glands that produce these hormones, it may be argued that there are corresponding psychological patterns of reaction. But until it can be shown—leaving aside pathological cases—that there are such differences, and until it can be shown that the types of behavior of normal individuals that have been referred to these differences are not really due to earlier associations, the argument hangs in the air.

There is another related question that should not be forgotten. Most individuals meet in the course of their lives a vast number of situations to which they react. It is, in my opinion, premature to assume that the associations formed in babyhood may not be changed or completely reversed later, and, if so, an entirely new set of reactions established for the time being. If this can take place, it does not seem unlikely that the type of reaction existing at any one time will often be the one that has been along the line of least resistance, which might be assumed to be the one to which the physical type most easily adjusts itself.

How far the general physique (tall or broad, fat or thin, etc.) of the individual is an important factor in determining his set of psychological reactions is presumably a question for psychologists to discuss. From the genetic point of view there can be little doubt but that most of these bodily differences are inherited. Granted that physique furnishes an element of behavior, it remains to be proved that in the long run the adjustments of the individual will be along the line of reaction correlated with physique, rather than with very early associations or with predominating social influences in later life. Everyone is familiar with men of very different physique living outwardly the same kinds of lives in general. Even if social restraint is admitted as the most outstanding explanation of the result, it does not follow that there may still not have been inherited differences that have been submerged. It is also conceivable in a race predominatingly of a given physical type that the social system followed may in time come to have an intimate relation to the physical type in certain economic or climatic environments. All these possibilities have been at one time or another exploited by writers of all shades of opinion and have furnished the would-be well-wishers of science with material for popular exposition.

The occurrence of identical twins has supplied the biologists with materials that convincingly establish the far-reaching effects of physical inheritance in man. Cytology has made clear why identical twins resemble each other and why fraternal twins differ from each other. Identical twins, if studied experimentally, should be expected to supply excellent material to test the significance in behavior of hereditary psychic factors. Galton was amongst the first to take advantage of this opportunity. He records in his *Inquiries into Human Faculty* (1883) that through a questionnaire he had about eighty returns of cases of close similarity. He gives many interesting anecdotes about the similarities in the traits of some of the identical twins but, since in most cases the twins were for several years reared together, this kind of evidence is inconclusive. Nevertheless, taken as a whole, it cannot fail to leave the impression that the similarities in some at least of the psychic differences are not due to the environment, for, when comparison with fraternal twins is made, no such close resemblance is found. Galton's comment on his evidence is interesting:

> The last point to which I shall allude regards the tastes and dispositions of the thirty-five pairs of twins. In sixteen cases—that is, in nearly one-half of them—these were described as closely similar;

in the remaining nineteen they were much alike, but subject to certain named differences. These differences belonged almost wholly to such groups of qualities as these: The one was the more vigorous, fearless, energetic; the other was gentle, clinging and timid; or the one was more ardent, the other more calm and placid; or again, the one was the more independent, original and self-contained; the other the more generous, hasty and vivacious. In short, the difference was that of intensity or energy in one or other of its protean forms; it did not extend more deeply into the structure of the characters. The more vivacious might be subdued by ill-health, until he assumed the character of the other; or the latter might be raised by excellent health to that of the former. The difference was in the keynote, not in the melody.

Galton also comments on the late histories of the twins that had been "closely similar" up to their early manhood and womanhood. In some cases the resemblance in "body and mind" had continued unaltered up to old age notwithstanding very different conditions of life. In other cases the parents ascribed such discontinuity as was found to some form of illness.

> In not a single instance have I met with a word about the growing dissimilarity being due to the action of the firm free will of one or both of the twins, which had triumphed over natural tendencies; and yet a large proportion of my correspondents happen to be clergymen, whose bent of mind is opposed, as I feel assured from the tone of their letters, to a necessitarian view of life.

His general summing up is:

> We may, therefore, broadly conclude that the only circumstance, within the range of those by which persons of similar conditions of life are affected, that is capable of producing a marked effect on the character of adults, is illness or some accident which causes physical infirmity. The twins who closely resembled each other in childhood and early youth, and were reared under not very dissimilar conditions, either grow unlike through the development of natural characteristics which had lain dormant at first, or else they continue their lives, keeping time like two watches, hardly to be thrown out of accord except by some physical jar. Nature is far stronger than Nurture within the limited range that I have been careful to assign to the latter.

A recent and more detailed study of the psychological traits of a pair of identical twins has been made by Muller (1925). The babies had been separated when two weeks old, and did not see each other until they were eighteen, and afterwards only occasionally. They were thirty years old when the tests were made. Two intelligence tests were used, the Army Alpha Test and the Otis Advanced Intelligence Test. The total scores were almost identical, indicating superior intelligence. On the other hand, when other methods were used that are supposed to test "volitional traits," the results were different, and show, Muller thinks, the influence of the training or experience that each twin had undergone. Muller concludes that most sections of the intelligence tests show a high correlation with the genetic basis of intelligence so far established "when they are applied to individuals brought up in the same general territory and social class," which is the case with these twins. If there were no such genetic basis, the chance for these twins to have been so much alike would be less than 1 in 200. In regard to the non-intelligence tests, the evidence is in the opposite direction and may indicate differences in past experience, or the tests may be inadequate for the purpose of finding genetic similarities

Newman (1920) has more recently examined several identical twins reared apart, using several psychological tests. In one case he found that the mental traits differed more than the emotional traits, which is the reverse relation of that found in Muller's case. In another case, the twins, separated at one and one-half years of age and living apart for nineteen years, were brought up under very different educational conditions, but the other environments were not very dissimilar. "In every test of mental capacity, whether of so-called native ability or of achievement, G., the more highly educated twin has distinctly the superior mind." In contrast to this, the twins were unusually similar in all the tests of emotional traits. In a third case, the boys, separated at the age of two months, did not meet until they were twenty-two years old. One (C) had lived in a city environment; the other (O), rural or small town. Both graduated from high school. In mental ability they were nearly identical; in educational achievement the boy educated in the larger town ranked higher. Their "personalities," however, were quite different. One (C) was more reserved, self-centered, experienced, and less friendly; the other (O) was more temperamental and emotional. More recently, Hirsch (1930) has brought together most of the literature of recent years relating to twins and reported on a number of new cases in which physical and mental measurements were made. There is little in these cases that is not covered by the more thoroughly examined cases given above.

Conclusions

If the evidence discussed in the preceding review makes it seem probable that the doctrine of the inheritance of acquired characters gives no secure basis on which to bring about an intimate alliance between zoölogy and psychology, and if the statistical method developed by Galton and the Pearson school of biometricians, when applied to mixed populations, fails to give us the specific information that Mendel's principles supply, genetics may still have other bearings on the study of human psychology.

The psychological problems are immeasurably complicated by the fact that human behavior is influenced to a great extent by associations, conditioned reflexes, and experiences in general that the social environment of man effects from babyhood through all the formative periods of man's life. Until more definite information is obtainable concerning mental traits and emotional reactions, some of us remain extremely skeptical of the crude and often forced attempts that have been made so far to determine what is inherited and what is acquired after birth.

A comparison of the facts of Mendelian heredity relating to plants and animals with what is known of human heredity leaves no doubt, as far as physical characters are involved, that the same rules apply to both. The extraordinary physical resemblance of identical twins to each other establishes on the soundest basis the fact that heredity plays an all-important rôle in the inheritance of structural characters. But it is extremely hazardous to carry over this inference to the psychic character of man where there is no certainty as to what extent his behavior is determined by heredity and by environment. Until suitable methods have been applied that are discriminative, conclusions will be largely a question of personal opinion or conviction. It need scarcely be urged again that identical twins under controlled conditions may supply much of the needed information.

BIBLIOGRAPHY

ADAMI, J. G. 1901. An address on the theories of inheritance, with special reference to the inheritance of acquired conditions in man. *Brit. Med. J.*, No. 2109, 1317-1323.

AMMON, O. 1895. Die Vererbung erworbener Eigenschaften. *Naturwiss. Woch.*, 10.

ASSHETON, R. 1898. An account of a blastodermic vesicle of the sheep of the seventh day, with twin germinal areas. *J. Anat. & Physiol.*, 32, 362-372.

BATESON, W. 1902. Mendel's principles of heredity, a defence. London: Macmillan. Pp. xiv+212.

————. 1906. An address on Mendelian heredity and its application to man. *Brit. Med. J.*, 11, 61-67.

BAUER, J. 1924. Die konstitutionelle Disposition zu inneren Krankheiten. (3rd ed.) Berlin: Springer. Pp. xii+794.

BERNSTEIN, F. 1925. Zusammenfassende Betrachtungen über die erblichen Blutstrukturen des Menschen. *Zsch. f. Abst.-Vererb.*, 37, 237-270.

BREWER, W. H. 1892. On the hereditary transmission of acquired characters. *Agric. Sci.*, 6.

————. 1893. On the hereditary transmission of acquired characters. *Agric. Sci.*, 7.

BROWN-SÉQUARD, C. E. 1869. Nouvelles recherches sur l'épilepsie due à certaines lésions de la moelle épinière et des nerfs rachidiens. *Arch. de physiol.*, 2, 211-220, 422-441, 496-503.

————. 1870-71a. Faits nouveaux concernant la physiologie de l'épilepsie. *Arch. de physiol.*, 3.

————. 1870-71b. Remarque sur l'épilepsie causée par la section du nerf sciatique chez les cobayes. *Arch. de physiol.*, 3, 153-160.

————. 1872. Quelques faits nouveaux relatifs à l'épilepsie qu'on observe à la suite de diverses lésions du système nerveux chez les cobayes. *Arch. de physiol.*, 4.

————. 1880. Transmission par hérédité de certaines altérations des yeux chez les cobayes. *Gaz. méd. de Paris*, 2.

————. 1882. Faits nouveaux établissant l'extrême fréquence de la transmission, par hérédité, d'états organiques morbides produits accidentellement chez les ascendants. *C. r. Acad. des sci.*, 94, 697-700.

————. 1892. Hérédité d'une affection due à une cause accidentelle. Faits et arguments contre les explications et les critiques de Weismann. *Arch. de physiol.*, 24, 686-688.

————. 1893. Transmission héréditaire de caractères acquis. *Arch. de physiol.*, 25.

BUTLER, S. 1878. Life and habit. London & New York: Dutton. Pp. x+310.

————. 1882. Evolution, old and new. (2nd ed.) London: Fifield. Pp. 384.

CHAMPY, C. 1924. Les caractéres sexuels considérés comme phénomènes du développement et dans leur rapports avec l'hormone sexuelle. Paris: Doin. Pp. 376.

COPE, E. D. 1896. The primary factors of organic evolution. Chicago: Open Court. Pp. xvi+547.

CREW, F. A. E. 1927. Organic inheritance in man. Edinburgh & London: Oliver & Boyd. Pp. 242.

CUÉNOT, L. 1903. L'ovaire du tatou et l'origine des jumeaux. *C. r. Soc. de biol.,* **55,** 1391.

CUNNINGHAM, J. T. 1892. The evolution of flat-fishes. *Nat. Sci.,* **1.**

————. 1895. The origin of species among flat-fishes. *Nat. Sci.,* **6,** 169, 233.

————. 1896. Lyell and Lamarckism. *Nat. Sci.,* **8,** 326-331.

————. 1900. Sexual dimorphism in the animal kingdom. London: Black. Pp. xi+317.

DANFORTH, C. H. 1919. Resemblance and difference in twins. *J. Hered.,* **10,** 399-410.

DAVENPORT, C. B. 1919. A strain producing multiple births. *J. Hered.,* **10,** 382-384.

————. 1920*a.* Influence of the male in the production of human twins. *Amer. Natur.,* **54,** 122-129.

————. 1920*b.* Heredity of twin births. *Proc. Soc. Exper. Biol. & Med.,* **17,** 75-77.

————. 1924. Influence of endocrines on heredity. *Proc. & Addr. Amer. Asso. Stud. Feeble-Mind.,* **29,** 132-147.

DELAGE, M. Y. 1903. L'hérédité et les grands problèmes de la biologie générale. (2nd ed.) Paris: Reinwald. Pp. xix+912.

DETLEFSEN, J. A. 1923. Are the effects of long-continued rotation in rats inherited? *Proc. Amer. Phil. Soc.,* **62.**

————. 1925. The inheritance of acquired characters. *Physiol. Revs.,* **5,** 244-278.

DEUTSCHMANN, —. 1880. Ueber Vererbung erworbener Augenaffectionen bei Kaninchen. *Klin. Monatsbl. f. Augenhk.,* **18,** 507-513.

DINGFELDER, J. 1887. Beitrag zur Vererbung erworbener Eigenschaften. *Biol. Zentbl.,* **7,** 427-432.

————. 1889. Beitrag zur Vererbung erworbener Eigenschaften. *Biol. Zentbl.,* **8,** 210-217.

DUPUY, E. 1890. De le transmission héréditaire des lésions acquises. *Bull. scient. de France et Belge,* **1,** 445-448.

DÜRKEN, B. 1923. Ueber die Wirkung farbigen Lichtes auf die Puppen des Kohlweiszlings (*Pieris brassicae*) und das Verhalten der Nachkommen. *Arch. f. mikr. Anat. u. Entwickmech.,* **99,** 223-389.

EIMER, G. H. T. 1890. Organic evolution as a result of the inheritance of acquired characters according to the laws of organic growth. (Trans. by J. T. Cunningham.) London: Macmillan. Pp. xxviii+435.

ELDRIDGE, S. 1925. The organization of life. New York: Crowell. Pp. 470.

EMERY, C. 1897. Gedanken zur Descendenz und Vererbungstheorie: IX. Variationsrichtungen und Germinalselektion. *Biol. Zentbl.,* **17,** 142-146.

EWART, J. C. 1899. The Penycuik experiments. London: Black. Pp. xciii+177.

————. 1901. Experimental contributions to the theory of heredity. Reversion and telegony. *Trans. Highland & Agric. Soc. Scotland.* Pp. 54.

FAIRCHILD, D. 1919. Twins. *J. Hered.,* **10,** 387-398.

FARABEE, W. C. 1905. Inheritance of digital malformations in man. *Mem. Peabody Museum, Harvard*, **3**, 69-77.

FERNANDEZ, M. 1909. Beiträge zur Embryologie der Gürteltiere: I. Zur Keimblätterinversion und spezifischen Polyembryonie der Mulita (*Tatusia hybrida* Desm.). *Morph. Jahrb.*, **39**, 302-333.

FINDLAY, G. F. 1924. The effect of different species' lens antisera on pregnant mice and rats and their progeny. *Brit. J. Exper. Biol.*, **1**, 201-213.

FISCHER, E. 1901. Experimentelle Untersuchungen über die Vererbung erworbener Eigenschaften. *Allg. Zsch. f. Entom.*, **6**.

FOREL, A. 1905. Richard Semon's Mneme als erhaltendes Prinzip im Wechsel des organischen Geschehens. *Arch. f. Rassen- u. Gesellschbiol.*, **2**, 169-197.

FRANTZ, H. M. 1919. Dementia praecox in twins. *J. Nerv. & Ment. Dis.*, **50**, 325-330.

GALTON, F. 1883. Inquiries into human faculty and its development. London: Dent. Pp. xix+261.

———. 1889. Natural inheritance. London: Macmillan. Pp. ix+259.

———. 1892. Hereditary genius. London: Macmillan. Pp. 379.

———. 1897. The average contribution of each several ancestor to the total heritage of the offspring. *Proc. Roy. Soc. London*, **61B**, 401-413.

———. 1901. The possible improvement of the human breed under the existing conditions of law and sentiment. *Nature*, **64**, 659-665.

———. 1905. Eugenics: its definition, scope and aims. *Papers Sociol. Soc., London*, **1**, 43-100.

———. 1906. Eugenics: its definition, scope and aims. *Papers Sociol. Soc., London*, **2**, 1-53.

GATES, R. R. 1923. Heredity and eugenics. London & New York: Macmillan.

GIARD, A. 1890. L'hérédité des modifications somatiques. *Rev. scient.*, **46**, 705-713.

———. 1904. Controverses transformistes. Paris.

GOWAN, J. W. 1922. Identical twins in cattle. *Biol. Bull.*, **42**, 1-6.

GRIFFITH, C. R. 1922. Are permanent disturbances of equilibration inherited? *Science*, **56**, 676-678.

GUYER, M. F. 1916. Being well-born. Indianapolis, Ind.: Bobbs-Merrill. Pp. 374.

———. 1921. Immune sera and certain biological problems. *Amer. Natur.*, **55**, 97-115.

———. 1922a. Orthogenesis and serological phenomena. *Amer. Natur.*, **56**, 116-135.

———. 1922b. The production and transmission of certain eye defects. *Trans. Int. Cong. Ophthal.*, **1**, 669-689.

———. 1923. The germ cell and serological influences. *Proc. Amer. Phil. Soc.*, **62**.

———. 1928. The possibility of modifying germ plasm. *Proc. 3rd Race Betterment Conf.*, 50.

GUYER, M. F., & SMITH, E. A. 1918. Studies on cytolysins: I. Some prenatal effects of lens antibodies. *J. Exper. Zoöl.*, **26**, 65-82.

———. 1920. Studies on cytolysins: II. Transmission of induced eye defects. *J. Exper. Zoöl.*, **31**, 171-224.

———. 1924. Further studies on inheritance of eye defects induced in rabbits. *J. Exper. Zoöl.*, **40**, 449.

HERBST, K. 1919. Der Einfluss gelber, weiszer und schwarzer Umgebung auf die Zeichnung von *Salamandra maculosa*. *Heidelberg. Akad. d. Wiss.*, **1**.

HERING, E. 1870. Ueber das Gedächtniss als eine allgemeine Funktion der organisierten Materie. Vienna: Akad. d. Wiss. Pp. 26. Also in *Wien. Almanach*, **20**, 253-278.

HERTWIG, O. 1905. Ergebnisse und Probleme des Zeugungs- und Vererbungslehre. Jena: Fischer. Pp. 30.

HERTWIG, O., & HERTWIG, G. 1923. Allgemeine Biologie. (6th and 7th ed.) Jena: Fischer. Pp. xvii+822.

HIRSCH, N. D. M. 1930. Twins: heredity and environment. Cambridge, Mass.: Harvard Univ. Press. Pp. 157.

HUXLEY, J. S., & CARR-SAUNDERS, A. M. 1924. Absence of prenatal effects of lens-antibodies in rabbits. *Brit. J. Exper. Biol.*, **1**, 215-248.

HYATT, A. 1894. The phylogeny of an acquired characteristic. *Proc. Amer. Phil. Soc.*, **32**, 349-647.

JENKINS, R. L. 1927. Twin and triple birth ratios. *J. Hered.*, **18**, 389-394, 504.

JENKINSON, J. W. 1903. A reinvestigation of the early stages of the development of the mouse. *Quar. J. Micr. Sci.*, **43**, 61-81.

JHERING, H. v. 1885. Ueber die Fortpflanzung Gürteltiere. *Sitzber. d. preuss. Akad. d. Wiss.*, **105**, 1051-1053.

JOHANNSEN, W. 1903. Ueber Erblichkeit in Populationen und in reinen Linien. Jena: Fischer. Pp. 68.

JONES, D. F. 1925. Genetics in plant and animal improvement. New York: Wiley. Pp. 568.

KAMMERER, P. 1911. Die Abstammungslehre. Jena: Fischer. Pp. iv+489.

————. 1924. The inheritance of acquired characteristics. New York: Boni & Liveright. Pp. 414.

KIDD, W. 1901. Use-inheritance—illustrated by the direction of hair on the bodies of animals. London: Black. Pp. 47.

————. 1907. The sense of touch in mammals and birds. London: Black. Pp. 176.

KRAEPELIN, E. 1919. Dementia praecox and paraphrenia. (Trans. by R.ʼ M. Barclay.) Edinburgh: Livingstone. Pp. 331.

KRETSCHMER, E. 1925. Physique and character. (Trans. by W. J. H. Sprott.) London: Kegan Paul. Pp. 266.

LE DANTEC, F. 1900. L'hérédité, clef des phénomènes biologiques. *Rev. gén. scient.*, **11**.

————. 1906. Les influences ancestrales. Paris: Flammarion. Pp. xi+306.

LENDL, A. 1889. Hypothese über die Entstehung von Soma- und Propagationszellen. Berlin: Friedlander. Pp. v+78.

LENZ, F. 1912. Ueber die krankhaften Erbanlagen des Mannes und die Bestimmung des Geschlechts beim Menschen. Jena: Fischer. Pp. 177.

LESLIE, G. 1882. On hereditary transmission of disease. *Edinburgh Med. J.*, **27**, 795-799.

LILLIE, F. R. 1923. Supplementary notes on twins in cattle. *Biol. Bull.*, **44**, 47-78.

LITTLE, C. C., & BAGG, H. J. 1924. The occurrence of four inheritable morphological variations in mice and their possible relation to treatment with X-rays. *J. Exper. Zoöl.*, **41**, 45-91.

LUSH, J. L. 1924. Twinning in Brahma cattle. *J. Hered.*, **15**, 25-28.

MACAULIFFE, L. 1925. Les mechanismes intimes de la vie. Paris: Legrand. Pp. 290.

MACDOWELL, E. C. 1919. The influence of parental alcoholism upon habit formation in albino rats. *Proc. Soc. Exper. Biol. & Med.*, **16**, 125.

MacDowell, E. C., & Vicari, E. M. 1921. Alcoholism and the behavior of white rats: I. The influence of alcoholic grandparents upon maze-behavior. *J. Exper. Zoöl.*, **33**, 209-291.

————. 1923. Alcoholism and the behavior of white rats: II. The maze-behavior of treated rats and their offspring. *J. Exper. Zoöl.*, **37**, 417-456.

Maciesza, A., & Wrzosek, A. 1911. Experimentelle Untersuchungen über die Vererbung der durch Ischiadicusverletzung hervorgerufenen Brown-Séquard-schen Meerschweinchen- Epilepsie. *Arch f. Rassen- u. Gesellschbiol.*, **8**, 1-24, 145-163.

McCartney, E. S. 1926. Acquired and transmitted characters in Greek lore of heredity. *Mich. Acad. Sci., Arts & Letters*, **21**.

McCordock, H. A., & Congdon, C. C. 1924. Suppurative otitis of the albino rat. *Proc. Soc. Exper. Biol. & Med.*, **22**, 150-154.

McDougall, W. 1927. An experiment for the testing of the hypothesis of Lamarck. *Brit. J. Psychol. (Gen. Sec.)*, **17**, 267-304.

————. 1930. Second report on a Lamarckian experiment. *Brit. J. Psychol. (Gen. Sec.)*, **20**, 201-218.

Mendel, G. J. 1865. Versuche über Pflanzen Hybriden. *Verhandl. d. Naturforsch. Verein in Brünn*, **4**, 3-47.

Meyer, S. 1906. Gedächtnis und Vererbung. *Arch. f. Rassen- u. Gesellschbiol.*, **3**, 629-645.

Miles, M. 1892. Heredity of acquired characters. *Amer. Natur.*, **26**, 887-900.

Mohr, O. L. 1919. Mikroskopische Untersuchungen zu Experimenten über den Einfluss der Radiumstrahlen und der Kältewirkung auf die Chromatin-reifung und das Heterochromosom bei *Decticus verruccivorus* (♂). *Arch. f. mikr. Anat.*, **92**, 300-368.

Morgan, T. H. 1923. The modern theory of genetics and the problem of embryonic development. *Physiol. Revs.*, **3**, 603-627.

————. 1924a. Mendelian heredity in relation to cytology. Sec. XI of *General cytology*, ed. by E. V. Cowdry. Chicago: Univ. Chicago Press; Cambridge, England: Univ. Press. Pp. vii+754.

————. 1924b. Are acquired characters inherited? *Yale Rev.*, **13**, 712-729.

————. 1924c. Human inheritance. *Amer. Natur.*, **58**, 385-409.

————. 1925. Evolution and genetics. Princeton, N. J.: Princeton Univ. Press. Pp. 211.

————. 1926. Genetics and the physiology of development. *Amer. Natur.*, **60**, 489-575.

————. 1928. The theory of the gene. New Haven, Conn.: Yale Univ. Press. Pp. xvi+343.

Morgan, T. H., Sturtevant, A. H., Muller, H. J., & Bridges, C. B. 1923. The mechanism of Mendelian heredity. (Rev. ed.) New York: Holt. Pp. 262.

Muller, H. J. 1925. Mental traits and heredity. *J. Hered.*, **16**, 433-448.

————. 1927a. Artificial transmutation of the gene. *Science*, **66**, 84-87.

————. 1927b. The problem of genic modification. *Verhandl. d. V. int. Kong. f. Vererbung*, Berlin, 234.

————. 1928. The production of mutations by X-rays. *Proc. Nat. Acad. Sci.*, **14**, 714-726.

————. 1930. Radiation and genetics. *Amer. Natur.*, **64**, 220-251.

Murray, G. R. 1925. A study of twins in health and disease. *Lancet*, **208**, 529-532.

Myerson, A. 1925. The inheritance of mental diseases. Baltimore, Md.: Williams & Wilkins. Pp. 400.

NEWMAN, H. H. 1912. The ovum of the nine-banded armadillo. Growth of the ovocytes, maturation, and fertilization. *Biol. Bull.,* **23**, 100-140.

――――. 1913*a*. The modes of inheritance of aggregates of meristic (integral) variates in the polyembryonic offspring of the nine-banded armadillo. *J. Exper. Zoöl.,* **15**, 145-192.

――――. 1913*b*. The natural history of the nine-banded armadillo of Texas. *Amer. Natur.,* **47**, 513-539.

――――. 1915. Heredity and organic symmetry in armadillo quadruplets: I. Modes of inheritance of band anomalies. *Biol. Bull.,* **29**, 1-32.

――――. 1916. Heredity and organic symmetry in armadillo quadruplets: II. Modes of inheritance of double scutes and a discussion of organic symmetry. *Biol. Bull.,* **30**, 173-209.

――――. 1917. The biology of twins. Chicago: Univ. Chicago Press. Pp. 195.

――――. 1923. The physiology of twinning. Chicago: Univ. Chicago Press. Pp. 230.

――――. 1927. Evolution, genetics, and eugenics. Chicago: Univ. Chicago Press. Pp. 639.

――――. 1928*a*. Studies of human twins: I. Methods of diagnosing monozygotic and dizygotic twins. *Biol. Bull.,* **55**, 283-297.

――――. 1928*b*. Studies of human twins: II. Asymmetry reversal, or mirror imaging in identical twins. *Biol. Bull.,* **55**, 298-315.

――――. 1931. Palm print patterns in twins. On the use of dermatoglyphics as an aid in the diagnosis of monozygotic and dizygotic twins. *J. Hered.,* **22**, 41-49.

NEWMAN, H. H., & PATTERSON, J. T. 1909. A case of normal identical quadruplets in the nine-banded armadillo, and its bearing on the problems of identical twins and of sex determinaton. *Biol. Bull.,* **17**, 181-187.

――――. 1910. Development of the nine-banded armadillo from the primitive streak stage to birth: with special reference to the question of specific polyembryony. *J. Morph.,* **21**, 359-424.

――――. 1911. The limits of hereditary control in armadillo quadruplets: a study of blastogenic variation. *J. Morph.,* **22**, 855-926.

OGILVIE, G. 1901. Some remarks on the inheritance of acquired immunity. *Brit. Med. J.,* No. 2105, 1070-1072.

ORNSTEIN, B. 1889. Ein Beitrag zur Vererbungsfrage individuel erworbener Eigenschaften. *C. B. dtsch. Gesellsch. f. Anthrop. u. Ethnog., München,* **20**, 49-53.

ORR, H. B. 1893. A theory of development and heredity. London: Macmillan. Pp. 255.

ORTH, J. 1887. Ueber die Entstehung und Vererbung individueller Eigenschaften. In *Festschrift für A. v. Kolliker zur Feier seines siebenzigsten Geburtstages gewidmet von seinen Schülern.* Leipzig: Engelmann. Pp. iv+444.

OSBORN, H. F. 1889. Palaeontological evidence for the transmission of acquired characters. *Rep. Brit. Asso. Adv. Sci.,* **59**, 621-623. Also in *Amer. Natur.,* **23**, 561-566. Also in *Nature,* 1889-90, **41**, 227-229.

――――. 1891. Are acquired variations inherited? *Amer. Natur.,* **25**, 191-216.

――――. 1892. Present problems in evolution and heredity. *Med. Rec.,* **41**, 197, 253, 449, 533.

――――. 1895. The hereditary mechanism and the search for the unknown factors of evolution. *Biol. Lectures, Woods Hole,* **3**, 79-100.

――――. 1896. Ontogenetic and phylogenetic variation. *Science,* **4**, 786-789.

PACKARD, A. S. 1893. The life history of certain moths of the family Cochliopodidae with notes on their spines and tubercles. *Proc. Amer. Phil. Soc.,* **31**, 83-108.

————. 1894. On the inheritance of acquired characters in animals with a complete metamorphosis. *Proc. Amer. Acad. Sci.*, **29**, 331-370.

PARKER, G. H. 1926. Identical twins with dementia praecox. *J. Hered.*, **17**, 137-143.

PAULY, A. 1905. Darwinismus und Lamarckismus. Munich: Reinhardt. Pp. 335.

PEARSON, K. 1897. Mathematical contributions to the theory of evolution: III. Regression, heredity, and panmixia. *Phil. Trans.*, **187A**, 253-318.

————. 1898. Mathematical contributions to the theory of evolution. On the law of ancestral heredity. *Proc. Roy. Soc. London*, **62B**, 386-413.

————. 1900a. The grammar of science. (2nd ed.) London: Black; New York: Macmillan. Pp. xviii+548.

————. 1900b. Mathematical contributions to the theory of evolution. On the law of reversion. *Proc. Roy. Soc. London*, **66B**, 140-164.

————. 1903a. The law of ancestral heredity. *Biometrika*, **2**, 211-228.

————. 1903b. On the inheritance of the mental and moral characters in man, and its comparison with the inheritance of physical characters. (Huxley lecture, 1903.) *Trans. Anthrop. Instit. Great Britain & Ireland*, 179-237.

————. 1904a. A Mendelian's view of the law of ancestral inheritance. *Biometrika*, **3**, 109-112.

————. 1904b. On the laws of inheritance in man: II. On the inheritance of the mental and moral characters in man, and its comparison with the inheritance of the physical characters. *Biometrika*, **3**, 131-190.

————. 1904c. Mathematical contributions to the theory of evolution: XII. On a generalized theory of alternative inheritance, with special reference to Mendel's laws. *Phil. Trans.*, **203A**, 53-86.

————. 1904d. On the criterion which may serve to test various theories of inheritance. *Proc. Roy. Soc. London*, **73B**, 262-280.

PEARSON, K., & LEE, A. 1901. Mathematical contributions to the theory of evolution: VIII. On the inheritance of characters not capable of exact quantitative measurement. *Phil. Trans.*, **195A**, 79-150.

————. 1903. On the laws of inheritance in man: I. Inheritance of physical characters. *Biometrika*, **2**, 357-462.

PICTET, A. 1905. Influence de l'alimentation et de l'humidité sur la variation des papillons. *Mem. Soc. Phys. et Hist. nat., Genève*, **35**, 46-127. Also in *Nature*, **72**, 632.

POPENOE, P. 1922. Twins reared apart. *J. Hered.*, **13**, 142-144.

POULTON, E. B., & CUNNINGHAM, J. T. 1894. Acquired characters. *Nature*, **51**, 126-127.

POULTON, E. B., & OSBORN, H. F. 1897. Organic selection. *Science*, **6**, 583-587.

PRZIBRAM, H. 1910. Experimental-Zoölogie: III. Phylogenese. Leipzig: Deuticke. Pp. viii+315.

RAYMOND, P. 1905. L'hérédité morbide. Paris: Vigot. Pp. 381.

REH, L. 1894. Zur Frage nach der Vererbung erworbener Eigenschaften. *Biol. Zentbl.*, **14**, 71-75.

REIBMAYR, A. 1899. Die Immunisierung der Familien bei erblichen Krankheiten (Tuberculose, Lues, Geistesstörungen). Leipzig & Vienna: Deuticke. Pp. 51.

REID, G. A. 1897. Characters, congenital and acquired. *Science*, **6**, 896-902, 933-947.

————. 1905. Principles of heredity, with some applications. London: Dutton. Pp. 372.

RIGNANO, E. 1907. Ueber die Vererbung erworbener Eigenschaften. Hypothese einer Zentroepigenese. Leipzig: Engelmann. Pp. 399.

English: 1911. Inheritance of acquired characters, an hypothesis of heredity, development, and assimilation. (Trans. by B. C. H. Harvey.) Chicago: Open Court. Pp. 413.

ROMANES, G. J. 1892. Darwin and after Darwin: I. Darwinian theory. Chicago: Open Court. Pp. xvi+460.

――――. 1895. Darwin and after Darwin: II. Heredity and utility. Chicago: Open Court. Pp. x+334.

――――. 1897. Darwin and after Darwin: III. Isolation and physiological selection. Chicago: Open Court. Pp. vi+181.

ROSANOFF, A. J. 1913. Dissimilar heredity in mental disease. *Amer. J. Insan.*, **70**, 1-105.

ROSANOFF, A. J., & ORR, F. I. 1911. A study of heredity in insanity in the light of the Mendelian theory. *Amer. J. Insan.*, **68**, 221-261.

ROSENTHAL, J. 1889. Zur Frage der Vererbung erworbener Eigenschaften. *Biol. Zentbl.*, **9**, 510-512.

ROUX, W. 1881. Der Kampf der Teile im Organismus. Leipzig: Engelmann. Pp. viii+244.

RUEDIN, E. 1916. Studien über Vererbung und Entstehung geistiger Störungen: I. Zur Vererbung und Neuentstehung der Dementia Praecox. Berlin: Springer. Pp. v+172.

RYDER, J. A. 1889. Proofs of the effects of habitual use in the modification of animal organisms. *Proc. Amer. Phil. Soc.*, **26**, 541-558.

――――. 1890. A physiological hypothesis of heredity and variation. *Amer. Natur.*, **24**, 85-92.

――――. 1893. The inheritance of modifications due to disturbances of the early stages of development, especially in the Japanese domesticated races of gold-carp. *Proc. Acad. Nat. Sci.*, Philadelphia, **45**, 75-94.

――――. 1894. Dynamics and evolution. *Biol. Lectures, Woods Hole*, **2**, 63-81.

――――. 1895. A dynamical hypothesis of inheritance. *Biol. Lectures, Woods Hole*, **3**, 23-54. Also in *Science*, **1**, 597, 617.

SCHRÖDER, C. 1903. Ueber experimentell erzielte Instinktsvariationen. *Verhandl. d. zool. Gesellsch.*, **13**.

SECÉROV, S. 1912. Die Umwelt des Keimplasmas: II. Der Lichtgenuss im Salamandra-Körper. *Arch. f. Entwickmech.*, **33**, 682-702.

SEMON, R. 1905a. Ueber der Erblichkeit der Tagesperiode. *Biol. Zentbl.*, **25**, 241-252.

――――. 1905b. Die Mneme als erhaltendes Princip im Wechsel des organischen Geschehens. *Biol. Zentbl.*, **25**, 365-368.

――――. 1907. Beweise für die Vererbung erworbener Eigenschaften; ein Beitrag zur Kritik der Keimplasmatheorie. *Arch. f. Rassen- u. Gesellschbiol.*, **4**, 1-46.

――――. 1911. Die Abstammungslehre: XV. Können erworbene Eigenschaften vererbt werden? Jena: Fischer. Pp. iv+489.

――――. 1912. Das Problem der Vererbung "erworbener Eigenschaften." Leipzig: Engelmann. Pp. viii+203.

SIEMANS, H. W. 1924. Die Zwillingspathologie. Berlin: Springer. Pp. iv+103.

――――. 1927. The diagnosis of identity in twins. *J. Hered.*, **18**, 201-209.

SIOLI, ―. 1885. Ueber direkte Vererbung von Geisteskrankheiten. *Arch. f. Psychiat.*, **16**, 113-150.

SNYDER, L. H. 1924. The inheritance of the blood groups. *Genetics*, **9**, 464-478.

――――. 1925. Human blood groups and their bearing on racial relationships. *Proc. Nat. Acad. Sci.*, **11**, 406-407.

————. 1926. Human blood groups: their inheritance and racial significance. *Amer. J. Phys. Anthrop.,* **9**, 233-263.

SOLLIER, P. 1889. Du rôle de l'hérédité dans l'alcoholisme. Paris: Lecrosnier et Babé. Pp. 227.

SOMMER, M. 1900. Die Brown-Séquardische Meerschweinschenepilepsie und ihre erbliche Uebertragung auf die Nachkommen. *Beitr. z. path. Anat. u. allg. Path.,* **27**, 289-330. Summary by H. E. Ziegler in *Zoöl. Zentbl.,* **20**, 1-16.

SOMMER, R. 1907. Familienforschung und Vererbungslehre. Leipzig: Barth. Pp. vii+232.

SPENCER, H. 1864 & 1866. Principles of biology. (1st ed., 2 vols.) New York: Appleton. Pp. viii+475; viii+566. (2nd ed. of Vol. I, 1889. Pp. xii+706.)

————. 1890. The inheritance of acquired characters. *Nature,* **41**, 414-415.

————. 1893a. The inadequacy of natural selection. *Contemp. Rev.,* **63**, 155-166.

————. 1893b. Professor Weismann's theories. *Contemp. Rev.,* **63**. Also in *Pop. Sci. Mo.,* **43**, 473-490.

————. 1893c. A rejoinder to Professor Weismann. *Contemp. Rev.,* **63**.

————. 1894. Weismannism once more. *Contemp. Rev.,* **64**, 592-608.

STOCKARD, C. R. 1923. Experimental modification of the germ-plasm and its bearing on the inheritance of acquired characters. *Proc. Amer. Phil. Soc.,* **62**.

STOCKARD, C. R., & PAPANICOLAOU, G. 1916. A further analysis of hereditary transmission of degeneracy and deformities by the descendants of alcoholized mammals: I and II. *Amer. Natur.,* **50**, 65-88, 144-177.

————. 1918. Further studies on the modification of the germ-cells in mammals: the effect of alcohol on treated guinea pigs and their descendants. *J. Exper. Zoöl.,* **26**, 119-226.

SZILY, A. V. 1924. Die Ontogenese der idiotypischen Spaltbildungen des Auges, des Mikrophthalmus, und der Orbitalcysten. *Zsch. f. Anat. u. Entwickgesch.,* **74**, 1-230.

THOMSON, J. A. 1908. Heredity. (2nd ed.) London: Murray; New York: Putnam (1910). Pp. xvi+605.

TOLMAN, E. C. 1924. The inheritance of maze-learning ability in rats. *J. Comp. Psychol.,* **4**, 1-18.

VICARI, E. M. 1924. The non-inheritance of the effects of training. *Science,* **59**, 302.

WARD, J. 1913. Heredity and memory. Cambridge, England: Cambridge Univ. Press. Pp. 56.

WATSON, J. B. 1914. Behavior: an introduction to comparative psychology. New York: Holt. Pp. xii+439.

WEISMANN, A. 1885. Die Kontinuität des Keimplasmas, als Grundlage einer Theorie der Vererbung. Jena: Fischer. Pp. vi+122.

————. 1886. Zur Frage nach der Vererbung erworbener Eigenschaften. *Biol. Zentbl.,* **6**, 33-48.

————. 1888. Ueber die Hypothese einer Vererbung von Verletzungen. *Naturforsch. Versamml. in Köln,* 45-57.

————. 1891 & 1892. Essays upon heredity and kindred subjects. (2 vols.) Oxford: Clarendon Press. Pp. xv+471; v+226.

————. 1893. The germ-plasm: a theory of heredity. (Trans. by W. W. Parker and H. Rönnfeldt.) London: Scribner's. Pp. xxii+447.

————. 1894. The effect of external influences on development. (Romanes Lecture.) (Trans. by G. Wilson.) Oxford: Clarendon Press.

————. 1896. On germinal selection as a source of definite variation. Chicago: Open Court. Pp. xii+61. (2nd ed., 1902.)

154   HANDBOOK OF GENERAL EXPERIMENTAL PSYCHOLOGY

————. 1904. The evolution theory. (2 vols.) (Trans. by J. A. Thomson and M. R. Thomson.) London: Arnold. Pp. 416; 405.

————. 1906. Richard Semon's "Mneme" und die "Vererbung erworbener Eigenschaften." *Zsch. f. Rassen- u. Gesellschbiol.*, **3**, 1-27.

WETTSTEIN, R. v. 1903. Der Neo-Lamarckismus und seine Beziehungen zum Darwinismus. Jena: Fischer. Pp. 30.

WHEELER, W. M. 1927. The physiognomy of insects. *Quar. Rev. Biol.*, **2**, 1-36.

WIGGAM, A. E. 1923. Twins again. *J. Hered.*, **14**, 311-322.

WILDER, H. H. 1919. Physical correspondence in two sets of duplicate twins. *J. Hered.*, **10**, 410-421.

WINDLE, B. C. A. 1891. Teratological evidence as to the heredity of acquired conditions. *J. Linnaean Soc.*, **23**, 448-502.

————. 1892. A note on identical malformations in twins. *J. Anat. & Physiol.*, **26**, 295-299.

WOODS, F. A. 1919. Twins prove the importance of chromosomes. *J. Hered.*, **10**, 423-426.

ZELENY, C. 1921. The relative numbers of twins and triplets. *Science*, **53**, 262.

ZIEGLER, E. 1886. Können erworbene pathologische Eigenschaften vererbt werden, und die entstehen erbliche Krankheiten und Missbildungen? Jena: Fischer. Pp. 44.

ZIEGLER, H. E. 1905. Die Vererbungslehre in der Biologie. Jena: Fischer. Pp. 76.

CHAPTER 3

THE MECHANISM OF REACTION

ALEXANDER FORBES
Harvard Medical School

In attacking the problem of the mechanism of reaction one naturally seeks to interpret the fundamental activities which constitute the basis of behavior in terms of physical law. The scientist should not be complacent in the assumption that all laws of matter, animate or inanimate, are known. But the hasty assumption that vital phenomena which do not appear to exemplify the known laws of matter are not subject to physical law tends to confuse and obstruct progress. The law of the conservation of energy is no more violated by living matter than by other material systems. Those vital phenomena which baffle our attempts at explanation in terms of physical law should be regarded as complexities as yet unraveled, rather than as evidence that physical law does not apply to living things. As the marvels of physiology are elucidated by research, they show not so much new laws of life, breaking away from physics and chemistry, as examples of the ingenuity with which the physical laws and physical properties of matter have been utilized in the process of evolution.

NEUROMUSCULAR EVOLUTION

A study of the mechanism of reaction can perhaps best be approached through a consideration of the development and specialization of function in the neuromuscular system in the course of evolution. The protozoa are animals in which all the functions essential to life exist in a single cell. The ameba, for example, is capable of digestion and assimilation of food, respiration, metabolism, excitation, conduction, motion, and reproduction. All these functions are performed by the single cell which constitutes the animal. In the present discussion we are concerned with the functions of excitability, conductivity, and motility, which, taken together and supplemented by secretion and certain other types of energy liberation, comprise the physical basis of reaction. Excitability may be defined as the capacity for responding with functional activity to changes in environment. Conductivity means the capacity to transmit a functionally active state from one part of the living substance to another. Motility is exemplified in the ameba by the formation of pseudopodia and the flowing of cytoplasm from place to place; in ciliated protozoa and in ciliated epithelium of higher forms, by the beating of slender and flexible cilia; and in the major activities of all the animals higher in the scale than protozoa, by contraction of muscle.

The protozoa, having all necessary functions lodged in a single cell, are self-contained and complete in a very small compass, but their responses are

155

stereotyped and only slightly adaptable to altered conditions. Their range of activities is thus extremely limited. Jennings (1899) has shown that the ciliate protozoan paramecium reacts to mechanical and chemical stimuli by the uniform response of reversing temporarily the beat of the cilia in such a manner that the animal backs a short distance, changes course, and proceeds again forward. This single response serves well enough to enable the paramecium to avoid obstacles and dangers in its path, but when the experimenter places a drop of strong acid behind the animal this same response causes it to back into the injurious substance and perish.

With the aggregation of cells into the large coordinated groups which constitute the bodies of higher animals, we find the needs of the organism served by the specialization of the functions of excitability, conductivity, and contractility in tissues differentiated for the purpose. Coordination is served by the mechanical arrangement of the body, as in the operation of the tube-feet of the starfish by means of the water-vascular system, or, more familiarly, in the action of the bones and joints of the vertebrate. Coordination is also effected by the production of special substances by glands and their distribution through the circulation. These two types of coordination will not be considered in detail here, for in this discussion the emphasis will be placed on coordination by the neuromuscular mechanism.

Conductivity and excitability are intimately related, for conduction involves excitation of each successive region which becomes functionally active. Yet we find in the fully developed nervous system a differential development of excitability and conductivity; that is, some structures are differentiated for the purpose of receiving stimuli, while others are differentiated for conduction.

The early steps in the evolution of the differentiated neuromuscular mechanism have been admirably sketched by Parker (1919). His observations on sponges have led him to the conclusion that the first step toward a neuromuscular mechanism is the specialization of the contractile function in muscle. The sponge is an animal with primitive muscle cells but with no trace of nerves. The function of the muscles is to close certain openings through which a current of water passes. They can be called into action by a variety of stimuli, but their response to these stimuli is always very sluggish.

In the sea-anemone (a coelenterate) there are sensory cells in the integument, leading by slender nervous branches to the muscle cells (Figure 1), marking the first stage in the evolution of a nervous system. This animal possesses a quicker and more effective type of response. Yet the nervous processes of these sensory cells are very short, and, although the nerve net formed by them and the ganglionic cells renders nervous transmission possible from almost any part of the sea-anemone to almost any other part, the coordination is chiefly local. This is illustrated by the fact that a tentacle, when removed from the animal and held in sea water, gives almost exactly the same kind of response to the stimulus of food that it did before removal from the animal. The nervous system, consisting of innumerable cells distributed throughout the integument, each connected

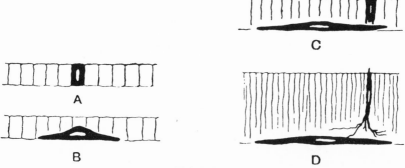

FIGURE 1

DIAGRAM TO ILLUSTRATE THE EARLY STAGES IN THE DIFFERENTIATION OF THE
NEUROMUSCULAR MECHANISM

A, epithelial stage; *B*, differentiated muscle cell at stage of sponge; *C*, partially
differentiated nerve cell in proximity to fully differentiated muscle cell; *D*, nerve
and muscle cell of coelenterate stage.
(From G. H. Parker's "The Origin and Significance of the Primitive Nervous
System," *Proc. Amer. Phil. Soc.*, 1911.)

only with its neighbors by short processes, is not characterized by any one
dominant center. Summing up the structural features and the evidence
from experiments on the animal's behavior, Parker (1914) concludes:
"The nervous system in the sea-anemone is diffuse rather than centralized."
Parker (1914) has summarized this evolutionary sequence as follows:

> Muscle arose first and the simple *effectors*[1] thus produced were
> the first element of the neuromuscular mechanism. These effectors
> were directly stimulated and consequently slow in action. They
> afforded centers around which nervous tissues first differentiated in
> the form of sense organs or *receptors*[1] whose function it was to
> serve as triggers to initiate muscle action quickly. As these receptors
> became more highly developed, a third element, the central nervous
> organ, rose from the nervous elements between the receptor and
> the effector. This organ, the *adjustor*,[1] served as a means of con-
> ducting and modifying the sensory impulses on their way from the
> receptor to the effector and ultimately it also served as a storehouse
> for the nervous experience of the individual and as the seat of its
> intellectual life.

The next important step above the coelenterates appears in the worms.
In the earthworm we find at the anterior end a centralized brain. This is
connected with the skin by sensory nerve fibers and with the muscles by
motor nerve fibers. Within the brain are the so-called association or
internuncial neurons, nerve cells which often form connecting links in the
conduction path between the sensory and the motor nerve fibers. Three
salient steps have been made from the stage of the sea-anemone. The
nerve fibers or conducting processes of the nerve cells have become

---

[1]Italics ours.

very much longer, thus providing the mechanism for rapid coordination between different parts.   Motor neurons have evolved, that is, nerve cells whose function it is to conduct impulses to the muscles.   A centralization of control has occurred; the central end of the sensory fibers, the association neurons, and the points of origin of the motor neurons being grouped together in a brain.

Correlated with this development we find in the behavior of the animal

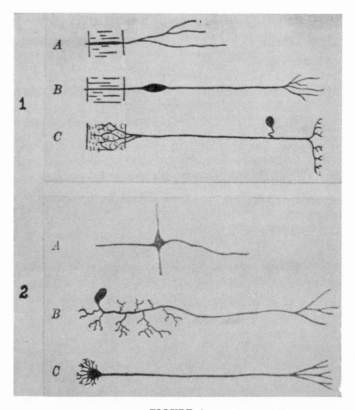

FIGURE 2

1. Stages in the Differentiation of Sense Cells

A, sensory protoneuron from a coelenterate; *B,* sensory neuron from a mollusk; *C,* primary sensory neuron from a vertebrate. In each instance the peripheral end of the cell is toward the left, the central toward the right.

2. Stages in the Differentiation of Nerve Cells

A, protoneuron from the nerve net of a coelenterate; *B,* motor neuron of an earthworm; *C,* primary motor neuron of a vertebrate. In *B* and *C* the receptive end of the neuron is toward the left, the discharging end toward the right.

(From G. H. Parker's *The Elementary Nervous System,* 1919, by permission of the publishers, J. B. Lippincott Co., Philadelphia.)

an increased efficiency of coordination. "The earthworm responds to a large range of stimuli by appropriate and characteristic reactions, and its movements justify the conclusion that its reflex arcs, like those of higher animals, involve receptors, an adjustor, and effectors." Evidence is cited suggesting that the behavior of the earthworm may be modified by experience (Parker, 1914).

Parker points out that the three classes of nervous cells which occur in man are also represented in the earthworm. Thus the fundamental plan upon which the central nervous system of higher animals is organized is already laid down in an elementary form in the worm. Of course, the steps are many and important by which the nervous system is brought from the crude stage of the worm to that which makes possible the dominating intelligence of man, but perhaps the most important single element in the development is the increase in the number of association neurons. As Stiles (1924) has put it: "With the addition of intermediate links between the receptor and the effector departments the reaction becomes less and less predictable . . . more and more . . . subject to reinforcement, suppression, or modification under the influence of changing circumstances."

Although the basic plan of neuromuscular organization, common to all higher forms, is already present in the earthworm, further development includes not only vast changes in the number of neurons and in the complexity of their arrangement, but also significant changes in the forms of the individual neurons. Parker gives a synopsis of the more salient changes, noting that in the evolving sensory neuron the cell body migrates from the peripheral to the central end of the conducting path, and in the motor neuron the cell body migrates toward the receptive end of the structure (Figure 2). Thus in each case the cell body comes to occupy a central and therefore protected position in the body of the animal. Correlated with these changes is another of special significance: instead of the primitive nerve net, in which there is continuity between the conducting fibers of adjacent cells, the neurons make junction with one another at synapses at which there is believed to be contact but no protoplasmic continuity, and which are capable of conduction in only one direction. The typical vertebrate neuron, exemplified by the motor neurons of the spinal cord and most of the internuncial neurons of the central nervous system, consists of a nucleated cell body with short, finely branching processes called dendrites, and a longer process, the axon, which conducts the impulses to the next neuron, or, in the case of motor neurons, to the muscle. At the end of the axon are branches which, in the case of sensory and internuncial neurons, connect with the dendrites or cell body of another neuron.

We arrive, then, at the general plan of neuromuscular organization found in the vertebrates, including man. The nervous system, embryologically of ectodermal origin, is made up entirely of neurons, histologically distinct units, linking the receptors and effectors. The simplest type of vertebrate reflex arc, providing for response to an external stimulus, is shown in Figure 3, which illustrates the arrangement of the neurons and their central and peripheral connections. External stimuli in some in-

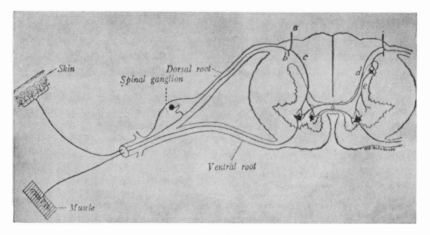

FIGURE 3

DIAGRAMMATIC SECTION THROUGH SPINAL CORD AND A SPINAL NERVE TO
ILLUSTRATE THE THREE MAIN CLASSES OF NEURONS *in situ*

A receptive neuron is shown in the dorsal root, a motor neuron in the ventral, and internuncial neurons in the cord itself (*e* and *o*).

(From S. W. Ranson's *Anatomy of the Nervous System,* 1920, by permission of the publishers, W. B. Saunders Co., Philadelphia.)

stances act on free nerve endings at the peripheral ends of the sensory neurons; in other instances these endings are connected with specialized sensory cells.   In either case this portion of the reflex mechanism is termed the receptor.   The working of the reflex arc is described by Parker (1919) as follows:

> The receptors are connected by nerve-fibers with the central nervous organ or adjustor composed of the central ends of the sensory and the motor neurones and of the internuncial neurones. Here the impulses arriving from the receptors are directed toward the appropriate groups of muscles by which the animal may respond to the stimulus and, if the animal is highly organized, impressions are made upon the adjustor which, as memories, may become more or less permanent parts of the animal's nervous equipment. Finally the adjustors are connected by nerve-fibers with the third set of elements, the effectors, which as muscles, electric organs, glands, etc., enable the animal to react on the environment. Thus three physiological categories are to be distinquished which in the order of their sequence in action are sense organs or receptors, central nervous organs or adjustors, and muscles or other effectors.

Not only is this general plan common to all the vertebrates but so also are many of the anatomical details of the grouping and arrangement of the neurons.   In man, as in all other vertebrates, we find sensory neurons connecting all points of the integument and all the organs of special sense with the centers in the spinal cord and brain.   The spinal cord is that portion of the central axis of the nervous system which lies outside of the cranium, or brain case.   All the sensory neurons receiving impulses from the limbs, from the integument of the trunk, and from most of the internal viscera enter the spinal cord in segmentally arranged bundles known as dorsal roots.

The spinal cord is composed of white matter consisting of nerve fibers, and gray matter consisting of nerve cells and the terminal branches through which the neurons make connection with each other.   The gray matter comprises the local nerve centers or adjustors which exercise immediate control over the activity of the muscles of the limbs and trunk.

The brain is structurally a continuation of the spinal cord.   Histologically it is similar in that it is made up of white matter, consisting of axons (conducting paths), and gray matter consisting of cell bodies, dendrites, and terminal branches.   In the lower vertebrates (e.g., fishes) the brain is a comparatively small enlargement at the anterior end of the spinal cord. As we ascend in the phylogenetic scale it becomes larger, till in man it is many times the size of the cord.   This increase in relative size of the brain is clearly correlated with intelligence and complexity of behavior.   The anatomy of the brain in man is extremely complex, and the millions of neurons of which it is composed vary greatly in size, shape, and arrangement, but they all possess the fundamental structures—dendrite, cell body, and axon (or "neurite"), and they all fall into the three categories already named — sensory, internuncial, and motor.

Besides the central nervous system, comprising brain and spinal cord, vertebrates possess an autonomic nervous system consisting of outlying neurons whose cell bodies are grouped in ganglia more or less remote from the brain and spinal cord, but connected with these central structures by neurons arising in the latter.   This system is sometimes called the vegetative system, as its function is the regulation of the activities of the digestive tract, the smooth muscles of the circulatory system, glands, and other viscera not subject to voluntary control nor participating directly in the immediate reactions to the environment in the manner characteristic of the skeletal muscles.

There is also present in the digestive tract of vertebrates a nerve net resembling the primitive nervous system of the coelenterate.   This nerve net, in contrast with the central nervous system, is devoid of synapses. Thus in the higher forms we find in conjunction with some smooth-muscle cells, resembling as they do the muscle cells of sponges and coelenterates, a primitive nervous system which has survived almost unchanged through the course of evolution.   Its extent, however, is insignificant compared with the synaptic nervous system which, in the higher forms, has assumed the dominant rôle.

It is important to note that, though all parts of the vertebrate body are coordinated by the nervous system, the conducting paths lead to or from the centers in the spinal cord or brain, never directly from organ to organ. Exceptions to this general rule are found in certain "axon reflexes," in which the blood vessels are controlled by impulses starting centripetally in one branch of a peripheral neuron and passing centrifugally from the point of branching to an effector innervated by the adjacent branch, without traversing a synapse.

EFFECTORS

The effectors at the disposal of the animal kingdom are of several kinds. There are nettling cells in coelenterates. There are cilia, slender processes which beat like the limb of a swimming animal. Cilia are found in protozoa, in which they serve the purpose of locomotion. They are found in the tentacles of many aquatic animals from coelenterates to polyzoa; they are found on epithelial surfaces of metazoa from coelenterates to mammals; in these cases they serve to move the surrounding fluid. There are chromatophores or pigment-bearing cells, capable of contracting and expanding and thus altering the appearance of the integument which contains them. These are found mostly in vertebrates. There are glands composed of cells which produce various substances, deriving the constituents from the body fluids or the blood stream. These include sweat glands, digestive glands, endocrine glands which pour their secretions into the blood stream, and glands producing such special secretions as the sepia whereby the squid makes a sort of aquatic smoke screen to confuse its adversaries. Glandular function is found in all classes of animals from protozoa to man. There are luminous organs in various forms beginning near the bottom of the animal scale and appearing as high in the scale as fishes. There are electric organs in certain fishes, specialized for the purpose of giving electric shocks to hostile creatures. Finally, there are muscles, which by contracting serve the purpose of motility. As we have seen, they are first specialized in sponges, and they constitute the most widespread type of effector in all classes of metazoa. In the vertebrates muscles are of two main types — smooth and striated. The smooth muscles are the more primitive type, resembling the muscles of the sponge and the sea-anemone; their contraction is slow and usually of comparatively sustained character. They are found chiefly in the walls of the blood vessels and the hollow viscera. Striated muscle is specialized for rapid contraction. It moves the limbs, trunk, neck, jaws, tongue, larynx, and eyes. Because of its attachment to bony structures it is designated skeletal muscle. It serves the purpose of locomotion and all manner of other activities. It is normally classified as "voluntary." The heart muscle, though striated, is not subject to voluntary control and is physiologically intermediate in character between smooth muscle and skeletal muscle.

Of the above-named types of effector, the nettling organs are independent of the nervous system, being called into functional activity by the direct action of external stimuli. Cilia are usually independent effectors but in some cases are under nervous control. Chromatophores, glands, luminous organs, and muscles are in some cases under nervous control and in some cases not. Electric organs, which morphologically are akin to muscles, are always under nervous control.

CONDUCTION

In considering the nature of the functional evolution which has enabled the neuromuscular mechanism to perform its intricate task, we shall deal first with conduction, for though, according to Parker, the specialization of muscle for the purpose of contraction preceded the specialization of nerve for conduction, protoplasmic conduction is the more fundamental property and is common to both muscle and nerve.

When the motor nerve of a vertebrate is stimulated, no visible change appears in the nerve itself, but the innervated muscle promptly responds by a vigorous contraction. An invisible disturbance has been propagated along the nerve fibers at a much higher speed than the conducted disturbance in undifferentiated protoplasm, such as that of epithelial cells and protozoa. The nerve fiber is highly specialized for the purpose of rapid and efficient conduction—up to 100 meters a second in mammalian motor nerves.

Excitation. Despite the obvious differences between nerve and muscle, both as to structure and function, the fundamental nature of their mode of excitation and conduction has many important features common to both tissues. Both nerve and muscle may be excited by various classes of stimuli, mechanical, thermal, chemical, and electrical. There is reason to believe that the essential element in all forms of stimuli is an electric disturbance. The study of electrical excitation of nerve and muscle has thrown a great deal of light on the nature of their functional activity. The researches of Nernst (1899, 1908), Lapicque (1926), Lucas (1910), and Hill (1910) have included quantitative measurements upon the relation between intensity and duration of a current sufficing to excite a given tissue. These researches have revealed the fact that when an electric current is passed through a portion of a nerve or muscle fiber a local change occurs which is limited to the region through which the current flows. If this local change does not attain a certain critical intensity, it produces no remote effects whatever; if it is made sufficiently intense, however, it will set up a disturbance which is conducted away from the point of stimulation over the entire length of the fiber. The "local excitatory process," as it was designated by Adrian and Lucas (1912), persists for a time after the stimulating current has ceased to flow, and its rate of subsidence is characteristic of each tissue.

The prevailing interpretation of experiments on this subject is that the local excitatory process consists in a concentration of ions at some point in the tissue. Only when this concentration reaches a certain requisite value does a propagated disturbance sweep over the fiber. In spite of quantitative differences between nerve and muscle, especially as to time relations, the curves correlating the requisite intensity of the exciting current with its duration have the same shape. The basic principle of electrical excitation is clearly the same for both tissues. A typical curve is shown in Figure 4. It will be noted that the curve ceases at a certain point to approach the base line, and is thereafter horizontal. This means that, up to a certain point, increasing the duration decreases the strength of cur-

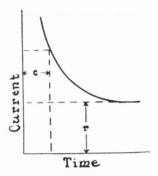

FIGURE 4
TYPICAL CURVE CORRELATING DURATION WITH STRENGTH OF A CONSTANT CURRENT
WHICH BARELY SUFFICES TO EXCITE
Abscissae, duration; ordinates, strength of current. r=rheobase. c=chronaxie.
(Taken from observations by Lucas on sartorius muscle of toad in K. Lucas' "The
Excitable Substances of Amphibian Muscle," *J. Physiol.*, 1907-08.)

rent required to excite, but beyond that point further increase in duration
is immaterial. The excitation time, as revealed by such a curve, is probably a significant property of any excitable tissue. Since it is difficult to
measure the precise point at which the curve becomes horizontal, a constant
has been introduced (Lucas, 1906-07), which Lapicque (1926) designates
chronaxie, for the purpose of measuring the time element in excitation.
The minimal voltage of a constant current of indefinite duration is termed
the *rheobase.* For the purpose of measurement a voltage double the
rheobase is chosen; *chronaxie* is the least duration at which such a voltage
will excite the tissue. This measure of time varies from about 0.2σ in
mammalian medullated nerve to 100σ in the case of smooth muscle.

Excitation time as measured by chronaxie has been invoked as playing
an important rôle in neuromuscular coordination. Whatever significance
this may have in the mechanism of nerve and muscle, it should be noted
that chronaxie alone is not a reliable measure, for excitation time is adequately portrayed only bv a complete "strength-duration curve" (Lambert,
Skinner, and Forbes, 1933).

Propagated Disturbance. Even more striking evidence of the essential
similarity in nerve and muscle is found in the many identical features revealed by the propagated disturbance which results when the local excitatory process becomes sufficiently intense. This disturbance has been known
classically in the case of nerve as the "nerve impulse," in the case of muscle
as the "wave of excitation." The single designation *propagated disturbance* (Adrian and Lucas) is a noncommittal and fitting name for it in
both tissues. Perhaps the most noteworthy feature of this functional response is the electric change by which we may follow its progress along the
fibers. A suitable galvanometer or electrometer connected with a nerve
or muscle reveals a wave of lowered electrical potential sweeping along the

fiber, the active portion being negative with respect to the inactive regions in front of and behind the advancing wave. This effect, as observed in a recording galvanometer, is commonly called the "action current," or "action potential."[2] Records from both nerve and muscle made with the apillary electrometer by Adrian (1921) and from nerve with the cathode ray oscillograph by Gasser and Erlanger (1922) and Bishop (1927) show that the electric disturbance rises rapidly to a maximum and then dies away more slowly, the decline lasting several times as long as the rise to maximum. The actual duration of the initial rise in mammalian motor nerve is about 0.3σ; in the most rapidly responding skeletal muscle it is about four times as long. Records of action currents in nerve and muscle, made with a string galvanometer, are shown in Figures 5 and 6. Recent

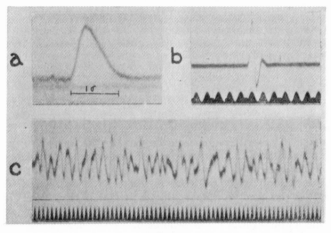

FIGURE 5

RECORDS OF ACTION CURRENTS IN NERVE AND SKELETAL MUSCLE MADE WITH STRING GALVANOMETER

a—monophasic action current of frog's sciatic nerve recorded with amplifier and short-string galvanometer (Forbes, Davis, and Emerson); *b*—diphasic action current of gastrocnemius muscle of frog; *c*—action currents of human forearm flexor muscles during voluntary contraction, electrodes applied to the skin. In *a, b,* and *c* the response was in each case evoked by a single stimulus (induction shock). In *a,* $1\sigma = 1.3$ cm.; the small initial excursion shows escape of stimulating current. In *b* and *c,* time is shown below by shadow of tuning fork vibrating 100 d.v. per sec.

[2]The classical designation "action current" for the electric response of nerve or muscle has largely been replaced by the term "action potential." The change is associated with the introduction of amplifiers which draw a negligible amount of current from the tissue and therefore give a truer record of the potential changes than is possible with an unaided galvanometer. There is no essential difference in the phenomenon as observed by the different methods; the word "current" is therefore retained in those portions of the chapter which have not been rewritten in revision.

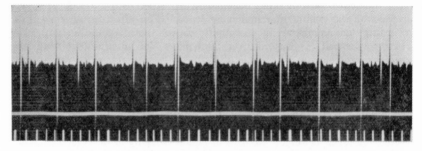

FIGURE 6

ELECTRIC RESPONSE FROM HUMAN FOREARM MUSCLE (FLEXOR DIGITORUM SUBLIMIS)
DURING WEAK FLEXION OF FINGER, REVEALING ISOLATED RESPONSES OF TWO
MOTOR UNITS (GROUPS OF MUSCLE FIBERS INNERVATED BY SINGLE
NEURON) DISCHARGING AT SLIGHTLY DIFFERENT FREQUENCIES

Action potentials were led off with localizing concentric electrodes, through amplifier, to DuBois oscillograph. Constancy of tension shown by mechanical myograph line below electrical record. Time shown below in 0.02-sec. intervals. Record by D. B. Lindsley.

work by Gasser and Erlanger (1930) and Gasser and Graham (1932) and others has shown the action potential of nerve to be composed of two parts, which they call the "spike" and the "after-potential." They are differentiated because they can be made to vary independently under experimental conditions. The spike potential subsides almost to zero in a period about three times as long as the rising phase. The after-potential in fresh nerve lasts about five times as long as the spike, and is greatly prolonged by fatigue. A similar differentiation of two successive parts in the action potentials of cardiac and skeletal muscle was found by Bishop and Gilson (1927). Rosenblueth, Leese, and Lambert (1933) have recently found in smooth muscle two stages of electric response, apparently corresponding to those found in striated muscle, but even more clearly separated in time.

A probable clue to the physical significance of the action potential is the "current of injury," which flows through a galvanometer connected at one terminal with the uninjured surface of a nerve or muscle, and at the other with the transversely cut end or otherwise injured portion of the tissue. The cut end or injured portion is negative with respect to the uninjured surface, just as during the passage of an impulse the active region is negative with respect to the inactive region. Furthermore, although it is impossible to infer the actual magnitude of the potential difference involved in either the action current or the current of injury, "since the circuit through the instrument is shunted to an unknown degree by idle tissue and fluid" (Davis, 1926), it is probably significant that the potential difference appears to be of the same order of magnitude in the two cases (presumably between 50 and 100 millivolts).

The most probable interpretation of all these observations is embodied in the *membrane theory,* which was developed for nerve by Ostwald (1890) and Bernstein (1902) and somewhat extended by Lillie (1920, 1922). This theory assumes a semipermeable membrane which normally maintains a difference in concentration of electrolytes, and hence a difference of potential, between the protoplasm within and the external surface of the fiber. The current of injury, obtained by transverse section of the fiber, constitutes probably its most direct measure, for the electrode at the cut end is applied as directly as possible to the exposed inside portion of the fiber. On the membrane theory the action current, which marks the passage of an impulse, is due to a transient increase in permeability resulting in a partial or complete depolarization moving progressively along the fiber. Even though there is no recording instrument there must be a local bioelectric current (Lillie, 1922) in consequence of the action potential. This current is assumed to flow from the positive outer surface in front of the disturbance, along the outer sheath, and through the surrounding fluid to the active region, at that point inward through the depolarized membrane to the inside of the fiber, and back again along the inside (see Figure 7).

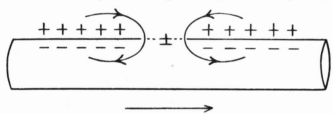

FIGURE 7

DIAGRAM TO ILLUSTRATE THE MEMBRANE THEORY OF CONDUCTION IN NERVE AND MUSCLE

The arrow below indicates the direction of the propagated disturbance. The general course of the bio-electric currents is shown by the curved arrows.

It is further assumed that this current constitutes the stimulus which calls into action the next section of the nerve and thus causes the wave of activity to progress. The cessation of the action current is assumed to depend on the spontaneous restoration of the polarized state as the wave of activity passes on.

This theory is reinforced by the analogy of the behavior of an iron wire with a film of oxide on its surface immersed in nitric acid. The wave of electrochemical activity which can be made to pass along the wire furnishes a striking counterpart of the nerve impulse in certain respects (Lillie, 1922). The close similarity of nerve and muscle with respect to both action currents and currents of injury leads to the conclusion that the mechanism of conduction must be fundamentally alike in the two tissues. In support of the membrane theory Lillie (1914) has called attention to the correlation between the rate of rise of action current and velocity of conduction in various types of nerve and muscle. The hypothetical membrane cannot be identified with any particular part of the structure of the nerve fiber.   Bishop (1927) and Bishop and Erlanger (1926) show features of the action potential which suggest the progress of chemical reactions, and in discussing the membrane theory they warned against any oversimplified and static explanation; they regard both action and resting potentials as the resultants of balanced reactions.

Refractory Phase.   Another feature common to nerve and muscle, and of the greatest importance, is the *refractory phase*.   When a propagated disturbance is initiated it sweeps over the tissue, leaving it refractory to further stimulation for a brief interval of time (Bramwell and Lucas, 1911).   Following the absolute refractory phase when the tissue cannot respond, there is a period of recovery, the relative refractory phase, during which the threshold of excitation is abnormally high, and the size of the response which can be evoked is subnormal, both returning gradually to normal.   Adrian has shown that in the case of a nerve immersed in a slightly acid fluid there is, following the relative refractory phase, an apparently *supernormal* phase in the recovery of excitability.   He further showed that the excitability becomes no greater than would be found if the same tissue were in neutral fluid.   The supernormality is only relative, due to the fact that in an acid medium the final resting stage is subnormal when compared with the condition of the tissue at neutrality (Adrian, 1920).   Gasser and Erlanger (1930) have more recently shown that the supernormal phase may still be found after a nerve has been removed from acid, and they give reason for correlating it with a prolonged afterpotential.

TABLE 1

	Duration of action potential		Refractory phase		Velocity of conduction (meters per sec.)
	Rising phase	Total	Absolute	Total (including relative)	
Medullated nerve (mammalian) at body temperature (37°C.)	0.2σ	0.6σ	0.6σ	—	100
Non-medullated nerve (mammalian) at body temperature	3.5σ	10σ	4σ	—	1
Medullated nerve (frog sciatic) 22°C.	0.3σ	2σ	2σ	8σ	30
Skeletal muscle (frog sartorius) 24°C.	3.0σ	20σ	3σ	11σ	2

The values, compiled from various sources, are only approximations.   The duration of action potential refers to the spike.   For total duration of both action potential and refractory phase the approximations are very rough because the decline of the action potential and the return of excitability to normal are both so gradual that precise determination of their duration is impossible.

The recent work of Erlanger and Blair (1931*a*) affords convincing evidence that the relative refractory phase in nerve is essentially a post-cathodal depression left by the action potential.   In this we have not only a simplified picture of nerve function, but also added support for the membrane theory of conduction.

Just as the action current is briefer in the case of nerve than in muscle and the velocity of conduction more rapid, so is the refractory phase briefer.   There is not a strict proportionality but a very clear correlation as regards quickness of function in its various aspects (see Table 1).

The recent work of Gasser and Erlanger (1930) and Gasser and Graham (1932) seems to show that the entire refractory period, absolute and relative, is coextensive with the spike potential.   They contend that this potential change, although correlated with depolarization of the membrane, is probably secondary to an underlying chemical reaction.

ALL-OR-NONE LAW

It has long been known that, when a single stimulus is applied directly to a muscle or to its motor nerve, the size of contraction which may be evoked is apparently graded according to the strength of stimulus from the threshold, below which the stimulus is ineffective, to a maximal value, above which further increase in the strength of stimulus causes no further increase in the size of contraction.   Lucas (1909), by using a very small muscle and a delicate means of recording the size of the contractile twitch, showed that the increase in contraction as the stimulus was gradually increased in strength occurred in a series of definite steps, and after each step was reached there was no further increase in the size of contraction until the next step.   Pratt (1917), using even more refined methods, brought out this same effect more strikingly.   These observations can be interpreted only as meaning that each step represents the threshold of stimulation for a new fiber or group of fibers, and that the contractile effort of the individual fiber is the same whether the stimulus be strong or weak. Adrian (1922), using the pore-electrode, showed that the action current of muscle likewise increases by a series of definite steps, the level being maintained constantly throughout the extent of each step, and that therefore the electric response, as well as the contractile effort of the individual muscle fiber, obeys the *all-or-none law*.

Gelfan and Gerard (1930) have found that certain striated muscle fibers, when stimulated through microscopic electrodes, can be made to yield localized contractions of graded amount.   This occurs only when the stimulus is too weak to initiate conduction; as soon as true conduction is started, the usual all-or-none response ensues (cf. Lucas, 1907-08, p. 266).

Adrian in 1912 attacked the question of the all-or-none character of the nerve impulse by a new method.   When a portion of a nerve is subjected to a narcotic, the impulse is blocked, provided the narcotic is sufficiently concentrated and applied for a long enough time.   Apparently the duration of action of a narcotic necessary to abolish conduction depended on the length of the narcotized region. From this it was concluded that the impulse became progressively weaker as it traversed the narcotized portion of nerve. This is the classical conception of *"decrement."* Proceeding on the assumption of decremental conduction in a narcotized region, Adrian demonstrated that if a nerve impulse is allowed to traverse a region of narcosis almost but not quite long enough to extinguish the impulse, it will, on emerging into an unnarcotized region, apparently regain its initial size. These and other observations (1914) involving narcotization led to the conclusion that *the size of the nerve impulse in the individual fiber is independent of the strength of stimulus,* i.e., *that it obeys the all-or-none law.*

Kato in 1924 pointed out that the assumed decremental conduction in a narcotized region, which had thus been used to furnish evidence for the all-or-none law in normal nerve, constituted an exception to the all-or-none law itself. He and his colleagues showed that the dependence of the duration of narcosis upon the length of the narcotized region was limited to regions less than 7 mm. long. Beyond 7 mm. the length of the narcotized region was immaterial. In shorter lengths the observed relation is in part explainable through diffusion near the edge of the narcotizing chamber with a resulting gradient of concentration of the narcotic. These experimenters also showed that when the nerve impulse enters a region of uniform narcosis the electric response falls to a reduced level, but instead of growing progressively smaller, as the decrement theory assumed, it remains constant in size as long as the degree of narcosis is constant. On emerging from the narcotized region to normal nerve the electric response at once regains its initial size. Davis, Forbes, Brunswick, and Hopkins (1926), working independently, afforded complete confirmation of Kato's conclusion. These experiments, although disproving the premise of decrement in narcosis, upon which Adrian's chain of evidence rested, nevertheless confirmed his main conclusion and placed the all-or-none law on a firmer foundation than ever. Davis, Forbes, Brunswick, and Hopkins contended on theoretical grounds that there must be a brief transitional decrement as the impulse passes from a normal region to one of partial narcosis. Cooper in 1926 reported observations which appeared difficult to reconcile with Kato's view of decrementless conduction. The difficulty has been met by Rice and Davis (1928), and we may definitely abandon the idea of progressive decrement in uniformly narcotized nerve, with the reservation that on theoretical grounds there must be some degree of transitional decrement, even if only of molecular dimensions, and the question of extent remains yet to be determined. Perhaps the strongest case for the all-or-none law in nerve is the reasoning which Adrian brought to bear on the problem in 1914. Since the impulse is set in motion as soon as the local excitatory process reaches the requisite value "and the refractory state accompanying the disturbance will prevent any subsequent change in the local conditions from affecting its size in any way," the all-or-none relation is a necessary logical consequence (cf. Ritchie, 1932).

The evidence that the impulse regains its full size on emerging from a narcotized into a normal region shows that *the energy of the impulse comes not from the stimulus but from the fiber.* This fact taken together with the refractory phase, denoting a temporary depletion of the source of energy, shows that the nerve impulse is dynamically like an explosive re-action or the burning of a fuse, rather than like a sound wave or an electric current in an inert conductor. A disturbance of this class must be funda-mentally independent of the strength or character of the stimulus which evokes it, provided this be adequate. It should be noted that the membrane theory of conduction harmonizes well with the all-or-none character of the response, for, if the essential feature of the impulse is a breaking-down of the polarized state of the membrane, it is evident that such a change cannot go beyond complete depolarization.

The all-or-none law of response is now well established for nerve and skeletal muscle. This law, frequently misunderstood, in reality states that *propagated disturbance evoked by a single stimulus in a single functional unit of nerve or muscle is always as large as that functional unit is capable of producing at the moment when the response is evoked, no matter how strong the stimulus may be.* In other words, the size of the propagated disturbance is independent of the strength of the stimulus, provided this is adequate (Forbes and Cattell, 1924). The size of response may be varied by varying the condition of the tissue; for instance, the energy released in a muscle twitch may be varied by altering the load to which the contract-ing muscle is subjected. The size of response varies with the degree of recovery from a previous response. But under all these conditions the size of response is independent of the strength of stimulus.

The recent researches of Adrian (1926, 1926-27, 1928) and Adrian and Zotterman (1926a, 1926b) have shown quite clearly the all-or-none char-acter of sensory nerve impulses and the fact that, while their magnitude is constant, their frequency is correlated with the strength of the stimulus applied to the sensory receptor. Thus sustained tension applied to a small strip of frog's muscle, containing a single receptor for muscle sense, set up in the afferent nerve a regular succession of impulses varying in frequency from 100 per second with the maximum load to 5 per second with a very weak pull. If the tension applied was constant, the frequency of the nerve impulses declined gradually during its application.

Metabolism in Nerve

It has long been known that both nerve and muscle require oxygen in order that they remain functionally active, and that muscle gives off carbon dioxide as a result of its contractile activity. Until recently observers failed to detect any carbon-dioxide production in nerve, and this fact made many lean to the view that nerve was an inert conductor. More recently Tashiro (1913), Parker (1924-25, 1925-26, 1925-28), and Fenn (1927) have shown that minute quantities of carbon dioxide are produced by nerve even at rest, and that this quantity is measurably increased during activity, as is also the oxygen consumption (Fenn, 1926-27).

The heat production of muscle is well known and has been extensively studied with quantitative methods by A. V. Hill and his associates. Recently, with refined methods, Downing, Gerard, and Hill (1926) demonstrated heat production in nerve. From experiments with various frequencies of stimulation, Gerard, Hill, and Zotterman (1927) inferred that the amount of heat from a single impulse traversing a gram of nerve is a millionth of a calorie. This is very much less than the heat production in muscle, which is of the order of 0.003 calorie per gram for a single functional response. In the matter of heat production there is a further qualitative similarity and quantitative difference between nerve and muscle, in that each tissue shows an immediate heat production, which results during functional activity, and a delayed heat production, which occurs at a slower rate but lasts for several minutes after activity has ceased. In the case of muscle contracting for a short time, the delayed heat production amounts to about half the total. In the case of nerve the delayed heat production amounts to about nine-tenths of the total and lasts as long as ten minutes after the cessation of activity (Downing, Gerard, and Hill, 1926). Clearly the activity of nerve, as well as of muscle, is metabolic.

Gasser and Erlanger (1930), differentiating the two components of the electric response, spike and after-potential, related the latter to some oxidative process probably involving the removal of metabolites and reforming a substance essential to normal activity. This likens the phenomena to those observed in muscle, to be described presently.

FATIGUE

One of the most striking apparent differences between nerve and muscle is in relation to fatigue. If an isolated muscle is made to contract by a rapid series of stimuli, it will soon become obviously fatigued and the ability to contract will fall off to a small fraction of its initial value. A nerve, on the other hand, will conduct a hundred impulses or more a second and continue to do so for hours without apparent exhaustion. From this fact it has been inferred that nerve was unfatigable. But recently Field and Brücke (1926) showed that with continued stimulation the refractory phase of a nerve is greatly prolonged. Gerard (1927a) showed that oxygen consumption and heat production in nerve become less if stimulation is continued at high frequency than if it is intermittently interrupted with periods of rest. In some recent experiments (Forbes and Rice, 1929), the action current of nerve has been found to grow smaller in a prolonged series of responses at high frequency (Levin, 1927). Gerard (1927b) emphasized the fact that, in the case of nerve, continued activity at a given frequency of stimulation does not result in a decline of activity to the point of exhaustion, but that an equilibrium is reached at a reduced level of functional activity, and this level may be maintained for a long time. Increase in the frequency of stimulation causes the functional level to fall farther and attain a new equilibrium; decrease in frequency causes a partial restoration to a higher equilibrium level. Davis and Davis (1932) found a similar effect in muscle. Gerard proposes the term *"equilibration"* to signify the difference between this condition and the type of fatigue that progresses to exhaustion. The fact that fatigue can be demonstrated in nerve tends to make the difference between nerve and muscle quantitative rather than qualitative in this respect, as well as in other features of functional activity.

Gerard (1927c) has attempted to bring together the facts which have emerged from the chemical and dynamic studies of nerve in a provisional theory. He shows how a cycle of three related reactions might give rise to the known phenomena of refractory phase and equilibration fatigue.

We have considered in some detail the functional properties of nerve and muscle. Of the excitable tissues, medullated nerve and striated muscle are the two most highly differentiated for the special functions of conduction and contraction respectively. It has been shown that, in spite of their differences, the essential nature of the conduction process is apparently the same in both. That, in tissues so different in structure and embryonic ancestry, these essential elements of function should be the same, is a matter of profound significance. It suggests the inherent propensity to react in this way as perhaps a basic property of living cells in general.

An important conclusion which follows from the all-or-none character of the nerve impulse, and which is not yet as well recognized as it might be, is the fact that, whatever the functional properties of the gray matter may be, the nervous system must utilize impulses of the kind which we have been describing wherever they are transmitted through axons, whether in the peripheral nerves or in the white matter of the brain and cord (Martin, 1922). It has been customary in the past to treat nerves as if they were pipe lines in which continuous streams of nervous energy could be graded as to intensity, much as one grades the flow of water by opening and shutting a faucet. It is evident that this mode of treatment is fundamentally wrong. We must recognize that the impulses mediating sensation in the afferent nerves, the impulses in the axons of the internuncial neurons of the entire central nervous system, and, finally, the impulses which traverse the efferent nerves to evoke responses in muscle or gland, are all successive disturbances of the transient, all-or-none type.

MUSCULAR CONTRACTION

It has already been noted that nerve and muscle are differentiated and specialized for the two distinct functions, conduction and contraction, and yet that fundamental properties of the propagated disturbance are the same in both. It remains to mention the salient properties in which muscle differs from nerve. The conduction process in muscle is incidental to its prime function, contraction. Hill (1926a) says "a muscle is essentially a mechanism for transforming chemical into mechanical energy."

Anatomically, skeletal muscle is made up of fibers varying roughly from 20 to 80 microns in diameter, each consisting of a large number of *myofibrils*. The myofibrils show a banded or striated structure, due apparently to alternate transverse layers of two kinds of material called "isotropic" and "anisotropic."

It is noteworthy that the progagated disturbance set up by a single stimulus, as measured by the action current, is of far briefer duration than the resulting contraction. The action current in some of the limb muscles of the cat reaches its maximum in about 2σ and is practically over in 10σ. Sherrington (1921) and Cooper and Eccles (1930) have perfected myographs for recording accurately and without lag the tension developed in isometric contraction, i.e., contraction when the muscle is not allowed to shorten and the contractile effort is revealed as tension. Cooper and Eccles find the contraction time (to maximum tension) in the isometric twitch in various muscles in the cat to be approximately as follows: soleus, 100σ; gastrocnemius, 30σ; internal rectus of the eye, 7 to 10σ. A record of such an isometric contraction from a skeletal muscle in the cat is shown in Figure 8, together with the diphasic action current marking the underlying propagated disturbance; this record shows the simple twitch evoked by a single stimulus. Fulton (1926) has made ingenious use of isometric recording in the analysis of spinal reflexes.

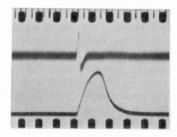

FIGURE 8

RESPONSE OF CAT'S GASTROCNEMIUS MUSCLE IN RESPONSE TO SINGLE BREAK-SHOCK STIMULUS APPLIED TO POPLITEAL NERVE

Lower line, record of isometric lever; upper line, string-galvanometer record of diphasic action current. Time recorded in 0.01-second intervals by vertical lines above the perforations at the top of the picture.

It is an old observation that a muscle will contract more powerfully if subjected to a moderate initial load. "The maximum work can be obtained only by variable load, which at every length during the contraction is exactly equal to the maximum tension the muscle can exert at that length" (Hill, 1913). The extensive researches of Hill (1911, 1913, 1920-21, 1926a, 1926b, 1928) have solved many problems in the thermodynamics of muscular contraction. Heat production occurs in several distinct stages.

> Immediately on stimulation there is a large and rapid evolution of heat; this, in a contraction of short duration, represents about half the 'initial' energy: it is complete long before the moment when the maximum tension is attained; then follows relaxation, accompanied by the

evolution of the other half of the 'initial' heat. In a prolonged contraction there is another equally obvious phase, that associated with a constant rate of heat-production, lasting as long as the contraction is maintained. (Hill, 1926a)

As already mentioned, this initial heat production is followed by a recovery heat production, very much more gradual but slightly larger in amount, and lasting in muscle as long as 15 minutes. The initial heat production occurs, as does contraction, even if the muscle is isolated in an atmosphere deprived of oxygen. The recovery heat production occurs only in the presence of oxygen. Hill concludes that the initial energy liberation is non-oxidative, but that recovery is an oxidative process. He has likened the recovery process to a combustion engine driving a dynamo which recharges a storage battery.

The chemical changes which underlie the contraction of muscle have recently been investigated in fruitful researches which make an important chapter in physiology, beyond the scope of this summary. For a review of the experiments and literature the reader is referred to Hill (1932a).

CHEMICAL MEDIATION

Recently evidence derived from many ingenious experiments has pointed convincingly to the conclusion that nerve impulses in the autonomic system activate the smooth muscles which they innervate through the mediation of chemical substances produced where the nerve fiber impinges on the muscle cell. It is believed that the nerve endings of the sympathetic division of the autonomic system produce as a mediator adrenin or a closely similar substance, whereas the nerve endings of the parasympathetic division produce acetylcholine. Cannon and Rosenblueth (1933) have found evidence leading to the view that the mediator combines with receptive substances existing in the muscle cell, and that these receptive substances are of two kinds, excitatory and inhibitory. When the receptive substance is excitatory the combination causes contraction of the muscle cell; when inhibitory, lengthening (Cannon, 1933).

This new conception of smooth-muscle function suggests a fundamental similarity to the activity of glands whose function is the production of chemical substances.

Rosenblueth (1934b), on the basis of various findings in relation to the skeletal neuromuscular unit and to smooth muscle, has outlined the chain of events which occurs when a nerve impulse evokes a response in the innervated muscle. The sequence is as follows: nerve impulse; propagated disturbance in muscle; chemical mediator, which in some cases combines with a receptive substance and which causes the response in the muscle (contraction with liberation of heat). The first two steps are quantal, i.e., all-or-none; the remaining steps are subject to gradation. The formulation of this sequence may be a generalization applicable to all effectors—skeletal muscle, smooth muscle, and gland.

GLANDS

Glands constitute an important group of effectors whose function is tc elaborate substances serving various purposes in the life of the organism. Glands are of two classes: those whose secretion is poured into a duct, whence it is led to the surface of the body or into an internal cavity such as the intestinal tract, and the endocrine organs, whose secretion is taken up by the blood stream as it circulates through the substance of the gland. The former class performs a variety of services relating to digestion and the elimination of waste, which are concerned only indirectly with the subject of this chapter.   The glands of internal secretion play a variety of rôles in the coordination of body activity, and, in such instances as the adrenal glands, play an active part in the mechanism of immediate reaction of the organism to its environment (Cannon, 1929).

CENTRAL NERVOUS FUNCTIONS

Let us now turn to a consideration of the special functions of the central nervous system.   The gray matter of the brain and cord comprises the adjustor mechanism.   Its functional properties can best be approached through a study of the simplest reflexes involving the synapse between neurons.

The contrast between nerve trunk and reflex arc may be viewed from the angle of the diversity of purpose which the structures serve.   The nerve fiber apparently exists for the purpose of transmitting messages to remote parts, rapidly, economically, and without modification.   The central structure appears to serve as a junctional point where messages from many regions may be correlated, relayed, and distributed to other regions.   In this respect the fibers and centers may be likened to the wires and central offices, respectively, of a telephone system.

Anatomically, the nerve fiber is characterized by its comparative simplicity, extending as it does for great distances without branching or changing much in size or form.   In contrast with this, the gray matter presents a picture of the most prodigious complexity, with intricate end-branches and dendrites providing the connections for extensive coordination of conducting paths.

Finally, the contrast between nerve trunk and reflex arc may be viewed from the angle of functional differences.   Sherrington in 1906 summarized the differences between conduction in nerve trunk and reflex arc, the most important of which are as follows.   Reflex conduction shows:

a.   *slower speed* as judged by latency of response;

b.   *after-discharge,* i.e., persistence of response after stimulation has ceased, often for several seconds;

c.   *summation,* single stimuli in many reflexes failing to produce any response, whereas a repeated series is effective;

d.   *irreversibility,* conduction from afferent to efferent neurons being possible, but in the reverse direction through the central structure, impossible;

e. fatigue on continued stimulation, in contrast with the nerve trunk, which exhibits extraordinary resistance to fatigue;

f. greater *variability of threshold* or ease with which responses can be evoked;

g. far greater *dependence on blood supply and oxygen,* and correspondingly greater *susceptibility to anaesthetics;*

h. reinforcement by allied reflex arcs;

i. inhibition, afferent nerves having the property of suppressing as well as initiating central activity.

Histological research has not yet settled conclusively whether there is indeed a true surface of separation between connecting neurons, or whether there is actual protoplasmic continuity. The indisputable structural difference between the reflex arc and the nerve trunk lies in the intricately branching system of connections, on the one hand, and the isolated, unbranched arrangement on the other (Loeb, 1903).

Lucas (1917), whose crucial experiments did much to elucidate the fundamental nature of conduction in nerve and muscle, raised the following question:

> Are we to suppose that the central nervous system uses some process different from that which is the basis of conduction in peripheral nerves, or is it more probable that the apparent differences rest only on our ignorance of the elementary facts of the conduction process? If we had a fuller knowledge of conduction as it occurs in peripheral nerve, should we not see Inhibition, Summation, and After-discharge as the natural and inevitable consequences of that one conduction process working under conditions of varying complexity?

The scope of this idea is large. A reduction of the elements of neural activity underlying consciousness and behavior to the single basis of the nerve impulse, many of whose physical properties are now known, would be a generalization comparable to the reduction of all the various chemical elements to their constituent protons and electrons.

Lucas further suggested

> that we should inquire first with all care whether the elementary phenomena of conduction, as they are to be seen in the simple motor nerve and muscle, can give a satisfactory basis for the understanding of central phenomena; if they cannot, and in that case only, we shall be forced to postulate some new process peculiar to the central nervous system.

A task of cardinal importance in the study of the nervous system is to determine the extent to which the peripheral type of conduction can serve to explain the known facts of central or reflex function. Does every neural disturbance sweep over the conducting paths open to it, leaving them refractory, so that sustained activity must be intermittent? Or is there something at the synapse which can pass into a sustained state of activity uninterrupted by refractory phase and capable perhaps of gradation?

Spinal Reflexes. In mammals the reflexes most accessible to study are the spinal reflexes, involving contraction of the limb muscles. It is possible to isolate the local centers which coordinate the movements of the hind limbs by transecting the spinal cord in the thoracic region. In that way the lumbar enlargement of the spinal cord, which contains all the motor neurons innervating the muscles of the hind limbs, is cut off from the influence of the brain and higher centers in the cord. This operation makes it possible to study the extent to which a local coordinating mechanism exists in these lower centers. Transection of the spinal cord between the brain and the cervical enlargement containing the local centers for the forelimbs makes possible the study of the local reflexes in both the hind limbs and the forelimbs and the coordination of the two pairs of limbs with each other. This operation destroys the respiratory center and makes it necessary to employ artificial respiration to keep the animal alive. Transection of the brain-stem, just in front of the cerebellum, eliminates the entire cerebrum, and with it consciousness and spontaneous activity. It does not interfere with spontaneous respiration or with certain coordinating effects of the lower centers of the brain, and it permits the study of spinal reflexes under conditions which are in some respects more nearly normal than those obtaining when the spinal cord is severed below the medulla oblongata. This operation is known as decerebration. The most striking immediate effect is the development of extensor rigidity, a condition described and studied by Sherrington. All the extensor muscles of the limbs go into a state of sustained contraction and remain in this condition for many hours, in fact as long as the animal can be maintained in a normal condition as regards temperature and circulation. As Sherrington (1906, p. 302) has pointed out, the extensor muscles are those which support the animal's weight against the force of gravity and their sustained contraction is to be looked on as a postural reflex. Its reflex nature has been demonstrated by the fact that any interruption of the path from the receptors of muscle sense, located within the muscles and tendons, to a nerve center in the hind-brain and back to the extensor muscles through their motor neurons, abolishes the rigidity.

All three of these operations have been used extensively by Sherrington in the study of spinal limb reflexes. The initial operation is performed under deep surgical anaesthesia and thereafter the reflexes may be studied after the local centers have been freed from the effects of the anaesthetic. In the case of decerebration or transection of the cord at its junction with the brain, the cerebrum, which is the center of consciousness, is destroyed, and the animal thereafter becomes a reflex automaton in which the reflex mechanism may be studied without the possibility of pain. In the case of low spinal transection in the thoracic region, there is no nervous connection between the lumbar centers coordinating the muscles of the hind limbs and the rest of the central nervous system; thus the hind-limb reflexes may be studied without provoking any sensation whatever in the animal.

These methods have yielded a great mass of information about the mammalian limb reflexes (Sherrington, 1910a). Only the more constant and important of these reflexes will be described here. When a skin surface or a sensory nerve in the hind limb is strongly stimulated in either a spinal or decerebrate animal, the regular reflex response is a rapid flexion of the hip, knee, and ankle in the stimulated leg. Usually this is accompanied by a slightly more gradual but equally strong extension of the same three joints in the opposite hind leg. These two reflex responses are called the *flexion reflex* and the *crossed extension reflex*. Their purposive significance has been pointed out by Sherrington (1906). If a normal animal steps on a thorn or otherwise brings his foot in contact with an injurious object, the natural defensive reaction is withdrawal of the foot, which is best effected by a flexion of hip, knee, and ankle. That the body may be supported during this reaction requires the contraction of the extensor muscles of the opposite hind limb. The crossed coordination whereby flexion in one hind limb is accompanied by extension in the other is found not only in the defensive reaction just described but also in normal progression. A walking animal such as a cat or dog normally flexes the joints of one leg while extending those of its mate; rhythmical progression movements, in which this coordination is beautifully demonstrated, can easily be evoked in a cat or dog after low spinal transection. Many of Sherrington's observations have shown a functional linkage between the flexor motor center of each hind limb and the extensor motor center of its mate.

One of the most interesting and striking features of these limb reflexes is the reflex inhibition shown in the reciprocal innervation of antagonistic muscles. If the flexor and extensor muscles of the knee joint contract simultaneously, they work against each other. Sherrington (1906, 1910*a*, 1910*b*, 1913) has shown that reflex excitation of one group of muscles is accompanied by reflex inhibition of the antagonistic group, which insures their relaxation and the elimination of wasteful opposition. Thus in the flexion reflex there is not only reflex excitation of the flexor muscles but simultaneously a reflex inhibition of the extensors. This is especially well demonstrated during decerebrate rigidity, in which, as has been already stated, the extensor muscles are in a state of sustained contraction. If an extensor muscle is isolated it is found that when the powerful afferent stimulus which evokes the flexion reflex is applied the extensor muscle relaxes instantly; this is due to central inhibition.

Other examples of inhibitory action are known elsewhere in the body, as, for example, the inhibition of the heart by the vagus nerve. The stimulation of the vagus causes a slowing or cessation of the heart beat; this occurs even when the vagus nerve is severed from the central nervous system and the peripheral portion stimulated. There is an important difference between such peripheral inhibition and reflex inhibition of skeletal muscles. The heart muscle has the property of spontaneous contraction; therefore peripheral inhibition is a necessity if the heart beat is to be slowed to less than its spontaneous rate. Vertebrate skeletal muscle has no tendency to spontaneous contraction; normally it contracts only when excited by the discharge of impulses from the central nervous system. If motor nerve impulses cease, muscular contraction ceases. There are no special inhibitory impulses set up in the motor nerves to stop contraction in the skeletal muscles (Verworn, 1900; Forbes, Whitaker, and Fulton,

1927); reflex inhibition consists in stopping the discharge of motor impulses from the reflex center (Cobb, 1928). This law, as far as is known, applies universally to vertebrates; exceptions have been found in certain arthropods in which the striated muscle of the claw is subject to peripheral inhibition by stimulation of the appropriate nerve (Biedermann, 1887).

There are certain interesting differences between the reflex contractions of flexor and extensor muscles (Liddell and Sherrington, 1923a). The flexion reflex usually starts very quickly, and if the stimulus is strong all the motor neurons which participate in the reflex begin discharging impulses at once; thus the muscular contraction has a brisk and rapid onset not differing much from the twitch evoked by applying a maximal stimulus to the motor nerve. Forbes and Gregg (1915a), stimulating an afferent nerve with single induction shocks and recording the action current in the motor nerve which innervates the flexor muscle in the hind leg of a cat, showed that the time consumed by the disturbance traversing the spinal cord is only about 4σ. Forbes and Miller (1922), recording the action current which marked the entrance of afferent impulses into the brain, found that when a single stimulus was applied to the sciatic nerve of a decerebrate cat the first clearly recognizable impulses reached the medulla oblongata about 8σ after the stimulus was applied, or not less than 6σ after the afferent impulses had reached the spinal cord. Leese and Einarson (1934) have detected impulses reaching the medulla approximately 4σ after the arrival of the afferent volley at the spinal cord. This is nearly synchronous with the discharge of impulses in the flexor motor neurons. From these observations it is evident that in the flexion reflex the motor response is actually initiated by the spinal cord before the afferent impulses make the animal aware of the stimulus by reaching the cerebral cortex (Forbes, Cobb, and Cattell, 1923). Recent measurements by Gasser and Graham (1933) seem to show a somewhat slower velocity of conduction in the spinal cord than do those of Leese and Einarson, but the sequence of events is not materially altered thereby. Such prompt and uniform conduction through the arc of the flexion reflex forms the basis of a machine-like regularity of response, apparently not differing very greatly from that found in the nerve-muscle preparation, in which the motor nerve is stimulated and the muscle responds without the interposition of any reflex mechanism.

In the case of the crossed extension reflex the condition is quite different. This probably involves more internuncial neurons than the flexion reflex; at all events, the conducting path has to cross the median plane of the spinal cord. The reflex is more variable than the flexion reflex and is much less regularly evoked by single stimuli applied to the afferent nerve. In decerebrate animals several successive stimuli are often needed. Its latency is considerably longer, the time occupied in traversing the gray matter (*reduced reflex time*) being never less than 12σ (Forbes and Cattell, 1924). It never begins with a full discharge of the center such as is found in the flexion reflex, but instead its onset is gradual. Liddell and Sherrington

(1923*a*) have shown that the first few stimuli evoke response only in a relatively small percentage of the motor neurons which ultimately take part if the stimulation is continued long enough. Gradually more and more motor neurons are brought into action as the reflex develops. They call this process *"recruitment"* (1923*b*). The after-discharge of the crossed extension reflex is much more prolonged than that of the flexion reflex. In the decerebrate animal this is partly due to the secondary reflex effect caused by stimulation of the intramuscular receptors (muscle sense) which set up a *proprioceptive reflex* (Sherrington, 1906), resulting in a sustained contraction of the extensor muscle. Even when the afferent part of the proprioceptive reflex arc is interrupted by severing the dorsal roots of the spinal nerves, the crossed extension reflex shows a more prolonged after-discharge than does the flexion reflex. The crossed extension reflex usually disappears first in a moribund animal. It appears to involve a more delicate and vulnerable mechanism than that which mediates the flexion reflex.

Let us now consider the specific differences between nerve-trunk and reflex conduction appearing in the facts now known and, following Lucas' suggestion, see whether reflex phenomena can reasonably be interpreted in terms of the all-or-none type of conduction established for peripheral nerve. It is granted that the reflex utilizes the all-or-none type of response in the axon; the question is whether a similar type of response accounts for conduction through the synapse. A few years ago the question was still open. Observations which have been made in the last four years have rendered it increasingly probable that a different type of mechanism exists in the reflex centers.

Conduction Time. Jolly (1911) found the reduced reflex time of the knee-jerk to be about 2σ, or somewhat less than that of the flexion reflex. The actual distance traversed within the cord is very short; the velocity of conduction in the most rapid fibers of peripheral nerve is about 100 meters a second; therefore it is evident that conduction through the central part of the reflex arc is much slower than in peripheral nerve. This fact, however, does not demand a qualitatively different kind of conduction; the difference may be purely quantitative. Rapid conduction is a highly specialized property of medullated nerve fibers. It is altogether likely that the finer terminal branches and dendrites in the synaptic region resemble more closely the primitive tissues as regards their speed of conduction. The very much greater delay in the reflex response to weak stimuli, described by Sherrington, amounting, in the case of the scratch reflex, to 2 or 3 seconds, involves a different principle, for in these cases the response was evoked only by repeated stimulation. The problem thus becomes one of the summation of propagated disturbances and will be dealt with as such presently.

After-Discharge. The continued discharge of impulses in the motor neurons for several seconds after the cessation of afferent stimulation, especially notable in the crossed extension reflex, appears to be at variance with the principle of peripheral conduction in which the disturbance

sweeps over the tissue, leaving it refractory.   There appears to be instead
a condition of sustained activity.   But in the gray matter we are not
dealing with isolated, unbranched paths, as in the nerve trunk, but with a
complex system in which one afferent fiber is probably connected with many
central neurons through extensive branching; in such a system sustained
activity might be built up of disturbances of the same kind as peripheral
nerve impulses.   We might assume only sufficiently elaborate and extensive paths including chains of neurons, each adding a considerable measure
of synaptic delay, to account for after-discharge without introducing a
functional capacity in any way at variance with the all-or-none principle.
The most prolonged after-discharge of the crossed extension reflex would
require a sort of central reverberation, that is, some central paths would
be traversed repeatedly.   Lorente de Nó (1933) has demonstrated histologically the existence of paths in the central gray matter which might
well serve as "closed self-exciting chains," and thus provide the mechanism
for "reverberation."   On the other hand, the recent work of Rosenblueth
(1934a), in which reflex acceleration and inhibition of the heart rate are
used as indicators, furnishes cogent evidence for the view that the prolonged after-discharge, lasting sometimes for minutes, is caused by the
production and persistence of a chemical substance in the central structures.

  Summation.   Many reflexes cannot be evoked by a single volley of
afferent impulses; a succession is required—sometimes as many as forty or
fifty stimuli must be applied to bring about the reflex contraction (Sherrington, 1906).   In the normal nerve-muscle preparation a single adequate stimulus evokes a full-sized response.   Adrian and Lucas (1912)
were able to find conditions which made possible a summation of propagated
disturbances in the nerve-muscle preparation.   If the neuromuscular junction was sufficiently fatigued, a single impulse in the nerve failed to evoke
contraction in the muscle.   But if a second stimulus was applied during
the supernormal phase of recovery following the relative refractory period,
a contraction could be evoked.   They were also able to duplicate this
effect by interposing a narcotized region in the nerve between the stimulating electrodes and the muscle.   Their original interpretation in terms
of decremental conduction must be revised; and as long as we have no
exact knowledge of the physical nature of conduction in the synapse we
cannot hope to form a precise picture of the mechanism of summation.

  A chemical substance, which the evidence of after-discharge has led
Rosenblueth to postulate, would provide a simple explanation also of the
phenomena of summation.

  Irreversibility.   The synapse has a valve-like property which enables
impulses to pass from afferent to internuncial or motor neurons but not
in the reverse direction.   Several proposals have been made for explaining
this in accordance with the hypothesis that the action potential in one
neuron is the stimulus which excites the next, by making various assumptions as to the duration of the action current on one side of the synapse
in relation to the time element of excitation (chronaxie) on the other
side, or the strength of the action current in relation to the rheobase

threshold, or some combination of the time and intensity factors (Lillie, 1914; Gerard, 1931). By a proper combination of these factors it is possible to picture a conceivable arrangement which would provide the observed irreversible conduction. But these schemata are theoretical speculations, unsupported by evidence.

If we accept the implications of Rosenblueth's (1934*a*) experiments as to the mediation of reflex effects by a substance produced at the synapse, it would be simpler to explain irreversible conduction on the assumption that the end-branches of the afferent neuron have the power to produce the substance, whereas the dendrites of the motor neuron have not.

Fatigue. It is easy to demonstrate fatigue in the reflex arc. Its fatigability contrasts strikingly with the relative unfatigability of the nerve trunk. Gerard and Forbes (1928) recently showed that fatigue in the flexion reflex was apparently of the equilibration type, the size of response falling to a reduced level depending on the frequency with which the responses are evoked; thus the reflex arc qualitatively resembles the nerve trunk. Quantitatively there is a great difference, the degree of fatigue being very much greater in the reflex arc.

Sherrington (1906, p. 218), Lee and Everingham (1909), and Forbes (1912) gave evidence of various sorts tending to show that the fatigue in the reflex arc occurs in the particular channel of approach to the motor center, rather than in the discharging motor neurons themselves. This tends to place fatigue in the synapse, which is the structure to which Sherrington ascribed most of the functional properties peculiar to the reflex arc (1906, p. 16). Stiles (1920) has drawn attention to the fact that the finer branches of the neurons in the synaptic region are highly attenuated and that therefore we should expect any material required for the transmission of the impulse to be more rapidly exhausted here than in the larger fibers.

Variability of Threshold. Sherrington emphasized the fact that the threshold of reflex excitation is more variable than that of the isolated nerve. This appears paradoxical. In view of the all-or-none law of the nerve impulse, it is hard to see how the threshold of the reflex can be other than the threshold of the afferent nerve fibers. Lutz (1918) compared the threshold for reflex contraction on stimulating the afferent nerve in the frog with the threshold for muscular contraction when the stimulus was applied directly to the motor nerve in the same animal. When the animal was cooled, the threshold for the reflex rose nine times as much per degree centigrade as did the threshold of the nerve-muscle preparation. The reflex threshold presumably depends on the number of afferent fibers excited and is not the same as the threshold of the most excitable fiber among them (Forbes, 1922, p. 377). This consideration emphasizes the importance of the branched character of the central connections (cf. Sherrington, 1929, p. 342). The treatment of a reflex arc as consisting typically of a single afferent fiber connected through a synapse with a single motor fiber is misleading in that it ignores the extensive interconnection of many afferent neurons with many motor neurons. If a number of converging impulses give a more effective stimulus to the motor neuron than a single impulse, it implies a phenomenon of spatial summation, which might be explained by the combining of action potentials in overcoming a high synaptic threshold. But this effect becomes essentially identical with temporal summation (considered above) if interpreted on the basis of a chemical substance (cf. Rosenblueth, 1934a).

Dependence on Blood Supply and Susceptibility to Anaesthetics. Reflex centers are strikingly dependent on blood supply as compared with peripheral nerves. A concentration of ether or other anaesthetic in the blood sufficient to abolish all ordinary reflexes does not appreciably affect the function of the peripheral nerves. On the other hand, a nerve without its blood supply will ultimately lose its function, and anaesthetics in sufficient concentration will abolish function in a nerve trunk. Thus it appears that, both in dependence on blood supply and oxygen and in susceptibility to anaesthetics, the difference between the reflex arc and the nerve trunk is only one of degree. It has been shown (Forbes, 1922, p. 386) that there is an adequate basis for the observed differences in the known properties of the synaptic part of the conducting path.

Mutual Reinforcement between Allied Arcs. Sherrington (1906) has given several instances of reinforcement of the activity of one reflex arc by stimulation of an allied arc. This phenomenon appears to fall readily into the category of effects just discussed under variation of reflex threshold. If those effects can be explained by convergence of individual afferent paths, so can reinforcement. Camis (1909-10) found that contraction in the flexion reflex was greater if evoked by simultaneous stimulation of two nerves containing afferent fibers from different parts of the hind foot than could be evoked by stimulating either nerve alone. This might be ascribed to the connection of the afferent fibers of the two nerves with different motor neurons, but there is evidence from other sources (Cooper, Denny-Brown, and Sherrington, 1926) that both sets of afferent paths are connected centrally with many of the same motor neurons. Central reinforcement may depend in part on additional motor neurons involved in the reinforcing reflex, but it probably also depends in part on convergence of conducting paths from various sources at common points in the nervous system.

Reflex Inhibition. This phenomenon apparently involves something wholly different from ordinary conduction, for, whereas the nerve impulse ordinarily induces functional activity, the central inhibitory process suppresses activity. The afferent impulses entering the spinal cord cause a cessation of the discharge of motor impulses from the center.

In 1885 Wedensky showed that when a series of stimuli is applied to the nerve of a slightly fatigued nerve-muscle preparation, if the frequency of stimulation is increased beyond a certain point, contraction in the muscle is replaced by relaxation. Since in this instance increasing the excitatory input results in an actual decrease in muscular response, the effect presents a superficial resemblance to inhibition. Lucas (1911-12) showed that the Wedensky effect depends on a succession of nerve impulses so rapid that each is set up in the relative refractory period following the preceding impulse, and consequently is subnormal and therefore unable to excite the muscle (cf. Kato, 1929a, 1929b). Lucas (1911-12, 1917) suggested that this effect might be a clue to reflex inhibition (cf. Adrian, 1924). He showed how an internuncial neuron made to conduct impulses so frequent as to be subnormal and terminating in a synapse which subnormal impulses were unable to pass would serve as a block to all excitatory impulses which must traverse it in order to cause a reflex response.

Further developments of this suggestion, modified to meet the requirements imposed by more recent observations, have been outlined (Forbes, 1921, 1922; Forbes, Davis, and Lambert, 1930), but it has become increasingly difficult to fit the hypothesis to the rapidly growing body of experimental evidence (Forbes, Smith, Lambert, Caveness, and Derbyshire, 1933), until the proposed interpretation of inhibition has become so improbable as to be of little more than historical interest. Inhibition presents a serious obstacle to the interpretation of reflex functions in terms of the all-or-none type of conduction without recourse to a different sort of phenomenon.

Other Reflex Effects. A number of important facts concerning spinal reflexes must be accounted for by any hypothesis relating to the mechanism in the spinal centers. Sherrington (1908) observed a balancing of the antagonistic effects of excitation and inhibition by stimulating simultaneously afferent nerves from opposite sides of the animal with graded strengths of stimuli. The balancing of opposite central effects seems to show what he called an *algebraic summation,* the degree of muscular contraction being intermediate between the full contraction evoked by the excitatory stimulus alone and the relaxation caused by the inhibitory stimulus alone. This effect has been especially studied in the case of the extensor muscle, which is excited in the crossed extension and inhibited in the flexion reflex. It appears that a maximal stimulus, that is, one strong enough to excite all the fibers, applied to an afferent nerve evoking the flexion reflex, always produced complete inhibition of the extensor, and no strength of excitatory stimulus could break through it. Algebraic summation apparently occurs only when some of the afferent fibers are not excited; it apparently depends on leaving some of the extensor motor neurons uninhibited (Forbes, 1921). Yet the observations of Creed and Eccles (see Creed, Denny-Brown, Eccles, Liddell, and Sherrington, 1932), Sherrington (1929), and Forbes, Davis, and Lambert (1930) seem to show the possibility of grading excitation in the individual motor neuron, as evidenced by balanced excitatory and inhibitory effects.

Various reversals of reflex effect are described by Sherrington and Sowton (1911a, 1911b). Interesting examples are the change from reflex excitation to reflex inhibition under the influence of moderate chloroform anaesthesia, and the postural reversal which Sherrington (1906) and Magnus (1910) have found in certain reflexes. The type of response to a given stimulus is in some cases determined by the posture existing when the stimulus is applied. Thus Sherrington has been able under certain conditions to evoke flexion in an extended limb by the same stimulus which evokes extension in a flexed limb. These effects have been discussed (Forbes, 1922, p. 396) in connection with Lucas' question as to whether reflex phenomena conform to the principles of conduction as manifested in peripheral nerve, and at that time no clear evidence was found in them demanding the assumption of a qualitatively different function in the reflex arc.

ELECTRIC RESPONSE IN GRAY MATTER

A number of recent researches have revealed electric responses in the gray matter of the central nervous system which differ in certain features from those of peripheral nerve trunks. Gasser and Graham (1933), leading from the spinal cord and stimulating sensory spinal nerves, recorded first a spike potential whose duration and other properties identified it with the volley of impulses in the axons entering the cord in the dorsal roots, i.e., the fibers to which the stimulus was applied. Following this spike was a much slower series of potential changes, devoid of spikes or notches and therefore interpreted as marking the activity of a structure other than the axons. Their evidence suggests that these smooth-contoured waves arise in some part of the internuncial neurons, either in the cell body or in the synapse.

Adrian and Buytendijk (1931) recorded even slower potential waves, associated with respiration, in the brain of the goldfish and considered them the characteristic response of nerve cells, or their dendrites, as distinguished from axons.

Application of leading-off electrodes to the cerebral cortex by Bartley and Newman (1931), Perkins (1933), Fischer (1932), Kornmüller (1933), and Bartley and Bishop (1933a, 1933b) has revealed "spontaneous" electric disturbances, also of slower time relations than those associated with axons. These investigators have also obtained by this means responses to optical and acoustic stimuli in the appropriate portions of the cortex.

Evidently there are electric responses peculiar to the nervous structures in the gray matter. The duration of these waves is from 10 to 50 times as great as that of the spike potential in the more rapidly responding axons. If it is established that the nerve center comprises structures whose function is essentially different from that of the axon, the slow potential changes recorded in the gray matter may well be associated with their activity.

THEORETICAL CONSIDERATIONS

In spite of all that has been written it is unknown whether the locus of the special properties of the reflex center lies in the highly attenuated branches of the axons and dendrites or in the synaptic connection between adjacent cells or in the cell body, all of which differ histologically from axons, or whether it lies in the combination of all of these structures. Sherrington emphasized the conspicuous property of summation in the reflex arc, whereby repetition of the afferent impulse renders a subliminal effect supraliminal. He said, "This result is explicable if at some central situation there be a structure which is something other than a nerve-fiber, and has, unlike nerve-fiber, no absolute refractory phase, and has, as have many other cell-structures including skeletal muscle-fiber itself, a property of summating its successive reactions when these are not too far apart in time." He further pointed out that the ionic change, which on the membrane theory underlies the progress of the nerve impulse, may be expected, on reaching the limiting membrane, which may well exist at the synapse, to lead to a different condition from that which obtains in the axon. This suggestion implies that successive impulses, on reaching the synapse, cause a cumulative ionic concentration, which is impossible in the continuous nerve fiber. Sherrington denoted the "exciting state or agent" E, but was noncommittal as to its nature. He assumed merely that it differs from the nerve impulse in that it may be graded in intensity, being built up by successive impulses, outlasting them and subsiding more slowly, and involving no subsequent refractory phase. Therefore the designation of this hypothesis as a "chemical theory" (Fulton, 1926; Gerard, 1931) is unwarranted.

To explain inhibition, Sherrington postulated "a state or agent which produces lessening or total disappearance of E," and this he designated I. He suggested that this might be of the nature of diffusion or adsorption of the excitation-ions, or "a neutralization of them, chemical or electrical." Reflex inhibition, on this view, would depend on the fact that impulses in the inhibitory afferent nerve, on arrival at the synapse, set up the state I, which could be graded in amount according to the number of afferent impulses, just as E could be graded in the excitatory reflex arc. This hypothesis can be very simply applied to the observed facts of balancing ("algebraic summation") of the opposed reflex effects, excitatory and inhibitory, in the spinal center, as well as to the facts of summation and after-discharge. In the more recent discussions it has been customary to denote these hypothetical central excitatory and inhibitory states "$c. e. s.$" and "$c. i. s.$"

More recently Eccles (1931) and Eccles and Sherrington (1931a, 1931b, 1931c, 1931d) have presented a quantity of important new evidence on the behavior of the reflex centers. They find that in the flexion reflex if a second afferent volley follows 5 or 6σ after the first, the reduced reflex time of the second response is only 0.5σ, as compared with 3σ to 4σ in the case of the first. This is taken as evidence that most of the central delay is due to the building-up of the $c. e. s.$, the response to the second stimulus occurring only in those motor neurons which did not respond to the first, but in which the $c. e. s.$ was built up almost to threshold value. This and other facts point to a "subliminal fringe" comprising those motor neurons in whose synapses the $c. e. s.$ exists but lacks sufficient intensity to excite the reflex discharge. Their experiments suggested that when reflex discharge is set up in a motor neuron the *c. e. s.* which has accumulated at the synapse is thereby removed. An antidromic impulse sent up the motor neuron into the center by artificial stimulation also removes the "pre-formed *c. e. s.*" They accept the membrane theory of the nerve impulse, and, extending its principles to the central structures, argue against the view that the central excitatory state can be a chemical substance.

Adrian and Buytendijk, on the basis of their observations on the brain of the goldfish, already mentioned, suggest that the nerve cells undergo a relatively enduring depolarization of their membranes, which becomes a source of stimulation to the axon arising therefrom. In this behavior they note the analogy to an injured region at the cut end of a mammalian peripheral nerve, which Adrian (1930) found to constitute a sustained source of excitation to certain types of axons in the nerve. Although the time relations of the central disturbance in the goldfish experiment differ widely from those of the axon response, it is a striking fact that the electric sign is similar, and that so close a parallel is found in the injured nerve.

The Oxford school (see Creed, Denny-Brown, Eccles, Liddell, and Sherrington, 1932) continues to be noncommittal as to the essential nature of the central excitatory state. They contend, however, that it is built up by afferent impulses, and that it cannot become supraliminal, on the ground that when its intensity reaches the threshold of the motor neuron it sets up an impulse therein and in so doing becomes depleted. In these respects they liken it to the local excitatory process (Lucas, 1917), which was originally supposed to consist in a concentration of ions at a certain point in the excitable cell. In terms of the membrane theory they look on this as a partial depolarization of the cell membrane, remaining subliminal for the setting-up of a propagated disturbance until its intensity reaches the neuron threshold. Its depletion on initiating a nerve impulse in the next neuron likens it to the local excitatory process, which has been shown also to be depleted on initiating a nerve impulse (Forbes, Ray, and Griffith, 1923). If the *c. e. s.* is indeed a depolarization of the membrane, the fact that it can be graded in intensity and shows no refactory phase differentiates it from the depolarization which on the membrane theory constitutes the nerve impulse in the axon. A consistent picture may be conceived if we concede that the central depolarization is never supraliminal.

This view, involving gradations of *c. e. s.* only in the subliminal range of intensities and denying the possibility of its ever attaining a supraliminal value, robs it of its power to explain the phenomena of after-discharge. This fact is recognized by the Oxford school, and in order to explain prolonged after-discharge they postulate continued bombardment of the central structure by afferent impulses approaching through delay paths. Rosenblueth (1934a), on the basis of the observations already cited (p. 299), emphasizes the heavy demand imposed on neuron detours (delay paths) if they are to explain, even with the aid of "reverberation," the most prolonged after-discharges, amounting, in the reflexes he observed, to several minutes. He further argues that the continuity of the curve of subsidence of after-discharge and the fact that after-discharge is a continuous function of the frequency of maximal afferent stimulation cannot be explained on the delay-path basis without highly improbable assumptions. Both of these phenomena are easy to explain on the basis of chemical mediation (cf. Fulton, 1926, and Samojloff and Kisseleff, 1927).

It is tempting to avoid the introduction of additional hypotheses by interpreting the *c. e. s.* on the basis of depolarization, as the Oxford school and Adrian and Buytendijk have suggested; but the recent work of Kibjakow (1933), reinforced by the subsequent observations of Feldberg and Gaddum (1933), affords convincing evidence of chemical mediation in the transference from cell to cell in the sympathetic ganglia. If this fact is indeed established, it would be surprising if the same mechanism did not obtain in the synapses of the central nervous system.

If after-discharge depends on the continued production of a chemical mediator, there appears to be a contradiction between this view and that of the Oxford school, which contends that the central excitatory state cannot become supraliminal. This conflict might be resolved by the assumption that the chemical mediator, when formed, spreads through a central reservoir, at the end of which it acts upon the motor neuron. At the point where it sets up the motor nerve impulse it might be locally depleted, as the observations of the Oxford school suggest, its concentration falling to zero locally on the initiation of a nerve impulse. The total quantity in the reservoir, however, might well remain supraliminal and continue to be a source of excitation.

The assumption here proposed is noncommittal as to what part of the central structure is to be identified with the reservoir of the mediator, and at what point the motor nerve impulse is initiated. Eccles and Sherrington (1931c) argue on anatomical grounds that if a motor neuron be excited at any point, either through antidromic impulses from the axon or through one of its dendrites, the propagated disturbance will traverse the entire surface of the cell body and the dendrites to their terminations. On this view the mediator would be formed in the end-branches of the afferent or internuncial neuron and the motor nerve impulse would be initiated at the synapse. But the above-mentioned inference from anatomical considerations is unproved, and it is conceivable that the antidromic impulse stops at the axon hillock. If so, we might then conceive of the formation of the mediator in the cell body and the initiation of the motor nerve impulse at the axon hillock. On this view the motor nerve impulse would commence at the beginning of the axon, which is the structure known to be differentiated for the all-or-none type of response.

The Oxford school has suggested that inhibition may be due to the stabilization of the polarized membrane, rendering it more difficult to depolarize by the excitatory impulses. It is difficult to see how an afferent impulse, presumably the same sort of disturbance as an excitatory impulse, can exert an opposite effect on arriving at that portion of the cell membrane to which it is conducted, unless it does so by causing the production of a special inhibitory substance which neutralizes the chemical mediator of excitation. Since excitatory and inhibitory substances have been established in the effectors of the autonomic system, and since there is cogent evidence of an excitatory mediator in the nerve centers, it is a simple step to assume such an inhibitory substance in the nerve centers as well. This assumption is supported by the evidence of Rosenblueth (1934a) that the inhibitory after-effect, on cessation of the afferent stimuli, may endure fully as long as the after-discharge following excitatory stimuli. If we make this assumption, it is probably easier to conceive of the interaction of excitatory and inhibitory substances as occurring in the cell body than in the end-branches of internuncial neurons or at the synaptic membrane where the latter make contact with the motor neurons.

Perhaps the most plausible working hypothesis at present is that excitatory and inhibitory nerve endings impinging on a neuron liberate in the cell body antagonistic excitatory and inhibitory substances respectively, and that the resultant concentration of the excitatory substance at the axon hillock determines the discharge of nerve impulses in the axon.

Tonus

The extraordinary persistence of long-sustained contraction in the extensor muscles in decerebrate rigidity has led some observers to infer that it involves a function, "tonus," quite distinct from contraction which causes motion. This problem has been extensively discussed in recent literature (Cobb, 1925; Fulton, 1926; Forbes, 1929a), and the preponderance of testimony indicates that in the case of skeletal muscle no essentially different function is involved in the sustained contraction from that involved in the execution of movements. There is some evidence that certain autonomic nerve fibers may innervate skeletal muscle fibers as well as the so-called somatic motor nerve fibers which conduct the impulses evoking contraction. This view has been doubted by Hinsey (1927) and Bremer (1932). There is further evidence suggesting that if such autonomic fibers do innervate the skeletal muscle fibers they may possibly exert some physicochemical effect on them, perhaps resembling secretion in gland cells, an effect which does not directly evoke contraction but which may modify contraction induced through the motor nerves. The testimony of various observers (Asher and Scheinfinkel, 1928; Bouman, 1931; Maibach, 1928; Nakanischi, 1927) is in some respects conflicting, and it is perhaps premature to accept the conclusion as established.

GRADATION OF MOTOR ACTIVITY

Since the all-or-none law applies both to the nerve impulse and to the muscle response, it is evident that gradation in the strength of contraction must depend either on the number of muscle fibers in action or the frequency of response in each, or on both (Forbes and Gregg, 1915*b*). Adrian and Bronk (1929) have recently determined the frequencies of impulses in the individual motor neuron in the cat in various spinal reflexes. In the flexion reflex the gradation of strength of muscular contraction appears to depend largely on the frequency of impulses; this lies between 5 and 50 per second. In the crossed extension reflex the nerve-impulse frequency is usually in the neighborhood of 70 per second, and gradation depends largely on the number of fibers participating. In the tonic contraction of decerebrate rigidity these authors found the frequency of impulses in the individual fiber to be in the neighborhood of 10 to 20 per second.

It was shown by Forbes and Olmsted (1925) that many of the motor nerve impulses involved in the crossed extension reflex are subnormal, indicating that they fall in the relative refractory period following their predecessors. From this it was inferred that the frequency was over 300 per second. The subsequent observation by Field and Brücke (1926) that the refractory period is greatly prolonged on continued stimulation shows that the inference as to frequency was not justified and reconciles the observations with those of Adrian and Bronk (see Forbes, Barbeau, and Rice, 1931). The muscle fibers may not always follow the frequency of the motor nerve impulses, but it seems probable that they generally do.

A typical electromyogram, taken from the muscles of the human forearm during voluntary contraction, is shown in Figure 5*c*. The action currents of the muscle-fiber groups are sometimes synchronized and sometimes not, consequently the resultant composite picture presents an irregular rhythm.

In the matter of gradation there is an important difference between skeletal muscle and smooth muscle, for, whereas in skeletal muscle there are independent motor units and gradation depends entirely on the number of motor units excited and the frequency of impulses in each, smooth muscle is differently organized, having no motor units. It has been shown that the nerve impulses which activate smooth muscle cause the formation of chemical mediators which diffuse from cell to cell throughout the mass of the muscle. The nerve impulses which liberate the mediator are quantal in nature (all-or-none), but the substance liberated by them is subject to unlimited gradation in its concentration. Thus for the smooth muscle as a whole the step-wise increase in response characteristic of skeletal muscle is absent. When smooth muscle is excited chemically, as by adrenin in the blood stream, there is complete gradation.

INTEGRATION

The nervous system in higher animals is characterized not merely by the orderly working of definite reflexes, but more especially by the integration of these reflexes into adaptive patterns of behavior. As Mac-Curdy (1928) points out, an essential in coordination is speed of conduction. That the muscles should efficiently serve the body as a whole, it is necessary that the coordinating impulses should travel from the nerve centers to the muscles in much less time than the duration of the contractions. This result is achieved by the high speed of conduction in medullated nerve fibers.

Lennox and Cobb (1928) speak of *long-circuiting* and *encephalization* as the evolutionary steps whereby more association neurons, especially those of the brain, are interposed in the reflex path (see Figure 9). These

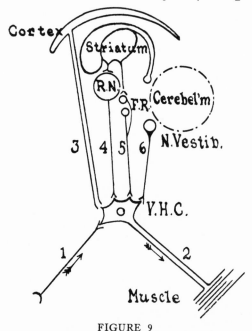

FIGURE 9

DIAGRAM OF THE VARIOUS NEURON LEVELS WHICH PLAY UPON THE MOTOR NEURONS AND CAUSE CONTRACTIONS IN THE MUSCLE

Afferent impulses may come in from a sense-organ and directly affect the ventral horn cell by way of the simple reflex arc (*1*). The cortico-spinal tract (*3*) sends down highly integrated impulse-complexes which take precedence over the simpler ones from the nucleus ruber (*R.N.*), the formatio reticularis (*F.R.*), and the nucleus vestibularis (*N. Vestib.*), which traverse, respectively, the rubro-spinal tract (*4*), the reticulo-spinal tract (*5*), and the vestibulo-spinal tract (*6*). But it is the combination of pyramidal (*3*), extra-pyramidal (*4* and *5*), vestibular (*6*), and spinal (*1*) impulses, all harmoniously playing on the motor cell, that causes normal synergic movement.

(From W. G. Lennox and S. Cobb's "Epilepsy," *Med. Monog.*, 1928.)

developments provide for delayed response and its modification by virtue of experience, and thus lead to intelligent behavior and abstraction.

Sherrington (1906) has described the irradiation of reflexes. As a peripheral stimulus becomes stronger, the central effect becomes greater, which means, in view of the all-or-none law, that more impulses reach the center in a given time. An interesting consequence of this increase is the spread of reflex activity into relatively remote centers in the nervous system. For instance, associated with a powerful flexion reflex is not only extension of the crossed hind limb but extension of the forelimb on the same side and flexion of the forelimb on the opposite side. This coordinated pattern plays a significant part in the act of walking. Other instances of integration are the postural effects described by Magnus (1910). Proprioceptive impulses arising in the neck muscles, and depending on their posture, modify the postural reflexes in the limb muscles and to some extent their response to local afferent stimuli. As previously stated, a possible interpretation of postural reversal in terms of Wedensky inhibition has already been proposed (Forbes, 1922). MacCurdy (1928) has criticized this proposal on the ground that it not only depends on fixed frequencies of impulses in the center but also fails to account for the increased activity of the extensor centers caused by impulses from the hind-brain in decerebrate rigidity. The latter difficulty can be met by assuming that the impulses from the brain approach the motor neurons through another path and thus do not add to the frequency of impulses in that channel of approach wherein the inhibitory interference of impulses is assumed to occur. On the other hand, the effect might be more simply interpreted on Sherrington's assumption of an excitatory state which neutralizes the inhibitory state.

We may conclude that no decisive evidence has been offered to prove that after-discharge, summation, inhibition, and other reflex functions reveal anything which cannot be interpreted in physical terms, either on the basis of Lucas' suggestion as to the arrangement of qualitatively similar nerve impulses or on Sherrington's suggestion of a balancing of excitatory and inhibitory states.

The introduction of a "vital force" to replace the operation of physical law in the functioning of living matter seems to arise from two causes, the staggering complexity which the behavior of living matter presents and a natural unwillingness to place those faculties which we cherish in ourselves on the same level with machines.

The difficulty arising from the complexity of organisms is due largely to the attempt to make excessively simple explanations fit the behavior of structures whose intricacy should warn us at the outset of the improbability of finding any complete explanation with the means at our disposal. Clearly, with many millions of nerve cells in the gray matter, each presenting a bewildering array of branching fibers for connection with other cells, there is room for prodigiously complex activity through the mere factor of arrangement, even if the underlying activity is always the same in kind. It is true, as MacCurdy says (1928), that "no adequate mechanistic explanation of reflex phenomena has ever been achieved"; but a completely adequate explanation would require virtual omniscience (cf. Forbes, 1929b).

The second cause of the "vitalist" point of view rests on a confusion of the means with the end. It seems to me that the only sound method when dealing with the material aspect of living matter, as we must in objective physiology, is to treat it consistently on a physical basis. This position is best expressed by Lloyd Morgan (1901), "Monism regards nature and experience as one and indivisible, and all apparent dualism, as a dualism of aspect, distinguishable in thought, but indissoluble in existence." The application of this view to biology has been discussed elsewhere (Forbes, 1927) and is admirably set forth in the closing chapter of Hill's *Living Machinery*.

The fact that music is transmitted to the ear by sound waves and nothing but sound waves—physical events not only analyzable but reproducible—does not rob it of its beauty or any other attribute essential to its musical nature. The character of the music depends on the arrangement of the sound waves. To explain how afferent nerve impulses evoke efferent impulses, we need not assume in the center a vital force which cannot be interpreted physically. But to understand the broader significance of behavior we must recognize the fact of arrangement or integration. Just as the arrangement of sound waves enables them to express something to whose meaning the physical analysis of the waves themselves gives no clue, and as an author uses ink and paper to express thoughts depending on the particular distribution of the ink, so the nerve impulses and elementary reflexes, by virtue of their integrated arrangement, serve the purposes of conscious life.

Summary

1. The protozoa possess, within the limits of the single cell of which each animal consists, all the functional properties essential to life. In the metazoa, the evolution of the neuromuscular system, which is the chief basis of active behavior, begins with the differentiation of muscle cells, whose function is contraction. Next appear primitive nerve cells, which receive stimuli and, being differentiated for the purpose of conduction, transmit impulses to the muscle cells and thus evoke appropriate motions. From this simple beginning we can trace the development of the nervous system to the vertebrate pattern, in which receptor cells are connected through afferent nerve fibers with spinal and cerebral nerve centers (adjustors), and these, in turn, are connected through motor nerve fibers with muscle cells and other types of effectors.

2. The effectors, by which the animal reacts upon its environment, are of various types, the most important of which are ciliated cells, glands, and muscle cells.

3. The functional properties upon which the working of the neuromuscular system depends are excitability, conduction, and (in the case

of muscle) contraction.   Excitability and conduction are common to nerve and muscle.   In spite of the structural and functional differences between these two highly specialized tissues, the fundamental nature of the propagated disturbance is the same in both.   This community of function is shown by the nature of electrical excitation, by the electric response, or action current, which marks the propagation of the disturbance along the active fiber, by the refractory phase, which follows the disturbance, and by its all-or-none character.

4.   The all-or-none law is an important feature of the functional response in nerve and in striated muscle.   According to this law, the response in a single functional unit, although it may vary in size according to the condition of the tissue, cannot be varied in size or character by varying the strength of stimulus.   If the stimulus be adequate, the response will be as large as the tissue is capable of yielding at the moment. Gradation of both sensory disturbance and motor response depends on the number of nerve fibers involved and the frequency of impulses in each fiber.   The usual frequencies found in those neural discharges which have been so far investigated lie between 10 and 100 per second.

5.   In both nerve and muscle, functional activity involves metabolism, as shown by heat production, consumption of oxygen, and production of CO_2.   In this respect there is a great quantitative difference, for the amount of metabolic activity in nerve is so much smaller than in muscle that only the most refined of modern methods have sufficed to measure it.   Correspondingly slight is fatigue in nerve; yet it has recently been demonstrated and found to resemble qualitatively fatigue in muscle.

6.   Muscular contraction involves the transformation of chemical into mechanical energy.   Glycogen furnishes the energy which through a chain of chemical reactions results in the development of tension and liberation of heat.

7.   The action of autonomic nerves in causing contraction of smooth muscle has been shown to involve chemical mediators.

8.   The functions of the nerve centers, in which they differ from the conducting axons in peripheral nerves, are typified in the spinal reflexes. Numerous evident differences have been described by investigators, notably, in the case of the reflex, greater fatigability and susceptibility to drugs, irreversible conduction, and the presence of after-discharge, summation, and inhibition.

9.   Many hypotheses have been proposed to explain the functions peculiar to the reflex center.   Some of these, based on the observation of electric disturbances, similar in sign, but of slower time relations than the action potential in the nerve trunk, involve the conception of a partial depolarization of the cell membrane.   Recent evidence points to the probability of the release of chemical substances as the basis of central excitatory and inhibitory effects.

10.   Tonus is a state of sustained contractile tension in a muscle.   It has been believed by some to involve a different kind of function from

contraction, but most of the evidence indicates that there is no essential qualitative difference between tonic and other forms of contraction.

11. Integration in the central nervous system, whereby the impulses in the constituent neurons are made the vehicle of the higher activities of man, is a matter of arrangement and interaction. It is not necessary to assume that it involves a "vital force."

Bibliography

ADRIAN, E. D. 1912. On the conduction of subnormal disturbances in normal nerve. *J. Physiol., 45*, 389-412.

————. 1914. The all-or-none principle in nerve. *J. Physiol., 47*, 460-474.

————. 1920. The recovery process of excitable tissues: I. *J. Physiol., 54*, 1-31.

————. 1921. The recovery process of excitable tissues: II. *J. Physiol., 55*, 193-225.

————. 1922. The relation between the stimulus and the electric response in a single muscle fibre. *Arch. néerl. de physiol., 7*, 330-332.

————. 1924. Some recent work on inhibition. *Brain, 47*, 399-416.

————. 1926. The impulses produced by sensory nerve-endings: I. *J. Physiol., 61*, 49-72.

————. 1926-27. The impulses produced by sensory nerve-endings: IV. Impulses from pain receptors. *J. Physiol., 62*, 33-51.

————. 1928. The basis of sensation: the action of the sense organs. London: Christophers; New York: Norton. Pp. 122.

————. 1930. The effects of injury on mammalian nerve fibres. *Proc. Roy. Soc. London, 106B*, 596-618.

————. 1932. The mechanism of nervous action: electrical studies of the neurone. (*The Eldridge Reeves Johnson Foundation Lectures.*) London: Oxford Univ. Press; Philadelphia: Univ. Pa. Press. Pp. x+103.

ADRIAN, E. D., & BRONK, D. W. 1928. The discharge of impulses in motor nerve fibres: I. Impulses in single fibres of the phrenic nerve. *J. Physiol., 66*, 81-101.

————. 1929. The discharge of impulses in motor nerve fibres: II. The frequency of discharge in reflex and voluntary contractions. *J. Physiol., 67*, 119-151.

ADRIAN, E. D., & BUYTENDIJK, F. J. 1931. Potential changes in the isolated brain stem of the goldfish. *J. Physiol., 71*, 121-135.

ADRIAN, E. D., & LUCAS, K. 1912. On the summation of propagated disturbances in nerve and muscle. *J. Physiol., 44*, 68-124.

ADRIAN, E. D., & MATTHEWS, B. H. C. 1933. Observations on the electrical activity of the cortex. *J. Physiol., 80*, 1P-2P.

ADRIAN, E. D., & ZOTTERMAN, Y. 1926a. The impulses produced by sensory nerve-endings: II. The response of a single end-organ. *J. Physiol., 61*, 151-171.

————. 1926b. Impulses produced by sensory nerve-endings: III. Impulses set up by touch and pressure. *J. Physiol., 61*, 465-483.

ASHER, L., & SCHEINFINKEL, N. 1928. Fortgesetzte Untersuchungen über die zeitlichen Erregungsverhaltnisse unter dem Einfluss von sympathischen und parasympathischen Giften. *Zsch. f. Biol., 88*, 540-552.

BARTLEY, S. H. 1933. Action potentials of the optic cortex under the influence of strychnine. *Amer. J. Physiol., 103*, 203-212.

BARTLEY, S. H., & BISHOP, G. H. 1933a. The cortical response to stimulation of the optic nerve in the rabbit. *Amer. J. Physiol.*, **103**, 159-172.

————. 1933b. Factors determining the form of the electrical response from the optic cortex of the rabbit. *Amer. J. Physiol.*, **103**, 173-184.

BARTLEY, S. H., & NEWMAN, E. B. 1931. Studies on the dog's cortex: I. The sensori-motor areas. *Amer. J. Physiol.*, **99**, 1-8.

BERITOFF, J. 1929. On the conduction time of the nervous impulses through the central nervous system. *Amer. J. Physiol.*, **90**, 281-282.

BERNSTEIN, J. 1902. Untersuchungen zur Thermodynamik der bioelektrischen Ströme. *Pflüg. Arch. f. d. ges. Physiol.*, **92**, 521-562.

BIEDERMANN, W. 1887. Zur Kenntniss der Nerven und Nervenendigungen der quergestreiften Muskeln der Wirbellosen. *Sitzber. Wien. Akad. d. Wiss., Math.- naturwiss. Kl.*, Abt. 3, **96**, 8-38+20 figures.

BISHOP, G. H. 1927. The form of the record of the action potential of vertebrate nerve at the stimulated region. *Amer. J. Physiol.*, **82**, 462-477.

————. 1933. Cyclic changes in excitability of the optic pathway of the rabbit. *Amer. J. Physiol.*, **103**, 213-224.

BISHOP, G. H., & ERLANGER, J. 1926. The effects of polarization upon the activity of vertebrate nerve. *Amer. J. Physiol.*, **78**, 630-657.

BISHOP, G. H., & GILSON, A. S. 1927. Action potentials accompanying the contractile process in skeletal muscle. *Amer. J. Physiol.*, **82**, 478-495.

BISHOP, G. H., & HEINBECKER, P. 1930. Differentiation of axon types in visceral nerves by means of the potential record. *Amer. J. Physiol.*, **94**, 170-200.

BLAIR, E. A., & ERLANGER, J. 1933. A comparison of the characteristics of axons through their individual electrical responses. *Amer. J. Physiol.*, **106**, 524-564.

BOUMAN, H. D. 1931. Beitrag zur Kenntnis der Erregungsleitung vom Nerven zum Muskel. *Arch. néerl. de physiol.*, **16**, 168-213.

BRAMWELL, J. C. B., & LUCAS, K. 1911. On the relation of the refractory period to the propagated disturbance in nerve. *J. Physiol.*, **42**, 495-511.

BREMER, F. 1932. Le tonus musculaire. *Ergeb. d. Physiol.*, **34**, 678-749.

CAMIS, M. 1909-10. On the unity of motor centres. *J. Physiol.*, **39**, 228-234.

CANNON, W. B. 1929. Bodily changes in pain, hunger, fear and rage. (2nd ed.) New York: Appleton. Pp. xvi+404.

————. 1933. Chemical mediators of autonomic nerve impulses. *Science*, **78**, 43-48.

CANNON, W. B., & ROSENBLUETH, A. 1933. Studies on conditions of activity in endocrine organs: XXIX. Sympathin E and I. *Amer. J. Physiol.*, **104**, 557-574.

CHILD, C. M. 1924. Physiological foundations of behavior. New York: Holt. Pp. xii+330.

COBB, S. 1925. Review on the tonus of skeletal muscle. *Physiol. Revs.*, **5**, 518-550.

————. 1928. Physiology, psychiatry, and the inhibitions. *Arch. Neur. & Psychiat.*, **19**, 981-996.

COOPER, S. 1926. The conduction of a nervous impulse in a narcotized region of nerve. *J. Physiol.*, **61**, 305-318.

COOPER, S., DENNY-BROWN, D. E., & SHERRINGTON, C. 1926. Reflex fractionation of a muscle. *Proc. Roy. Soc. London*, **100B**, 448-462.

COOPER, S., & ECCLES, J. C. 1930. The isometric responses of mammalian muscles. *J. Physiol.*, **69**, 377-385.

CREED, R. S., DENNY-BROWN, D., ECCLES, J. C., LIDDELL, E. G. T., & SHERRINGTON, C. S. 1932. Reflex activity of the spinal cord. Oxford: Clarendon Press. Pp. vii+183.

CREED, R. S., & ECCLES, J. C. 1928. The incidence of central inhibition on restricted fields of motor units. *J. Physiol.*, **66**, 109-120.

DAVIS, H. 1926. The conduction of the nerve impulse. *Physiol. Revs.*, **6**, 547-595.

DAVIS, H., & DAVIS, P. A. 1932. Fatigue in skeletal muscle in relation to the frequency of stimulation. *Amer. J. Physiol.*, **101**, 339-356.

DAVIS, H., FORBES, A., BRUNSWICK, D., & HOPKINS, A. McH. 1926. Studies of nerve impulse: II. The question of decrement. *Amer. J. Physiol.*, **76**, 448-471.

DAVIS, H., PASCUAL, W., & RICE, L. H. 1928. Quantitative studies of the nerve impulse: III. The effect of carbon dioxide on the action current of medullated nerve. *Amer. J. Physiol.*, **86**, 706-724.

DOWNING, A. C., GERARD, W. R., & HILL, A. V. 1926. The heat production of nerve. *Proc. Roy. Soc. London*, 1926, **100B**, 223-251.

ECCLES, J. C. 1931. Studies on the flexor reflex: III. The central effects produced by an antidromic volley. *Proc. Roy. Soc. London*, **107B**, 557-585.

ECCLES, J. C., & HOFF, H. E. 1932. The rhythmic discharge of motor neurones. *Proc. Roy. Soc. London*, **110B**, 483-514.

ECCLES, J. C., & SHERRINGTON, C. 1931a. Studies on the flexor reflex: I. Latent period. *Proc. Roy. Soc. London*, **107B**, 511-534.

————. 1931b. Studies on the flexor reflex: II. The reflex response evoked by two centripetal volleys. *Proc. Roy. Soc. London*, **107B**, 535-556.

————. 1931c. Studies on the flexor reflex: IV. After-discharge. *Proc. Roy. Soc. London*, **107B**, 586-596.

————. 1931d. Studies on the flexor reflex: V. General conclusions. *Proc. Roy. Soc. London*, **107B**, 597-605.

ERLANGER, J. 1926-27. Analysis of the action potential in nerve. In *Harvey Lectures*, Ser. 22. Philadelphia: Lippincott. Pp. 90-113.

ERLANGER, J., & BLAIR, E. A. 1931a. The irritability changes in nerve in response to subthreshold induction shocks, and related phenomena including the relatively refractory phase. *Amer. J. Physiol.*, **99**, 108-128.

————. 1931b. The irritability changes in nerve in response to subthreshold constant currents, and related phenomena. *Amer. J. Physiol.*, **99**, 129-155.

FELDBERG, W., & GADDUM, J. H. 1933. The mechanism of the nervous discharge of adrenaline. *J. Physiol.*, **80**, 12P-13P.

FENN, W. O. 1926-27. Oxygen consumption of frog nerve during stimulation. *J. Gen. Physiol.*, **10**, 767-779.

————. 1927. Gas exchange of nerve during stimulation. *Amer. J. Physiol.*, **80**, 327-346.

FIELD, H., & BRÜCKE, E. T. 1926. Ueber die Dauer des Refraktärstadiums des Nervens bei Ermüdung und Erholung. *Pflüg. Arch. f. d. ges. Physiol.*, **214**, 103-111.

FISCHER, M. H. 1932. Elektrobiologische Erscheinungen an der Hirnrinde: I. *Pflüg. Arch. f. d. ges. Physiol.*, **230**, 161-178.

FORBES, A. 1912. The place of incidence of reflex fatigue. *Amer. J. Physiol.*, **31**, 102-124.

————. 1921. The modification of the crossed extension reflex by light etherization and its bearing on the dual nature of spinal reflex innervation. *Amer. J. Physiol.*, **56**, 273-312.

————. 1922. The interpretation of spinal reflexes in terms of present knowledge of nerve conduction. *Physiol. Revs.*, **2**, 361-414.

————. 1927. Spiritualism and telepathy. *Harvard Grad. Mag.*, **36**, 189-202.

————. 1929a. The problem of tonus in skeletal muscle in relation to sympathetic innervation. *Arch. Neur. & Psychiat.*, **22**, 247-264.

————. 1929b. Mechanism in nerve centers. *Nature*, **124**, 911-912.

FORBES, A., BARBEAU, A., & RICE, L. H. 1931. Evidence from the alcohol block method on the frequency of motor nerve impulses in the flexion reflex. *Amer. J. Physiol.*, **98**, 484-510.

FORBES, A., & CATTELL, McK. 1924. Electrical studies in mammalian reflexes: IV. The crossed extension reflex. *Amer. J. Physiol.*, **70**, 140-173.

FORBES, A., COBB, S., & CATTELL, H. 1923. Electrical studies in mammalian reflexes: III. Immediate changes in the flexion reflex after spinal transection. *Amer. J. Physiol.*, **65**, 30-44.

FORBES, A., DAVIS, H., & LAMBERT, E. 1930. The conflict between excitatory and inhibitory effects in a spinal center. *Amer. J. Physiol.*, **95**, 142-173.

FORBES, A., & GREGG, A. 1915a. Electrical studies in mammalian reflexes: I. The flexion reflex. *Amer. J. Physiol.*, **37**, 118-176.

————. 1915b. Electrical studies in mammalian reflexes: II. The correlation between strength of stimuli and the direct and reflex nerve response. *Amer. J. Physiol.*, **39**, 172-235.

FORBES, A., & MILLER, R. H. 1922. The effect of ether anesthesia on afferent paths in the decerebrate animal. *Amer. J. Physiol.*, **62**, 113-139.

FORBES, A., & OLMSTED, J. M. D. 1925. The frequency of motor nerve impulses in the crossed extension reflex as shown by the alcohol block method. *Amer. J. Physiol.*, **73**, 17-62.

FORBES, A., RAY, L. H., & GRIFFITH, F. R., JR. 1923. The nature of the delay in the response to the second of two stimuli in nerve and in the nerve-muscle preparation. *Amer. J. Physiol.*, **66**, 553-617.

FORBES, A., & RICE, L. H. 1929. Quantitative studies of the nerve impulse: IV. Fatigue in peripheral nerve. *Amer. J. Physiol.*, **90**, 119-145.

FORBES, A., SMITH, O. C., LAMBERT, E. F., CAVENESS, W. F., & DERBYSHIRE, A. J. 1933. The central inhibitory mechanism investigated by means of antidromic impulses. *Amer. J. Physiol.*, **103**, 131-142.

FORBES, A., WHITAKER, L. R., & FULTON, J. F. 1927. The effect of reflex excitation and inhibition on the response of a muscle to stimulation through its motor nerve. *Amer. J. Physiol.*, **82**, 693-716.

FULTON, J. F. 1926. Muscular contraction and the reflex control of movement. Baltimore, Md.: Williams & Wilkins; London: Baillière (1927). Pp. xv+644.

GASSER, H. S. 1928. The relation of the shape of the action potential of nerve to conduction velocity. *Amer. J. Physiol.*, **84**, 699-711.

GASSER, H. S., & ERLANGER, J. 1922. A study of the action currents of nerve with the cathode ray oscillograph. *Amer. J. Physiol.*, **62**, 496-524.

————. 1930. The ending of the axon action potential, and its relation to other events in nerve activity. *Amer. J. Physiol.*, **94**, 247-277.

GASSER, H. S., & GRAHAM, H. T. 1932. The end of the spike potential of nerve and its relation to the beginning of the after-potential. *Amer. J. Physiol.*, **101**, 316-330.

————. 1933. Potentials produced in the spinal cord by stimulation of dorsal roots. *Amer. J. Physiol.*, **103**, 303-320.

GELFAN, S. 1933. The submaximal responses of the single muscle fibre. *J. Physiol.*, **80**, 285-295.

GELFAN, S., & BISHOP, G. H. 1932. Action potentials from single muscle fibres. *Amer. J. Physiol.*, **101**, 678-685.

GELFAN, S., & GERARD, R. W. 1930. Studies of single muscle fibres: II. A further analysis of the grading mechanism. *Amer. J. Physiol.*, **95**, 412-416.

GERARD, R. W. 1926-27. The two phases of heat production of nerve. *J. Physiol.,* **62**, 349-363.

————. 1927*a*. Studies on nerve metabolism: I. The influence of oxygen lack on heat production and action current. *J. Physiol.,* **63**, 280-298.

————. 1927*b*. Studies on nerve metabolism: II. Respiration in oxygen and nitrogen. *Amer. J. Physiol.,* **82**, 381-404.

————. 1927*c*. The activity of nerve. *Science,* **66**, 495-499.

————. 1931. Nerve conduction in relation to nerve structure. *Quar. Rev. Biol.,* **6**, 59-83.

GERARD, R. W., & FORBES, A. 1928. "Fatigue" of the flexion reflex, and a note on action currents and "equilibration" in the cat's peroneal nerve. *Amer. J. Physiol.,* **86**, 178-205.

GERARD, R. W., HILL, A. V., & ZOTTERMAN, Y. 1927. Effect of frequency of stimulation on heat production of nerve. *J. Physiol.,* **63**, 130-143.

GERARD, R. W., & MARSHALL, W. H. 1933. Nerve conduction velocity and equilibration. *Amer. J. Physiol.,* **104**, 575-585.

GERARD, R. W., MARSHALL, W. H., & SAUL, L. J. 1933. Cerebral action potentials. *Proc. Soc. Exper. Biol. & Med.,* **30**, 1123.

GOTCH, F. 1902. The submaximal electric response of nerve to a single stimulus. *J. Physiol.,* **28**, 395-416.

HILL, A. V. 1910. A new mathematical treatment of changes of ionic concentration in muscle and nerve under the action of electric currents, with a theory as to their mode of excitation. *J. Physiol.,* **40**, 190-224.

————. 1911. The position occupied by the production of heat, in the chain of processes constituting a muscular contraction. *J. Physiol.,* **42**, 1-43.

————. 1913. The absolute mechanical efficiency of the contraction of an isolated muscle. *J. Physiol.,* **46**, 435-469.

————. 1920-21. The four phases of heat-production of muscle. *J. Physiol.,* **54**, 84-128.

————. 1926*a*. The laws of muscular motion. *Proc. Roy. Soc. London,* **100B**, 87-108.

————. 1926*b*. Muscular activity. Baltimore, Md.: Williams & Wilkins; London: Baillière. Pp. 125.

————. 1927. Living machinery. New York: Harcourt, Brace. Pp. 327.

————. 1928. The rôle of oxidation in maintaining the dynamic equilibrum of the muscle cell. The absolute value of the isometric heat coefficient TL/H in a muscle twitch, and the effect of stimulation and fatigue. The absence of delayed anaërobic heat in a series of muscle twitches. The recovery heat-production in oxygen after a series of muscle twitches. *Proc. Roy. Soc. London,* **103B**, 138-191.

————. 1932*a*. The revolution in muscle physiology. *Physiol. Revs.,* **12**, 56.

————. 1932*b*. Chemical wave transmission in nerve. Cambridge, England: Univ. Press; New York: Macmillan. Pp. x+74.

HINSEY, J. C. 1927. Some observations on the innervation of skeletal muscle of the cat. *J. Comp. Neur.,* **44**, 87-195.

HOWELL, W. H. 1925. Inhibition. *Physiol. Revs.,* **5**, 161-181.

JENNINGS, H. S. 1899. The psychology of a protozoan. *Amer. J. Psychol.,* **10**, 503-515.

JOLLY, W. A. 1911. On the time relations of the knee-jerk and simple reflexes. *Quar. J. Exper. Physiol.,* **4**, 67-87.

KATO, G. 1924. The theory of decrementless conduction in narcotised region of nerve. Tokyo: Nankodo. Pp. 166.

————. 1926. The further studies on decrementless conduction. Tokyo: Nankodo. Pp. 163.

KATO, G., et al. 1929a. Explanation of Wedensky inhibition: Part I. Amer. J. Physiol., **89**, 471-481.

————. 1929b. Explanation of Wedensky inhibition: Part II. Explanation of "paradoxes Stadium" in the sense of Wedensky. Amer. J. Physiol., **89**, 692-714.

KIBJAKOW, A. W. 1933. Über humorale Übertragung der Erregung von einem Neuron auf das andere. Pflüg. Arch. f. d. ges. Physiol., **232**, 432-443.

KORNMÜLLER, A. E. 1933. Bioelektrische Erscheinungen architektonischer Felder. Eine Methode der Lokalisation auf der Grosshirnrinde. Dtsch. Zsch. f. Nervenhk., **130**, 44-60.

LAMBERT, E. F., SKINNER, B. F., & FORBES, A. 1933. Some conditions affecting intensity and duration thresholds in motor nerve, with reference to chronaxie of subordination. Amer. J. Physiol., **106**, 721-737.

LAPICQUE, L. 1926. L'excitabilité en fonction du temps. La chronaxie, sa signification et sa mesure. Paris: Presses universitaires de France. Pp. 371.

LEE, F. S., & EVERINGHAM, S. 1909. Pseudo-fatigue of the spinal cord. Amer. J. Physiol., **24**, 384-390.

LEESE, C. E., & EINARSON, L. 1934. Conduction time in the afferent tracts of the spinal cord of the cat in relation to the flexion reflex. Amer. J. Physiol. (in press).

LENNOX, W. G., & COBB, S. 1928. Epilepsy. Medicine, **7**, 105-290.

LEVIN, A. 1927. Fatigue, retention of action current and recovery in crustacean nerve. J. Physiol., **63**, 113-129.

LIDDELL, E. G. T., & SHERRINGTON, C. S. 1923a. A comparison between certain features of the spinal flexor reflex and of the decerebrate extensor reflex respectively. Proc. Roy. Soc. London, **95B**, 299-339.

————. 1923b. Recruitment type of reflexes. Proc. Roy. Soc. London, **95B**, 407-412.

LILLIE, R. S. 1914. The conditions determining the rate of conduction in irritable tissues and especially nerve. Amer. J. Physiol., **34**, 414-445.

————. 1920. The nature of protoplasmic and nervous transmission. J. Phys. Chem., **24**, 165-191.

————. 1922. Transmission of physiological influence in protoplasmic systems, especially nerve. Physiol. Revs., **2**, 1-37.

LOEB, J. 1903. Comparative physiology of the brain and comparative psychology. New York: Putnam. Pp. x+309.

LORENTE DE NÓ, R. 1933. Vestibulo-ocular reflex arc. Arch. Neur. & Psychiat., **30**, 1-47.

LUCAS, K. 1906-07. The analysis of complex excitable tissues by their response to electric currents of short duration. J. Physiol., **35**, 310.

————. 1907-08. On the rate of variation of the exciting current as a factor in electrical excitation. J. Physiol., **36**, 253-274.

————. 1909. The "all or none" contraction of the amphibian skeletal muscle fibre. J. Physiol., **38**, 113-133.

————. 1910. An analysis of changes and differences in the excitatory process of nerves and muscles based on the physical theory of excitation. J. Physiol., **40**, 225-249.

————. 1911-12. On the transference of the propagated disturbance from nerve to muscle, with especial reference to the apparent inhibition described by Wedensky. J. Physiol., **43**, 46-90.

————. 1917. The conduction of the nervous impulse. London: Longmans. Pp. 113.

Lutz, B. R. 1918. Threshold values in the spinal frog: II. Variations with change of temperature. *Amer. J. Physiol.,* **45,** 515-527.

MacCurdy, J. T. 1928. Common principles in psychology and physiology. Cambridge, England: Cambridge Univ. Press. Pp. xvii+284.

Magnus, R. 1910. Zur Regelung der Bewegungen durch das Zentralnervensystem: III and IV. *Pflüg. Arch. f. d. ges. Physiol.,* **134,** 545-597.

Maibach, C. 1928. Untersuchungen zur Frage des Einflusses des Sympathikus auf die Ermüdung der quergestreifter Muskulatur. *Zsch. f. Biol.,* **88,** 207-226.

Martin, E. G. 1922. The application of the "all-or-nothing" principle of nervous conduction to the interpretation of vasomotor reflexes. *Amer. J. Physiol.,* **59,** 400-412.

Morgan, C. L. 1901. Introduction to comparative psychology. (Rev. ed.) London: Scott. Pp. xiv+382.

Nakanischi, M. 1927. Ueber den Einfluss des sympathischen Nervensystem auf Skelettmuskeln. *J. Biophys.,* **2,** 19-30.

Nernst, W. 1899. Zur Theorie der elektrischen Reizung. *Gött. Nachr., Math.-phys. Kl.,* 104-108.

————. 1908. Zur Theorie des elektrischen Reizes. *Pflüg. Arch. f. d. ges. Physiol.,* **122,** 275-314.

Orbeli, L. A. 1923. Die sympathische Innervation der Skelettmuskeln. *J. Petrograd Med. Instit.,* **6,** 8. Abstract in *Med. Sci. Abstrs. & Revs.,* 1924, **10,** 486.

Ostwald, W. 1890. Elektrische Eigenschaften halbdurchlässiger Scheidewände. *Zsch. Phys. Chem.,* **6,** 71-82.

Parker, G. H. 1911. The origin and significance of the primitive nervous system. *Proc. Amer. Phil. Soc.,* **50,** 217-225.

————. 1914. The origin and evolution of the nervous system. *Pop. Sci. Mo.,* **84,** 118-127.

————. 1919. The elementary nervous system. Philadelphia & London: Lippincott. Pp. 229.

————. 1924-25. The production of carbon dioxide by nerve. *J. Gen. Physiol.,* **7,** 641-669.

————. 1925-26. The carbon dioxide excreted in one minute by one centimeter of nerve fiber. *J. Gen. Physiol.,* **9,** 191-195.

————. 1925-28. The excretion of carbon dioxide by frog nerve. *J. Gen. Physiol.,* **8,** 21-31.

————. 1932. Humoral agents in nervous activity. Cambridge, England: Univ. Press. Pp. x+79.

Perkins, F. T. 1933. A study of cerebral action currents in the dog under sound stimulation. *Psychol. Monog.,* **44,** No. 197, 1-29.

Pratt, F. H. 1917. The all-or-none principle in graded response of skeletal muscle. *Amer. J. Physiol.,* **44,** 517-542.

————. 1930. On the grading mechanism of muscle. *Amer. J. Physiol.,* **93,** 9-18.

Rice, L. H., & Davis, H. 1928. Uniformity of narcosis in peripheral nerve. *Amer. J. Physiol.,* **87,** 73-84.

Ritchie, A. D. 1932. The all-or-none principle. *Biol. Rev.,* **7,** 336-349.

Rosenblueth, A. 1932. The chemical mediation of autonomic nervous impulses as evidenced by summation of responses. *Amer. J. Physiol.,* **102,** 12-38.

————. 1934a. Central excitation and inhibition in reflex changes of heart rate. *Amer. J. Physiol.,* **107,** 293-304.

————. 1934*b*. The all-or-none principle and the nerve effector systems. *Quar. Rev. Biol.* (in press).

ROSENBLUETH, A., FORBES, A., & LAMBERT, E. 1933. Electric responses in the submaxillary gland. *Amer. J. Physiol.,* **105**, 508-517.

ROSENBLUETH, A., LEESE, C. E., & LAMBERT, E. 1933. Electrical potentials in smooth muscle. *Amer. J. Physiol.,* **103**, 659-680.

ROSENBLUETH, A., & RIOCH, D. 1933. Temporal and spatial summation in autonomic systems. *Amer. J. Physiol.,* **106**, 365-380.

SAMOJLOFF, A., & KISSELEFF, M. 1927. Zur Charakteristik der zentralen Hemmungsprozesse. *Pflüg. Arch. f. d. ges. Physiol.,* **215**, 699-715.

SHERRINGTON, C. S. 1906. The integrative action of the nervous system. New York: Scribner's. Pp. xvi+411.

————. 1908. On reciprocal innervation of antagonistic muscles: Thirteenth note. On the antagonism between reflex inhibition and reflex excitation. *Proc. Roy. Soc. London,* **80B**, 565-578.

————. 1910*a*. Flexion-reflex of the limb, crossed extension-reflex, and reflex stepping and standing. *J. Physiol.,* **40**, 28-121.

————. 1910*b*. Reciprocal innervation of antagonistic muscles: Fourteenth note. On double reciprocal innervation. *Proc. Roy. Soc. London,* **81B**, 249-268.

————. 1913. Reflex inhibition as a factor in the coördination of movements and postures. *Quar. J. Exper. Physiol.,* **6**, 251-310.

————. 1921. Break-shock reflexes and supramaximal contraction-response of mammalian nerve-muscle to single shock stimuli. *Proc. Roy. Soc. London,* **92B**, 245-258.

————. 1925. Remarks on some aspects of reflex inhibition. *Proc. Roy. Soc. London,* **97B**, 519-545.

————. 1929. Some functional problems attaching to convergence. *Proc. Roy. Soc. London,* **105B**, 332-362.

SHERRINGTON, C. S., & SOWTON, S. C. M. 1911*a*. Chloroform and reversal of reflex effect. *J. Physiol.,* **42**, 383-388.

————. 1911*b*. Reversal of the reflex effect of an afferent nerve by altering the character of the electrical stimulus applied. *Proc. Roy. Soc. London,* **83B**, 435-446.

STILES, P. G. 1920. Types of fatigue. *Amer. J. Pub. Health,* **10**, 653-656.

————. 1924. The nervous system and its conservation. (3rd ed., rev.) Philadelphia: Saunders. Pp. xi+272.

TASHIRO, S. 1913. Carbon dioxide production from nerve fibers when resting and when stimulated; a contribution to the chemical basis of irritability. *Amer. J. Physiol.,* **32**, 107-145.

————. 1925. Ueber de physikochemischen Bedingungen der Erregungsleitung in Nerven: II. Der Einfluss der Ionenkonzentration und des osmotischen Druckes. *Zsch. f. Biol.,* **83**, 399-414.

VERWORN, M. 1900. Zur Kenntniss der physiologischen Wirkungen des Strychnins. *Arch. f. Physiol.,* 385-414.

WEDENSKY, N. 1885. Ueber einige Beziehungen zwischen der Reizstärke und der Tetanushöhe bei indirekter Reizung. *Pflüg. Arch. f. d. ges. Physiol.,* **37**, 69-72.

CHAPTER 4

THE LABYRINTHINE AND POSTURAL MECHANISMS

J. G. DUSSER DE BARENNE
Yale University

INTRODUCTION

The vestibular apparatus in the internal ear is one of the important receptors, though only one of several, reflexly influencing equilibrium and posture of the animal body.

In all vertebrates from the selachians upward the vestibular apparatus, or labyrinth, as distinguished from the cochlear or auditory part of the inner ear, consists of the three semicircular canals with their cristae and ampullar receptors and of the *sacculus* and *utriculus* with their maculae and otolithic receptors. The utricular otolith is called *lapillus,* the saccular otolith *sagitta.* In fishes, amphibians, and birds the sacculus shows a local dilatation, the *lagena,* with a separate macula. Of the mammals, only the lowest, the monotremata, have a lagena; in all other mammals it is absent.

The receptors in the cristae and maculae consist of more or less cylindrical sensory epithelial cells around which begin the ramifications of the afferent peripheral vestibular neurons, which have their bipolar ganglion cells in the ganglion of the vestibular nerve. The axons of these cells enter the medulla as fibers of the vestibular nerve and end around the cells of the primary vestibular nuclei.

Each of the sensory epithelial cells carries a long extension, a sense-hair. These cilia are embedded in a gelatinous mass, which covers the surface of the crista or macula. Whether the hairs are free in canals in the jelly, as Kolmer (1923) claims, or not, is questionable. In the cristae the gelatinous mass covering the sensory epithelium is called the *cupula;* it is cone-shaped and protrudes through the whole width of the ampullar cavity, touching its opposite wall and thus blocking the ampulla and the canal (Steinhausen, 1931*a,* 1931*b,* 1932*a,* 1932*b,* 1933*a,* 1933*b*). The shape of the macular otoliths is different: they are oblong, and thinner than the cupulae; their surface is curved (de Burlet and Koster, 1916; de Burlet and de Haas, 1924). The gelatinous mass covering the macular epithelium is covered with small crystals of microscopical dimensions, the *statoconia* or *otoconia.* For details regarding the macroscopical and microscopical anatomy of the labyrinth see Alexander (1923) and Kolmer (1923).

Although Wells (1792), Erasmus Darwin (1794), and Purkinje (1820) had already studied some of the subjective and objective phenomena (vertigo, nystagmus, falling reactions) observable during and after rotation and had found the importance of the position of the head during rotation, vestibular physiology may be considered as having begun with the experiments of Flourens (1824, 1842) in which he damaged or destroyed the membranous semicircular canals in pigeons and rabbits. These lesions resulted in forced movements of the head and body which bore a distinct relation to the canals which were damaged—the destruction of the horizontal canals, for instance, resulted in forced movements of the head in the horizontal plane. Flourens interpreted these symptoms as showing that the semicircular canals exert a "modifying force" on the movements of the animals. This, of course, is a quasi-explanation, actually denoting ignorance of the true functions of the labyrinth. Flourens' observations were confirmed in the main points by Harless (1864), Brown-Séquard (1853), Czermak (1879), Vulpian (1866), and others. All the authors explained the reactions of the animals as being due to some kind of acoustic perceptions. In 1816 Autenrieth claimed that the semicircular canals were the organs utilized in the perception of the direction of sound and this view remained prevalent until Goltz in 1870 pointed the way to the modern conception. In a short, important paper this author stated for the first time the fundamental division of the internal ear into two different parts: (1) an auditory part, the cochlea, and (2) the labyrinth, which he claimed to be "a receptor for the equilibrium of the head and indirectly of the body," although he did not exclude the possibility that this part of the internal ear might also have some auditory function.

Late in 1874 and early in 1875, separated by an interval of only a few weeks, three fundamental papers were published independently by Mach (1874), Breuer (1874), and Crum Brown (1875), in which each of these authors gave an almost identical explanation of the functions of the cristae of the semicircular canals, namely, that movement of the endolymph during positive and negative acceleratory movements stimulates the ampullar nerve endings and thus gives rise to the subjective and objective vestibular phenomena. Mach at first conceived, just as Breuer and Crum Brown did, an actual movement of the endolymph as the adequate stimulus, but changed his view the next year for the conception that the acceleratory momentum of the endolymph, working as pressure, acts directly as a stimulating force upon the ampullar receptors.

We need not go into the details of this much-debated controversy; the work of Rossi (1914, 1921), Maier and Lion (1921), and others, and especially the recent observations and photographs of Steinhausen, in which he demonstrated the existence of actual movements of the cupulae in the living animal (pike) under acceleratory and caloric stimulation of the semicircular canals, have settled this point definitely.

Important also is the second paper by Breuer (1875), in which he differentiated between the receptors in the ampullae of the semicircular canals and the receptors in the maculae (of the sacculus and utriculus), stating that the ampullae are the receptors for the reflexes due to rotations and that the maculae are the receptors for those reflexes which he called "positional reflexes" (*Reflexe der Lage*), i.e., those due to to the position of the head in space, and for reflexes upon progression movements.

Högyes (1881) was the first to study various rotatory and post-rotatory reflexes on the eye muscles with graphic methods and to attempt the localization of these reflexes in the central nervous system. In 1892 Ewald published his well-known monograph on the physiology of the labyrinth of the pigeon. In many respects his technique has been, and still is, exemplary. In 1907 Bárány introduced the physiologically and clinically important method of caloric vestibular stimulation through the syringing of the external auditory canal. The outstanding contribution to vestibular physiology during the first quarter of this century is undoubtedly the work of Magnus and his school, culminating in his monograph on *Körperstellung* of 1924.

Important recent contributions to human vestibular physiology are those of Dodge (1904, 1921a, 1921b, 1923a, 1923b, 1923c) and of Fischer and his co-workers, especially Wodak. Fischer (1928) has given a very instructive review of this field in his monograph on *Die Regulationsfunktion des menschlichen Labyrinths*. See also the monograph by Grahe (1926).

Attention should be drawn also to the recent work of Tait (1926), Tait and McNally (1925, 1929a, 1929b), McNally (1932, 1933), and McNally and Tait (1925, 1933) on the frog, in which section of the branches of the vestibular nerves to each of the receptors, separately and in all possible combinations, was performed with meticulous care and operative skill, and the physiological results investigated. Versteegh (see de Kleijn and Versteegh, 1927) was the first to succeed in isolated transection of the utricular nerve in the rabbit. Lorente de Nó's contributions (1925, 1926, 1927-28, 1927, 1931) to the physiology of the labyrinthine ocular reflexes and their neural pathways in the brain-stem should be mentioned also. The last contribution which I wish to mention here is the demonstration of the cupula and its movements during rotation and caloric stimulation in the living animal by Steinhausen.

These, I think, are some of the highlights in vestibular physiology.

METHODS

The functions of the vestibular apparatus can be studied by the same methods as are used in other domains of physiology, namely, by excitation and by elimination. Vestibular *stimulation* can be effected either by rotation or rectilinear movements, or thermically, mechanically, or electrically. Rotation and progression are the physiologically adequate forms of stimulation for the receptors in the ampullae; only acceleration acts as a stimulus by actual displacement of the endolymph and the cupulae, thus giving rise to excitation of the ampullar receptive nerve endings.

Important from the physiological and clinical points of view is the caloric stimulation by simple syringing of the external auditory canal with water above or below body temperature. This method permits the investigation of each labyrinth separately without the necessity of any operative exposure of the internal ear. Local heat application to exposed individual semicircular canals has also been used in physiological research. The mechanical stimulation of the separate canals has been extensively used by Ewald (1892) in his classical experiments with the "pneumatic hammer." This method has also been used recently by Steinhausen.

Electrical stimulation is usually accomplished by transversal galvanization of the posterior part of the head or by galvanization of the individual exposed canals.

For the *elimination* of the labyrinths various procedures may be followed. In many of the laboratory animals (guinea pig, rabbit, cat, and dog) the ventral approach through the bulla ossea is the best [Högyes (1881); for a full description see de Kleijn (1912)]. In the monkey the approach is made through the mastoid, as in man. In the guinea pig the labyrinth can be temporarily eliminated without damage by injection of a small amount of 5–10-per-cent cocaine solution through the tympanic membrane into the middle ear (cavum tympani). This method of pharmacological elimination can also be used with the rabbit and the cat by injection of cocaine solution into the labyrinth through the tympanic cavity and the round window; this, however, obviously incurs damage to the labyrinth. In the case of the frog the best and easiest method is the route through the roof of the mouth (Schrader, 1887). For the methods involved in the isolated transection of the nerves to the individual labyrinthine receptors see McNally (1932, 1933).

THE LABYRINTHINE REFLEXES

Since Breuer's work it has been customary to divide the various labyrinthine reflexes into two main groups: the statokinetic and the static reflexes.

The *statokinetic* reflexes are those labyrinthine reflexes elicited by active or passive movements of the head or of the whole animal. However, it is not the movement as such, i.e., not velocity, that is the stimulus, but rather changes in velocity, i.e., acceleration. A change from rest to movement or from movement to rest, or a change from a greater to a lesser velocity or vice versa, acts as a stimulus. If a rotation or rectilinear movement is uniform over a sufficiently long period the reflexes occurring at the onset of this movement pass off. A well-known example of an observation of this kind is the cessation of the perception of rotation if the rotation is continued long enough at uniform speed.

Thus positive or negative acceleration, either angular or rectilinear, is the stimulus in this group of labyrinthine reflexes; they may be called, therefore, the *labyrinthine acceleratory reflexes*.

The second group, that of the *static* reflexes, is characterized by the fact that, rather than through acceleration, these reflexes are elicited through the position of the head, i.e., the position of the labyrinths in space. Therefore, they may be called the *labyrinthine positional reflexes*. Whereas the acceleratory reflexes are transient—some of them even abrupt, dying away soon after the cessation of the acceleration—the positional reflexes are "tonic"; they persist as long as the position of the labyrinths in space remains unchanged.

These reflexes play an important rôle in the posture of animals, i.e., in the integration of the nervous mechanism through which normal posture of the body is effected. It must be kept in mind, however, that equilibrium and posture in animals are by no means regulated exclusively through mediation of the labyrinths; other nervous mechanisms are also active in this respect (see p. 214).

The impulses originating in the various receptors of the labyrinth(s) are transmitted to the central nervous system along the vestibular nerve(s) and flow back to the peripheral effectors along various pathways. Most important among these effectors are the striped muscles of various parts of the body—the external muscles of the eye, controlling the position of the eyeballs; the muscles of the neck, regulating the position of the head; and the muscles of the limbs and the trunk.

Autonomic effectors also can be influenced by labyrinthine impulses. This is evidenced by the occurrence of vomiting during or after vigorous rotation. In recent years many direct observations on changes in heart rate, blood pressure, and movements of the intestinal tract during vestibular excitation or after elimination of the labyrinths have been made known (Spiegel, 1926, and his co-workers; Le Heux and de Kleijn, 1931).

We shall now begin our discussion of the various labyrinthine reflexes according to the division given below. The two fundamental groups were distinguished by Breuer. The further subdivision is based on the fundamental work of Magnus and his school. It was thought advisable, however, to give a rearrangement of the various groups, differing from the grouping given by Magnus and de Kleijn, and to bring under the heading "acceleratory reflexes" those groups of reflexes in which it can safely be assumed at present that movement of the endolymph is the excitatory factor for the receptive vestibular nerve endings.

In the reflexes upon electrical (galvanic) vestibular stimulation another mechanism is probably involved, at least primarily, namely, direct electrical stimulation of the nerve endings or of the vestibular nerve fibers themselves. Some authors claim that endolymph currents also occur under galvanic stimulation of the canals. It was thought permissible, therefore, to include these reflexes under Group I rather than to put them under a separate heading.

We thus come to the following division of the various labyrinthine reflexes:

I. *Acceleratory reflexes* (statokinetic reflexes, "Reflexe auf Bewegung" of Breuer)

    A. Reflexes upon rotational (angular) acceleration
        1. On the muscles of the eye(s)
        2. On the muscles of the neck
        3. On the muscles of the limbs and the trunk

B. *Reflexes upon linear acceleration*
C. *Reflexes upon caloric stimulation*
D. *Reflexes upon mechanical stimulation*
E. *Reflexes upon electrical stimulation*

II. *Positional Reflexes* (static reflexes, "Reflexe der Lage" of Breuer)
  A. *Tonic reflexes on the eye muscles* (compensatory deviations of the eye[s])
  B. *Tonic reflexes on the muscles of the neck* (head)
  C. *Tonic reflexes on the muscles of the limbs and the trunk*
  D. *Labyrinthine righting reflexes* (Magnus)

I. *Labyrinthine Acceleratory Reflexes*

A. Reflexes upon Angular Acceleration

1. *Reflexes on the eye muscles.* The typical reaction upon rotation on the eye muscles in vertebrates is vestibular eye nystagmus. The primary reaction is a slow deviation of both eyes in the direction opposite that of the rotation. This slow phase of vestibular eye nystagmus can be seen in fishes (Lee, 1892, 1894, 1894-95; Kubo, 1906; Maxwell, 1923, 1920a, 1920b; and others), but is more obvious and constant in higher vertebrates, especially in mammals. When the eyes have moved in the direction of the slow deviation they return toward the normal position with a quick, jerky movement. Typical vestibular nystagmus elicited through excitation of the vestibular receptors thus consists of alternating slow and quick movements of both eyes. Because the direction of the quick phase usually can be determined much more easily than the direction of the initial slow phase, it has become accepted in vestibular physiology and clinical studies to denominate the direction of the nystagmus as that of the quick phase. Thus rotation to the *left* (with the head of the human subject flexed about 20° ventrally) elicits a (mainly) horizontal nystagmus to the *left.*

Usually three types of vestibular nystagmus are distinguished: horizontal, vertical, and rotatory. The direction of the nystagmus depends upon the position of the labyrinth(s) in space during the vestibular stimulation and upon this stimulation as such.

Vestibular nystagmus is essentially a brain-stem reflex. It can be elicited in the decerebrate animal and after extirpation of the cerebellum. Högyes (1881) has shown that it can also be elicited after transection of a neuraxis at the level of the calamus scriptorius. This narrows down the centers necessary for the production of typical vestibular nystagmus to the portion of the brain-stem between the posterior colliculi and the medulla. De Kleijn has shown that normal vestibular nystagmus can be induced in rabbits even when the oculomotor and the trochlear nuclei have been eliminated by posterior decerebration and all external eye muscles extirpated with the exception of the abducens. This experiment is not quite conclusive, since Dusser de Barenne and de Kleijn (1928) later found that the four slips of the retractor bulbi muscle in the rabbit (usually innervated by the sixth cranial nerve) suffice to produce normal vestibular nystagmus.   De Kleijn's experiment should, therefore, be repeated after extirpation of the retractor bulbi muscle.   There is little doubt, however, that in such a revised experiment the result would be the same as it was in de Kleijn's original experiment since de Kleijn and Schenk (1931) have elicited rotational vestibular nystagmus with quick and slow phases in an anencephalic child in which the cerebral hemispheres, the cerebellum, and the anterior parts of the brain-stem with the oculomotor and the trochlear nuclei were absent and in which only the posterior portion of the brain-stem, containing the abducens nuclei, was present; of the ocular muscles only the abducens was present in each eye (in man a retractor bulbi muscle is not present).   One must realize, however, that these experiments, with recording of one or two eye muscles after the method of Bartels-Topolanski, give only an incomplete picture. Under normal conditions the mechanisms involved are much more complicated as follows from the fact shown by Lorente de Nó and by Dusser de Barenne and de Kleijn that all six external eye muscles and in the rabbit also the four retractor slips participate in the production of a vestibular nystagmus.

It is generally accepted that the slow phase of vestibular nystagmus is a reflex elicited through the vestibular stimulation carried along the vestibular nerve and its bulbar nuclei to the nuclei of nerves for the eye muscles and to the eye muscles themselves.   The origin of the quick phase is much debated as yet.

In 1883 Bechterew found that in the dog a typical vestibular nystagmus with slow and quick phases appears if first one labyrinth is extirpated and then, after a few weeks, the second labyrinth.   During the interval between the two labyrinthectomies the nystagmus due to the first operation vanishes.   The nystagmus appearing after the extirpation of the second labyrinth is of the same direction as that following the first labyrinthectomy.   This is Bechterew's compensatory nystagmus.   The occurrence of this type of nystagmus has been regarded by Magnus and de Kleijn (1926a), Spiegel and Sommer (1931), and others as strong evidence against Maupetit's (1908) view that the quick phase is a labyrinthine reflex.   I cannot accept this objection to Maupetit's view, although I agree that it is probably incorrect.   From Bechterew's results we should then have to conclude also that the slow phase cannot be of vestibular origin.   So far as I can see, the conclusion to be drawn from his results should be that in that type of nystagmus both phases, the quick and the slow, are of central origin, produced by unbalanced activities of the central neural mechanisms, just as is any nystagmus which is elicited by some means in an animal which is bilaterally labyrinthectomized [lesion of the vestibular nuclei in the brain-stem (Spiegel and Sato, 1926) or galvanization of the head (Groebbels, 1922)].   The main objection to Maupetit's thesis is the fact that on habitual rotation the quick phase disappears gradually, whereas the slow phase, expressing itself then as a slow deviation, remains (Dodge, 1921b).   This indicates that the mechanisms of the two phases are different and that, while the slow phase is undoubtedly a vestibular reflex, the quick phase is probably of central origin.

It has also been claimed (Bartels, 1910a, 1910b, 1911a, 1911b; Marburg, 1912; Brunner, 1919, 1921) that the quick phase is a proprioceptive reflex, originating in the eye muscles through the proprioceptive impulses set up by their contraction during the slow phase of nystagmus. This view is certainly incorrect for de Kleijn has shown that after novocainization of the eye muscles, which eliminates the proprioceptive impulses, typical vestibular nystagmus with a slow and a quick phase can still be elicited.

Granting, then, that the quick phase is probably of central origin, as Bárány (1906), Köllner and Hoffman (1922), Dodge (1921b), Magnus and de Kleijn (1926b), Fischer (1928), and many others think, there is still the problem of whether it originates in the vestibular nuclei, as Spiegel claims, in the nuclei of the eye muscles, or in other centers of the brain-stem. This question is still unanswered. However, we cannot enter here into a discussion of this complicated problem.

For a discussion of the vestibular pathways in the brain-stem and allied problems the reader is referred to Lorente de Nó's papers.

The direction of the rotational nystagmus varies with different positions of the head of the animal in space and also depends upon whether the animal is one in which the eyes are placed in the sides or in the front of the head. For particulars see Magnus and de Kleijn's papers (1923).

The reflexes discussed here are those which appear upon positive rotational acceleration. Reflexes which occur upon negative rotational acceleration are well known and have been even more extensively investigated than the rotational reflexes. To this group belong all the phenomena observable at and after cessation of a rotation. Probably the post-rotational eye reflexes were the first vestibular phenomena observed.

The earliest convincing quotation on post-rotational nystagmus which I have been able to find is in an interesting booklet by William Charles Wells (1792)—*An Essay upon Single Vision with Two Eyes together with Experiments and Observations on Several Other Subjects in Optics* —on page 97 of which one finds this statement:

> To have the same thing proved in another way, I desired a person to turn quickly around, till he became very giddy; then to stop himself and look steadfastly at me. He did so, and I could plainly see that, although he thought his eyes were fixed, they were in reality moving in their sockets, first toward one side, and then toward the other.

Interesting also, though not quite as clear in their direct connection with post-rotational nystagmus, are his observations on pages 95-97, immediately preceding the quoted passage; these have to do with pseudomotion of objects in the field of vision after violent rotation. There Wells describes the opposite pseudo-motion after rotations in opposite directions as well as the influence upon these motions of different positions of the head. He concludes that these apparent motions of still objects must be caused by involuntary eye movements.

The post-rotational nystagmus has also a slow and a quick component, the directions of which are opposite to those of the slow and quick phases of the nystagmus during rotation; the slow jerk of the post-rotational nystagmus is in the direction of the previous rotation, its quick component in the opposite direction. The intensity of the post-rotational nystagmus is very different, not only in various animals, but even in the same animal on different days under strictly similar conditions of rotation (Dusser de Barenne and de Kleijn, 1923). In observations on rotational and post-rotational nystagmus it is essential to exclude visual stimuli, at least in the higher animals. In fishes no evidence of interference of visual or optical stimuli with these vestibular reflexes has as yet been found; in regard to amphibians the statements in the literature are contradictory. In birds (pigeons) visual stimuli certainly have a rôle, while in the mammals which have the eyes situated laterally in the head (guinea pigs, rabbits) these optic stimuli do not seem to play an important rôle. In the higher mammals whose eyes are frontally placed, however, the influence of optical stimuli becomes very troublesome and must be excluded in any study of vestibular reflexes. Rotation or rectilinear motion of the environment gives rise to typical nystagmus: the well-known optic nystagmus.

Steinhausen (1931a, 1931b, 1933) has succeeded in making visible the cupula on the ampullar cristae in the surviving preparation of the head of the pike and in the living pike by injection of a minute quantity of Chinese ink into a semicircular canal. In this way he could show that the cupula actually moves during rotation and caloric labyrinthine stimulation. He found that an abrupt rotation to the left over only a small angle, with the head in the normal position, gives rise to a short, quick deviation of the cupula in the ampulla of the left horizontal canal toward the utriculus (ampullopetal current) and results in a deviation of both eyes of the animal to the right. If the rotation to the left is sustained, a more lasting deviation of the cupula occurs simultaneously with a horizontal nystagmus of the eye with the quick component to the left. With mechanical stimulation Steinhausen showed that the effect was the same whether the deviation of the cupula was caused by pressure on one side of the cupula or by suction on the other side.

Steinhausen's observations and calculations are in agreement with the important mathematical investigations of Schmaltz (1924, 1925a, 1925b, 1927, 1932), to which the reader is referred.

The observation that deviation of the cupula toward the canal (ampullofugal current) is not followed by eye movements in the pike is interesting (see page 218 for asymmetry of effect of electrical stimulation). Ewald (1892) had found in his "hammer" experiments that an ampullopetal current in the horizontal canal of the pigeon elicits stronger reactions than an ampullofugal current. For the anterior and posterior canals he found that an ampullopetal current excites less than an ampullofugal current. This difference led him to conclude that in the case of the anterior and posterior canals the ampullopetal current of the endolymph exerts an inhibitory influence.

The assumption of Mach and Crum Brown that the ampullar receptor of a canal is excited only through rotation in one direction and that of the corresponding canal only by rotation in the opposite direction is incorrect. Breuer has shown that after unilateral labyrinthectomy a blinded pigeon reacts with deviation of the head on rotation in either direction. This has also been observed in mammals. De Kleijn and Versteegh (1933) have found that in a unilaterally labyrinthectomized rabbit in which also the ampulla of the posterior canal of the other labyrinth was destroyed (leaving only two canals) post-rotational nystagmus in all three directions (horizontal, vertical, and rotatory) could be elicited. These observations prove the incorrectness of the almost generally accepted assumption that each ampullar crista is responsible for nystagmus in one particular direction.

After extirpation of both labyrinths these rotational and post-rotational reflexes can no longer be elicited, provided optical stimuli are excluded (Högyes, 1881).

The two labyrinths are not stimulated equally during and after rotation. This can be shown in the following way: After unilateral extirpation of one labyrinth, for instance the left one, an animal will show a spontaneous nystagmus (with the quick phase toward the left), which gradually disappears in the course of a few days, the length of time varying in different species. If, after cessation of this spontaneous nystagmus, such an animal is rotated, for instance to the right, the rotational nystagmus is strong, the post-rotational nystagmus weak. After rotation to the left, the rotational nystagmus is weak, the post-rotational nystagmus strong. This shows that, in the intact animal, during the rotation to the right the rotational nystagmus is predominantly produced through the excitation of the right labyrinth, the post-rotational nystagmus through the excitation of the left labyrinth.

Innumerable investigations have been made on human subjects. Positive and negative angular accelerations give rise to opposite rotational perceptions, as has been known since the work of Purkinje (1820), Mach (1875), Breuer (1874, 1875, 1891), and Crum Brown (1875).

Wodak and Fischer (see Fischer, 1928) have described the occurrence of several periods of rotational illusions after vigorous uniform rotation. They could perceive up to six or seven positive and negative phases following each other alternately and gradually becoming smaller and smaller. The total duration of these fluctuating, antagonistic illusions may be as long as 15 to 20 minutes. Dodge (1921b) observed two such post-rotational illusions of rotation after less vigorous rotation. It is hardly conceivable that these subjective phenomena should be caused by pendular currents of the endolymph; their probable explanation is the assumption of gradually declining, fluctuating after-discharges of central processes in the vestibular centers or other parts of the central nervous system (Fischer and Wodak, Dodge).

The threshold for rotational perceptions lies at an acceleration of 1-2° per second (Mach, 1875; Mulder, 1908; Dodge).

Different positions of the head during rotation around a vertical axis result, in the human subject, in entirely different rotational perceptions, i.e., the apparent plane of rotation is quite different with different head positions. With the horizontal canals in the horizontal plane, which is the case when the head is tilted slightly forward (15°), the apparent plane of rotation is horizontal, as is the actual plane of rotation. With the head in intermediate positions, the apparent plane of rotation is different from the actual (horizontal) plane of rotation. Cyon (1908) has claimed that each corresponding pair of semicircular canals[1] has a specific spatial function, i.e., that each of the pairs of canals serves for the perception of rotation in one of the axes of space. This is incorrect. Each pair of corresponding canals, when put in the horizontal plane, can elicit the perception of horizontal rotation.

Perception of rotation, though mainly due to vestibular excitation, can be induced also through other receptors (vision excluded). As such, stimuli from cutaneous, proprioceptive, and also probably interoceptive receptors play a rôle (Kreidl, 1906; Dodge, 1921b; Fischer, 1928). Fischer has shown this in totally deaf subjects whose labyrinths were inexcitable, but he found that these stimuli give rather poor information as to the direction, beginning, and end of the rotation. Leiri (1927), on the other hand, believes that these impulses are of primary importance in rotational perception. Although it may be that in ordinary life these secondary stimuli are of more importance than under the strict conditions of the vestibular experiment (the subject in a revolving chair and with head, body, and limbs fixed), I think that Leiri is wrong in stating that the perception of rotation is due only to these involuntary reflex activities set up by the labyrinthine excitation.

The rotational reflexes on the eyes, the rotational and post-rotational nystagmus of the eyes, are the main objects of investigation in human vestibular physiology and pathology. Normally the vestibular nystagmus in the human subject also shows a slow and a quick phase. Care must be taken to exclude any interference of neck and pelvic reflexes. A rotational velocity of 10 revolutions in 20 seconds (Bárány) in a revolving chair has been generally accepted as standard method for clinical investigation.

Buys (1924, 1925) has investigated the post-rotational nystagmus after prolonged uniform rotation to eliminate the effects of the onset of the positive acceleration. For other special types of rotation see the papers by Dodge (1923a) and Fischer (1928). The duration of post-rotational nystagmus in human subjects is also found to be variable (Bárány and Wittmaack, 1911; Holsopple, 1923a, 1923b; Buys). Often a "secondary," post-rotational nystagmus of reversed direction has been observed (Bárány). Fischer and Wodak (1922) have observed as many as three or more successive antagonistic phases of post-rotational nystagmus.

Dodge (1921a) has determined the latency of this nystagmus by means of his optical recording methods and has found it to be 40 to 90 σ; the most common value was 50 σ.

It has been claimed that the post-rotational nystagmus on repeated rotation decreases gradually and may disappear entirely. Dodge (1921b)

----

[1]The corresponding pairs are: (1) the two horizontal canals, (2) the left posterior and right anterior canals, and (3) the left anterior and right posterior canals.

has shown that this is true only for the quick phase; the initial slow deviation persists, though this also may decrease a little.

2. *Reflexes on the muscles of the neck (head).* During rotation a typical slow deviation of the head in the direction opposite to that of the rotation appears. This is a constant phenomenon from the amphibians upward throughout the whole animal scale. In reptiles with long necks this deviation of the head may be as much as 90-120° (Trendelenburg and Kühn [lizard], 1908). Often, but not always, a quick return movement of the head succeeds the slow deviation, and then a typical head nystagmus is present.

At the cessation of rotation a deviation of the head opposite to that seen during rotation occurs, sometimes followed also by a quick phase in the opposite direction.

All these reactions occur also in decorticate animals and even in animals in which the hemispheres, basal ganglia, and optic thalami have been extirpated. After bilateral labyrinthectomy these reactions are permanently abolished if optical stimuli are excluded. Breuer showed this in the pigeon, and his results have been confirmed by all later investigators. It has been shown in mammals also. For the principal phenomena in human subjects see Section 3 immediately following.

3. *Reflexes on the muscles of the limbs and the trunk.* The first instance of such reflexes was observed in the frog by Dusser de Barenne (1918). If a normal frog is hung vertically by a thread through the praemaxilla and the thread is given a slight twist so that the animal slowly turns around its longitudinal axis, for instance to the left, the hind legs often assume a typical asymmetrical position. The right hind leg is extended, abducted, and tilted slightly forward and the toes are spread; the left hind leg is bent at the knee and ankle and brought a little dorsally, and the toes are more flexed than in the resting hanging position. At the end of the turning movement, when the opposite swing to the right starts, the position of the hind legs becomes reversed, the left hind leg now becomes extended, the right hind leg more flexed. Similar reflexes are often observable in the forelegs also.

These alternating reflexes are of labyrinthine origin. They are abolished by bilateral labyrinthectomy, but are still present after section of the three upper cervical posterior roots. This demonstrates that they are not due secondarily to neck reflexes, arising in the muscles of the neck, upon the muscles of the hind legs (see page 221). Magnus (1922) later observed labyrinthine rotational reflexes on the muscles of the limbs and pelvis in the monkey, and Grahe (1924) has described such reflexes in the rabbit.

Most of the observations in human subjects are on the post-rotational phenomena. It is important that after cessation of the rotation the subject keep his head in the same position as during the rotation.

If a subject is rotated 10 times in 20 seconds to the left with the head in the normal position or slightly tilted forward (20°, to put the horizontal canals in the horizontal plane) and at cessation of the rotation stands up with both arms stretched forward, it will be seen that the head turns to the left, also the body and the arms; the right arm is raised, the left lowered. This position Fischer and Wodak (1922) have called the *position of a discus thrower*. If this rotation of the body is not checked, the subject may fall over toward the left and backward. Here again a few antagonistic, gradually decreasing phases can be observed for a period as long as half an hour (Fischer and Wodak).

Part of this complex picture has been known for years. The deviation of the arms was described by Bárány as *Abweichreaktion,* the difference in the level of the arms as *Armtonusreaktion* (Fischer and Wodak).

These authors distinguish this complex from their "fall reaction," which is evoked by sudden changes in the position of the head during or immediately following the rotation. For details see Fischer's monograph (1928). Bárány's pointing and past-pointing tests (*Zeigeversuch* and *Vorbeizeigen*) are also related to these phenomena; however, we cannot enter into a discussion of them at this time.

B. Reflexes upon Linear Acceleration (reflexes upon progression movements). Reflexes belonging to this group became known in animals much later than those upon rotational acceleration. Ach (1902) observed in the frog closure of the eyeslit upon abrupt vertical movement. More frequent is a movement of the head and the front legs during such progression movements: flexion during an upward movement, extension during the downward movement (Fischer, 1926). Analogous reactions of the head and the four limbs in mammals have been described by de Kleijn and Magnus as the "lift reaction." To this group of reflexes belongs one in which the toes of both hind legs are spread when an animal which has been held in the air vertically by the skin of the neck or the skin under the forelegs is lowered abruptly. Wilson and Pike (1912) described a "drop reflex" in the dog under similar conditions—a powerful extension of both hind legs. De Kleijn and Magnus found an analogous reflex in the front legs of the guinea pig upon vertical downward progression when the animal was held in the air by the pelvis with the head hanging downward. Fleisch (1922) has reported evidence of eye movements during linear acceleration in the rabbit.

Dependable observations on reflexes upon linear acceleration in man are scarce. Mach as early as 1875 had pointed out that only acceleration stimulates. He gives as a threshold for the perception of vertical acceleration an acceleration of 12 cm. per second. Fischer (1928) has observed some indication of post-accelerative phasic subjective phenomena analogous to those reported in rotation experiments. Breuer (1875) claimed that these reflexes originate in the otoliths. Magnus and de Kleijn, Kobrak, and others consider the ampullae as the receptors for these reflexes (see discussion on pages 225-228).

C. Reflexes upon Caloric Stimulation. Syringing of the external auditory canal with cold water has been found to produce vertigo, sometimes even vomiting (Brown-Séquard, 1860; Schmidekam, 1868; and others). The early workers interpreted these reactions as due to stimulation of the sensory nerve endings in that part of the skin of the auditory canal which is innervated by the ramus auricularis nervi vagi. A number of investigations have been made wherein heat and cold have been applied directly to the membranous canals. Such stimulation results in various vehement reactions. It was Bárány (1906, 1907) who first fully recognized the importance of this method of caloric vestibular stimulation as it is known today. The advantages of the method are (1) that no operative procedure is necessary and there is no contra-indication to this method in human beings unless there is a perforation of the tympanic membrane, and (2) that each labyrinth can be stimulated and investigated separately, which is impossible with the rotational methods. Syringing of one auditory canal with water below body temperature produces, after a latency which varies in different subjects and also depends upon the temperature and the amount of water used, a typical vestibular nystagmus of the eyes with the quick phase toward the side which is not stimulated. If the syringing is done with water above body temperature the quick phase of the caloric eye nystagmus is toward the syringed side. The direction of the nystagmus is dependent also upon the position of the head, that is, upon the position of the labyrinth(s) in space.

Bárány (1910b) also found on caloric stimulation of one labyrinth a bilateral deviation of the arms in "pointing" when they were stretched forward (*Vorbeizeigen*, past-pointing).

The observations on nystagmus which Bárány made on human subjects were immediately confirmed in the principal points by observations which Kubo (1906) made on rabbits.

The origin of this caloric nystagmus has been much discussed. The correct explanation has been given by Bárány (1907), who states that the difference between the temperature of the water and that of the body gives rise to local cooling or warming of the semicircular canals and thereby to endolymph currents which excite the ampullar receptors and thus provoke the nystagmus. This hypothesis has received strong support from experiments by de Kleijn and Storm van Leeuwen (1917), which also show that the direction of the caloric nystagmus depends upon the position of the canals in space. For a discussion of the various hypotheses advanced to explain the genesis of caloric nystagmus see Magnus and de Kleijn (1926).

Steinhausen has also performed local heating of the horizontal canal in the surviving preparation of the head of the pike and in the living animal and has observed deviation of the cupula under these conditions.

Bárány used rather cold or warm water in large quantities. Kobrak (1923) has shown that a few cubic centimeters of water, differing by only a few degrees (C.) in temperature from the body temperature, are sufficient to produce marked nystagmus. Fischer and Wodak state that differences in temperature of even a few tenths of a degree and quantities of water as small as 1 or 2 cc. are sufficient to produce typical rotational illusions. Bilateral, equal syringing usually gives rise to complicated phenomena; only in a few special positions of the head is such a bilateral caloric stimulation without effect [the "absolute indifferent positions" of Fischer and Veits (1927)].

D. *Reflexes upon Mechanical Stimulation.* Obviously mechanical stimulation of the labyrinth is possible only after dissection and exposure of of the various membranous canals.

The first conclusive experiments upon this type of reflex are those of Ewald (1892), who succeeded in establishing very concise, controllable mechanical stimulation with his "pneumatic hammer." By plugging the canal under investigation at some point with a "plombe" and compressing it between this point and the ampulla with his hammer, Ewald studied the effect of ampullopetal and ampullofugal endolymph currents and found that these two currents resulted in antagonistic reflex movements of the head and the eyes. In the horizontal canals the ampullopetal current proved to be the stronger stimulus, while in the vertical canals the ampullofugal current was the more effective. See also page 212 above.

In the human subject mechanical stimulation of the labyrinths is possible only in abnormal conditions, i.e., in cases in which the tympanic membrane and the bone wall of a semicircular canal is perforated. In such a case pressure or suction exerted by means of a rubber balloon in the external auditory canal may evoke symptoms of vestibular stimulation (*Fistelsymptom*).

E. *Reflexes upon Electrical Stimulation.* Electrical stimulation of the labyrinth with galvanic currents has been used in a great number of investigations. Breuer (1874, 1875, 1891), who was one of the first to attempt such stimulation of the individual canals, thought that spread of the electrical current to the other parts of the labyrinth could be excluded, but Ewald (1892) realized that this form of stimulation was not very satisfactory because it did not lend itself well to sharply localized excitation. The result of such electrical stimulation is that, with the cathode applied to one labyrinth, for instance the left, and the anode to the breast of the animal (pigeon), the head is rotated toward the right; with the electrodes reversed, the head is rotated toward the left.

How the galvanic current acts is as yet not quite certain. The most plausible conception is that proposed by Bárány, i.e., that there is a direct excitation of the ampullar nerve endings or of the vestibular nerve fibers themselves. This view is corroborated by Steinhausen's finding that local galvanization of a canal results in deviation of the eyes without any movement of the cupula. With the anode on the utricular side and the cathode on the canal, eye deviation occurred (threshold, .5 m.a.) ; with the current reversed no eye movements were elicited, not even with 5 m.a. Brünings and Groebbels claim that the galvanic current may induce cataphoretic endolymph currents.

In animal experimentation it is always advisable to exclude visual stimuli during vestibular experiments, the more so as it is impossible to get information about "subjective" phenomena in animals. With human subjects also it is nearly always desirable to exclude vision since this usually gives rise to complications. However, a great number of investigations have been carried out on rotational perception with simultaneous optical perception. For a discussion of the phenomena under these complicated conditions see Fischer's monograph (1928, p. 35).

We now turn to the second group of labyrinthine reflexes, that of the positional reflexes.

II. *Labyrinthine Positional Reflexes*

The segregation of this group of reflexes dates from Breuer (1875), although isolated observations had already been made by earlier observers.

As was pointed out previously, it is characteristic of these reflexes that they are not elicited by acceleration but by the position of the head, i.e., the position of the labyrinths, in space. This follows from the fact that the final positional reflex is always the same for a given position of the head in space, regardless of the preceding positions (Breuer, 1875). They are usually designated as "tonic" labyrinthine reflexes because they are present as long as the position of the labyrinths in space remains unchanged.

A. Tonic Reflexes on the Eye Muscles (compensatory deviations of the eyes). Tonic reflexes on the eye muscles are easily observable in fishes (Breuer, 1891; Loeb, 1891; Lee, 1892, 1894, 1894-95; Nagel, 1896; Maxwell, 1923). Benjamins (1918) has made accurate quantitative studies of these reflexes in fishes.

If a fish is rotated around the horizontal longitudinal axis into one of the side positions the eyes deviate. If the right side of the animal is up, the right eye is deviated toward the lower border of its eyeslit and the left eye is turned toward the upper border of its eyeslit. When the animal is held in a right side position, i.e., with its left side up, the deviation of the eyes is reversed from that mentioned above. In the intermediate positions intermediate deviations are observed. If the animal is held in various positions as it is rotated around a transverse horizontal axis perpendicular to the longitudinal axis of the body compensatory deviations of the eyes in the form of their rolling around the axis of vision are observable.

In mammals also these reflexes are readily demonstrable, at least in the lower forms whose eyes are located on the sides of the head. In the higher mammals which have frontally placed eyes the importance of these labyrinthine reflexes is greatly reduced; visual fixation has become dominant.

As early as in 1854 von Gräfe had studied these reflexes in rabbits in various positions (rotation around the bitemporal axis), although he did not at that time differentiate between positional and acceleratory reflexes.

In studying these reflexes various precautions must be observed. Rotational reflexes must be excluded; to do this it is necessary to change the position of the animal very slowly and to wait after each change of position long enough to let such reflexes wear off if they are elicited. Care must be taken to avoid neck reflexes by a change of the position of the head with respect to the body.

Accurate measurements in mammals were made for the first time by van der Hoeve and de Kleijn (1917). Investigations with graphic registration were made by Lorente de Nó (1925, 1926), and, with an improved technique, by Dusser de Barenne and de Kleijn (1931). Lorente de Nó claimed that in these tonic labyrinthine eye reflexes the principle of reciprocal innervation of antagonistic eye muscles is not present—that simultaneous contraction of antagonistic muscles often occurs. Dusser de Barenne and de Kleijn could not confirm this statement and usually found reciprocal innervation present; in only a few cases it was not evident. (See also Huddleston and de Feo, 1928.) In animals whose eyes are situated frontally in the head it is very difficult to investigate these reflexes because of the "voluntary" eye movements. A few qualitative investigations have been made by Magnus in the monkey.

In human subjects a great number of investigations have been made. Almost all of the observations prior to the discovery of the tonic neck reflexes (see Section B following) were made with lateral deviation of the head and are therefore open to serious criticism. Delage was the only experimenter who placed the whole body in the deviated position without changing the position of the head with respect to the body. Most of the methods used to determine the amount of counter-rolling are not satisfactory. Fischer (1927) has made careful studies of these tonic eye reflexes in man, using the after-image method and excluding neck reflexes. He found counter-rolling over 6-8°.

Individuals whose labyrinths are inexcitable show very little compensatory deviation of the eyes, though it is not entirely absent. Either a mechanical factor is active in such cases or, as Fischer thinks, such minimal deviation in these subjects is due to other exteroceptive and proprioceptive stimuli (asymmetrical stimulation of body receptors in the deviated position).

B. *Tonic Reflexes on the Muscles of the Neck* (head). Tonic reflexes on the muscles of the neck are unknown in fishes so far as I know.

In amphibians Goltz (1870) described elevation of the head of a frog when the board on which the animal was sitting was tilted so that the head was below the horizontal level. Tilting the animal around its longitudinal axis resulted in a rotated position of the head so that the higher side was lowered. Greene and Laurens (1923) observed similar tonic reflexes on the head in Amblystoma, and Trendelenburg and Kühn (1908) reported similar reflexes in the lizard and the turtle.

Beautiful positional reflexes on the neck muscles can be seen in birds. In fact it was in the pigeon that Czermak (1863) made the first observations on these positional reflexes and observed that the head of the bird is kept in normal position in space irrespective of the position of the body. Breuer (1874) showed that this is true also if visual stimuli are excluded. Later observations were made by Trendelenburg (1906a, 1906b), Trendelenburg and Kühn (1908), Huxley (1913), and Groebbels (1922).

Huxley and Noël-Paton in 1913 simultaneously found evidence of labyrinthine positional reflexes on respiration in the duck.

Many of the above-mentioned phenomena might be classified, and perhaps more appropriately, as labyrinthine righting reflexes (see group D following).

In mammals true tonic reflexes on the neck muscles were observed by Magnus in 1911 (see Magnus and de Kleijn, 1912) in the decerebrate rabbit, cat, and dog. Strong "tonic" contraction of the extensor muscles of the neck is found if the animal is held in supine position with the slit of the mouth between the horizontal plane and 45° above it. If the animal is placed in the prone position (180° different from the former position) without changing the position of the head with respect to the body, it is found that the extensor muscles of the neck are relaxed and that the flexors are in strong contraction. Intermediate positions result in intermediate degrees of contraction of the extensors and flexors of the neck, respectively. In the normal adult human subject tonic neck reflexes are not known. Landau (1923, 1925) has described a tonic dorsiflexion of the head with opisthotonus and extension of the legs in infants from six to eighteen months old when the child is held horizontally in the air by its thorax with the abdomen downward. The primary dorsiflexion of the head is possibly a labyrinthine righting reflex on the head. (See Section D following.) The opisthotonus and the extension of the legs are in all probability evoked secondarily, through mediation of a tonic neck reflex, by the righting of the head; these phenomena disappear immediately when the head is forcibly bent downward (Schaltenbrand, 1925a, 1925b). A labyrinthine component is not probable since passive dorsiflexion of the head does not produce the opisthotonus and extension of the legs; for this a strong contraction of the neck muscles is necessary.

C. Tonic Reflexes on the Muscles of the Limbs and the Trunk. These reflexes were first observed by Magnus and form the basis of his excellent work and that of his many collaborators, especially de Kleijn, which has extended over more than fifteen years. It is necessary to distinguish between two groups of reflexes: (1) the tonic labyrinthine reflexes on the limb muscles and (2) the tonic neck reflexes on the limb muscles. Although the second group is not actually labyrinthine in origin, it is advisable to include a discussion of it here. Tonic labyrinthine reflexes on the limb muscles are those reflexes which are produced through changes of the position of the labyrinths, i.e., of the head, in space without changing the position of the head with respect to that of the body. The best procedure in investigating this group of reflexes is to enclose the head, neck, and thorax in a plaster cast. In this way it has been found by Magnus and de Kleijn (1912) that the contraction of the extensor muscles of both forelegs and both hind legs is always influenced in the same direction by these tonic labyrinthine reflexes, either augmented or diminished. There is one position of the head in space in which the contraction of the extensor muscles of the limbs is maximal and one in which it is minimal. These two positions differ by 180°.

The tonic labyrinthine reflexes on the limb muscles can best be studied in the decerebrate preparation in which the extensors of the limbs and the trunk show a certain degree of decerebrate rigidity and in which disturbing influences from cortical reflexes ("voluntary" movements, etc.) are excluded.

The second group, that of the tonic neck reflexes on the limb muscles, can be studied after extirpation of both labyrinths. These reflexes are more complicated. Rotation and turning[2] of the head evoke antagonistic changes in the muscles of the legs of both sides; the extremities on the side toward which the jaws point (the "jaw-legs") show increased extension through contraction of the extensors, inhibition of the flexor muscles. Raising of the head in the sagittal plane gives rise to augmentation of the extension of the front legs; on lowering the head (ventral flexion) the extension of these legs diminishes. In rabbits the hind legs react in the same direction as the front legs when the head is raised and lowered. In guinea pigs, cats, dogs, and monkeys the hind legs show antagonistic reactions, i.e., if the front legs exhibit extension when the head is raised, the extension of the hind legs diminishes, and vice versa. To evoke these reactions the movement of the head must be executed in the middle portion of the cervical spine. Magnus and Storm van Leeuwen (1914) have found that the afferent impulses for these reflexes in the cat pass along the posterior roots of the three cervical segments; in the rabbit the posterior roots of the fourth segment participate also. Magnus has claimed that these reflexes, found in the decerebrate animal, must also be present in the animal with intact central nervous system. This was proved experimentally by Dusser de Barenne (1914), who showed that these reflexes occur not only when the head is moved passively but also during active movements of the animal.

In the normal life of the animal both groups act together and their integration results in rather complex reflexes. The picture is still more complicated by the fact that in some animals the tonic labyrinthine reflexes dominate, whereas in others the tonic neck reflexes are the stronger, while in still other animals the two groups are of about equal importance.

The relative strength of the two reflexes in a given animal can be determined by turning the head while the decerebrate animal is in side position. If both forelegs react in the same direction the tonic labyrinthine reflexes are dominant; if both forelegs react antagonistically the neck reflexes are the more important in that particular animal. If only the upper foreleg is influenced by the turning of the head, while the lower foreleg does not react, the two groups of reflexes balance (Magnus).

A characteristic of these reflexes is their long latency. In the decerebrate preparation Magnus and de Kleijn found latencies of 1/3 of a second to

---

[2]Magnus has defined rotation (*Drehen*) as the movement of the head of the animal around its sagittal axis, which connects the snout and the occiput; during a rotation toward the right the skull is directed toward the right, the jaws toward the left. Turning (*Wenden*) is the movement of the head around a dorsoventral axis which goes vertically through the middle of the skull and the basis; when the head is turned to the right the snout points toward the right and the occiput toward the left.

6 seconds for the tonic neck reflexes; the latencies of the tonic labyrinthine reflexes varied even more, the figures running from 1/4 of a
second to 23 seconds. In these reflexes the principle of antagonistic
(reciprocal) innervation of antagonistic muscles (Sherrington) is clearly
demonstrable. Magnus (1924) and Beritoff (1915a, 1915b) have studied
and recorded these reflexes in isolated muscles.

After unilateral labyrinthectomy the tonic labyrinthine reflexes on the
limb muscles are unchanged, showing that one labyrinth influences the limb
muscles of both sides of the body.

In the normal adult human subject tonic neck reflexes on the limb muscles have not been demonstrated with any degree of certainty. Quix
(1922, 1923) has described many reactions which he ascribes to otolithic
reflexes: flexion and extension of the head around a bitemporal axis produces utricular reflexes (symmetrical flexion and extension of the limbs
respectively); sideward deviation of the head produces saccular effects
which are asymmetrical abduction or adduction of the limbs. These
statements are theoretical deductions from anatomical investigations of
the position of the otoliths in the human labyrinth. Quix has tried to
prove his deductions in experiments with the pointing-reaction, in itself a
very complicated motor mechanism. Another serious objection against his
experimental results is that he does not consider the influence of tonic
neck reflexes!

In abnormal human subjects with various organic lesions of the central
nervous system (idiotic children, infants with delivery traumata, adults
with pyramidal lesions) such tonic labyrinth reflexes on the limb and
trunk musculature have often been observed. The first cases were
observed by Magnus and de Kleijn. Then Brouwer (1917), de Bruin
(1914), Gamper (1926a, 1926b), Pette (1924, 1925), Stenvers (1918),
Simons (1923), Walshe (1923a, 1923b), Boehme and Weiland (1918),
Jonkhoff (1920), and others added observations. A review of this literature may be found in Fischer's monograph (1928). Whether or not
the "induced tonus changes" of Goldstein and Riese (1923a, 1923b, 1925),
and the "automatoses" of Zingerle (1924, 1925a, 1925b, 1926) belong
in this group of tonic labyrinthine reflexes is a controversial matter.

D. *The Labyrinthine Righting Reflexes.* Although this group of reflexes will be discussed more fully in describing the importance of the
righting reflexes in animal posture (see page 229), it seems advisable to
state here what these reflexes mean. If an animal which has a long neck
(reptile, bird, mammal) is held in the air, the head is held in the normal
position in space, even if optical stimuli are excluded. This normal
position of the head is maintained although the position of the body
may be changed to abnormal positions (Czermak, 1863). Breuer (1874)
showed that this ability to keep the head in normal position in space is
abolished by bilateral labyrinthectomy. This "fixation" of the head in
space, irrespective of the position of the body, is due to the influence of the
labyrinthine righting reflexes of Magnus.

For a discussion of the subjective phenomena during abnormal positions of the body, the positional perceptions (*Lage-Empfindungen*), see Fischer's monograph (1928).

THE RESULTS OF LABYRINTHECTOMY

The phenomena which appear after unilateral and bilateral labyrinthectomy in various animals have been studied by a great number of investigators: Flourens (1824), Breuer (1874, 1875, 1891), Goltz (1870), Högyes (1881), Ewald (1892), Winkler (1907), and many others. In the light of their recent work, Magnus and his collaborators—especially de Kleijn and Storm van Leeuwen—and Tait and McNally have again taken up the study of these complicated phenomena, particularly of those appearing after unilateral labyrinthectomy. They divide these symptoms into direct, or primary, and indirect, or secondary, symptoms.

The most important primary symptom which follows unilateral labyrinthectomy is, in all species investigated by Magnus (frog, guinea pig, rabbit, cat, dog, and monkey [macacus]), a rotation of the head and neck toward the side of the operation. This rotation is in these animals a permanent symptom and can be shown and more or less quantitatively estimated when the animal is held up in the air by the pelvis with the head pointing downward (fundamental rotation [*Grunddrehung*]). It is a reflex elicited from the remaining labyrinth (labyrinthine righting reflex). In the rabbit and the cat another primary symptom, also resulting from the activity of the labyrinth left intact, is a spiral torsion of the vertebral column of the neck and trunk; in the other species which were mentioned above this torsion of the trunk is a secondary symptom (neck righting reflex) since it disappears after correction of the abnormal primary position of the head. In the rabbit and the cat this mechanism is also active, of course, and enforces the primary torsion of the trunk.

Through the activity of the righting reflexes from the body on the head an animal with only one labyrinth can right its head toward the normal position in space when put on a plane surface. The righting reflexes from the body on the body allow the animal to maintain or regain the normal position of the body even when the head is not in its normal position in space (see page 230).

The abnormal position of the limbs in the unilaterally labyrinthectomized animal (adduction of the homolateral limbs, abduction and extension of the contralateral extremities) is a secondary symptom, elicited through tonic neck reflexes (de Kleijn, 1914). This is demonstrated by the fact that these abnormal positions of the limbs disappear immediately when the head is returned passively to its normal position in space. Only during the first period after the unilateral labyrinthectomy can a slight decrease in the "tonus" of the homolateral limb muscles be observed even when the head is in the normal position.

After unilateral labyrinthectomy the lower mammals (guinea pig, rabbit) often show rolling movements. In many of the older investigations these forced movements dominate the whole picture, at least for the first days or weeks after the operation. For the greater part they are probably due to complicating lesions. With the improvement of the technique of labyrinthectomy the rolling movements are much less marked, even in the guinea pig and the rabbit; in the higher mammals (cat, dog, and monkey) they are usually absent. In man, forced rolling movements do not occur after uncomplicated unilateral labyrinthectomy. Magnus and de Kleijn claim that these rolling movements are paroxysms of progression movements, during which the animal turns around its longitudinal axis and "screws itself through space" because of the torsion of the head and vertebral column. The rolling movements can be stopped by correcting this abnormal position of the head and do not occur after bilateral section of the first three cervical posterior roots, which eliminates the occurrence of tonic neck reflexes and righting reflexes from the neck on the limb muscles.

The only symptom which has not been explained satisfactorily as yet is the slight decrease of muscle tonus in the homolateral extremities for a short period after the unilateral labyrinthectomy. As has been stated before, this deficit is present even with the head in normal symmetrical position. Therefore it cannot be explained by asymmetrical tonic neck reflexes. In the dog it is present only for a few hours; in the rabbit and the monkey, for four to five weeks after the operation. After bilateral labyrinthectomy the tonus in the muscles of all four limbs and of the vertebral column is greatly diminished for some time, but this deficit gradually disappears, at least in the mammal. This is the main objection against the generalization made by Ewald (1892) that the labyrinth is *the* receptor for muscle tonus. The muscles of the body receive impulses which regulate and adjust their tonus from a great many sources (from exteroceptive, proprioceptive, and from other receptors), all of which participate in the elaboration of the normal tonus of the striped musculature.

The fact that the effects of labyrinthectomy are less pronounced in the higher animals and least so in man is important. It indicates that the influence of the labyrinth on the motor mechanisms becomes less and less as one ascends the vertebrate scale.

The problem of the *functional localization in the labyrinth* still offers many perplexities.

Breuer had stated as early as in 1874 that the acceleratory reflexes originate in the ampullar cristae, whereas the positional reflexes arise in the otolithic receptors. Only the reflexes upon linear acceleration he thought to be of otolithic origin. Since then many investigators have in general confirmed Breuer's conception.

Lee (1892, 1894, 1894-95), Lyon (1899), and Maxwell (1923) have found that the compensatory deviations of the eyes and the fins in fishes are present after extirpation of all six canals. Loeb (1891) established the fact that they disappear after extirpation of the otoliths. Extirpation of the sacculus is without effect upon these reflexes (Lyon, Maxwell); after elimination of the utriculi they are abolished (Maxwell). Recently

Versteegh (in the rabbit)) and McNally (1932, 1933) (in the frog) found that all vestibular reflexes, especially all positional reflexes known at present, can be observed to be apparently normal after elimination of the sacculus. On the other hand, Benjamins and Huizinga claimed that in the pigeon the compensatory deviations of the eyes around the optical axis are saccular reflexes. Von Frisch and Stretter (1932) stated that in fishes the sacculus definitely has auditory functions.

Magnus and de Kleijn (1926) accepted Breuer's conception, but regarded the reflexes upon linear acceleration as ampullar reflexes. Guinea pigs in which they had thrown off the otoliths from the maculae by violent centrifuging [method of Wittmaack (1909)] showed absence of positional reflexes with preservation of all acceleratory reflexes, including those upon linear acceleration. Subsequently Magnus and de Kleijn, Hasegawa (1931), and de Kleijn and Versteegh (1931) have found that tonic labyrinthine reflexes can still be observed in guinea pigs in which all otolithic membranes have been thrown off. These findings are of course more significant than those in which the positional reflexes are lost after removal of the otolithic membranes.

Thus one is led to the conception either that the positional reflexes originate, at least mainly, in the cristae of the semicircular canals or that these reflexes can still be elicited through otolithic receptors in which the membranes are absent. The only way to decide between these two possibilities is, of course, by section of the nerves of the otolithic receptors. Such section is possible at present only in the frog (McNally); in the mammals (rabbit) only the bilateral destruction of the sacculus and the unilateral section of the utricular nerve have been accomplished (Versteegh).[3] The corresponding results of these two investigators with regard to the sacculus have already been given. So far as the utriculus is concerned, the results of McNally's painstaking investigations can be summarized as follows:

The first important result is that in frogs in which only the two utricles are eliminated the righting reflex is normal. Such animals show a very marked tremor during any attempt to move. Forward progression is in some way interfered with, a deficiency which expresses itself in the fact that the animal "is loath to jump." Responses to quick tilting are very marked.

In frogs in which all labyrinthine receptors were eliminated with the exception of the two utricles, McNally (1933) observed the following phenomena: The resting position is symmetrical and essentially normal, though there is a slight widening of the base of support. The righting reflex is present though not quite so prompt as in the normal animal. During movement disturbances become obvious. Jumping is done clumsily and the animal may stumble toward any side on landing. Then a slow

---

[3] The author is greatly indebted to Dr. McNally and Dr. Versteegh, who kindly put at his disposal their most recent observations and opinions in this difficult chapter on vestibular physiology.

rhythmic pendular motion sets in and only gradually comes to rest. The reactions to quick tilting movements are unbalanced, the striking thing being that the first response is a movement in the direction of the tilt; in the normal frog the reaction to a tilt is in the opposite direction. It is more than a simple inertia reaction, as can be shown by the different reaction after total bilateral labyrinthectomy. Slow tilting of a frog which has only its two utricles left results in true compensatory reactions. It is interesting that these compensatory reactions occur in definite steps or shifts.

A frog in which only one utricle is left is still able to right; it shows pendular reactions to movements. Its position is asymmetrical, the animal leaning down to the side of the absent utricle, though less than after total unilateral labyrinthectomy. Upon correction of this abnormal position, the animal may remain in normal symmetrical position for quite a while, until it is disturbed or makes a spontaneous movement. Then the asymmetrical position appears again. McNally concludes from all these facts that the utricular receptor is not signalling constantly, but only in response to slight displacement of the otolithic membrane. That gliding of the otolith can act as a stimulus has also been suggested by Lorente de Nó.

For the results of isolated destruction of the various canallar receptors in the frog the reader is referred to the recent paper by McNally and Tait (1933).

Versteegh reports that all the rabbits in which he succeeded in cauterizing one utricular nerve died after a few days. Only recently has he been able to keep such an animal alive over a period of several months. The only permanent symptom was a *"Grunddrehung"* of 90° of the head. The anatomical control of this experiment is not yet finished.

Dr. Versteegh closed the résumé which he sent to me as follows:

> We must keep in mind the possibility that the labyrinth functions more as a whole, that all the various reflexes originate in the various receptors, although perhaps in the normal animal some of the receptors are more important for certain of the reflexes than the others. Thus it would be conceivable that in partial labyrinthine lesions the remaining parts could compensate the functional defects. One would then have to abandon the idea that each subdivision of the labyrinth subserves a special group of labyrinthine reflexes.

Since positional reflexes can still be observed after elimination of all otolithic membranes, the discussion of the vexing problem as to whether the otoliths are excited when their membranes are hanging or pressing upon the otoliths is futile for the present.

Magnus and de Kleijn thought that the otoliths are excited when their membranes are hanging, that the otolithic excitation is least when the membranes press upon the maculae. They reached this conception from the observation that the positional reflexes are maximal when the labyrinths are in the position in space in which, according to anatomical studies, the otolithic membranes hang down from the maculae, whereas these reflexes are minimal in the position in which the otoliths press upon the maculae.   Other investigators, especially Quix, defended the opposite view.

It would be inopportune to enter into this discussion now.   Only when it has been established definitely—especially in the mammal, with its greater variety of labyrinthine reflexes—which of these are otolithic and which are not will it be time to attack this problem.

We must now enter into a brief exposition of the problem of *animal posture* and its *central mechanisms*.

ANIMAL POSTURE AND ITS CENTRAL MECHANISMS

As a starting-point for our discussion we may take the striking differences with regard to postural activity between three well-known preparations of one of the higher mammals, e.g., of the cat: the decapitate, the decerebrate, and the decorticate preparations.

The *decapitate* preparation, in which the neuraxis is transected at the transition of the medulla and the spinal cord, usually at the level of the first cervical segment, shows no special distribution of muscle "tonus" when put in the side position.   Standing is impossible.   When the animal is put upon its four legs and left to itself the limbs collapse under the weight of the body and the preparation sinks down.   The head also follows gravity and hangs down.[4]

In the chronic "low" spinal preparation (transection, for instance, at L.I) of the cat and the dog, it has been known for many years that some postural activity reappears in the extensor muscles [reflex standing (Goltz and Freusberg, Sherrington); see also the recent investigations of Ranson and Ingram (1932*a*, 1932*b*, 1932*c*) and of Hinsey, Ranson, and McNattin (1930)].

Quite different from the picture offered by the decapitate preparation is that of the *decerebrate* preparation in which the brain-stem is transected at the level of the posterior colliculi.   Such a preparation shows the well-known decerebrate rigidity (Sherrington), a sustained contraction especially of the extensor muscles (muscles of the lower jaw, extensors of the vertebral column and of the limbs) which counteracts gravity when the animal is standing.   Recently Wachholder (1928) has pointed out that the flexor muscles also participate to some degree in decerebrate rigidity.

Thus this preparation can stand when put upon its four legs, although

---

[4]The generally accepted view that all postural activity is absent in the acute decapitate preparation or in the hind legs of the acute "low" spinal animal is incorrect.   Dusser de Barenne and Koskoff (1932, 1934) have recently found, immediately after spinal transection, prompt onset of a strong flexor rigidity (F.R.) in the hind legs of the decapitate and spinal preparation of the male cat and dog (and to some extent also in the female) as soon as the posterior part of the body is brought in the symmetrical prone position on the table.   Marked changes in this F.R. are elicited in the hind legs on rotation of the front part of the body.   As strong priapism is usually present during the mating season when the hind quarters are in the symmetrical prone position, this F.R. can be interpreted as a caricature of the normal postural copulation pattern in the male cat and dog.

all "voluntary" muscular activity is abolished by the elimination of the brain. The preparation shows "reflex standing," a caricature of normal standing because of the unbalanced overactivity of the extensors over the flexor muscles. If the preparation is put on its four legs and pushed over to either side it falls down and remains in the side position. It cannot "spontaneously" sit up or stand up. Active progression and locomotion are absent.[5]

It is in such decerebrate animals that, as has been discussed above (page 229), Magnus has found his tonic reflexes (labyrinthine and neck reflexes), which are the functional elements of all postural activity.

It was also pointed out above that these tonic labyrinthine and neck reflexes unmistakably play a rôle in the life of the normal animal.

The *decorticate* mammal (guinea pig, rabbit, cat, dog) in which the cortex of both hemispheres has been removed (whether the optic thalami and the striatum have also been removed is irrelevant in this respect) shows quite another picture and its postural and progressional activities approximate much more closely those of the normal animal. Decerebrate rigidity is either entirely absent or present only for a short period of time and in a moderate degree. Within a few hours after the extirpation of both cerebral hemispheres the decorticate animal "spontaneously" assumes a normal sitting and standing position and can walk around fairly normally. In the "chronic" stage progression and locomotion are almost entirely normal, and disturbances are observable only upon special investigation.

The fourth fundamental fact which should be mentioned in this connection is that a *decerebellate* animal can sit up fairly normally and can stand and walk, though with obvious and permanent impairment. Immediately after the extirpation of the cerebellum these activities are abolished, but they gradually return, and within a few weeks the animal can assume a more or less symmetrical sitting position and has regained the ability to stand and move around.

From these four fundamental observations it follows (1) that in the lower mammals posture and progression are essentially *subcortical* mechanisms and (2) that the centers controlling these functions lie in the brain-stem, between the levels of the subthalamic region and the medulla.

Magnus (1924) has given a masterly analysis of this complex postural activity and has shown that at least *four groups of righting reflexes* cooperate in such activity.

If one watches the awakening of a normal or decorticate rabbit from general anaesthesia it can be seen that the first sign of the wearing-off of the narcosis is the fact that the animal lifts its head from the side position and turns it toward the normal symmetrical position. This righting of

---

[5]That sometimes paroxysms of alternative, abortive progression movements occur is well known. They are due to secondary lesions of the remaining parts of the brain-stem (hemorrhages). These observations do not invalidate the above statement, since they never result in an actual displacement of the body as in normal walking or progression.

the head is due to Magnus' first group of righting reflexes, namely, the *labyrinthine righting reflexes on the head.*

This group of righting reflexes is also responsible for the fact that a rabbit when held in the air always keeps its head in the normal position in space. The labyrinthine origin of this group of reflexes can easily be demonstrated by the result of bilateral labyrinthectomy. After that operation the rabbit with intact central nervous system or the decorticate rabbit when held in the air can no longer right its head—the head hangs down, simply following gravitational forces. But as soon as such a bilaterally labyrinthectomized animal is laid down in the side position on a table its head assumes the normal symmetrical position in space. This is due to a second group of righting reflexes, arising from the asymmetrical stimulation (exteroceptors, proprioceptors) of the body surface upon the contact of the lower flank with the table. This asymmetrical stimulation of the flanks evokes *righting reflexes from the body on the head.* This is shown further by the fact that upon establishment of a more or less symmetrical stimulation of both flanks by application of a board with weight on the upper flank of the animal the head immediately falls back into the side position. As soon as the board is removed the head is lifted from the table and turned toward the normal symmetrical position in space (Magnus' board-experiment).

The next step in the recovery from general anaesthesia is the righting of the body after the righting of the head. First the front part of the body, the forelegs with the thorax, is righted. This is due to a third group of righting reflexes, the *neck righting reflexes.* If the head is brought back in side position, the body falls back into the side position, at least in this stage of recovery from general anaesthesia. For if the rabbit is fully recovered from the narcosis one finds that the body of the animal assumes normal sitting position from any side position, even when the head is held in side position by the experimenter. This righting of the body, although the head is in an abnormal position, is due to the fourth group of reflexes, the *righting reflexes from the body on the body.* These reflexes are also active after bilateral labyrinthectomy, and the board-experiment then yields the same results as in the case of the righting reflexes from the body on the head.

These four groups of righting reflexes determine the righting of the head and body in the decorticate mammal (guinea pig, rabbit, cat, dog, and monkey) and in the guinea pig and rabbit with intact central nervous system. In the cat, dog, and monkey a fifth group of righting reflexes can be shown to be active, namely, that of the optic righting reflexes (Magnus).

Whereas the head of a bilaterally labyrinthectomized rabbit is not righted when the animal is held in the air by the pelvis, the behavior of the labyrinthectomized cat, dog, and monkey is different under these conditions. These animals still show prompt righting of the head when held in the air, although both labyrinths are extirpated. As soon as the eyes are blindfolded, the head falls or hangs down, following gravity. Since

visual activity is eliminated after decortication, optic righting reflexes are
also absent in the decorticate cat, dog, and monkey.

The fact that the first four groups of righting reflexes are present in
the decorticate animal shows that the central mechanisms governing these
reflexes are located subcortically. Even a transection of the brain-stem
immediately posterior to the hypothalamic region and frontal to the anterior colliculi leaves these reflexes intact (Magnus). Rademaker (1924)
attempted to localize these various reflexes in the brain-stem and arrived
at the following conclusions:

The labyrinthine righting reflexes and the body righting reflexes on the
body have their center in the magnocellular part of the red nuclei. The
centers of the body righting reflexes on the head are probably not the
red nuclei, but are located in the immediate neighborhood of these nuclei.
The neck righting reflexes have their centers farther caudally in the
brain-stem; they are present in the decerebrate preparation, absent after
transection of the brain-stem at the level of the trochlear nucleus. The
centers for the labyrinthine reflexes on the eyes lie in the brain-stem
between the level of the entrance of the eighth cranial nerve and the
nuclei of the eye muscles. Rademaker's idea that the red nuclei are the
centers of the labyrinthine righting reflexes and the body righting reflexes on the body and that the rubrospinal tracts are the efferent central
pathways for these reflexes is probably incorrect. Several experimenters
have reported normal righting reflexes in animals with absence or only
very little evidence of decerebrate rigidity after isolated destruction and
degeneration either of the red nuclei or of the rubrospinal tracts (Lorente
de Nó, 1925, 1926; Mussen, 1927, 1932; Keller and Hare, 1932; Ranson and co-workers). It may be well to emphasize the fact that the
positive observation, namely, preservation of normal righting reflexes after
degeneration of the magnocellular division of the red nuclei and the
rubrospinal tracts which originate from those nuclei, is the significant fact
and eliminates negative observations. With these more recent observations the question of the exact location of the centers for these righting
reflexes has become problematic; they probably lie within close proximity
of the red nuclei.

All the various groups of righting reflexes known today are present
after extirpation of the cerebellum (Dusser de Barenne, 1923*a;* Rademaker, 1931). This does not mean, however, that the cerebellum has
no influence on these reflexes and on posture in general. Ever since the
beginning of experimental physiology of the cerebellum it has been recognized that this part of the central nervous system is of paramount importance in posture. The investigations of Magnus, Schoen, Pritchard,
and Rademaker have shown some of the neural mechanisms, besides the
righting and tonic reflexes, that are active as postural mechanisms. For
a full discussion the reader is referred to the papers of these investigators.

Many of the reflex mechanisms involved here fall under the attitudinal
reflexes (*Haltungsreflexe* of Magnus and de Kleijn, 1928), which regulate and control the contraction and distribution of the tonus of the muscles

of the limbs and the body, and, by that, the position of the various parts of the body and the fixation in the individual joints.

Magnus and de Kleijn subdivide these attitudinal reflexes into various groups: the local, the segmental, and the general attitudinal reflexes. The prototype of the first group is the *positive support reaction* of a limb (Schoen, Pritchard), by which the whole extremity is converted into a rigid column capable of supporting the weight of the body. This support reaction can be studied advantageously in the decerebellate dog. Proprioceptive and exteroceptive impulses from the distal parts of the limb play a rôle in its elaboration (dorsiflexion of the wrist and ankle, contact of the sole of the foot with the ground). In the decerebellate dog this positive support reaction, elicited through exteroceptive stimuli, is very active and has been described by Rademaker (1931) as *magnet* reaction; the slightest touch to the sole of a hind foot of such an animal, when the animal is held in the air or in the supine position, suffices to produce a strong tonic extension of this leg. In the forelegs the magnet reaction is not present when the animal is in the supine position, but only when it is held in the prone position. Touching of the dorsum of the foot does not produce the magnet reaction.

In contrast with the positive support reaction the *negative support reaction* loosens up the extremity. When the contact of the leg with the ground is taken away, or when the distal joints are flexed passively, the extremity immediately loosens its rigid extension and can easily be flexed again. Part of the positive and negative support reaction is determined by mechanical factors. Among the neural activities which enter into the positive support reaction are the myotatic reflexes of Liddell and Sherrington (1924), described previously by Paul Hoffmann (1922) as *Eigenreflexe*. Application of a pull, i.e., of an abrupt augmentation of tension, on a muscle elicits in this same muscle a reflex contraction; upon removal of the tension the muscle relaxes again. But not only these local myotatic reflexes, confined to the muscle which is stretched, play a rôle. Schoen and Pritchard, in their analysis of the support reaction, have shown that the stretch put up in one muscle reflexly elicits contraction of many other synergistic muscles acting upon other parts of the same limb. In the positive support reaction not only the antigravitational muscles contract, but simultaneously with their contraction their antagonists also contract. Under these conditions one finds a fundamentally different functional relationship between these two groups of muscles from that in phasic movements, in which reciprocal antagonistic innervation (Sherrington) prevails. In this same group of local attitudinal reflexes belong also Rademaker's (1931) *placing* and *hopping* reactions. The *placing* reactions (*Stehbereitschaft,* readiness for standing) are those reflexes through which the animal puts its legs in the adequate position for standing as soon as some part of the body (the snout or the skin of the dorsum of the foot for the front legs, the tip of the tail or the skin of the dorsum of the foot for the hind legs) touches a surface. These reflexes occur also when vision is excluded, though they can be induced by visual stimuli alone.

These placing reactions are temporarily abolished after extirpation of the cerebellum; they are permanently lost after extirpation of the cerebral cortex. After extirpation of one cerebral hemisphere they are abolished only in the contralateral extremities. This indicates that they are cortical reflexes. Recently Bard (1933) has demonstrated conclusively that these placing reactions are controlled exclusively by the sensorimotor area of the cortex. They are permanently abolished after extirpation of this part of the cortex; they are present, apparently normal, after extirpation of the whole cortex with the exception of the sensorimotor area. Brooks (1933) has demonstrated that this strict cortical localization holds true also for the placing reactions in the rat.

The typical, elegant flexion and extension of the toes and foot on soft stroking of the dorsum of the foot of an animal which is held in the air (the *Berührungsreflexe* of Munk) are also permanently lost after extirpation of the cerebral cortex. Whether these reflexes also belong to the placing reactions, as Rademaker claims, is controversial; I am not convinced that this conception is correct, especially not since I have observed a cat for twelve months after total extirpation of the cerebellum and found the placing reactions permanently abolished,[6] whereas the *Berührungsreflexe* of Munk were apparently normal. This observation seems to indicate that these two reflexes are different.

The *hopping* reactions are those reflexes which result in displacement of a leg when it is brought far enough out of the symmetrical standing position. Excessive adduction or abduction, forward or backward movement of the proximal joints of a limb, either passively or by moving the surface on which the leg is standing, results in corrective displacement of this limb. In the dog these hopping reactions are temporarily abolished after decortication, but return after a few weeks; they remain, however, permanently impaired (markedly retarded and hypermetric). In the cat and the rat the hopping reactions are permanently abolished after decortication, and in these animals the same strict cortical localization holds for these hopping reflexes as for the placing reactions (Bard, 1933; Brooks, 1933).

The loss or impairment of the placing and hopping reactions is an important factor in the deficient correction of abnormal postures of the limbs in animals which have lesions of the sensorimotor cortex or are without cortex, as has been known for many years. To some extent these reactions also cooperate in standing, though they are not essential in this respect, since totally decorticate animals (the lower mammals, cat, and dog) are capable of fairly normal standing and locomotion.

The *segmental* attitudinal reflexes are those in which the attitude of one extremity influences that of the other. Fundamentally they belong to the large group of contralateral reflexes, of which the well-known

---

[6]This is unusual in the decerebellate animal, and I cannot as yet offer an explanation for it. Still I think that this point does not invalidate the conclusion drawn from this observation.

crossed extension reflex (Goltz, Freusberg, Sherrington) is the prototype. This reflex, however, is a spinal reflex, whereas the segmental attitudinal reflexes are essentially brain-stem reflexes. Rademaker and Magnus have studied these reflexes extensively in normal animals and in the decerebellate dog and cat, in which these reflexes are usually present in exaggerated form. The "shifting reaction" (*Schunkelreaktion* of Rademaker, 1931) belongs to this group. If one stands a dog on three legs, holding the fourth leg—for instance the right foreleg—in one's hand, a contraction can be felt to occur in the extensor muscles of this leg, especially in the triceps, when the body of the animal is shifted passively toward the right. As soon as this displacement of the body passes beyond a certain stage, powerful extension of the whole right front leg occurs. If the body is brought back toward the normal symmetrical position over the three legs on which the animal is standing the extension of the right front leg disappears and flexion occurs. Thus one can produce alternative extensions and flexions of the foreleg by rocking the body sideways. These lateral tilting reactions are reflex phenomena produced by the changes in the tension of the adductors of the contralateral front leg, on which the animal stands; exteroceptive impulses are not essential. This is demonstrated by the fact that the tilting reactions are still present after sectioning of the cutaneous nerves of the leg on which the animal stands (stand-leg); they are abolished after section of the posterior roots of that leg. Analogous reactions, resulting in stepping forward or backward, occur if the body is shifted passively backward or forward. The hopping reactions also occur if the surface on which the animal stands is tilted in one direction or another.

These shifting reactions are essentially brain-stem reflexes, as is shown by the fact that they are present though impaired (retarded, hypermetric) in the decorticate and decerebellate animal. Rademaker and Garcin (1932, 1933) have investigated these and other reactions in the human being by putting the subject on a board or bed which could be tilted in various directions.

It is unnecessary to enter here into more details of these and other reflex activities and their integration and modification through various procedures (labyrinthine reflexes, neck reflexes, and so on). We may refer for such details to Rademaker's monograph (1931), which is a condensation of many years of patient research in close collaboration with Magnus, the man who has opened up this entire field of neurophysiological research. An extensive review of this book was published by Mussen (1932).

From this short discussion it will be clear that animal posture is the result of an enormously complex nervous integration. Some of the mechanisms involved are essentially subcortical, but cortical, cerebellar, and other subcortical (labyrinthine) and spinal mechanisms greatly influence the activities of these postural brain-stem mechanisms.

The functional importance of these various integrating mechanisms is different as one ascends the animal scale. The diminution in importance of the vestibular apparatus as a control mechanism for equilibrium and posture in the higher animals is one of the aspects of the complicated problem of functional encephalization and corticalization of nervous functions. The other sides of this problem bear also on equilibrium and posture. Thus it is evident that posture is a very complex functional picture, differing in many ways from species to species and reaching its greatest complexity in man with his upright gait.

In conclusion, we may make a few remarks about some other related findings in human beings.

In 1923 Foix and Thévenard described as postural reflexes (*réflexes de posture*) the fact that in many muscles a reflex contraction occurs when the origin and insertion of the muscle are approached passively. This observation was described in 1877 by Westphal for the tibialis anticus in the case of pseudo-sclerosis as "paradoxical contraction." The occurrence of this reflex in normal subjects was demonstrated in 1913 by Wertheim Salomonson and was called by him the "shortening-reflex." The French neurologists have subsequently found that this reflex phenomenon can be observed in many muscles of the normal human subject. Their denomination of these reflex phenomena as postural reflexes is a very unhappy one; it is too far fetched and can lead only to confusion. What would be the advantage of designating the myotatic or stretch reflexes, for instance the knee-jerk, as postural reflexes, although in the last analysis these reflexes are of course of importance with regard to posture? And so it is with the shortening-reflex of Wertheim Salomonson, which in organic lesions of the central nervous system with spastic conditions often becomes enormously increased as Westphal's paradoxical contraction. For a discussion of these reflexes see also Delmas-Marsalet (1927).

It has previously been stated that in many human subjects with organic lesions of the central nervous system which involve the pyramidal tract typical, constant tonic labyrinthine and neck reflexes may be observed. Are they also present in the normal subject? Minkowski (1924, 1925*a,* 1925*b*) found them in the prematurely born human fetus of three or four months' age. Schaltenbrand (1925*a,* 1925*b*), Landau (1923, 1925), Peiper, and others have found tonic neck reflexes in a small minority (10-15 per cent) of infants. Hoff and Schilder (1927) claim to have observed these reflexes in 70 per cent of the children observed by them. Landau has found his well-known positional reflex (dorsiflexion of head, opisthotonic extension of spinal column and legs when the child is held in a prone position in the air) in about 10 per cent of children during their first year after birth. Whether this is a labyrinthine positional reflex, as Hoff and Schilder think, or partly a neck reflex (Fischer) is controversial. I am inclined to accept the latter conception because, as Fischer also points out, a strong active contraction of the extensor muscles of the neck is necessary to elicit this reflex; passive dorsiflexion of the head does not produce it.

The question as to whether in the normal adult human subject typical tonic labyrinthine reflexes are present is by no means settled as yet. Magnus (1924), Schaltenbrand (1925a, 1925b), and others categorically deny the occurrence of these reflexes in the normal adult. Fischer (1928) and Hoff and Schilder (1927) admit the existence of tonic neck reflexes but deny that of labyrinthine positional reflexes.

Goldstein and Riese (1923a, 1923b, 1925), Zingerle (1924, 1925a, 1925b, 1926), and Bychowski (1926) claim that labyrinthine and neck reflexes are easily demonstrable in normal man. The first-named of these investigators speak of "induced" tonus changes in various parts of the body (head, limbs, vertebral column) on passive or active movements of other parts. Zingerle has made analogous observations in his subjects. The difficulty in these investigations is that they require a more or less peculiar mental state. Zingerle's subjects were definitely neurotic patients and their mental state was decidedly abnormal, resembling to some extent a semihypnotic state ("automatose"). From the descriptions given, as well as from nearly all the accompanying figures, I have the impression that these phenomena cannot be identified with the true neurophysiological reflex phenomena of Magnus and de Kleijn. They represent, in my opinion, complicated psychogenic motor reactions, in which the abnormal mental state of the subject plays an important rôle. (See my abstract of Zingerle's paper in the *Zentralblatt für die gesamte Neurologie und Psychiatrie,* volume 42, page 635.)

Here should also be mentioned the *Lagebeharrungsversuch* of Hoff and Schilder (1927). If a subject extends both arms forward horizontally, then moves one of them downward and then attempts to return it (with eyes closed) to its original position, it is found that this arm is brought back into a lower position than it originally occupied. This observation is of interest as being indicative of influences of the position of a limb on subsequent movements of this limb. But it must be stated that this and other reactions described by these authors and others are by no means constant and typical. Many normal persons do not show these reactions and, if they do, the reactions are not always in the same direction. Voluntary activity can easily modify and obscure them. This shows that it is not permissible to bring them into parallelism with the true brain-stem reflexes of Magnus; their functional level is another, and their functional significance doubtful.

I think it should be emphasized that in many of these and similar investigations the authors show a tendency to generalize too readily, to see more analogies with the results of well-controlled animal experiments than are actually warranted. This attitude does not lead to really fruitful conceptions. On the contrary, it is my firm conviction that such statements are dangerous and may be even harmful, as premature generalizations nearly always are.

Schaltenbrand, Peiper, and other authors have made interesting observations on the sitting-up and standing-up from the recumbent position in young children.

Bibliography

Ach, N. 1901. Ueber die Otolithenfunction und den Labyrinthtonus. *Pflüg. Arch. f. d. ges. Physiol.*, **86**, 122-146.

Alexander, G. 1923. Makroskopische Anatomie der nervösen Anteile des Gehörorganes. In Vol. 1 of *Handbuch der Neurologie des Ohres*. Vienna: Urban u. Schwarzenberg. Pp. 1-100.

Bárány, R. 1906. Beitrag zur Lehre von den Funktionen der Bogengänge *Monatssch. f. Ohrenhk.*, **40**, 358-360.

————. 1907. Physiologie und Pathologie des Bogengangapparates beim Menschen. Vienna: Deuticke. Pp. 76.

————. 1908. Die modernen Untersuchungsmethoden des Vestibularapparates und ihre praktische Bedeutung. *Med. Klin.*, **4**, 1903-1905.

————. 1910a. Der Vestibularapparat und seine Beziehungen zum Rückenmark, Kleinhirn and Grosshirn. *Neur. Centbl.*, **29**, 748-754.

————. 1910b. Die nervösen Störungen des Cochlear- und Vestibularapparates. In Vol. 2 of *Handbuch der Neurologie*, ed. by Lewandowsky. Berlin: Springer. Pp. 919-958.

Bárány, R., & Wittmaack, K. 1911. Functionelle Prüfung des Vestibularapparates. *Verhandl. d. dtsch. otol. Gesellsch.*, **20**, 36-184, 207-224.

Bard, P. 1933. Studies on the cerebral cortex. Localized control of placing and hopping reactions in the cat and their normal management by small cortical remnants. *Arch. Neur. & Psychiat.*, **30**, 30-74.

Bartels, M. 1910a. Ueber Regulierung der Augenstellung durch den Ohrapparat. *Graefes Arch. f. Ophth.*, **76**, 1-97.

————. 1910b. Ueber die Regulierung der Augenstellung durch den Ohrapparat. *Graefes Arch. f. Ophth.*, **77**, 531-540.

————. 1911a. Ueber Regulierung der Augenstellung durch den Ohrapparat: III. Kurven des Spannungszustandes einzelner Augenmuskeln durch Ohrreflexe. *Graefes Arch. f. Ophth.*, **78**, 129-182.

————. 1911b. Ueber Regulierung der Augenstellung durch den Ohrapparat: IV. Die stärke Wirkung eines Ohrapparates auf das benachbarte Auge. *Graefes Arch. f. Ophth.*, **80**, 207-237.

Bechterew, W. 1883. Ergebnisse der Durchschneidung des N. acusticus, nebst Erörterung der Bedeutung der semicirculären Cänale für das Körpergleichgewicht. *Pflüg. Arch. f. d. ges. Physiol.*, **30**, 312-347.

Benjamins, C. E. 1918. Contribution à la connaissance des réflexes toniques des muscles de l'oeil. *Arch. néerl. de physiol.*, **2**, 536-544.

Beritoff, J. S. 1915a. On the reciprocal innervation in tonic reflexes from the labyrinth and the neck. *J. Physiol.*, **49**, 147-156.

————. 1915b. On the mode of origination of labyrinthine and cervical tonic reflexes and on the part in the reflex reactions of the decerebrate preparations. *Quar. J. Exper. Physiol.*, **9**, 199-229.

Boehme, A., & Weiland, W. 1918. Einige Beobachtungen über die Magnusschen Hals- und Labyrinthreflexe bei Menschen. *Zsch. f. d. ges. Neur. & Psychiat.*, **44**, 94.

Breuer, J. 1874. Ueber die Function der Bogangänge des Ohrlabyrinthes. *Wien. med. Jahrb.*, **4**, 72-124.

————. 1875. Beiträge zur Lehre vom statischen Sinne. *Wien. med. Jahrb.*, 87-156.

————. 1891. Ueber die Function der Otolithen-Apparate. *Pflüg. Arch. f. d. ges. Physiol.*, **48**, 195-306.

Brooks, C. 1933. Studies on the cerebral cortex: II. Localized representation of hopping and placing reactions in the rat. *Amer. J. Physiol.*, **105**, 162-171.

BROUWER, B. 1927. Ueber Meningo-Encephalitis und die Magnus–de Kleynschen Reflexe. *Zsch. f. d. ges. Neur. u. Psychiat.*, **36**, 161.

BROWN-SÉQUARD, C. E. 1853. Experimental researches applied to physiology and pathology. New York: Baillière. Pp. iv+124.

BRUIN, J. DE. 1914. Enkele neurologische gevallen uit de kinderpratijk. *Nederl. Maandsch. v. Verloskunde en vrouwenz. en v. kindergeneesk.*, **3**, 593-605.

BRUNNER, H. 1919. Bemerkungen zum zentralen Mechanismus des vestibulären Nystagmus. *Monatssch. f. Ohrenhk.*, **53**, 1-23.

―――. 1921. Zur Pathogenese der labyrinthär bedingten Stellungsanomalien des Kopfes und der Augen. *Monatssch. f. Ohrenhk.*, **55**, 331, 437.

BUDDENBROCK, W. v. 1926. Die Funktion der statischen Organe bei wirbelosen Tieren. In Vol 11, Pt. 1 of *Handbuch der normalen und pathologischen Physiologie*, ed. by A. Bethe, G. v. Bergmann, G. Embden, and A. Ellinger. Berlin: Springer: Pp. 791-796.

BURLET, H. M. DE, & HAAS, J. J. DE. 1924. Die Stellung der Maculae acusticae im Macacus-Schädel. *Zsch. f. Anat. u. Entwicklungsgesch.*, **71**, Abt. 1, 233-239.

BURLET, H. M. DE, & KOSTER, J. J. 1916. Zur Bestimmung des Standes der Bogengänge und der Maculae acusticae im Kaninchenschädel. *Arch. f. Anat.*, **59**.

BUYS, E. 1924. Contribution à l'étude du nystagmus oculaire de la rotation chez l'homme. *Rev. d'oto-neuro-occul.*, **2**, 641-721.

―――. 1925. Contribution à l'étude du nystagmus oculaire de la rotation chez l'homme. *Rev. d'oto-neuro-occul.*, **3**, 10-105.

BYCHOWSKI, G. 1926. Sur les réflexes de posture et d'attitude et sur les mouvements induits. *Rev. neur.*, **2**, 145-166.

CAMIS, M. 1930. The physiology of the vestibular apparatus. (Trans. from the Italian with annotations by R. S. Creed.) London: Oxford Univ. Press. Pp. xiv+310.

CRUM BROWN, A. 1875. On the sense of rotation and the anatomy and physiology of the semicircular canals of the internal ear. *J. Anat. & Physiol.*, **8**, 327-331.

CYON, E. v. 1908. Das Ohrlabyrinth als Organ der mathematischen Sinne für Raum und Zeit. Berlin: Springer. Pp. 452.

CZERMAK, J. 1879. Gesammelte Schriften: Abt. II. Leipzig: Engelmann. Pp. 625-628, 776-778.

DARWIN, E. 1794. Zoönomia; or the laws of organic life. Vol. 1. London: Johnson.

DELMAS-MARSALET, P. 1927. Les réflexes de posture élémentaires. Paris: Masson. Pp. 174.

DODGE, R. 1904. Participation of the eye movements in the visual perception of motion. *Psychol. Rev.*, **11**, 1-14.

―――. 1921a. A mirror recorder for photographing the compensatory movements of closed eyes. *J. Exper. Psychol.*, **4**, 165-174.

―――. 1921b. The latent time of compensatory eye-movements. *J. Exper Psychol.*, **4**, 247-269.

―――. 1923a. Habituation to rotation. *J. Exper. Psychol.*, **6**, 1-35.

―――. 1923b. Thresholds of rotation. *J. Exper. Psychol.*, **6**, 107-137.

―――. 1923c. Adequacy of reflex compensatory eye movements. *J. Exper Psychol.*, **6**, 169-181.

DUSSER DE BARENNE, J. G. 1914. Nachweis dass die Magnus—de Kleijnschen Reflexe bei der erwachsenen Katze mit intaktem Zentralnervensystem bei passiven und aktiven Kopf resp. Halsbewegungen auftreten und somit im normalen Leben der Tiere eine Rolle spielen. *Folia Neurobiol.*, **8**, 413-420.

————. 1918. Ueber eine neue Form von vestibulären Reflexen beim Frosch. *Psychiat. en neur. bladen*, 258-261.

————. 1923*a*. Die Funktionen des Kleinhirns: Physiologie und allgemeine Neuropathologie. In Vol. 1 of *Handbuch der Neurologie des Ohres*. Vienna: Urban u. Schwarzenberg. Pp. 589-672.

————. 1923*b*. Das Problem der Körperstellung. *Jahresber. ü. d. ges. Neur.*, **7**, 1-16.

DUSSER DE BARENNE, J. G., & KLEIJN, A. DE. 1923. Ueber vestibuläre Augenreflexe: V. Vestibularuntersuchungen nach Ausschaltung einer Grosshirnhemisphäre beim Kaninchen. *Graefes Arch. f. Ophth.*, **111**, 374-392.

————. 1928. Ueber vestibulären Nystagmus nach Extirpation von allen sechs Augenmuskeln beim Kaninchen: Beitrag zur Wirkung und Innervation des Musculus retractor bulbi. *Pflüg. Arch. f. d. ges. Physiol.*, **221**, 1-14.

————. 1931. On reciprocal innervation of eyemuscles in tonic labyrinthine reflexes. *Acta Oto-Lar.*, **16**, 97-116.

DUSSER DE BARENNE, J. G., & KOSKOFF, Y. D. 1932. Flexor rigidity of hind legs and priapism in the "secondary" spinal preparation of male cat. *Amer. J. Physiol.*, **102**, 75-86.

————. 1934. Further observations on flexor rigidity in the hindlegs of the spinal cat. *Amer. J. Physiol.*, **107**, 441-446.

EWALD, J. R. 1892. Physiologische Untersuchungen über das Endorgan des Nervus octavus. Wiesbaden: Bergmann. Pp. xiii+324.

FISCHER, M. H. 1926. Die Funktion des Vestibularapparates bei Fischen, Amphibien, Reptilien und Vögeln. In Vol. 11, Pt. 1 of *Handbuch der normalen und pathologischen Physiologie*, ed. by A. Bethe, G. v. Bergmann, G. Embden, and A. Ellinger. Berlin: Springer. Pp. 797-867.

————. 1927. Messende Untersuchungen über die Gegenrollung der Augen und die Lokalisation der scheinbaren Vertikalen bei seitlicher Neigung des Kopfes, des Stammes und des Gesamtkörpers: I. Neigung bis zu 40 Grad. *Graefes Arch. f. Ophth.*, **118**, 633-680.

————. 1928. Die Regulationsfunktion des menschlichen Labyrinths. *Ergeb. d. Physiol.*, **27**. Also Wiesbaden: Bergmann. Pp. viii+171.

FISCHER, M. H., & VEITS, C. 1927. Beiträge zur Physiologie des menschlichen Vestibularapparates: VI. Kippreflexe und Ruckreflexe. *Pflüg. Arch. f. d. ges. Physiol.*, **216**, 564-579.

FISCHER, M. H., & WODAK, E. 1922. Experimentelle Untersuchungen über Labyrinthreaktionen. *Zsch. f. Hals-, Nasen- & Ohrenhk.*, **3**, 198-214.

————. 1927. Beiträge zur Physiologie des menschlichen Vestibularapparates. *Pflüg. Arch. f. d. ges. Physiol.*, **216**, 565-597.

FLEISCH, A. 1922. Das Labyrinth als beschleunigungsempfindendes Organ. *Pflüg. Arch. f. d. ges. Physiol.*, **195**, 499-515.

FLOURENS, P. 1824. Recherches expérimentales sur les propriétés et les functions du système nerveux dans les animaux vertébrés. Paris: Baillière. See pp. 36-42, 52-58.

————. 1842. Recherches expérimentales sur les propriétés et les functions du système nerveux dans les animaux vertébrés. (2nd ed.) Paris: Baillière. See pp. 438-501.

FOIX, C., & THÉVENARD, A. 1923. Les réflexes de posture. *Rev. neur.*, **30**, 449-468.

FRISCH, K. V., & STRETTER, H. 1932. Untersuchungen über den Sitz des Gehörsinnes bei der Elritze. *Zsch. f. vergl. Physiol.*, **17**, 686-801.

GAMPER, E. 1926*a*. Bau und Leistungen eines menschlichen Mitteilhirnwesens (Arhinencephalie mit Encephalocele). Zugleich ein Beitrag zur Teratologie und Faserśystematik. *Zsch. f. d. ges. Neur. u. Psychiat.*, **7**, 154.

―――――. 1926*b*. Bau und Leistungen eines menschlichen Mitteilhirnwesens (Arhinencephalie mit Encephalocele) : II. Klinischer Teil. *Zsch. f. d. ges. Neur. u. Psychiat.*, **104**, 49-120.

GOLDSTEIN, K., & RIESE, W. 1923*a*. Ueber induzierte Veränderungen des Tonus (Halsreflexe, Labyrinthreflexe und ähnliche Erscheinungen). Ueber induzierte Veränderungen des Tonus beim normalen Menschen. *Klin. Woch.*, **2**, 1201-1206.

―――――. 1923*b*. Ueber induzierte Veränderungen des Tonus (Halsreflexe, Labyrinthereflexe und ähnlicher Erscheinungen) : III. *Klin. Woch.*, **2**, 2338-2340.

―――――. 1925. Ueber induzierte Veränderungen des Tonus (Halsreflexe, Labyrinthreflexe und ähnliche Erscheinungen) : IX. Ueber den Einfluss sensibler Hautreize auf die sogenannten vestibularen Reaktionbewegungen. Zugleich ein weiterer Beitrag zur Kenntnis der tonischen Erscheinungen. *Klin. Woch.*, **4**, 1250-1254.

GOLTZ, F. 1870. Ueber die physiologische Bedeutung der Bogengänge des Ohrlabyrinths. *Pflüg. Arch. f. d. ges. Physiol.*, **3**, 172-192.

GRAHE, K. 1924. Bogengangsreflexe auf die Extremitäten beim Kaninchen. *Pflüg. Arch. f. d. ges. Physiol.*, **204**, 421-430.

―――――. 1926. Die Funktion des Bogengangsapparates und der Statolithen beim Menschen. In Vol. 11, Pt. 1 of *Handbuch der normalen und pathologischen Physiologie*, ed. by A. Bethe, G. v. Bergmann, G. Embden, and A. Ellinger. Berlin: Springer. Pp. 909-984.

GREENE, F. W., & LAURENS, H. 1923. The effect of extirpation of the embryonic ear and eye on equilibration in *Amblystoma punctatum*. *Amer. J. Physiol.*, **64**, 121-143.

GRIFFITH, C. R. 1922. An historical summary of vestibular equilibrium. *Univ. Ill. Bull.*, **20**, No. 5. Pp. 178.

GROEBBELS, F. 1922. Die Lage- und Bewegungsreflexe der Vögel. *Zsch. f. Biol.*, **76**, 83-136.

HARLESS, J. C. F. 1864. Section in Vol. 4. of Wagner's *Handwörterbuch der Physiologie*. Pp. 422-423.

HASEGAWA, T. 1931. Die Veränderung der labyrinthinären Reflexe bei zentrifugierten Meerschweinchen. *Pflüg. Arch. f. d. ges. Physiol.*, **229**, 205-225.

HINSEY, J. C., RANSON, S. W., & McNATTIN, R. F. 1930. The rôle of the hypothalamus and mesencephalon in locomotion. *Arch. Neur. & Psychiat.*, **23**, 1-43.

HOFF, H., & SCHILDER, P. 1927. Die Lagereflexe des Menschen. Berlin: Springer. Pp. iv+182.

HOFFMANN, P. 1922. Die Eigenreflexe. Berlin: Springer. Pp. iii+106.

HÖGYES, A. [1881.] 1912. Ueber den Nervenmechanismus der assoziierten Augenbewegungen. (Trans. from the Hungarian by M. Sugár.) *Monats:ch. f. Ohrenhk.*, **46**, 685-740, 810-841, 1027-1083. Also Vienna: Urban u. Schwarzenberg.

HOLSOPPLE, J. Q. 1923*a*. Some effects of duration and direction of rotation on post-rotation nystagmus. *J. Comp. Psychol.*, **3**, 85-100.

―――――. 1923*b*. Factors affecting the duration of post-rotation nystagmus. *J. Comp. Psychol.*, **3**, 283-304.

HUDDLESTON, O. L., & FEO, H. E. DE. 1928. Reciprocal innervation of antagonistic eye muscles. *Proc. Soc. Exper. Biol. & Med.*, **25**, 435-437.

HUXLEY, F. M. 1913. On the reflex nature of apnoea in the duck in diving: I. The reflex nature of submersion apnoea. II. Reflex postural apnoea. *Quar. J. Exper. Physiol.*, **6**, 147-157, 159-182.

IVY, A. C. 1929. Physiology of vestibular nystagmus. *Arch. Otolar.,* **9**, 123-134.

JONES, I. H. 1918. Equilibrium and vertigo. Philadelphia: Lippincott. Pp. xv+ 444.

JONKHOFF, D. F. 1920. A case of cervical reflexes of Magnus and de Kleijn in man, and their importance for the prognosis. *Nederl. Tijdsch. v. Geneesk.,* **I**, 307.

KELLER, A. D., & HARE, W. K. 1933. The independence of righting reflexes and of normal muscular tone from the rubro-spinal tracts. *Amer. J. Physiol.,* **105**, 61.

KLEIJN, A. DE. 1912. Zur Technik der Labyrinthextirpation und Labyrinthausschaltung bei Katzen. *Pflüg. Arch. f. d. ges. Physiol.,* **145**, 549-556.

————. 1914. Zur Analyse der Folgezustände einseitiger Labyrinthextirpation beim Frosch. *Pflüg. Arch. f. d. ges. Physiol.,* **159**, 218-223.

KLEIJN, A. DE, & SCHENK, V. D. W. 1931. Ueber den Reflexbogen des vestibulären Augennystagmus beim Menschen. *Acta Oto-Lar.,* **15**, 439-450.

KLEIJN, A. DE, & STORM VAN LEEUWEN, W. 1917. Ueber vestibuläre Augenreflexe. *Graefes Arch. f. Ophth.,* **94**, 316-328.

KLEIJN, A. DE, & VERSTEEGH, C. J. R. 1927. Some remarks upon the present position of the physiology of the labyrinth. *J. Laryngol. & Otol.,* **42**, 649-655.

————. 1931. Labyrinthreflexe nach Abschleuderung der Otolithen-Membranen bei Meerschweinchen. *Proc. Roy. Soc. Amsterdam,* **34**, 831-835.

————. 1933. Labyrinthreflexe nach Abschleuderung der Otolithenmembranen bei Meerschweinchen. *Pflüg. Arch. f. d. ges. Physiol.,* **232**, 454-465.

KOBRAK, F. 1923. Ueber kalorische Schwach- und Kurzreize und hierbei in Frage kommende Gesetzmässigkeiten. *Passow-Schaefers Beitr.,* **19**, 321-325.

KÖLLNER, H., & HOFFMAN, P. 1922. Der Einfluss des Vestibularapparates auf die Innervation der Augenmuskeln. *Arch. f. Augenhk.,* **90**, 170-194.

KOLMER, W. 1923. Mikroskopische Anatomie des nervösen Apparates des Ohres. In Vol. 1 of *Handbuch der Neurologie des Ohres.* Vienna: Urban u. Schwarzenberg. Pp. 101-174.

————. 1926. Bau der statischen Organe. In Vol. 11, Pt. 1 of *Handbuch der normalen und pathologischen Physiologie,* ed. by A. Bethe, G. v. Bergmann, G. Embden, and A. Ellinger. Berlin: Springer. Pp. 767-790.

KREIDL, A. 1906. Die Funktion des Vestibularapparates. *Ergeb. d. Physiol.,* **5**, 572-598.

KUBO, J. 1906. Ueber die vom Nervus acusticus ausgelösten Augenbewegungen. *Pflüg. Arch. f. d. ges. Physiol.,* **115**, 457-482.

LANDAU, A. 1923. Ueber einen tonischen Lagereflex beim älteren Säugling. *Klin. Woch.,* **2**, 1253-1255.

————. 1925. Zur Motorik des älteren Säuglings. *Zentbl. f. d. ges. Neur. u. Psychiat.,* **40**, 372-.

LEE, F. S. 1892. Ueber den Gleichgewichtssinn. *Zentbl. f. Physiol.,* **6**, 508-512.

————. 1894. A study of the sense of equilibrium in fishes: I. *J. Physiol.,* **15**, 311-348.

————. 1894-95. A study of the sense of equilibrium in fishes: II. *J. Physiol.,* **17**, 192-210.

LE HEUX, J. H., & KLEIJN, A. DE. 1931. Disturbance of the movements of the alimentary canal after unilateral labyrinthextirpation in cats. *Proc. Roy. Soc. Sci. Amsterdam,* **34**, 836-839.

LEIRI, F. 1927. Ueber die Bedeutung des Vestibularapparats bei der Aviation. *Zsch. f. Hals-, Nasen- u. Ohrenhk.,* **17**, 381-391.

LOEB, J. 1891. Ueber Geotropismus bei Tieren. *Pflüg. Arch. f. d. ges. Physiol.,* **49**, 175-189.

LORENTE DE NÓ, R. 1925. Études sur l'anatomie et la physiologie du labyrinthe de l'oreille: I. *Travaux du lab. de recherches biol. de Madrid*, **23**, 259.

————. 1926. Études sur l'anatomie et la physiologie du labyrinthe de l'oreille: II. *Travaux du lab. de recherches biol. de Madrid*, **24**, 3.

————. 1927. Die Labyrinthreflexe auf die Augenmuskeln nach einseitiger Labyrinthextirpation. *Monatssch. f. Ohrenhk.*, **61**. Also Vienna: Urban u. Schwarzenberg (1928). Pp. v+205. (This is Part III of *Études sur l'anatomie et la physiologie du labyrinthe, etc.*)

————. 1927-28. Untersuchungen über die Anatomie und die Physiologie des Nervus octavus und des Ohrlabyrinths. *Travaux du lab. de recherches biol. de Madrid*, **25**, 157.

————. 1931. Ausgewählte Kapitel aus der vergleichenden Physiologie des Labyrinths. *Ergeb. d. Physiol.*, **32**, 73-.

LYON, E. P. 1899. A contribution to the comparative physiology of compensatory motions. *Amer. J. Physiol.*, **3**, 86-114.

MACH, E. 1875. Grundlinien der Lehre von den Bewegungsempfindungen. Leipzig: Engelmann. Pp. 127.

MAGNUS, R. 1922. Körperstellung und Labyrinthreflexe beim Affen. *Pflüg. Arch. f. d. ges. Physiol.*, **193**, 396-448.

————. 1924. Körperstellung. Experimentell-physiologische Untersuchungen über die einzelnen bei der Körperstellung in Tätigkeit tretenden Reflexe, über ihr Zusammenwirken und ihre Störungen. Berlin: Springer. Pp. xiii+740.

MAGNUS, R., & KLEIJN, A. DE. 1912. Die Abhängigkeit des Tonus der Extremitätsmuskeln von der Kopfstellung. *Pflüg. Arch. f. d. ges. Physiol.*, **145**, 455-548.

————. 1923. Experimentelle Physiologie des Vestibularapparates bei Säugetieren mit Ausschluss des Menschen. In Vol. 1 of *Handbuch der Neurologie des Ohres*. Vienna: Urban u. Schwarzenberg. Pp. 465-552.

————. 1926a. Funktion des Bogengangs- und Otolithenapparats bei Säugern. In Vol. 11, Pt. 1 of *Handbuch der normalen und pathologischen Physiologie*, ed. by A. Bethe, G. v. Bergmann, G. Embden, and A. Ellinger. Berlin: Springer. Pp. 868-908.

————. 1926b. Theorie über die Funktion der Bogengangs- und Otolithenapparate bei Säugern. In Vol. 11, Pt. 1 of *Handbuch der normalen und pathologischen Physiologie*, ed. by A. Bethe, G. v. Bergmann, G. Embden, and A. Ellinger. Berlin: Springer. Pp. 1002-1014.

————. 1930a. Körperstellung, Gleichgewicht und Bewegung bei Säugern. In Vol. 15, Pt. 1 of *Handbuch der normalen und pathologischen Physiologie*, ed. by A. Bethe, G. v. Bergmann, G. Embden, and A. Ellinger. Berlin: Springer. Pp. 29-54.

————. 1930b. Haltung und Stellung bei Säugern. In Vol. 15, Pt. 1 of *Handbuch der normalen und pathologischen Physiologie*, ed. by A. Bethe, G. v. Bergmann, G. Embden, and A. Ellinger. Berlin: Springer. Pp. 55-87.

MAGNUS, R., & STORM VAN LEEUWEN, W. 1914. Die akuten und die dauerenden Folgen des Ausfalls der tonischen Hals- und Labyrinthreflexe. *Pflüg. Arch. f. d. ges. Physiol.*, **159**, 157-217.

MAIER, M., & LION, H. 1921. Experimenteller Nachweis der Endolymphbewegung im Bogengangsapparat des Ohrlabyrinths bei adäquater und kalorischer Reizung. *Pflüg. Arch. f. d. ges. Physiol.*, **187**, 47-74.

MARBURG, O. 1912. Zur Lokalisation des Nystagmus. *Neur. Centbl.*, **33**, 1366-1371.

MAUPETIT, R. J. A. 1908. Étude clinique sur le nystagmus rhythmique provoqué. (Thèse méd.) Bordeaux. Pp. 72.

MAXWELL, S. S. 1920a. Labyrinth and equilibrium: I. A comparison of the effect of removal of the otolith organs and of the semicircular canals. *J. Gen. Physiol.*, **2**, 123-132.

————. 1920b. Labyrinth and equilibrium: II. The mechanism of the dynamic functions of the labyrinth. *J. Gen. Physiol.*, **2**, 349-355.

————. 1923. Labyrinth and equilibrium. Philadelphia: Lippincott. Pp. 163.

McKENDRICK, J. G. 1900. The internal ear. In Vol. 2 of Schäfer's *Text-book of physiology.* London: Pentland. Pp. 1164-1205.

McNALLY, W. J. 1932. Report upon an experimental investigation of equilibrial mechanism of frog's labyrinth. *Trans. Amer. Laryngol., Rhinol., & Otol. Soc.*, 36.

————. 1933. Some experiments upon the utricle. *Trans. Amer. Otol. Soc.*, 99-105.

McNALLY, W. J., & TAIT, J. 1925. Ablation experiments on the labyrinth of the frog. *Amer. J. Physiol.*, **75**, 155-179.

————. 1933. Some results of section of particular nerve branches to ampullae of four vertical semicircular canals of frog. *Quar. J. Exper. Physiol.*, **23**, 147-196.

MINKOWSKI, M. 1924. Zum gegenwärtigen Stand der Lehre von den Reflexen in entwicklungsgeschichtlicher und anatomisch-psychologischer Beziehung. *Schweiz. Arch. f. Neur. u. Psychiat.*, **15**, 239-259.

————. 1925a. Zum gegenwärtigen Stand der Lehre von den Reflexen in entwicklungsgeschichtlicher und anatomisch-physiologischer Beziehung. *Schweiz. Arch. f. Neur. u. Psychiat.*, **16**, 133-152.

————. 1925b. Zum gegenwärtigen Stand der Lehre von den Reflexen in entwicklungsgeschichtlicher und anatomisch-physiologischer Beziehung. *Schweiz. Arch. f. Neur. u. Psychiat.*, **16**, 266-284.

MULDER, W. 1908. Dissertatio inauguralis (for the degree of M.D.). Utrecht.

MUSSEN, A. T. 1927. Experimental investigations on cerebellum. *Brain*, **50**, 313-349.

————. 1932. Review of G. G. J. Rademaker's monograph (see Rademaker, 1931). *Arch. Neur. & Psychiat.*, **28**, 679-701.

NAGEL, W. 1896. Ueber kompensatorische Raddrehungen der Augen. *Zsch. f. Physiol. u. Psychol. d. Sinnesorg.*, **12**, 331-354.

————. 1905. Die Lage- Bewegungs- und Widerstandsempfindungen. In Vol. 3 of *Handbuch der Physiologie,* ed. by W. Nagel. Braunschweig: Vieweg. Pp. 734-806.

NOËL-PATON, D. 1913. The relative influence of the labyrinthine and cervical elements in the reproduction of postural apnoea in the duck. *Quar. J. Exper. Physiol.*, **6**, 197-207.

PETTE, H. 1924. Ueber tonische Hals- und Labyrinthreflexe beim Menschen. *Dtsch. Zsch. f. Nervenhk.*, **84**, 85-89.

————. 1925. Klinische und anatomische Studien zum Kapitel der tonischen Hals- und Labyrinthreflexe beim Menschen. *Dtsch. Zsch. f. Nervenhk.*, **86**, 193-219.

PIKE, F. H. 1923. The function of the vestibular apparatus. *Physiol. Revs.*, **3**, 209-239.

POLLAK, E. 1926. Beteiligung des Cochlear- und Vestibularapparates bei Dyskinesien und Dystonien. In Vol. 3 of *Handbuch der Neurologie des Ohres.* Vienna: Urban u. Schwarzenberg. Pp. 239-.

PRITCHARD, E. A. B. 1926. Die Stützreaktion; graphische Analyse am Hinterbein der Katze. *Pflüg. Arch. f. d. ges. Physiol.*, **214**, 148-168.

PURKINJE, J. 1820. Beiträge zur näheren Kenntniss des Schwindels aus heautognostischen Daten. *Med. Jahrb. d. österreich. Staates*, **6**, 79-125.

QUIX, F. H. 1922. Examen fonctionnel de l'appareil otolithique. *Cong. int. d'otol.,* Paris, 1-49.

――――. 1923. La fonction des otolithes. *Arch. néerl. de physiol.,* **8,** 425-468.

RADEMAKER, G. G. J. 1924. Die Bedeutung der roten Kerne, etc. Berlin: Springer. Pp. 340.

――――. 1931. Das Stehen, statische Reaktionen, Gleichgewichtsreaktionen und Muskeltonus unter besonderer Berücksichtigung ihres Verhaltens bei kleinhirnlosen Tieren. (*Monog. a. d. Gesamtgeb. d. Neur. u. Psychiat.,* vol. 59.) Berlin: Springer. Pp. 476.

RADEMAKER, G. G. J., & GARCIN, R. 1932. Note sur quelques réactions labyrinthiques des extremités chez l'animal et chez l'homme. *Rev. neur.,* **1,** 637-653.

――――. 1933. L'épreuve d'adaptation statique. *Rev. neur.,* **2,** 565-579.

RANSON, S. W., & INGRAM, W. R. 1932a. Results of stimulation of the tegmentum with the Henley-Clarke stereotaxic apparatus. *Arch. Neur. & Psychiat.,* **28,** 513-541.

――――. 1932b. Direct stimulation of red nucleus in cats. *J. Neur. & Psychopathol.,* **12,** 219-230.

――――. 1932c. Place of red nucleus in postural reflex. *Amer. J. Physiol.,* **102,** 466-475.

ROHRER, F., & MASUDA, T. 1926. Physikalische Vorgänge im Bogengangsapparat und Statolithenapparat. In Vol 11, Pt. 1 of *Handbuch der normalen und pathologischen Physiologie,* ed. by A. Bethe, G. v. Bergmann, G. Embden, and A. Ellinger. Berlin: Springer. Pp. 985-1001.

ROSSI, G. 1914. Di un modello per studiare gli spostamenti della endolinfa nei canali semicircolari. *Arch. di fisiol.,* **12,** 349-356.

――――. 1921. Considerazioni ed esperimenti nella funzione dei canali semicircolari. *Arch. ital. di anat. e di embriol.,* **18,** suppl., 1-18.

SCHALTENBRAND, G. 1925a. Normale Bewegungs- und Lagereaktionen bei Kindern. *Dtsch. Zsch. f. Nervenhk.,* **87,** 23-59.

――――. 1925b. Ueber die Entwicklung des menschlichen Aufstehens, etc. *Dtsch. Zsch. f. Nervenhk.,* **89,** 82-90.

SCHILDER, P. 1923. Das Körperschema: ein Beitrag zur Lehre vom Bewusstsein des eigenen Körpers. Berlin: Springer. Pp. 92.

SCHMALTZ, G. 1924. Versuche zu einer Theorie des Erregungsvorganges im Ohrlabyrinth. *Pflüg. Arch. f. d. ges. Physiol.,* **207,** 125-128.

――――. 1925a. Ueber die Reizvorgänge an den Endorganen des Nervus octavus. *Klin. Woch.,* **4,** 520.

――――. 1925b. Ueber die Reizvorgänge an den Endorganen des Nervus octavus: III. Die Vorgänge im Bogengang bei der kalorischen Reizung. *Pflüg. Arch. f. d. ges. Physiol.,* **208,** 424-444.

――――. 1927. Ueber die Reizvorgänge an den Endorganen des Nervus octavus; die Beziehung der M. H. Fischerschen Pulsionsreflexe zur Stromungsgeschwindigkeit der Endolymphe. *Pflüg. Arch. f. d. ges. Physiol.,* **217,** 389-396.

――――. 1932. The physical phenomena occurring in the semicircular canals during rotatory and thermic stimulation. *Proc. Roy. Soc. Med. London,* **25,** 359-381.

SCHMALTZ, G., & VÖLGER, G. 1924. Ueber die Temperaturbewegungen im Felsenbein bei der kalorischen Reizung des Vestibularapparates. *Pflüg. Arch. f. ges. Physiol.,* **204,** 708-717.

SCHOEN, R. 1926. Die Stützreaktion; graphische Analyse am Vorderbein der Katze. *Pflüg. Arch. f. d. ges. Physiol.,* **214,** 21-47, 48-102.

SCHRADER, M. E. G. 1887. Zur Physiologie des Froschhirns. *Pflüg. Arch. f. d. ges. Physiol.,* **41,** 75-90.

SHAMBAUGH, G. E. 1912. A discussion of the theory of the physiology of the semicircular canals. *Ann. Otol., Rhinol., & Laryngol.*, **21**, 806-813.

SIMONS, A. 1923. Kopfhaltung und Muskeltonus. Klinische Beobachtungen. *Zsch. f. d. ges. Neur. u. Psychiat.*, **80**, 499-549.

SOCIN, C., & STORM VAN LEEUWEN, W. 1914. Ueber den Einfluss der Kopfstellung auf phasische Extremitätenreflexe. *Pflüg. Arch. f. d. ges. Physiol*, **159**, 251-275.

SPIEGEL, E. A. 1926. Experimentelle Analyse der vegetativen Reflexwirkungen des Labyrinths. In Vol. 3 of *Handbuch der Neurologie des Ohres*. Vienna: Urban u. Schwarzenberg. Pp. 631-660.

————. 1927. Der Tonus der Skelettmuskulatur. Berlin: Springer. Pp. v+ 203.

SPIEGEL, E. A., & SATO, G. 1926. Experimentalstudien am Nervensystem: I. Ueber den Erregungszustand der medullären Zentren nach doppelseitiger Labyrinthausschaltung. *Pflüg. Arch. f. d. ges. Physiol.*, **215**, 106-119.

SPIEGEL, E. A., & SOMMER, I. 1931. Ophthalmo- und Oto-Neurologie. Berlin: Springer. Pp. 366.

STEIN, S. v. 1894. Die Lehre von den Funktionen der einzelnen Teile des Ohrlabyrinths. (Trans. from the Russian by G. F. Krzywicki.) Jena: Fischer. Pp. xx+697.

STEINHAUSEN, W. 1931a. Ueber den Nachweis der Bewegung der Cupula in der intakten Bogengangsampulle des Labyrinthes bei der natürlichen rotatorischen und calorischen Reizung. *Pflüg. Arch. f. d. ges. Physiol.*, **228**, 322-328.

————. 1931b. Ueber den experimentellen Nachweis der Ableukung der Cupula terminalis in der intakten Bogengangsampulle des Labyrinths bei der thermischen und adäquaten rotatorischen Reizung. *Zsch. f. Hals-, Nasen- u. Ohrenhk.*, **29**, 211-214.

————. 1932a. Ueber die Eigenbewegung der Cupula in den Bogengangsampullen des Labyrinths. *Pflüg. Arch. f. d. ges. Physiol.*, **229**, 439-440.

————. 1932b. Ueber die Wittmaacksche Turgor- und Drucktheorie und die Mach-Breuersche Theorie der Verlagerung der Cupula terminalis in den Bogengängen des Vestibularapparats. *Arch. f. Ohren-, Nasen- u. Kehlkopfhk.*, **132**, 134-166.

————. 1933a. Ueber die Funktion der Cupula in den Bogengansampullen des Labyrinthes. *Zsch. f. Hals-, Nasen- u. Ohrenhk.*, **34**, 201-211.

————. 1933b. Ueber die Beobachtung der Cupula in den Bogengangsampullen des Labyrinths des lebenden Hechts. *Pflüg. Arch. f. d. ges. Physiol.*, **232**, 500-512.

STENVERS, H. W. 1918. Un "stellreflex" du bassin chez l'homme. *Arch. néerl. de physiol.*, **2**, 669-673.

TAIT, J. 1926. Ablation experiments on the labyrinth of frogs. *Arch. Otolar.*, **4**, 281-295.

TAIT, J., & McNALLY, W. J. 1925. Rotation and acceleration experiments mainly on frogs. *Amer. J. Physiol.*, **75**, 140-154.

————. 1929a. A method of recording the responses of individual muscles to appropriate stimulation of the semicircular canals. (Demonstration) *Amer. J. Physiol.*, **90**, 536-537.

————. 1929b. Analysis of limb responses to semicircular canal stimulation in the frog. *Ann. Otol., Rhinol., & Laryngol.*, **38**, 1121-1144.

THÉVENARD, A. 1926. Les dystonies d'attitude. Paris: Doin. Pp. 191.

THORNVAL, H. 1926. Études expérimentales sur la fonction des organes des canaux semi-circulaires et celle des otolithes: I & II. Copenhagen: Levin & Munksgaard. Pp. 157.

————. 1927. Études expérimentales sur la fonction des organes des canaux semi-circulaires et celle des otolithes: III. Copenhagen: Levin & Munksgaard. Pp. 103.

TRENDELENBURG, W. 1906a. Ueber die Bewegung der Vögel nach Durchschneidung hinterer Rückenmarkswurzeln; ein Beitrag zur Physiologie des Zentralnervensystems der Vögel (nach Untersuchungen an *Columba domestica*). *Arch. f. Physiol.*, 1-16.

————. 1906b. Weitere Untersuchungen über die Bewegung der Vögel nach Durchschneidung hinterer Rückenmarkswurzeln. *Arch. f. Physiol., Suppl.*, 231-246.

TRENDELENBURG, W., & KÜHN, A. 1908. Vergleichende Untersuchungen zur Physiologie des Ohrlabyrinthes der Reptilien. *Arch. f. Anat. u. Physiol.*, 2, 160-188.

VAN DER HOEVE, J., & KLEIJN, A. DE. 1917. Tonische Labyrinthereflexe auf die Augen. *Pflüg. Arch. f. d. ges. Physiol.*, 169, 241-262.

VULPIAN, M. 1866. Leçons sur la physiologie générale et comparée du système nerveux. Paris. Pp. 600.

WACHHOLDER, K. 1928. Willkürliche Haltung und Bewegung insbesondere im Lichte elektrophysiologischer Untersuchungen. *Ergeb. d. Physiol.*, 26, 586-775.

WALSHE, R. M. R. 1923a. On certain tonic or postural reflexes in hemiplegia, with special reference to the so-called "associated movements." *Brain*, 46, 1-37.

————. 1923b. On variations in the form of reflex movements, notably the Babinski plantar response, under different degrees of spasticity and under the influence of Magnus and de Kleijn's tonic neck reflex. *Brain*, 46, 281-300.

WELLS, W. C. 1792. An essay upon single vision with two eyes together with experiments and observations on several other subjects in optics. London: Cadell.

WERTHEIM SALOMONSON, J. W. A. 1913. On a shortening reflex. *Proc. Roy. Soc. Sci., Amsterdam*, 15, 1092-1100.

WILSON, J. G., & PIKE, F. H. 1912. The effects of stimulation and extirpation of the labyrinth of the ear, and their relation to the motor system. *Phil. Trans. Roy. Soc. London*, 201, 127-160.

WINKLER, C. 1907. The central course of the nervus octavus. *Trans. Roy Soc. Sci., Amsterdam*, 14, 1-202.

WITTMAACK, K. 1909. Ueber Veränderungen im inneren Ohre nach Rotationen. *Verhandl. d. dt:ch. otol. Gesellsch.*, 18, 150-156.

ZINGERLE, H. 1924. Ueber Stellreflexe und automatische Lageänderungen des Körpers beim Menschen. *Klin. Woch.*, 3, 1845-1849.

————. 1925a. Klinische Studie über Haltungs- und Stellungsreflexe, sowie andere automatische Körperbewegungen beim Menschen. *J. f. Psychol. u. Neur.*, 31, 329-399.

————. 1925b. Weitere Untersuchungen über Automatose. *J. f. Psychol. u. Neur.*, 31, 400-418.

————. 1926. Klinische Studie über Haltungs- und Stellreflexe sowie andere automatische Körperbewegungen beim Menschen. *Zsch. f. d. ges. Neur. u. Psychiat.*, 105, 548-598.

CHAPTER 5

HUNGER AND THIRST

W. B. CANNON

Harvard Medical School

In the functioning of our bodies most of the essential processes are managed automatically. For example, after the act of swallowing, the entire complicated process of digestion is thus controlled. The constancy of body temperature, the constancy of the acid-alkali balance in the blood, the constancy of blood sugar, and numerous other conditions which are of prime importance for natural existence are assured by agencies which operate correctively whenever there is significant deviation from the normal state. Among these conditions is adequate provision of food and water. Food is continuously required in our bodies as a source of energy for muscular work and as a means of repair and renewal of worn or injured body structure. Water, likewise, is of the utmost importance; it forms the bulk of the blood and lymph and of the fluid inside of cells, it serves as a carrier for the transfer of food from the alimentary tract into the blood stream, it helps to make a lubricant between moving surfaces, and it plays an essential part in the control of body temperature. Clearly, both food and water are among the first necessities of the organism. At all times, however, they are both being spent. Volatile waste from the burning of food material in the body is carried away by every breath. Other, non-volatile waste is always passing out through the kidneys. Serving as a vehicle for the discharge of this waste is water. Also water is continuously being evaporated from the respiratory surfaces and by insensible perspiration from the skin as well.

Since food and water are steadily being lost from the body, the only way in which a constant supply can be maintained is by means of storage and gradual release. Food is stored in the well-known forms of fat and body starch or glycogen, and probably also as protein in small masses in the liver cells. Water is stored in tissue spaces and in tissue cells. As need arises, these stored reserves are set free for use. The reserves themselves, however, must be replenished. It is the function of hunger and thirst as automatic stimuli to make certain that the reserves of food and water are maintained.

HUNGER AND THIRST VERSUS APPETITE

In any discussion of hunger and thirst it is important at the outset, as Cannon (1929, Chap. XV) has emphasized, to distinguish carefully between these sensations and appetite. The experiences of hunger and thirst are so well known that their definition may be deferred until later. Appetite has been regarded as a mild form of hunger or thirst. It belongs, however, to a quite different category. Appetite is dependent upon previous experience which was of such agreeable character that there is a desire for repetition of it. Thus, we have an appetite for a particular food or drink in accordance with the pleasure which it has given, although there is no real state of hunger or thirst. We eat a delectable dessert at the end of a long meal when we are not at all hungry, and we take a drink that gives us pleasure when we are not thirsty. The appetite for food and drink may lead to the taking of both nutriment and fluid far beyond bodily requirements. These appetites are in the nature of invitations to indulgence, and, as will be seen, are quite different from either hunger or thirst. If, however, an appetite does not lead to the taking of food or drink, then the much more exacting demands of hunger or thirst appear and act as impelling agencies which insistently require the eating of food or the drinking of water or watery fluids.

The Nature and Basis of Hunger

Hunger has been described, and most persons recognize the correctness of the description, as a very disagreeable ache or pang or sense of gnawing or pressure which is referred to the epigastrium, the region just below the tip of the breast bone. In a large group of persons there are almost invariably two or three who declare that they have never felt this sensation; possibly they have never been in a situation where a serious deficiency of food prevailed, or appetite, habit, and immediate provision have led to the taking of food before hunger has arisen. Experience of hunger, however, is so commonly recognized in the terms above mentioned that it may be so defined.

Theories of Hunger. The older theories of hunger assumed that it was a "general sensation" which was based on a general bodily need for food. It was supposed that the lack of food in the circulating blood directly stimulated the cells of the brain, among others, and that the sensation thus arose. According to this view, the common reference of the sensation to the vicinity of the stomach was explained as due to an association developed by the disappearance of the hunger pang when food was taken into the stomach. There are, however, serious objections to this view, which may be summarized as follows:

1. The cells of the brain are relatively insensitive to chemical stimulation; indeed, they are insensitive also to most forms of mechanical stimulation. The brain may be cut and manipulated in a conscious individual without any experience of discomfort. Even if there were food deficiencies in the blood, it seems quite unlikely that they would affect the cells of the cerebral hemispheres.

2. In certain times of great general bodily need, as, for example, during fever, when food is not relished, when it is commonly not taken in considerable amounts and may be ill digested, when there is actual wasting of the body—when, in short, hunger as a general sensation should be most intense—it is in fact usually absent.

3. The swallowing of indigestible materials, such as scraps of leather, bits of moss, or even clay, has been reported as a means of stopping the sensation of hunger. Since these do not provide food which would supply exigent brain cells, banishment of the sensation by them indicates that the sensation is not dependent upon general bodily requirements of nutrition expressed particularly in the requirements of the cerebral cortex.

In addition to the foregoing reasons for not crediting the theory that hunger is a general sensation, it is noteworthy that that theory does not account for the quick onset of hunger. Many persons have reported that the hunger pang or ache appears abruptly. That there could be any critical change in a general bodily state which would account for this sudden appearance of the phenomenon is highly improbable. Furthermore, by careful attention to hunger pangs, they may be observed to recur rhythmically; they come and go with a fair degree of regularity. There are no such variations in bodily needs. It is incredible that plenty of food material would be available for use in the body one minute, and a minute later a serious deficiency would occur, and perhaps a minute thereafter the supply would be adequate again. Opposed to the theory that hunger has a diffuse origin in a general bodily need, the quick onset and the periodicity of the sensation raise obstacles which cannot be satisfactorily set aside.

The theory that hunger is a general sensation, moreover, fails to explain the local reference to the epigastrium. The supporters of that theory, to be sure, have declared that it is fallacious to ascribe the pang to a change there because it may be a "referred sensation," like the referred sensation of tingling, for example, experienced by a man who has lost the part of his body in which the tingling seems to originate. The justification for this criticism, however, depends upon whether there is, in fact, a local change in the vicinity of the epigastrium that is temporally associated with the sensation and that might reasonably account for the hunger pang which is actually felt. There is, indeed, evidence that changes occur in the stomach which would account for the sensation.

The Local Origin of Hunger Pangs. Various theories have been offered to account for the origin of the hunger sensation by events in the stomach. The emptiness of the organ, the presence of hydrochloric acid within it, and the turgescence of the secreting cells in the gastric wall have all been suggested as possible causes of the pangs. It is obvious, however, quite apart from other reasons which might be cited, that the quick onset and the frequently recurring periods of hunger are not consistent with these views. The stomach would have to be empty and full within two minutes, hydrochloric acid would have to be present or absent within the same period, and the gastric glands would have to be turgid and flaccid with similar speed. All these suppositions involve impossibly rapid changes.

The observations on fairly frequent and rhythmic recurrence of hunger pangs, together with associated sounds of moving air in the stomach region, led Cannon (1911, p. 204) to the idea that the pangs might be due to strong periodic contractions of the muscle of the gastric wall. In 1911 he made observations on Washburn (1912), who had accustomed himself

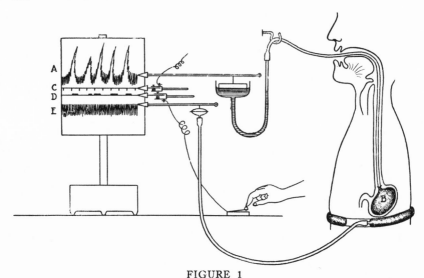

FIGURE 1

DIAGRAM SHOWING THE METHOD USED TO RECORD THE GASTRIC
HUNGER CONTRACTIONS

A, kymograph record of the increase and decrease of volume of the gastric
balloon, *B*. *C*, time record in minutes. *D*, record of the subjective experience of
hunger pangs. *E*, record of the pneumograph placed about the waist; this record
proves that the hunger contractions do not result from action of the muscles of
the abdominal wall.

to the presence of a rubber balloon in the stomach and to a tube in the
esophagus, which led from the gastric balloon to a recording apparatus
(see Figure 1). A pneumograph about the abdomen, which recorded
abdominal motions, gave assurance that the pressure changes recorded in
the stomach were not due to contractions of the abdominal musculature.
A key in the subject's right hand was pressed when he felt the sensation
of hunger. Volume changes in the gastric balloon, a time-marker for
minutes, the signal which registered the sensation, and respiratory changes
in the abdominal pneumograph were all recorded in the same vertical
line on a moving kymograph drum. In Figure 2 is reproduced the first
record obtained by use of this method.

As shown in Figure 2, there are powerful periodical contractions of
the empty stomach, lasting approximately 30 seconds and recurring at intervals which vary from 30 to 90 seconds, with an average of about 60 seconds.
As the reader will observe, the testimony of the subject that he experienced
a hunger pang was not recorded until the contraction had nearly reached
its peak. The sensation therefore was not the cause of the contraction—
the contraction was the cause of the sensation.

The observations made by Cannon and Washburn were soon confirmed
by Carlson (1912). He studied the phenomena of hunger in a man with

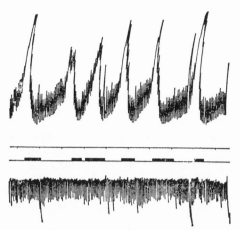

FIGURE 2

PHOTOGRAPH OF THE FIRST RECORD OF HUNGER CONTRACTIONS ASSOCIATED WITH
HUNGER PANGS, TAKEN MAY 17, 1911
One-half original size.
(From W. B. Cannon's "A Consideration of the Nature of Hunger," *Pop. Sci. Mo.*,
1912.)

a gastric fistula, and also in himself by becoming accustomed to a gastric
balloon as Washburn had done. In a series of interesting researches on
human beings and on various kinds of lower animals, Carlson (1913) and
his students have brought out many new aspects of the hunger pangs and
the relations of gastric contractions to them. Among the characteristics
of the phenomena, they have shown that hunger usually begins with occasional weak contractions of the empty stomach, and that these contractions become gradually more vigorous and appear at shorter intervals
until an acme of activity is reached which may end in a true spasm of
the gastric muscle. Either the single contractions or the spasm may be
associated with the typical, unpleasant ache or pang or gnawing sensation
which has long been recognized as the experience of hunger. After the
acme of activity has been reached, the stomach usually relaxes and remains
inactive for a period, whereupon it starts again with occasional weak contractions, and the cycle which has just been described is repeated. Carlson's subject with a gastric fistula reported that distention of the stomach
by means of the balloon or rubbing the mucous lining with a smooth
object did not cause sensations of hunger unless these procedures produced
contractions. It is definitely the contraction of the gastric muscle that
brings about the hunger pang.

By observations on the pressure changes in the stomach as recorded
from an intragastric balloon, at the same time that the gastric contractions
were examined by means of the X-rays, Rogers and Martin (1926) have
found that there are two types of activities in the stomach during the

hunger pang. At the height of a pang the lower portion of the stomach may be so strongly contracted that the cavity there may be completely obliterated. In addition, there may be unusually powerful peristalsis at such a rate that a second wave appears before the first one has disappeared.

Carlson and his students have studied with care the conditions which might influence the hunger contractions. The contractions, they have found, occur in a typical manner during sleep—a fact which explains in part the occasional restlessness of sleep. They are stopped by chewing and temporarily by swallowing, as Cannon (1911, p. 204) also had observed. It is well known that strong emotional states abolish all digestive activities of the alimentary tract; these states likewise abolish the gastric contractions associated with hunger. The contractions are weakened and may be completely checked by smoking, and apparently in this respect the efficacy of smoking varies according to the "strength" of the tobacco. The direct introduction of alcoholic beverages—undiluted beer and wines, and 10-per-cent alcohol—into the stomach through a gastric fistula caused cessation of the hunger contractions and also lessening of the tonus of the empty stomach. Very vigorous muscular exercise inhibits the periodic waves of hunger, but after the inhibition they are likely to recur with an intensity greater than before. Moreover, strong tightening of an abdominal belt nearly always leads to a stoppage of the contractions, when they are of weak or moderate strength, that lasts from five to fifteen minutes. The stoppage may be partial or complete, but in either case the contractions reappear despite continued pressure of the belt.

The interesting problem arises as to what induces the stomach, while empty, to contract with a vigor which is greater than that observed in the ordinary peristalsis recurring regularly during the digestion of a large meal. Reverting to the view that hunger is an expression of a general bodily need of nutriment, Müller (1924, pp. 524-530) has expressed the opinion that this need affects a part of the brain, which thereupon induces the gastric contractions and thus indirectly causes hunger pangs. That the powerful contractions are not due to extrinsic nervous influences, however, has been proved by completely isolating the stomach from the brain and spinal cord and later observing that the typical contractions occur, though at somewhat longer intervals than in normal animals (Carlson, 1913). Again, it is known that the elective source of energy for muscular contraction is carbohydrate food—glycogen or sugar. It seemed possible that a deficiency of this energy-yielding material might be signalized by excessive contractions of the smooth muscle of the stomach. Bulatao and Carlson (1924) observed that if the sugar concentration of the blood was reduced about 25 per cent by use of insulin the hunger contractions became more intense—an observation which has been noted subjectively in human beings who have received an overdose of insulin. That this effect is caused by the lowering of blood sugar and not by insulin was proved by La Barre and Destrée (1930). They followed the gradual drop of the glycemic level after removal of the liver and found that gastric contractions began to appear when the sugar percentage reached about 75 mg. per cent (i.e., about 25 per cent below normal), and that within limits their intensity and frequency increased rapidly as the percentage fell to lower levels. Bulatao and Carlson reported that on injection of sugar into the blood stream the hunger contractions were abolished. Although this evidence is suggestive, it cannot be regarded as definite proof that the hunger contractions are due to lack of circulating sugar, for the amount of sugar used to abolish the contractions was excessive both in amount and concentration as compared with normal blood sugar. Moreover, if a pyloric pouch or accessory stomach is made by isolating a part of that organ from its main body, the activity of the pouch is not affected by insulin or by intravenous injections of glucose (Quigley and Templeton, 1930). And, furthermore, Quigley and Halloran have observed that the *spontaneous hunger contractions* of normal or vagotomized dogs are not modified by intravenously infused glucose in a wide range of doses. The discrepancy between the behavior of the gastric side-pouch and the main body of the stomach, just mentioned, points to a local automatism as the primary factor rather than to the condition of the blood, for the character of the blood flowing to the pouch and to the main body of the stomach is necessarily the same. The problem as to the cause of the contractions, therefore, still remains unsettled.

The conception of the local, peripheral origin of hunger, developed in the foregoing paragraphs, has been criticized by Hoelzel (1927), who has emphasized a "central" origin of the sensation. He has not made clear, however, his definition of hunger; he intimates, indeed, that it is not a sensation but an urge to action, and he furthermore presses the point, which has been recognized by various observers, that hunger contractions may exist without producing the characteristic sensation. It is true that hunger does urge to action—indeed, as a rule, every disagreeable sensation is attended by an impulse which leads to such action as would result in abolishing the unpleasant experience. To magnify the impulse so extensively as to have it comprise all the subjective phenomena of hunger would appear to be a mistake. Again, in arguing that hunger contractions are not the source of hunger pangs because they may exist without producing the characteristic sensation, Hoelzel fails to recognize that many circumstances may prevent stimuli from having their usual effect. The same criticism can be brought against the statement of Christensen (1931) that in normal individuals he has not been able to find any relation between the presence or the strength of gastric contractions and the presence or intensity of hunger sensation. He did, indeed, find that in patients with disease of the stomach typical "hunger pains" were associated with vigorous contractions of the empty or nearly empty stomach. But even under these conditions strong contractions were recorded that were not associated with hunger pains. This is, however, negative evidence. A ticking clock may not produce the sensation of ticking because other stimuli are simultaneously affecting the nervous system or because, for instance, the nervous system may be dulled by sleep. That the ticking is not heard at times does not prove that it does not produce the sensation when it is heard. There is good evidence that by paying attention to hunger contractions and watching for them, their subjective results in hunger pangs may be intensified. It is also certain that by appeals to other interests hunger sensations may be largely eliminated from consciousness. Negative evidence, therefore, can have little force in opposition to the positive testimony of numerous investigators who, since the time when Cannon and Washburn studied the phenomenon, have found that the pangs of hunger have their immediate source in strong contractions of the gastric musculature.

The Nature and Basis of Thirst

Thirst is a sensation referred to the inner surface of the mouth and throat, especially to the root of the tongue and to the back part of the palate—a highly unpleasant sensation of dryness or stickiness. The tongue cleaves to the teeth or to the roof of the mouth, or a lump seems to be present at the back of the throat, and there is repeated swallowing in order to dislodge it. All accounts of well-marked thirst agree that its main characteristic is the dry mouth. King (1878), who described the experience of a United States cavalry troop which was lost for more than three days on a desert in the southwestern part of the United States, reported that on the third day there was no secretion of fluid into the mouth, that attempts to chew resulted in food sticking in the teeth, and that sugar did not dissolve on the tongue.

Other evidence which relates local dryness of the mouth with thirst is found in experiences which result in a rapid evaporation of the moisture of the mouth or a diminished production of fluid there. For instance, the breathing of hot, dry air, as well as prolonged speaking or singing, or the chewing of dessicated food such as dry crackers, will lead to the sensation of thirst and the desire for something to drink. Fear and anxiety likewise are associated with dryness of the buccal mucous membrane and may cause distressing thirst. Besides these local conditions, however, there are certain general bodily states which may produce the sensation. Profuse sweating, for example, or the excessive loss of fluid from the body in the course of disease as in the diarrhea of cholera or in the abundant discharge of water from the kidneys in diabetes, will provoke thirst to an intense degree. It is noteworthy that the withdrawal of milk from the body by a nursing infant induces in the mother a dominating desire for water. And after extensive hemorrhage thirst is tormenting—in the hospital wards after a battle the cry for water is almost universal.

In accordance with the evidence that thirst is due to local dryness of the mouth and also accompanies states of water need in the body as a whole, there have developed theories concerning the nature of the sensation similar to those developed for hunger; some experimenters have advocated the view that thirst is of local, peripheral origin, and others have argued that it is a general sensation.

Theories of Thirst. The theory that thirst has a general or diffuse origin has been based on the supposition that when there is a diminution of the water content of the body all parts may suffer from the deficiency; supporters of this theory explain the local reference to the back of the mouth as due to an association between the feeling of dryness there and the fairly quick disappearance of the feeling when water is taken. The analogy between this view and that of a conditioned local reference of hunger to the stomach is obvious. The evidence supporting the idea that thirst has a diffuse origin is in the main derived from certain general modes of treatment of thirst which affect the body as a whole and which abolish the sensation. For example, thirst may be promptly banished by the injection of water under the skin or into the intestines. The introduction of water by these routes does not moisten the pharynx, and yet the desire for water disappears. In commenting on this evidence the point may be made that the treatment, though general, may change the local conditions in the mouth and throat so that the sensation no longer arises from that region. If this should, indeed, be true, the abolition of thirst by general treatment would not prove that thirst has a diffuse, general origin, but rather would prove that it has a local origin in the pharynx. The main fact which must be kept in mind is that the thirsty man does not complain of a vague general condition, he complains of a parched and burning throat. That phenomenon must be accounted for in any theory of thirst which may be offered.

Müller (1924, pp. 530-537) has suggested that lack of water increases the concentration of crystalloid substances in the blood, that this excites a region in the base of the brain, and that this in turn discharges impulses which cause contractions of the esophagus which give rise to thirst sensation. Records of esophageal contractions are reported as being more pronounced after prolonged deprivation of water than they are when the water supply of the body is abundant. These records show, however, marked oscillations of the intensity of esophageal activity—such oscillations as cause the *hunger* sensation to be felt as recurrent and rhythmic. Since thirst is not experienced in this manner, but is a steady and persistent discomfort, the evidence that esophageal contractions cause the sensation seems unreliable. Furthermore, Müller's interpretation fails to take into account the central fact of thirst, which has been emphasized by all observers —the distressingly dry mouth and pharynx—and also the empirical testimony that this dryness of the mouth is, in fact, the source of the sensation. For example, persons suffering from severe thirst because of great losses of water through the kidneys have had their distress relieved when the sensitiveness of the nerve endings at the back of the mouth was destroyed by painting the region with cocaine. Moreover, sipping a small amount of water and temporarily moving it about in the mouth will stop the sensation. Also, holding in the mouth a substance which causes secretion of saliva—a bit of lemon, for instance—will lessen thirst. None of these procedures supplies water to the body, and yet the distress is mitigated. Their efficiency in bringing relief does not suggest, however, any rational account of the relation between the local dryness and the water lack in the organism as a whole. Such an account must explain how the dry mouth as a local condition may be a means of automatically indicating bodily need and of automatically leading to the satisfaction of the need. Clearly, an arrangement must be sought which, when the body requires water, would cause the mouth to become dry. This arrangement might reasonably be expected to be found only in animals which are continuously and rapidly losing water and which therefore must have repeated renewal of the water supply in order to maintain a normal condition. These clues have been followed (Cannon, 1929, Chap. XVI, or 1918).

Among vertebrates the fishes alone are strictly water-inhabiting animals; amphibia may live in air but they must remain near water so they may resort to it if they tend to become dry; only reptiles, birds, and mammals are strictly inhabitants of the air. The water in which fishes live wets constantly their body surface, and furthermore it is constantly passing through the mouth and out through the gills in providing for respiration. This stream of water moving through the mouth offers a continuous supply, and under such circumstances it seems improbable that thirst would arise. The conditions are quite different in the air-inhabiting forms. The body surface, which is in contact with the air, is dry. No longer is there a water current which keeps the mouth moist. Instead, there has been added to the structures of the head a nasal chamber through which an air current passes. It is noteworthy that at the back

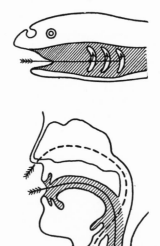

FIGURE 3

MIDSECTION OF THE HEAD OF A FISH AND THE HEAD OF A MAN TO SHOW THE NEW RELATIONS OF THE WATER COURSE FROM THE MOUTH TO THE GILL REGION IN AIR-INHABITING ANIMALS

Note that in the pharynx the air current passes to and fro across the ancient water course (which is cross-hatched).

of the mouth this current crosses the pharynx to reach the windpipe or trachea (see Figure 3). Microscopic examination shows that the lining of the nasal chamber and of the trachea is well provided with cells which secrete a mucous fluid. On the other hand, the lining of the back of the mouth and the pharynx consists of flattened epithelium in which there are very few of the secreting cells. The air which passes to and fro across this ancient water course would therefore tend specifically to dry the region. Prolonged speaking, singing, or smoking, which would deprive the pharynx of the advantage of previously moistened air, because the air would be drawn in mainly through the mouth and not through the nose, would be especially favorable to drying the mucous membrane at the crossing. The sensation of dryness and stickiness in this area, as already noted, is commonly recognized as thirst.

The question now arises, why does not the mucous membrane of the back of the mouth always feel dry and sticky? And since it does not always feel so, why does it feel so when the body is in need of water? Again, a comparison of water-inhabiting animals with air-inhabiting animals offers a suggestive clue. The study of comparative anatomy has revealed the fact that vertebrates which live in water do not possess buccal glands. Vertebrates which live in air, however, have such glands as newly developed features associated with their new type of environment. In the higher air-inhabiting forms the buccal glands have become evolved into the well-known salivary glands. There are three of these on each side of the mouth, each gland provided with a duct. The ducts empty either on the side of the mouth or under the tongue. The saliva which the glands produce has a water content varying between 97 and 99 per cent. It is a striking fact that mammalian forms which have returned to a water habitat after having developed as land animals, such as the whales and the porpoises, have no salivary glands or very small remnants. The theory which these facts suggest is that when water is lacking in the body the salivary glands are unfavorably affected, along with other structures, by the deficient water supply; that they differ from other structures, such as muscle, for example, in requiring a large amount of water for the performance of their function, which is that of pouring out a secretion consisting almost wholly of water; and, furthermore, that they occupy a peculiarly strategic position, for if they do not have water to utilize for secretion and are therefore unable to secrete, the mouth and pharynx become dry and thus the sensation of thirst arises. Such is the theory of thirst which would account for a local, peripheral source at the back of the mouth, when there is general bodily need of water.

Evidence That Thirst Is of Local Origin. The evidence that thirst results from a dryness due to deficiency of saliva may now be given:

1. The chewing of a tasteless gum for five minutes will result repeatedly in a fairly uniform amount of saliva. In observations which Cannon (1929) made upon himself this averaged about 14 cc. In an experiment in which no fluid was taken between 7:00 P.M. of one day and

3:00 P.M. of the next day, there was no diminution of the amount of saliva that resulted from the standard period of mastication until after 11:00 A.M. During the next three hours of the test the amount secreted was gradually reduced from approximately 14 cc. to less than 8 cc. Thereupon, at 3:00 P.M., 1000 cc. of water was drunk. A collection of saliva during each of the following four hours by the standard method proved that the discharge from the salivary glands had been promptly restored to approximately the previous amount and was there maintained. During the period when the saliva flow was diminishing, the sensation of thirst became prominent. After the water was drunk and the saliva was again secreted, the sensation of thirst disappeared. The coincident association of bodily need for water, diminished flow of saliva, and the sensation of thirst strongly suggests that the deficient functioning of the salivary glands signals the bodily need by causing the unpleasant sensation. The observations just described have been confirmed by Winsor (1930), who observed the effect of dehydration on the secretion of saliva from the parotid gland. The saliva was collected in a graduated tube connected to a suction cup set over the opening of Stenson's duct. The conditions studied were the chewing of a tasteless gum at a standard rate for 15 minutes, the "normal" salivary flow without special stimulation, and the effect of a dry buccal and pharyngeal mucosa due to breathing through the mouth. Under each of the three conditions the salivary output fell, until, 70 hours after the last drink, it was much reduced. The response to chewed gum was only one-sixth its former amount. A few minutes after drinking 1000 cc. of water the output was restored nearly to normal. Although Winsor admits that membranes around the base of the tongue are affected first when liquids are withheld from the body, and that the sensation of dryness there is ordinarily thought of as thirst, he calls it a "false thirst." The reason for this term lies in the observation that when the subject continues chewing gum and thus keeps the mouth moist, there appears, after the second day of water deprivation, a craving for liquids, or "true thirst." At that stage, it should be noted, the standard stimulus called forth less than half the usual flow of saliva. The saliva, furthermore, was being collected from the parotid, a "serous" gland. The saliva in the mouth, however, was admittedly very viscous. It was coming from the other glands which are largely "mucous." Has not Winsor reported on the fluid produced by one type of gland, and neglected to consider that the conditions in the mouth were caused by other types of glands? The viscous saliva, small in amount, would result in an unpleasant, sticky sensation, closely allied to the unpleasant sensation of dryness. The "craving for liquids" can be interpreted as an intensifying of the impulsive concomitant of the disagreeable state, the tendency to escape from it.

That "dehydration" will lessen the salivary output in lower animals as well as in man has been shown by Crisler and by Gregersen. Crisler (1928) observed that the conditioned secretion of saliva was practically abolished in dogs three to five days without water, and that, after drinking, the usual response was very quickly restored. Gregersen (1931) found that in dogs panting is accompanied by a remarkably uniform outflow of saliva from the submaxillary gland, as measured in a tube collecting from a permanent fistula of the duct. Deprivation of water greatly reduces the regular secretion and then drinking quickly restores the flow to its usual amount.

2. By wrapping the body in very warm blankets and applying hot water bottles it is possible to cause abundant sweating. Cannon found that the large loss of water from the body induced thereby lessens the output of saliva, which results from standard stimulation for a standard period, to about one-half what it was before the water loss. Associated therewith was a noteworthy dryness of the mouth and an unpleasant thirstiness. This condition was soon obviated by the drinking of water. Winsor (1930) likewise noted that when his subject reclined in a tub of hot water (96°-100° F.) for one hour the parotid secretion produced by chewing a tasteless gum for 15 minutes was reduced 50 per cent. Drinking water promptly restored the normal rate.

3. In another experiment Cannon (1929, Chap. XVI) showed that the subcutaneous injection of the drug atropine caused the salivary output resulting from mastication for a standard period to fall from 13.5 cc. to 1 cc. This occurred without any noteworthy loss of water from the body. Nevertheless, all the feelings of ordinary thirst were present. The unpleasant dry surface of the interior of the mouth, the sense of stickiness, the difficulty of speaking and swallowing—all these particular features of thirst appeared in association with the characteristic mass sensation. In this experiment atropine had its usual peripheral effect of stopping the flow of saliva; and by thus producing local dryness of the mouth it gave rise to the usual experience which attends that condition.

4. There is a well-established reflex secretion of saliva after the mouth becomes slightly dry. A very simple experiment is that of chewing an indifferent substance for five minutes and comparing the amount of saliva thus obtained with that which is obtained by breathing only through the mouth for five minutes. At first the passage of air to and fro through the mouth gradually dries the surface. As the surface becomes more and more dry, however, saliva is poured out and the amount collected as it flows forth may be considerably greater than that obtained by the chewing. The presence of this reflex indicates that salivary glands have as one of their special functions the moistening of the mouth. This observation is in harmony with the observations made by Pavlov (1910) that dry food is peculiarly effective in evoking a marked salivary discharge.

5. Many years ago Bidder and Schmidt (1852) tied in dogs the ducts of the salivary glands and made the interesting observation that such animals are always ready to drink water. The tying of the ducts, of course, has no effect on the water content of the body, but it is effective, like atropine, in causing a dryness of the mouth. Under these circumstances the animal acts as if quite as thirsty as an animal long deprived of water. The local dryness fully accounts for the observed behavior. Unfortu-

nately, Bidder and Schmidt did not detail the conditions of their experiment. Recently Montgomery (1931) has removed the salivary glands from dogs and has reported that in these animals, fed moist food (25 cc. of water added to 100 gms. of food), the average daily water intake was not increased. It is noteworthy that the buccal mucous membrane remained moist, and that the glands (other than salivary) of the nose, mouth, and pharynx produced a measurable amount of fluid (about 9 gms. per hour when the dog was awake). It seems quite possible that under these circumstances the glands of the mucous surfaces of the mouth and pharynx are adequate. Gregersen and Cannon (1932) have shown that if dogs deprived of the function of their salivary glands are placed in a warm room where they exhibit panting, i.e., where they are exposed to conditions which tend to dry the buccal mucous membrane, the water intake may be increased well over 100 per cent. Under conditions which make the mouth dry, therefore, a deficient salivary flow evidently causes thirst and a greater water intake even in the absence of bodily dehydration.

Gregersen (1932) has recently shown that when the times of drinking and the amount of water drunk are registered graphically, the water intake of dogs occurs almost entirely within the first few hours after they are fed, regardless of the time when food is given. If no food is given for 24 hours, the usual amount that is drunk is reduced to one-fourth the normal, or less. Furthermore, if the giving of water is delayed for some time after the feeding, the 24-hour intake is ordinarily much less than when water is given freely through the period immediately after the feeding. These typical features of the behavior of the animals are explained by the loss of water from the body into the contents of the digestive canal, in the abundant secretion of the digestive juices from the salivary glands, the gastric wall, the pancreas, the liver, and the mucosa of the small intestine. The water in these secretions, which pass out of the body into the lumen of the alimentary tract, is as if actually lost to the organism. There is temporarily a considerable reduction of the blood volume because of this water loss. Under these circumstances, the salivary glands are deprived of the main constituent of their secretion and are unable to keep satisfactorily moist the mucous membranes of the mouth. Thus is explained the behavior of the dogs in the few hours after they eat, when they drink abundantly. Thus is explained, also, their failure to drink if they have not been fed, and thus, also, is explained their failure to drink abundantly if there is considerable delay in giving them water after a meal, for the digestive juices which have been poured out have then been restored to the body again by absorption, and the need for water is no longer present.

6. Thirst as a consequence of fright and the attendant checking of salivary secretion are well known. Dr. H. J. Howard (1926), of Peking Union Medical College, has vividly reported his experiences when he thought he was about to be shot by Chinese bandits. "So I was going to be shot like a dog! My tongue began to swell, and my mouth to get dry. This thirst rapidly became worse until my tongue clove to the roof of my

mouth, and I could scarcely get my breath. The thirst was choking me
. . . I was in a terrible state of fear." He prayed for strength to meet
his approaching doom and soon fear left him as he determined to die like
a man. "Instantly my thirst began to disappear," he writes. "In less than
a minute it was entirely gone and by the time we had reached the gate I
was perfectly calm and unafraid." Again the intense and distressing
sensation of thirst was not associated with a real lack of fluid in the body
but resulted from a local condition in the mouth.[1]

The foregoing observations taken together support the conclusion that
thirst is normally the consequence of a drying of the mucous membrane of
the mouth and pharynx when the salivary glands fail to keep this region
moist. The continuous loss of water from the body through the kidneys,
through the respiratory passages and the skin does not cause any appreciable
change in the water content of the *blood* for a long period. Observations
made by Mayer (1900) have shown that there may be no demonstrable
change in the blood of a dog after three days of total deprivation of water.
It is clear that the blood is maintained in a constant state at the expense
of the water reserves in the tissues and in the cells of the body structures.
Among the structures which are called upon are the salivary glands. As
pointed out above, however, they require water for their proper service to
the organism. Not having water available they cannot perform that service and consequently the mouth becomes disagreeably dry. When water
is drunk it is at once made available for the salivary glands and they can
again perform their special function of keeping the buccal cavity moist and
lubricated.

The evidence cited above also offers a new explanation of the experiments which have been adduced to support the theory of thirst as a general
sensation. It is obvious that if a condition of thirst has arisen because
of bodily need for water the introduction of water under the skin or into
a blood vessel or by way of the intestines will result in a supply which will
allow the salivary glands to operate. The mouth, which has been dry
because of their failure to operate properly, will be moistened again, and
the sensation of thirst will disappear. Its disappearance will not result
directly from the satisfaction of a general bodily need but will result indirectly from the moistening of the buccal lining, which, when dry, produces a highly disturbing experience.

---

[1]In the first edition of this book the experiments of Pack (*Amer. J. Physiol.*,
1923, **65**, 346-349) were cited, in which rabbits were deprived of water for seven
days and, after some of them had been given pilocarpine to increase salivary
secretion, all were allowed to drink; the animals which had received the drug
drank much less than the others, a difference of behavior interpreted as due to
moistness of the mouth. Gregersen has confirmed Pack's observations but is
convinced that pilocarpine disturbs the animals so profoundly that Pack's conclusion is unwarranted. The same objection may reasonably be brought against
the experiments of Montgomery (*Amer. J. Physiol.*, 1931, **98**, 35-41), whose dogs,
when given pilocarpine after a thirst period of two days, did not drink less
than other dogs not given pilocarpine. Except in one test the drug made all
the dogs vomit. Obviously, the animals were far from being in a normal state.

In the foregoing discussions of the nature and physiological basis of hunger and thirst no attention has been given to the abnormal manifestations of these two states. There are instances of intense hunger beyond normal limits and also instances of unquenchable thirst as, for example, in diabetes insipidus. Such pathological states are of interest in connection with the physiological explanations for these sensations, but space will not permit discussion of them in this brief account.

The modes of action of the appetites for food and drink and of the sensations of hunger and thirst in maintaining the bodily supplies of nutriment and water may be regarded as typical of other arrangements in the organism which operate for the welfare of the individual or the race. As Perry (1926) has pointed out, behavior may be directed by both negative expectation—the riddance of disturbing stimulation—and by positive expectation—the prolongation or renewal of agreeable stimulation. Hunger and thirst belong to the first category. Also in this category may be classified the asphyxia of air-hunger, the tensions of "sex hunger," pain, and possibly also the discomfort of fatigue and the unpleasantness of confinement or physical restraint. Each of these states is associated with an impulsive factor; each one more or less vigorously spurs or drives to action; each may be so disturbing as to force the person who is afflicted to seek relief from the intolerable annoyance or distress. On the other hand, experience may condition behavior by revealing that the taking of food, drink, or exercise is accompanied by unanticipated delight. Appetites for the repetition of these experiences are thus established; the person beset by an appetite is tempted, not driven, to action—he seeks satisfaction, not relief. It is not to be supposed that the two motivating agencies—the pang and the pleasure—are as separate as they have been regarded in the foregoing discussion. They may be closely mingled; when relief is found, the appetite may simultaneously be satiated. In so far as an assurance of supplies for food and water is concerned, appetite, or the habitual taking of these provisions, is the prime effective agency. If the requirements of the body are not met, however, in this mild and incidental manner, hunger and thirst arise as powerful, persistent, and tormenting stimuli, which imperiously demand the taking of food before they will cease their goading.

BIBLIOGRAPHY

SECTION ON HUNGER

BULATAO, E., & CARLSON, A. J.   1924.   Influence of experimental changes in blood-sugar level on gastric hunger contractions. *Amer. J. Physiol.,* **69**, 107-115.

CANNON, W. B.   1911.   The mechanical factors of digestion. London: Arnold. Pp. 227.

———.   1929.   Bodily changes in pain, hunger, fear and rage.   (2nd ed.) New York: Appleton. Pp. xvi + 404.

CANNON, W. B., & WASHBURN, A. L.   1912.   An explanation of hunger. *Amer. J. Physiol.,* **29**, 441-454.

CARLSON, A. J.   1912.   The relation between the contractions of the empty stomach and the sensation of hunger. *Amer. J. Physiol.,* **31**, 175-192.

————. 1913. A study of the mechanisms of the hunger contractions of the empty stomach by experiments on dogs. *Amer. J. Physiol.,* **32**, 369-388.

————. 1916. The control of hunger in health and disease. Chicago: Univ. Chicago Press. Pp. 319.

CHRISTENSEN, O. 1931. Pathophysiology of hunger pains. Copenhagen: Busck. Pp. 41, 88.

HOELZEL, F. 1927. Central factors in hunger. *Amer. J. Physiol.,* **82**, 665-671.

KING, C. 1878. *Amer. J. Med. Sci.,* **75**, 404.

LA BARRE, J., & DESTRÉE, P. 1930. L'influence des variations glycémiques sur la motilité gastrique. *C. r. Soc. de biol.,* **103**, 532-533.

MÜLLER, L. R. 1924. Die Lebensnerven. Berlin: Springer. Pp. 614.

QUIGLEY, J. P., & HALLORAN, W. R. 1931. Effect of carbohydrate administration on gastro-intestinal motility. *Amer. J. Physiol.,* **97**, 552.

QUIGLEY, J. P., JOHNSON, V., & SOLOMON, E. I. 1929. Action of insulin on the stomach of normal fasting man. *Amer. J. Physiol.,* **90**, 89-98.

QUIGLEY, J. P., & TEMPLETON, R. D. 1930. Action of insulin on motility of the gastro-intestinal tract: III. *a.* Action on the pyloric pouch. *Amer. J. Physiol.,* **91**, 475-478.

ROGERS, F. T., & MARTIN, C. L. 1926. X-ray observations of hunger contractions in man. *Amer. J. Physiol.,* **76**, 349-353.

SECTION ON THIRST

BIDDER, F., & SCHIMDT, C. 1852. Die Verdauungssäfte und der Stoffwechsel. (Eine physiologischchemische Untersuchung.) Mitau & Leipzig: Reyher. Pp. 413.

CANNON, W. B. 1918. The physiological basis of thirst. *Proc. Roy. Soc. London,* **90B**, 283-301.

————. 1929. Bodily changes in pain, hunger, fear and rage. (2nd ed.) New York: Appleton. Pp. xvi + 404.

CRISLER, G. 1928. The effect of the withdrawal of water on the salivary conditioned reflex induced by morphine. *Amer. J. Physiol.,* **85**, 324-331.

GREGERSEN, M. 1931. Observations on the quantitative changes in salivary flow during dehydration. *Amer. J. Physiol.,* **97**, 107-116.

————. 1932. Conditions affecting the daily water intake of dogs as registered continuously by a potometer. *Amer. J. Physiol.,* **102**, 344-349.

GREGERSEN, M. I., & CANNON, W. B. 1932. The effect of extirpation of the salivary glands on the water intake of dogs while panting. *Amer. J. Physiol.,* **102**, 336-343.

HOWARD, H. J. 1926. Ten weeks with Chinese bandits. New York: Dodd, Mead. Pp. 272.

MAYER, A. 1900. Essai sur la soif. Paris: Jouve Boyer. Pp. 168.

MONTGOMERY, M. F. 1931. The rôle of the salivary glands in the thirst mechanism. *Amer. J. Physiol.,* **96**, 221-227.

MÜLLER, L. R. 1924. Die Lebensnerven. Berlin: Springer. Pp. 614.

PAVLOV, I. P. 1910. The work of the digestive glands: lectures. (Trans. by W. H. Thompson.) (2nd ed.) London: Griffin. Pp. 266.

PERRY, R. B. 1926. General theory of value. New York: Longmans, Green. Pp. 702.

WINSOR, A. L. 1930. The effect of dehydration on parotid secretions. *Amer. J. Psychol.,* **42**, 602-607.

CHAPTER 6

EMOTION: I. THE NEURO-HUMORAL BASIS OF EMOTIONAL REACTIONS

PHILIP BARD

The Johns Hopkins School of Medicine

For centuries bodily change has been the criterion of emotion. The rôle of the musculature of limbs, trunk, and face in producing the attitudes, expressions, and movements typical of the several emotions has been evident at all times. At a very early date observers began to pay special attention to the more obvious visceral activities which accompany affective states. Where little was known of the brain and its relation to the internal organs there was a natural tendency to locate the feeling of emotion in the reactive viscera. In the Book of Genesis we read that when Joseph recognized Benjamin "his bowels did yearn upon his brother." During Homeric times and throughout early Greek medicine psychic functions were generally attributed to thoracic and abdominal organs. Aristotle, who refused to attach much importance to the brain, made significant observations on the heart and by a reasonable process of thought came to regard that organ as the principal seat of psychic activity. To the influence of Aristotle and the writers of the Old Testament we largely owe such expressions of common parlance as "matters of the heart," "hard-hearted," and "bowels of mercy."

Galen (131-201 A.D.), whose authority dominated anatomical and physiological thought for fifteen centuries, first showed experimentally that voluntary movement and sensation are dependent upon the connection of the peripheral nerves with the brain. When Vesalius (1514-1562), the great founder of modern anatomy, confirmed and amplified many of Galen's neurological findings, it was definitely recognized that the brain is the seat of sensation and the organ to which voluntary movement must be referred. In addition, the brain, as the sensorium for the whole body, became, at the hands of Descartes, the site of emotional consciousness. It was then only a step to assume that emotional behavior is dependent upon cerebral processes.

It was easy enough for the writers who followed Vesalius to postulate a cerebral origin for the activities of skeletal muscles in emotion. To them these changes were obviously due to influences transmitted by the same cerebrospinal nerves which execute the dictates of the will, for they may be modified by the will acting through the same channels or may be mimicked by voluntary effort in the absence of any affective state. But in the case of the wholly involuntary visceral accompaniments of emotion the neural basis seemed less clear. To be sure Galen had described visceral nerves (see Soury, 1899) and Eustachius, the contemporary and rival of Vesalius, portrayed them in a way that almost rivals modern presen-

264

tations of the subject, but at that time their relation to the brain was unknown or incorrectly surmised. Yet the necessity for some connection between brain and viscera was impressed upon all who gave thought to the visceral reverberations of emotional excitement. In the light of recent work it is interesting to see how often during the seventeenth and eighteenth centuries the opinion was expressed that the influence which the emotions exert upon the internal organs is mediated by that peripheral group of nerves which is now called the sympathetic system. Certain writers of that period went so far as to locate the central control of the viscera in definite parts of the brain. Thomas Willis (1621-1675), who wrote the most complete account of the central nervous system of his time, placed it in the cerebellum. But these early conjectures, historically interesting as they are, lacked experimental support and it was not until the precise central origins, the general distribution, and the particular peripheral effects of the visceral nerves were worked out during the second half of the last century that a neural basis for the visceral aspects of emotional behavior could be accurately described.

The somatic[1] manifestations of such elementary states as fear and rage include external movements of offense and defense which are effective in preserving the organism at times of stress. Their utility has always been evident. But insight into the significance of the visceral alterations which occur concomitantly with the overt action has come only with recent physiological progress. On the basis of ample experimental findings we now recognize in them a cooperation of the viscera which is directly serviceable to the organism in preparing for and maintaining the appropriate external activities. The peripheral nervous mechanism for the somatic expression of emotion is the same as that involved in voluntary and reflex activities of the skeletal muscles. It consists of the familiar somatic components of the cranial and spinal nerves. On the other hand the viscera are connected with the central nervous system in a special manner, and it will be necessary to devote some attention to the general organization and functional importance of the visceral innervation before considering its rôle in producing emotional behavior. It will then be possible to turn to the central nervous mechanisms which activate both sets of peripheral paths during emotional excitement.

THE VISCERAL NERVES CONCERNED IN EMOTIONAL BEHAVIOR

The motor neurons which connect the central nervous system with skeletal muscle fibers have their cell bodies in the brain or spinal cord; one nerve cell bridges the gap between cerebrospinal axis and effector. The innervation of the secreting cells and the smooth muscle of the viscera is somewhat different. It is characterized by the fact that the axons which come into immediate functional relation with these effector cells belong to

---

[1]In the absence of a better term the word "somatic" is used throughout this chapter to describe the activities and innervation of skeletal muscle as contrasted with those of the viscera.

neurons which lie entirely outside the central nervous system. The cell bodies of these outlying neurons are typically grouped together in peripheral ganglia. There they make synaptic connections with axons arising in the central nervous system. The special feature of the innervation of the viscera lies in this fact that the path from central axis to effector is broken by a synapse. This arrangement is illustrated in Figure 1, which shows the essential difference between the somatic and visceral innervations. The neuron on the central side of the peripheral synapse is called *preganglionic* and that on the distal side *postganglionic*. From embryological studies we know that the postganglionic neurons originate in the central nervous system and, in the course of development, migrate outward to take their

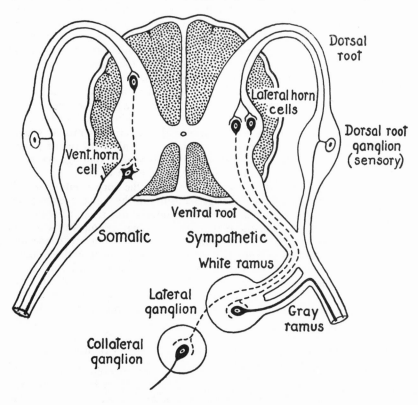

FIGURE 1

DIAGRAM ILLUSTRATING THE DIFFERENT ARRANGEMENTS OF NEURONS IN SOMATIC AND AUTONOMIC NERVOUS SYSTEMS

At left is shown simple spinal reflex arc of somatic system, at right that of sympathetic division of the autonomic system. At right the preganglionic neurons are represented by broken lines, the postganglionic by solid lines.

(After Gaskell. From J. J. R. McLeod's *Physiology and Biochemistry* in *Modern Medicine*, 5th ed., 1926, by permission of the publishers, C. V. Mosby Co., St. Louis.)

characteristic peripheral positions. They are thus the homologues of the motor fibers of the cerebrospinal system, while the preganglionic neurons have their counterparts in the centrally placed premotor neurons of that system. In Figure 1 this homology is illustrated by the use of broken lines.

One other morphological feature distinguishes the visceral from the somatic innervation. While the cerebrospinal fibers pass out from the central nervous system in an almost unbroken series, the preganglionic fibers issue in three distinct groups, as was first shown by Gaskell (1920). The first of these, the *cranial* outflow, is composed of visceral motor fibers in the third, seventh, ninth, and tenth pairs of cranial nerves. The fibers of the second division arise from all the thoracic and from the upper lumbar segments of the spinal cord and begin their peripheral course in the ventral roots of the corresponding spinal nerves; they form the *thoraco-lumbar* outflow. The third division, the *sacral* outflow, consists of fibers which proceed from the sacral spinal segments in a manner similar to the mode of origin of the thoraco-lumbar division. Visceral fibers do not issue in some of the cranial nerves, and the cervical and lower lumbar segments of the cord do not contribute to the preganglionic outflow (see Figure 2).

The entire visceral nervous system, postganglionic neurons and ganglia as well as preganglionic neurons, may be divided along the lines of these three divisions. Unfortunately the names applied to the three parts have varied from author to author and few are appropriate. The entire system composed of preganglionic and postganglionic neurons was called by Langley (1921), to whom we owe much of our knowledge of these structures, the *autonomic nervous system*. He used for the thoraco-lumbar division the old name *sympathetic* and classed the cranial and sacral divisions together under the term *parasympathetic*. This terminology is the one commonly used in current physiological literature and will be followed in the present discussion. The word sympathetic has been applied to each and all of the three divisions, but was originally introduced in 1732 by Winslow to describe the chain of ganglia and associated strands which we now know to be connected with the thoracic and lumbar segments of the spinal cord. Accordingly, Langley's use of the term has an historical justification. Since the cranial and sacral divisions possess certain common features which distinguish them from the middle division, they are conveniently described together as the parasympathetic system.

Strictly speaking, the autonomic system is made up entirely of motor nerves. Langley (1900, 1903) was unable to obtain any experimental evidence of a true reflex's being mediated through autonomic ganglia. There is no good evidence that these structures ever act as reflex centers for the nervous reactions of the viscera. Although visceral afferent fibers are found in many of the nerves of this system they have their cell bodies in the sensory ganglia of the cranial and spinal nerves and so belong to the cerebro-spinal system rather than to the autonomic.

The Sympathetic Division of the Autonomic System. The preganglionic fibers of this division have their cell bodies in the lateral horns of the

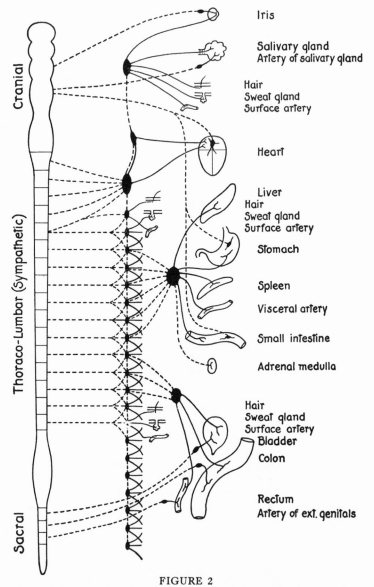

Iris

Salivary gland
Artery of salivary gland

Hair
Sweat gland
Surface artery

Heart

Liver
Hair
Sweat gland
Surface artery

Stomach

Spleen

Visceral artery

Small intestine

Adrenal medulla

Hair
Sweat gland
Surface artery
Bladder

Colon

Rectum
Artery of ext. genitals

Cranial

Thoraco-Lumbar (Sympathetic)

Sacral

FIGURE 2

DIAGRAM OF THE GENERAL ARRANGEMENT OF THE AUTONOMIC NERVOUS SYSTEM
The brain and spinal cord are represented at left. The nerves of the somatic
system are not shown. The preganglionic fibers are in broken lines, the postganglionic in solid lines. Further description in text.

(After figure in W. B. Cannon's *Bodily Changes in Pain, Hunger, Fear and
Rage*, 1915, by permission of the publishers, D. Appleton and Co., New York.)

gray matter of the thoracic and upper lumbar spinal segments (Gaskell, 1920). Emerging with the somatic motor fibers in the ventral roots, they leave the spinal nerves to form the white rami communicantes and course to the ganglia of the sympathetic system (see Figure 1). These ganglia fall into two distinct groups.

The lateral (or vertebral) ganglia are arranged in two chains, one on either side of the spinal column. These chains extend from the upper part of the neck to the pelvic region. In general, their ganglia have a segmental distribution, but in the upper thoracic and in the cervical regions several have united to form the large stellate and superior cervical ganglia (Figure 2). One characteristic of the vertebral ganglia is that they send postganglionic fibers to the spinal nerves. These fibers form the gray rami communicantes. Gray rami contribute to the composition of every spinal nerve while the white rami arise only from the thoracic and upper lumbar ventral roots. By means of the gray rami and spinal nerves, postganglionic fibers are carried to the blood vessels of skin and skeletal muscle, to the sweat glands, and to the smooth muscle of the hairs. Postganglionic fibers from the superior cervical ganglia join the fifth and one or two other pairs of cranial nerves to be distributed to the smooth muscle of the orbit and to the glands and blood vessels of the cranial region. From some of the lateral ganglia, notably those of the upper thorax, postganglionic fibers run directly to the organ innervated. This is so in the case of the cardiac accelerator nerves (Cannon, Lewis, and Britton, 1926).

The collateral (or prevertebral) ganglia are the ganglia of the so-called solar plexus (the semilunar and superior mesenteric ganglia), the inferior mesenteric ganglia, and some small nearby ganglia. These lie near the points of origin of the main arteries supplying the abdominal organs. From them postganglionic fibers proceed with the arteries to innervate the abdominal viscera and their blood vessels. These ganglia receive preganglionic fibers through white rami from the fifth thoracic to the second lumbar nerves. In this case the preganglionic fibers join the lateral chain, but continue to the collateral ganglia as the *splanchnic* nerves.

The fibers of the sympathetic system have a very wide distribution throughout the body. They include vasoconstrictor fibers to the small blood vessels of the abdominal organs, skin, and other parts, accelerator fibers to the heart, secretory fibers to the sweat glands, inhibitory fibers to the smooth muscle of the gastro-intestinal tract, motor fibers to smooth muscle of the hairs, fibers supplying the liver which carry impulses that act to release sugar into the blood, constrictor fibers to the spleen, dilator fibers to the bronchioles, cervical sympathetic fibers to the eyes causing dilatation of the pupils and retraction of the nictitating membranes (where these are developed) and projection of the eye forward in the orbit (exophthalmos), fibers to the pelvic viscera, and, finally, secretory fibers to the medullary portion of the adrenal glands.

The innervation of the adrenal medulla is peculiar. Elliott (1913) has shown that the secretory cells of this endocrine organ receive preganglionic fibers directly from the splanchnic nerves. This apparent exception to the rule that organs innervated by the autonomic system receive postganglionic fibers is explained by the fact that the secreting cell of the adrenal medulla is the morphological equivalent of the postganglionic sympathetic neuron. In the embryo both types of cells arise from a common central mass and in certain lower vertebrates they have a common peripheral distribution (Gaskell, 1920). It is not surprising, therefore, that the internal secretion of these glandular cells, adrenin, when circulating in the blood stream, acts upon any tissue in the same way as do nerve impulses conducted by sympathetic postganglionic fibers (Langley, 1921).[2] These facts make it clear that the adrenal medulla is an integral part of the sympathetic system.

Cannon (1929) has pointed out that besides the *extensiveness* of the distribution of its fibers another important feature of the sympathetic system is its arrangement for a *diffuse* discharge. It was found by Langley (1900, 1903) that the sympathetic preganglionic fibers issuing from any one spinal segment pass to a series of lateral ganglia, usually from six to nine in number, never to a single segmented ganglion, and he also obtained evidence that each preganglionic fiber sends branches to make synaptic connections with postganglionic neurons in several ganglia. This is a morphological condition which assures a widespread discharge over postganglionic fibers. Furthermore, a discharge of impulses over that single group of preganglionic fibers which innervates the adrenal medulla will throw into the blood stream a chemical agent capable of inducing practically all the changes which occur when the entire thoraco-lumbar outflow is active. The existence of these neuro-humoral arrangements for the production of extensive effects leads plainly to the conclusion that the sympathetic division of the autonomic system is organized to *act as a whole,* a view that has been particularly emphasized by Cannon (1929). Further support of this view has recently been given by Cannon and Bacq (1931), who, in continuation of the work of Newton, Zwemer, and Cannon (1931), have demonstrated that a sympathico-mimetic substance is given off into the blood stream when sympathetic impulses throw effector cells into activity. While this material has the properties of a hormone acting like adrenin, its immediate source is different and therefore it has been given the name *sympathin.* Rosenblueth and Cannon (1932) have found that sympathin and adrenin, liberated into the circulation at the same time, act cooperatively. More recently (1933) they have been able to show that both an inhibitory and an excitatory sympathin are produced.

This system of nerves has many duties in the animal economy. A certain fraction of the preganglionic outflow is constantly discharging and this tonic activity is in part responsible for a number of fairly constant bodily conditions. A continuous activity of vasoconstrictor fibers keeps the smooth muscle of the arterioles in a state of sustained contrac-

---

[2]The sweat glands have a sympathetic innervation, but are not affected by adrenin (Langley, 1921). This is the only known exception to the statement made above.

tion, a peripheral condition of major importance in maintaining an adequate arterial pressure. The pulse rate tends to remain relatively rapid because of the tonic discharge of cardio-accelerator fibers. Section of the cervical sympathetic trunk leads at once to constriction of the pupil, sinking of the eye into the orbit (enophthalmos), and, in animals which possess an active nictitating membrane, passive projection of that tissue over the front of the eye. This result demonstrates that a tonic discharge over cervical sympathetic fibers is responsible for the normal size of the pupil and for the normal position of the eye in the orbit. These tonic sympathetic discharges are of central origin. They may be decreased by inhibition or augmented by excitation of the central neural mechanisms in control of the preganglionic neurons. Certain sympathetic paths such as those to the sweat glands and smooth muscle of the hairs appear to be usually at rest and become active only when special conditions lead to excitation of their central connections. It is also true that one or more functional groups of sympathetic fibers may be affected without the involvement of other groups. A lowered arterial pressure may lead to compensatory augmented activity of the vasoconstrictor and cardio-accelerator mechanisms without extension of the response to other parts of the sympathetic system. Several instances of similar fractional activity in the sympathetic might be given. But the most general and the most significant aspect of the physiology of this system is its marked tendency to go into action as a whole.

Simultaneous activity of all parts of the somatic system of nerves would lead to a generalized muscular spasm such as occurs in strychnine poisoning. Under the influence of this drug the normal integrative action of the nervous sytem gives way to a diffuse discharge of impulses and mass incoordinate movements result. Does action as a whole in the sympathetic evoke similar disintegrated activity or do the many changes so induced combine to form a purposive effect? Physiological consideration of these changes shows the majority of them to be related in such a way that they cooperate to mobilize energy and to provide for its ready utilization. Energy transformation in the body involves an oxidation of foodstuffs with the production of carbon dioxide, other metabolites, and heat. Its principal seat is the skeletal musculature. When it is augmented, the active tissues demand more food, more oxygen, and the means of distributing and disposing of additional quantities of metabolites and heat. These requirements must be met by prompt internal responses. Activity in the sympathetic system is the immediate cause of many of them. It leads to an increase of the available potential energy by throwing more sugar into the blood. It stops unnecessary activity in the digestive system. By accelerating the heart and causing vasoconstriction in quiescent regions it produces a more rapid circulation through the active tissue. It thus provides a means of supplying additional food and extra oxygen to the site of augmented metabolism and makes possible an adequate removal of metabolites and heat. Sympathetic activity further facilitates the respiratory processes by dilating the bronchioles, and recent work by Izquierdo and

Cannon (1928) has given evidence that it may discharge into the blood an extra supply of the oxygen-carrying red corpuscles by causing contraction of the spleen. Through their action on the sweat glands sympathetic impulses provide for loss of excessive amounts of heat. Secreted adrenin not only supplements the effects of sympathetic impulses but is capable of acting as an antidote to the effects of fatigue in skeletal muscle (Cannon, 1929). It is therefore clear that when circumstances demand an increased energy output a tendency on the part of the sympathetic to discharge as a whole will lead to bodily changes which constitute a purposive reaction.

Cannon (1928a, 1929) has pointed out that the conditions under which the sympathetic actually does discharge as a unit are those which require a vigorous response to insure the maintenance of an essential bodily state or even of life itself. Such conditions include strong emotional excitement, pain, vigorous muscular exercise, asphyxia, exposure to cold, and states of lowered blood sugar (hypoglycemia). From the account just given it can be seen that in muscular activity with its increased energy output a diffuse and widespread discharge of sympathetic impulses would go far in mobilizing bodily resources. Since pain, asphyxiation, and strong emotion are likely to be accompanied or followed by muscular effort and struggle, the visceral changes evoked by sympathetic activity are appropriate in those states. When the warm-blooded animal is exposed to a lowered environmental temperature, reactions occur which prevent the threatened depression of body temperature. Restlessness and shivering produce additional quantities of heat. Activity in the sympathetic by giving extra blood sugar provides a readily combustible material for the extra heat production; by causing constriction of peripheral vessels and erection of hair it diminishes the heat loss from the body surface and by augmenting secretion of adrenin it supplies a substance which not only reinforces these changes but is capable of hastening combustion itself (Cannon, Querido, Britton, and Bright, 1927). The blood sugar, like the blood temperature, is kept at a fairly constant level. Normally it lies around 100 mg. per 100 cc. of blood. When this percentage is greatly diminished as by an excessive dose of insulin, so-called hypoglycemic reactions occur. They first appear when the sugar falls below 70 to 80 mg. and include pallor, a rapid pulse, dilatation of the pupils, and profuse sweating. Cannon, McIver, and Bliss (1924) have shown that with these signs of sympathetic activity there is an increment in medulliadrenal secretion of sufficient magnitude to check the rate of fall of the glycemic percentage. Since convulsions occur, and coma and death may ensue when the blood sugar reaches 45 mg., this sympathico-adrenal activity is of prime importance in warding off a dangerous deficiency. In short, each of these six situations constitutes a state of stress, an emergency, in which dire consequences threaten the integrity of the organism. In each, widespread sympathetic activity leads to changes which anticipate or ameliorate the danger. We owe the realization of this important fact to Cannon, who has described it as the *emergency function of the sympathico-adrenal system* (1928a, 1929).

This distinctive function of the mechanism naturally raises the question of its indispensability. It may be said at once that there is abundant evidence that the adrenal medulla, unlike the adrenal cortex, is not essential for life or even normal existence (Schafer, 1924). Recently Cannon, Lewis, and Britton (1927; see also Cannon, Newton, Bright, Menkin, and Moore, 1929) have successfully removed from cats both lateral sympathetic chains from superior cervical to coccygeal ganglia. After degeneration of the truncated postganglionic fibers animals thus operated upon possess no functional sympathetic nervous tissue. A number of such animals have lived in good health for over a year and so long as they are kept under quiet laboratory conditions they show no deficiencies of behavior. But when these "pansympathectomized" cats are confronted with a stressful situation, they are clearly at a disadvantage in comparison with their unoperated fellows. In cold weather, they lose heat rapidly, have a low body temperature, and they seek a warm place more than do normal cats. When excited their blood sugar does not rise and the hair is not erected. They lack any control over secretion of adrenin. Although they exhibit all the typical somatic signs of aggressive feeling when confronted with their enemy, the dog, they cannot summon the visceral support which is under sympathetic control. They would enter combat or take flight under serious disadvantages. These findings at once demonstrate the dispensability of the sympathetic and emphasize its emergency function.

The Parasympathetic Division of the Autonomic System. This second part of the autonomic, formed by classifying together the cranial and sacral divisions, is composed of fibers which bear nerve impulses to many organs situated in diverse parts of the body. The third cranial nerves supply motor impulses to the ciliary muscle and the sphincter of the pupil. The seventh and ninth nerves distribute secretory and vasodilator impulses to the salivary glands and the mucous membranes of the buccal region. The tenth pair of cranial nerves, the vagi, furnish inhibitory fibers to the heart and motor fibers to the glands and musculature of the gastro-intestinal tract. Turning to the sacral outflow we find the pelvic nerves (nervi erigentes) composed of fibers which cause contraction of colon, rectum, and bladder, and vasodilation in the external generative organs.

In the variety of its distribution and in the number of effects which it evokes, the parasympathetic resembles the sympathetic. Indeed, a majority of the viscera are innervated by both systems. But here the likeness ends. The most striking fact about the organization of the parasympathetic is that groups of preganglionic fibers reach out to ganglia which lie close to or within the organ innervated. The postganglionic fibers issuing from any one ganglion are short and supply a circumscribed mass of tissue (Figure 2). This *restricted distribution* is an arrangement whereby the central nervous system is able to exert effects upon single organs without at the same time affecting other organs. It is this feature which distinguishes the parasympathetic most sharply from the sympathetic where the organization is favorable to the production of simultaneous activity in a large number of viscera.

In accord with this fact is the absence of any parasympathetic hormone capable of acting extensively upon organs innervated by this system. Although it is well established that some sort of "vagus stuff" akin to the sympathin of the thoraco-lumbar system is given off by isolated organs when their vagal branches are stimulated (see Cannon, 1933), its influence in the intact animal appears to be quite local. Freeman, Phillips, and Cannon (1931) failed to obtain any evidence that stimulation of the vagus nerve below its cardiac branches is mediated chemically to organs innervated by parasympathetic fibers lying outside the abdominal vagal distribution. The adrenal medulla and the tendency of sympathetic impulses generally to yield to the circulating blood an effective sympathetic hormone have no counterparts in the parasympathetic division. The reason for this is clear. Action as a whole in this instance would lead to widespread coincident changes having no functional relation to one another; the result would be disorderly and purposeless. Constriction of the pupil, slowing of the heart, increased gastro-intestinal activity, contraction of the bladder and rectum, and engorgement of erectile tissue are not responses which are bound by any physiologic ties of integration.

Despite the lack of functional interrelation between the several groups of parasympathetic fibers, it is possible to describe in a general way the respective functions of the cranial and sacral divisions. Cannon (1929) has pointed out that the former may be regarded as a conserver of bodily resources. The tonic action of the cardio-inhibitory nerves under normal conditions and their augmented discharge when the heart is overtaxed by a high arterial pressure protect that organ from overactivity. Similarly, constriction of the pupil by reflex activation of third nerve fibers protects the retina from excessive light and even under ordinary intensities of illumination a tonic discharge of these parasympathetic fibers is a necessary condition for acute vision as anyone who has experienced the paralytic effects of atropine will testify. The conserving function of the cranial autonomic is perhaps best illustrated by its control over digestive processes. The secretory fibers of the seventh and ninth nerves are responsible for the secretion of saliva; vagal fibers, for much of the normal activity of esophagus, stomach, and small intestines. In this way the cranial parasympathetic contributes in a very definite manner to the nutrition of the body.

The sacral autonomic has been characterized (Cannon, 1929) as a group of mechanisms for emptying. Normally the contractions of bladder, colon, and rectum are reflex occurrences in which the adequate stimulus is distention by accumulation of contents. But it is notorious that these organs may be emptied during those strong emotional states which activate the sympathetic division, and we must recognize that vigorous sympathetic discharge may be accompanied by discharge via sacral autonomic fibers. The rhythmic contractions which empty the vasa deferentia and seminal vesicles at the height of sexual excitement and the supposedly analogous contractions of the uterus are not due to a sacral discharge—these organs are supplied only by fibers of sympathetic origin (Langley, 1900, 1903). However, a discharge of nerve impulses over sacral vasodilator fibers to the external genitalia of both sexes is the usual forerunner of these events and in the male it is commonly evoked by distention of the tubes and vesicles.

The Antagonism of the Two Divisions of the Autonomic System. Certain structures, namely, the internal generative organs, the blood vessels and glands and smooth muscle of the skin, the blood vessels of the portion of the digestive tract between mouth and rectum and of the glands opening into that portion, receive autonomic fibers only from the sympathetic system. Most of the visceral tissues, however, possess a double nerve supply, sympathetic and cranial or sympathetic and sacral (Langley, 1900, 1903). Wherever this occurs, the sympathetic and parasympathetic as a rule produce opposed effects. In the heart the sympathetic exerts a positive, the cranial a negative influence upon excitability, conduction and rate and strength of beat (Wiggers, 1923). In general, it can be said that the sympathetic sends inhibitory nerves to the smooth muscle of the entire gastro-intestinal tract except the sphincters. The parasympathetic, on the other hand, supplies motor fibers to the stomach and small intestine by way of the vagi and to the colon and rectum through the sacral outflow. The cranial innervation of the eye contracts the pupil, the sympathetic dilates it. While the parasympathetic sends vasodilator fibers to the salivary glands and external genitalia, these parts, in common with the rest of the body, receive a vasoconstrictor supply from the sympathetic.

The common opposition of the effects of sympathetic and parasympathetic impulses is the basis of certain reciprocal relationships between the functions of the two systems. It is well known, for example, that in the reflex widening of the pupil which follows painful stimulation central inhibition of the constant third nerve discharge to the sphincter of the pupil cooperates with augmented sympathetic discharge to the antagonistic radial muscle of the iris. This is quite similar to the reciprocal innervation of antagonistic skeletal muscles demonstrated by Sherrington (1906). In both cases the organization of the central neural mechanisms is such that an increased discharge of impulses to one muscle is accompanied by a diminished discharge to its antagonist. Now many visceral organs, unlike skeletal muscle, receive inhibitory as well as excitatory nerves. Where this occurs, as in the heart and blood vessels, the two sets of fibers may act in a reciprocal manner upon a single receptor. The acceleration of the heart during muscular exercise is the outcome partly of lessened vagal tone and partly of greater accelerator discharge (Bainbridge, 1923).

AUTONOMIC CONTROL OF THE VISCERA IN EMOTION

Only a little over a century ago Bichat declared (see Soury, 1899) that the brain *"n'est jamais affecté dans les passions; les organes de la vie interne en sont le siège unique."* This was a sporadic attempt to revive the ancient doctrine of the peripheral seat of the emotions. It grew out of a belief that the nerves of the viscera lie beyond the control of the central system, that they possess a complete autonomy of function. Such conjectures became untenable as soon as experimental work showed that the normal activity of visceral nerves is dependent upon their connections with the central nervous system and that these same nerves bring about the very changes which constitute the visceral aspects of emotional behavior.

The discovery of vasomotor nerves by Claude Bernard and of the functions of the extrinsic nerves of the heart by German physiologists indicated clearly that the pallor of fear and anger, the blush of shame, and the palpitations of the heart which accompany many emotional states are all due to autonomic fibers. When the secretory nerves of sweat glands were found to belong to the sympathetic system the "cold sweat" of fear and anxiety had a neural explanation. Erection of hair must have been long noticed as a symptom of strong emotion. It is discussed at some length by Darwin, who regarded erection of dermal appendages as perhaps the most general expressive movement common to reptiles, birds, and mammals. In 1870 Schiff (see Schiff, 1896, pp. 141-146) reported that the phenomenon as seen in the angry cat is abolished by section of sympathetic nerves; later Langley showed conclusively that all pilo-motor nerves belong to the sympathetic system.

Emotion and Digestion. Studies of both the chemical and mechanical factors of digestion have contributed generously to our understanding of the bodily resonance of emotion. They have shown that, while certain feelings and emotions are conducive to the secretion of digestive juices and tend to initiate and sustain gastro-intestinal motility, other affective states have a markedly depressive influence upon these processes.

It is a matter of common knowledge that the sight or smell of a favorite food may induce an abundant flow of saliva, a fact described by saying that "it makes the mouth water." This effect is not due to an inborn reflex, but to one that has been acquired in the course of individual experience because of the agreeable quality of the particular food in question (Pavlov, 1927). For this reason it is termed a "psychic" or "conditioned" secretion to distinguish it from the unconditioned, unlearned, similar response evoked by the mere presence of food or other material in the mouth. In both types of response the same secretory fibers of the cranial autonomic are activated, in the latter by the reflex machinery of the medulla oblongata, in the former by a more complicated central mechanism involving the cerebral cortex.

That there is also a psychic secretion of gastric juice has been shown by a number of investigators. Pavlov (1910), using dogs, has studied the secretion of a side pouch of the stomach prepared surgically in such a way that its cavity was separate from that of the rest of the stomach and opened to the surface of the body. When this arrangement was combined with an opening in the esophagus through which swallowed food was returned to the outside without reaching the stomach, in short when "sham feeding" could be done, the experimental conditions permitted a study of the effects of presentation, chewing, and swallowing of food upon the flow of gastric juice. It was then found that the sight, smell, or taking of food agreeable to the dogs resulted, after a short latent period, in a copious secretion from the side pouch. Since this result could not be obtained by the mere presence of solid matter or various chemical substances in the mouth and also failed to occur when foodstuffs indifferent to the animals were chewed and swallowed, it was concluded that the adequate stimulus for the response is the pleasure of seeing, smelling, or taking food which is relished. It was further shown by Pavlov that this agency causes stimulation of the gastric glands by discharging impulses over vagal fibers, for after cutting the nerves the swallowing of any amount of highly favored food does not induce the reaction.

While the pleasurable feelings which accompany the anticipation or taking of food promote the initial flow of digestive juices, disagreeable feelings and unpleasant strong emotions have the opposite effect. This has been noted in many studies of gastric secretion and is perhaps best illustrated by the experiments of Bickel and Sasaki (1905), who made use of a dog prepared after the manner of Pavlov. Under ordinary quiet conditions a five-minute bout of sham feeding produced, during the following 20 minutes, 66.7 cc. of normal gastric juice. At another time the dog was given a fictitious meal of the same duration after first being infuriated by the presence of a cat. Although he showed every sign of an eager appetite, the procedure yielded only 9 cc. of a thick mucous secretion during the 20-minute period corresponding to the previous observation. It was also found that an abundant psychic secretion which had begun as a result of sham feeding under tranquil conditions was almost wholly stopped by introducing the cat. Quite similar results of similar affective states have been obtained in human cases (Alvarez, 1929; Cannon, 1929) where injury has led to closure of the esophagus and made necessary a fistulous opening into the stomach through the side of the body by which food may be introduced.

It is evident from this work that a physiological process accompanying a pleasurable psychic state is inhibited when an unpleasant affective state intervenes. Recently Dumas (1928) has reported experiments showing the depressive influence of fear and pain upon gastric secretion. It is curious yet interesting that he should find that sexual excitement, which may be regarded as a strong but not unpleasant emotion, evokes, in dogs, an abundant secretion of saliva and gastric juice.

The motor activities of stomach and intestines are of two types. Rhythmic kneading movements mix the food with the digestive juices and bring the products of digestion in contact with the walls of the gut for absorption. Peristaltic contractions carry the food onward into fresh regions of digestion and absorption and move indigestible residues and excreted matter to a position where they may be voided. In his extensive studies of these mechanical factors of digestion by means of the Roentgen rays, Cannon (1911) encountered many instances of emotional influence. Cats which were restive and excited on being fastened to a holder failed to show gastric or intestinal peristalsis, whereas these movements proceeded normally in animals which submitted calmly to the restraint. Whenever signs of rage or distress or mere anxiety made their appearance there was an immediate cessation of gastro-intestinal movement. The reports of clinical observers are replete with evidence that this depressive effect of emotion lies at the root of many cases of acute and chronic "dyspepsia" (Alvarez, 1929; Cannon, 1929).

From what is known of the functions of the extrinsic nerves of the gastro-intestinal tract, it must be supposed that the neural basis for the disturbing effect of emotional excitement upon the mechanical aspects of digestion involves a sympathetic discharge. Stimulation of the splanchnic nerves causes diminished tonus and stoppage of contractions in stomach and intestines, and such is the effect of adrenin. On the other hand, the vagi exert a general motor influence. Certain results obtained by Cannon in his work on cats can leave little doubt that the inhibitory effect of emotion upon gastric motility is exerted over splanchnic fibers. It was found that slight interference with breathing, sufficient to evoke an emotional response, caused a complete stoppage of the stomach contractions, provided the splanchnic nerves were intact. After these had been severed and the vagi alone remained, the respiratory distress had no effect upon the stomach. Furthermore, evidence which will be presented in the next section makes it certain that a fit of anger is accompanied by a medulliadrenal secretion capable of producing marked physiological changes, among them depression of the gut.

Some of Cannon's findings have indicated that just as there is a psychic secretion of gastric juice there is also a "psychic tone" of the gastric musculature and that this is mediated by the vagus nerves. The importance of tonic contraction of the stomach muscle lies in the fact that it is necessary for gastric peristalsis. Although it may develop in a stomach disconnected from its extrinsic nerves, vagus stimulation does produce it. These facts raised the question as to the stage in the digestive process at which vagus influences affect gastric tone. It was then found that if the vagal supply to the stomach was cut just before an animal took food, the tonus of the stomach disappeared or remained minimal, and contractions of the gastric wall did not occur. In contrast to this was the effect of cutting the nerves after food had been eaten with relish; then the contractions which had started continued in a normal fashion. The indication here is that the pleasurable taking of food is accompanied by a vagal discharge which arouses the essential tonic condition in the gastric muscles. This may then be continued by local agencies. A recent paper by Alvarez (1929) gives abundant testimony of the operation of a psychic tone in the human digestive tract.

The data just given reveal that the opposed influences of affective states favorable and unfavorable to good digestion are expressed through parasympathetic and sympathetic nerves which are themselves typically antagonistic in their functional relations to the digestive organs.

The Emergency Function of the Sympathico-adrenal System in Strong Emotion. Anger, rage, and fear are the conditions par excellence for studying the bodily reverberations of emotion. The surface manifestations of these major affective states are truly remarkable. They have been studied, observed, and commented upon by a variety of philosophers, psychologists, physiognomists, artists, and natural historians. But the detailed examination of the deep-seated visceral alterations which occur when a strong emotion is in evidence has required the special methods of the physiologist.

As already related, physiological investigations have shown that, when sight and taste and smell of food are attended by agreeable sensations, the cranial autonomic goes into action to promote the processes of digestion and so fortifies the body against times of stress. Evidence has also been presented that interruption of this mild feeling of pleasure by fear or anger is accompanied by sympathetic activity that completely overthrows the quiet conserving processes. The significance of this lies in the fact that the inhibition of digestive functions is merely one of a multitude of effects produced by widespread sympathetic activity at this time. In the angry cat, for example, the hairs of the back and tail are erected, the pupils are dilated, and the eyes become prominent, the blood sugar rises, the heart is accelerated, and widespread vasoconstriction occurs. Likewise, the human being assailed by anger or fear shows a rapid heart, a high arterial pressure, wide pupils, sweating, and high glycemic percentages which lead to the appearance of sugar in the urine (Cannon, 1929).

In discussing the organization and physiology of the sympathetic system it was pointed out that conditions which demand an increased outlay of energy are characterized by unit action in this system. The bodily alterations so induced are of the utmost service to the organism. Strong emotion is only one of several conditions attended by these responses. When it is aroused, intense muscular effort is likely to ensue. It is then that the sympathetic most thoroughly fulfills its emergency function. Here it is that domination of the viscera by sympathetic impulses most notably mobilizes the bodily forces for immediate action.

It is a firmly established fact, generally agreed to, that artificial stimulation of the splanchnic nerves, by exciting the secretory fibers distributed to the adrenal medulla, causes a discharge of adrenin into the blood stream (Cannon, 1929; Schafer, 1924). Therefore, it might be expected that nerve impulses are sent out along these fibers and excite the adrenin-secreting cells whenever, under natural conditions, there is general sympathetic activity. Since adrenin has the same actions as sympathetic nerve impulses, it would, if secreted at such times, cooperate with those impulses to produce widespread effects. Whether this actually occurs or not is a question which was first taken up by Cannon in 1911. The positive results obtained by Cannon and his collaborators from carefully controlled experiments during the last twenty years have revealed the emergency function of the sympathetic system together with that of its constituent part, the adrenal medulla. The importance of these investigations can be described by saying that they have clearly established the function of an endocrine organ and thrown new light upon the action of the nervous system. As objective studies of emotion they have a special significance for the psychologist.

In this work two experimental methods have been employed to determine the secretory activity of the adrenal medulla in laboratory animals. The first involved the painless taking of samples of blood from the inferior vena cava just above the mouths of the lumbo-adrenal veins by means of a catheter introduced from below through the femoral vein. The adrenin content of caval blood was then tested before and after the experimental procedure by its effect upon rhythmically contracting strips of intestinal muscle which are characteristically inhibited by adrenin in dilutions as great as one part in many millions. Since adrenin is practically the only known substance occurring in blood which has this effect, and since adequate control experiments showed that the adrenal glands are alone able to confer the inhibitory power upon blood, it was considered that the method was reliable (Cannon, 1929). The second method of Cannon and his collaborators makes use of the completely denervated heart (Cannon, 1919; Cannon, Lewis, and Britton, 1926). When the extrinsic nerves of the heart, the vagal inhibitory fibers and the sympathetic accelerators, are cut, the only factors, aside from a rise in blood temperature, which are capable of increasing the heart rate are medulli-adrenal secretion, thyroid secretion, and a cardio-accelerating substance which, under certain conditions, may be liberated into the blood from the liver (Cannon, Lewis, and Britton, 1926). To observe the influence of any one of these humoral stimulating agencies it is necessary only to eliminate the other two. Since all are under nervous control, this may be accomplished by section of the appropriate nerves. The thyroid innervation is interrupted by removal of the stellate ganglia (a part of the usual method of denervating the heart); the innervation of the liver, by severing the hepatic nerves; and the nervous supply to the adrenals, by section of the splanchnics (more conveniently the adrenal factor is eliminated by removal of one gland and denervation of the other). With thyroid and hepatic influences disposed of, the denervated heart becomes a delicate indicator of circulating adrenin. Its reliability in this respect has been abundantly demonstrated.

In 1911 Cannon and de la Paz (see Cannon, 1929), using the catheter method, first showed that there is an emotional stimulation of medulli-adrenal secretion. They noted that, when a cat was frightened (or enraged) by a barking dog, blood drawn from the inferior vena cava just above the opening of the lumbo-adrenal veins repeatedly caused inhibition of the beating intestinal strip, whereas blood removed before the excitement had no effect, and, further, that excitement after removal of the glands did not yield the positive result. In a second report Cannon and Hoskins brought forth evidence that in anaesthetized animals the adrenal medulla is stimulated to secrete by asphyxia and by such sensory stimulation as would have caused very severe pain in a conscious animal. Thus began a long series of experiments in which it was shown that "painful" sensory stimulation and asphyxia, as well as emotional excitement, throw into effective action the secretory nerves of the adrenal medulla. All three of these agencies are closely related in the sense that they are emergency states and produce similar bodily changes.

Among the early investigations leading to the formulation of the emergency theory of sympathetic and adrenal functions were those carried out by Cannon in collaboration with Gray and Mendenhall (see Cannon, 1929) which showed that injected adrenin, stimulation of the splanchnic nerves, and fear and rage hasten the clotting of blood. The demonstration that the adrenals are necessary for the effect when produced by splanchnic stimulation and that emotional excitement evokes more rapid clotting only when the splanchnics are intact was further evidence for emotional activation of the adrenal medulla. The proposition that acceleration of clotting is an emergency function of the adrenin secreted during fright and fury needs no argument, for combat with possible injury and hemorrhage is foreshadowed by the circumstances which ordinarily evoke these emotions.

The relative difficulty and intricacy of the catheter method led Cannon to adopt the denervated heart as a preparation for detecting adrenal secretion. The latter is superior to the older method in one important particular, namely, that it tests the adrenin content of blood circulating in the animal under investigation. Since adrenin is an unstable compound that rapidly undergoes inactivation in the blood stream, the denervated heart permits a continuous record showing the duration and subsidence as well as the latency of the secretion. By means of the newer method Cannon in 1919 was able to confirm the results obtained with de la Paz eight years before. In 1925 Cannon and Britton used the denervated heart in connection with a "pseudaffective" state which they were able to produce in cats by ablation of the cerebral cortex and in which are manifested the activities typical of anger. This decorticate sham rage (described in detail in the next section of this chapter) occurs in fits during which there are all the signs of vigorous, widespread sympathetic discharge. In fifteen experiments it was found that the denervated heart had rates averaging 252 beats per minute during the fits of rage and 222 beats per minute during the intervening periods of quiet. After the adrenal glands had been removed, the rate averaged 156 and was increased only four to eight beats during activity. It was concluded that a greatly increased secretion of adrenin is associated with this form of emotional behavior.

The evidence for emotional secretion of adrenin obtained by Cannon and his associates has received, from the very beginning, abundant confirmation. As early as 1912, Elliott reported some observations on the "paradoxical dilatation" of the pupil which occurs after removal of the superior cervical ganglion and is due to increased sensitivity of the radial muscle of the iris to adrenin. He found that this response was evoked in anger, but only so long as the adrenals were intact and innervated. Elliott's findings were later confirmed by Kellaway. Recently Sataké, Watanabé, and Sugawara (1927) have studied the rate of medulliadrenal secretion by testing, with the intestinal strip, blood taken directly from the lumbo-adrenal vein. Their dogs were prepared for the experiment in advance by section of the sensory nerves of the loin, thus making it possible to obtain adrenal blood without anaesthesia and without disturbing the animals in the least. It was found that emotional excitement evoked by fastening the animals was accompanied by an increased secretion amounting to several times the rate in quiet existence. Such, in brief, is the direct support given Cannon's contention that the adrenal medulla becomes active in emotion. And from many investigators working in diverse parts of the world and using a variety of methods has come confirmation of his demonstration that other stressful experiences, pain, asphyxia, exposure to cold, hypoglycemia, all produce an augmented secretion of adrenin (Cannon, 1928a, 1929; Cannon, Lewis, and Britton, 1926). Contrary to this mass of positive evidence is the doctrine, vigorously put forward by Stewart and Rogoff some years ago, that the output of adrenin is constant and unchangeable (Stewart, 1922). This is not the place to weigh and counterweigh the opinions of Stewart and Rogoff. It is sufficient to point out that their theory was based implicitly upon negative results obtained by a method which, in the hands of the only other investigators who have used it, has contributed further evidence in favor of Cannon's view (Kodama, 1923; Sugawara, Watanabé, and Saito, 1926). Furthermore, the reader is advised that Cannon and his collaborators (Cannon, 1928a, Cannon and Britton, 1927; Cannon and Rapport, 1921a) have effectively answered, by appeal to experimental evidence, the many theoretical arguments advanced by Stewart and Rogoff in criticism of each and every method that has yielded results contrary to their own.

Most conclusive and most significant of all the evidence for emotional activation of the adrenal medulla is that recently reported by Cannon and Britton (1927). They made use of cats in which denervation of the heart and all other operative procedures were carried out by surgical methods. The emotional reactions of these animals were studied later while they were living normally in the laboratory. In such lasting preparations of the denervated heart emotional excitement induced by the presence of a barking dog or by restraint in a holder was invariably accompanied by marked increments in pulse rate. Characteristically they persisted for some time after the stimulus for them had ceased to act; after the cats had been excited by a dog for one minute they were removed from the scene of the disturbance and allowed to lie quietly on a cushion whereupon the faster pulse rate fell off gradually and attained the quiet rate only after 15 or 20 minutes. This result is similar to the prolonged inhibition of gastric secretion noted by Bickel and Sasaki and is related to the common experience that serenity and calmness are not restored for some time after an emotional upset. Control observations were made on the same animals by Cannon and Britton after extirpation of one adrenal and denervation of the other. Although such animals were quite healthy (due to retention of the essential cortex of one gland) and reacted with the same outward vigor to the emotional stimuli, the faster heart rate either wholly failed to occur or was so slight as to be explicable by a rise in temperature.

Of special interest was the finding, in these experiments of Cannon and Britton, that the output of adrenin varies directly with the intensity of the physical effort. For example, the increments in heart rate averaged 22 beats per minute when the excitement was accompanied by slight muscular activity (hissing, snarling, retraction of the ears, twitching of the tail) and 49 beats when it was attended by struggle or aggressive movements of attack. This shows that the bodily processes are more profoundly altered in the full expression of emotion than in the preparatory visceral changes alone. As pointed out by the authors, it follows that "when limitation of the bodily disturbances is desirable, control of the controllable factors, the voluntary muscles, would minimize the effects of an emotional storm." This new evidence is in contradiction to the view that suppression of the outward manifestations of strong emotion may lead to exaggeration of the visceral components of the response. Previous to the work of Cannon and Britton, the observations of Hartman, Waite, and Powell had furnished evidence that adrenal secretion is increased in muscular exercise and is proportional to the extent and duration of the activity.

Gradation of adrenal secretion with the vigor of somatic emotional behavior emphasizes the cooperation of the sympathetic system in activities involving energy changes in the body. The muscular activity which prevails or is likely to prevail in strong emotion is primarily dependent upon an increased oxygen supply. This requirement is met by adaptive changes in the circulatory and respiratory systems. The faster heart and vasoconstriction in the splanchnic region with shifting of blood to other parts are factors which increase the circulation rate and so multiply the number of round trips taken by the oxygen-carrying red blood corpuscles between the lungs and active tissues (skeletal muscles, central nervous system, and heart muscle itself). These changes are under sympathico-adrenal control. And recent work has revealed another sympathetic effect which is of service in supplying the increased oxygen demand of motion and emotion. Barcroft and his co-workers have proved that conditions of oxygen deficiency—asphyxia, hemorrhage, muscular exercise—cause the spleen to contract, and that when it contracts it discharges into the blood stream an extra supply of red blood corpuscles. Previously a higher concentration of red corpuscles in the blood after emotional excitement or injection of adrenalin had been observed by Lamson, but he attributed it to occurrences in the liver. Later Izquierdo and Cannon (1928) demonstrated a 20-per-cent increase in circulating red cells in cats excited by dogs and showed that the effect is splenic in origin and is due to sympathetic discharge to the spleen. As regards the coincident secretion of adrenin, their experiments failed to indicate how great a rôle, if any, it plays in producing this effect. But it can certainly support the sympathetic impulses which act directly upon the heart and splanchnic vessels to bring about the vascular adjustments so necessary to sustained muscular activity. Also, amounts of this hormone corresponding to the amounts secreted have the ability to produce a rapid recovery of the capacity of fatigued muscle to respond to stimulation (Cannon, 1929). Its remarkable action in restoring the ability of exhausted animals to continue running has been clearly shown in the work of Campos, Cannon, Lundin, and Walker (1929). It was also found by these investigators that cutting the sympathetic nerves to the liver results in a striking reduction of the working ability. They were unable to ascribe this effect to interference with any of the known functions of the liver nerves.

Another aspect of the sympathico-adrenal response in emotion which has a definite emergency value is the increase in blood sugar that it effects by causing a breakdown of the glycogen stores of the liver (glycogenolysis). The utility of such mobilization of carbohydrate lies in the fact that sugar is the optimum source of muscular energy. Since the kidneys do not permit sugar to escape until the percentage in the blood rises considerably above the normal level, the appearance of sugar in the urine, as a consequence of emotional excitement, is an indication of emotional hyperglycemia. Emotional glycosuria in man and animals is an old and frequent observation (Cannon, 1929). In 1911 Cannon, Shohl, and Wright (see Cannon, 1929) demonstrated its appearance in cats, found that it varied with the magnitude of the emotional disturbance, and showed that it could not be induced after removal of the adrenals. The latter observation suggested that medulliadrenal secretion is a prime factor in producing the change and that it is of more consequence than a direct sympathetic discharge to the liver. Desiring further evidence on this point, Bulatao and Cannon (1925) investigated it in animals manifesting decorticate rage. They found that when the true pseudaffective state developed the blood sugar rose, on the average, to nearly five times its normal percentage. Appropriate operative procedures showed that as a causative factor secreted adrenin is far more potent than impulses over the splanchnic branches to the liver. A recent study by Britton (1928) has again demonstrated the prepotency of the humoral factor in throwing into action the glycogenolytic processes. When normal cats were excited by an aggressive dog, there were marked increments in the glycemic percentage. These responses were scarcely modified after section of the sympathetic nerves to the liver. On the other hand, ablation of the medulla of both adrenal glands, although it had no influence upon the general affective response, abolished the rise in blood sugar. It is interesting that a parallelism in the visceral and somatic reactions was again revealed by these experiments. Even so, the release of considerable quantities of sugar into the blood stream when emotion is accompanied by only slight muscular activity seems to be in anticipation of a greater demand.

The experimental evidence presented in the foregoing paragraphs gives reality to the statement that in emotion the viscera are dominated by activity in the sympathetic division of the autonomic system. In the production of these changes sympathetic impulses and adrenin, itself secreted as a result of sympathetic discharge, cooperate. One change, the speeding of blood-clotting, is solely the result of increased adrenal secretion. Another, glycogenolysis, appears to be chiefly, if not entirely, due to the humoral factor. In the case of cardiac acceleration, the available evidence suggests that the direct neural influence is somewhat prepotent, the humoral important but supplementary; the same is probably true of splenic contraction and splanchnic vasoconstriction. It was previously thought that adrenin has an effect apart from sympathetic impulses in increasing the excitability of fatigued skeletal muscle, but the testimony of Orbeli (see Fulton, 1926) as to the beneficial influence of sympathetic impulses on fatigued muscle suggests that here, too, the neural agency may be of importance.

THE CENTRAL MECHANISMS FOR EMOTIONAL REACTIONS

At various times "the seat of the emotions" and the central mechanisms controlling emotional behavior have been sought at the highest level of the central nervous system, namely, the cerebral cortex. But however reasonable the assumption may be that the neural processes underlying emotional consciousness are cortical, it does not follow that the bodily changes which make up emotional behavior are due to a discharge of cortical origin. In fact certain considerations and many experimental facts indicate that the bodily responses typical of one strong emotion, rage, are operated by the more primitive parts of the brain.

First of all, there is the fundamental nature of the behavior attending this emotion. It is a behavior which is called forth by the urgency of certain definite circumstances and it is directed toward the preservation of the individual. It constitutes a reaction which is primitive, energetically purposive, and common to many different members of the vertebrate series. In short, it possesses many features in common with such elementary responses as sneezing, coughing, and sucking. An illuminating summary of the similarity of the rage reaction to these simple reflexes has been given by Cannon (1928b): "First, its occurrence in the early months of even so highly developed an organism as the human infant indicates that its neural pattern, like that of the reflexes mentioned above, is congenitally inwrought in the central nervous apparatus. Second, as in the reflexes, it is a prompt response to the appropriate stimulus. Again, it is a constant and uniform response—so much is this so, indeed, that there is no mistaking its character, whether it be manifested by the diverse races of man or by the lower animals. It is like the reflexes, also, in being a permanent mode of reaction; throughout life the characteristic display of the rage response may be suddenly evoked in all its elaborateness. Further, it is a response to a fairly definite stimulus—an inner stimulus which arises when there is a hampering or checking of motion or an opposition to one or another primary impulse. Finally, the rage response is like the simple reflexes in being useful." Obviously the rage response has all the earmarks of a subcortical reaction. Its prompt, uniform, and stereotyped character places it in sharp contrast to the type of behavior subserved by the cortex. The latter is characteristically complex, uncertain, temporary, and modifiable by experience. The behavior of an enraged cat is no more complex and no more the result of experience than are its postural and righting reflexes, which, as shown by the late Professor Magnus of Utrecht (1924), are managed in an automatic inborn manner by neural mechanisms which lie wholly in the brain-stem and spinal cord. As regards their degree of complexity and integration and their immunity to modification, there is every similarity between the reactions of an angry cat and those reactions of a falling cat which land it invariably upon all four feet.

The foregoing considerations certainly suggest that the expression of this emotion is dependent upon the older, more primitive divisions of the central nervous system. There is much experimental evidence to show that this is actually the case.

When a dog or cat is deprived of its cerebral cortices the capacity for the exhibition of anger is by no means abolished. After complete removal or disconnection of all parts of the cerebral cortex and with some injury to corpora striata and the dorsal part of the thalamus, Goltz's dog (1892) lived in good health for more than 18 months. The animal was reduced to a state of idiocy; it lost all of its learned behavior, showed no ability to regain the loss, and did not acquire any new modes of response. Its emotional activity was confined to a reaction, capable of regular elicitation, which closely resembled the picture of rage as seen in a normal dog. The same was true of the similar dog described by Rothmann (1923). Dusser de Barenne (1920) prepared and studied for months two decorticate cats which showed marked emotional responses to various disturbances, innocuous as well as mildly harmful; merely lifting the animals caused energetic movements of defense and those reactions so characteristic of the angry cat—spitting, growling, and erection of the hair. The trivial and often irrelevant nature of the conditions which would evoke the rage reaction in these four animals is noteworthy. It was readily induced in Goltz's dog by merely pinching the skin. Taking the animal from its cage invariably caused barking, growling, biting, and every evidence of violent protest in spite of the fact that this procedure was the usual sign for feeding and would have become quite agreeable to any normal dog. Snarling and growling were obtained in Rothmann's dog by gentle scratching of its back, and the presence of a fly on the creature's nose sent it into a fit of rage. It is disappointing that the reports of the emotional reactions of these animals mention only one symptom of sympathetic activity, the erection of hair in the case of the cats. Other superficial signs of sympathetic discharge were undoubtedly present, but were evidently overlooked. In the course of some recent work the writer has studied in the chronic condition four cats and three dogs in which the ablations varied from removal of neocortex to extirpation of all cerebral tissue above the hypothalamus. A description of the types of emotional response exhibited by these animals will be given below, but it may be stated here that many observations on them have confirmed and extended those of the earlier investigators and leave no doubt that the chronically decorticate cat or dog can express rage.

The observations of Goltz, Rothmann, and Dusser de Barenne, showing that cortical ablation renders the mammal excessively prone to the display of anger, led Cannon and Britton (1925) to make use of decorticate cats in the acute condition, i.e., animals which do not recover from the effects of the operation, for the study of emotional activation of the sympathetic. It was found that after disconnecting the cortex from the brain-stem there appeared upon removing the anaesthetic "a group of remarkable activities such as are usually associated with emotional excitement— a sort of sham rage." They included: lashing of the tail; arching of the trunk; thrusting and jerking of the limbs in the thongs which fastened them to the animal board, together with protrusion of the claws and clawing movements; snarling; movements of the head from side to side with attempts to bite; very rapid panting with mouth open and movements of the tongue to and fro. These somatic activities were accompanied by signs of a vigorous sympathetic discharge; erection of the tail hairs; sweating from the toe-pads; dilatation of the pupils; large increments in heart rate and arterial pressure; an abundant secretion of adrenin; and, as later shown by Bulatao and Cannon (1925), an increase in blood sugar up to five times the normal concentration. These activities occurred without special stimulation in "fits" lasting from a few seconds to many minutes with intervening periods of quiet during which a fit could be evoked by the slightest disturbance of the animal.

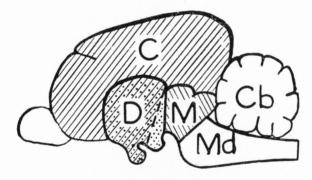

FIGURE 3

MEDIAN SECTION OF A MAMMALIAN BRAIN

C, cerebral cortex; *D*, diencephalon (indicated by dots); *M*, mesencephalon (midbrain); *Md*, medulla oblongata; *Cb*, cerebellum. The cross-hatching, from right downward to left, marks the portion of the brain which can be removed without interfering with the expression of rage.

(After figure in W. B. Cannon's "The Mechanism of Emotional Disturbance of Bodily Function," *New England J. Med.*, 1926.)

For years the decerebrate cat,[3] an animal with brain-stem transected at a mesencephalic level (Figure 3), has been employed in the analysis of reflex action (Sherrington, 1906). The testimony of all who have inves-

---

[3]Following Sherrington and in accord with the proper definition of the word *cerebrum* physiologists generally use the adjective *decerebrate* to designate the condition which ensues upon mesencephalic transection of the brain-stem. *Decerebration* and *decortication* are quite different procedures and should not be confused.

tigated such preparations is consistent in showing that they never exhibit the typical decorticate rage. The decerebrate cat of acute experiments displays marked rigidity of the antigravity muscles and this postural condition is not interrupted by movements nor is marked sympathetic discharge evident unless nociceptive stimuli be given. Woodworth and Sherrington (1904) have described certain responses, expressive of affective states, which they were able to evoke in decerebrate cats by strong stimulation of sensory nerves, but these "pseudaffective reflexes," as they were designated, "never amounted to an effective action of attack or escape." In contrast, the sham rage of the decorticate cat is elicited by the slightest disturbance of any kind, is astonishingly intense, and possesses a width and energy of expression that make it unmistakably the counterpart of the behavior of the enraged normal animal. This more general, more energetic, and more easily evoked activity must be dependent upon neural mechanisms which lie below the cortex and above the midbrain.

A delimitation of the subcortical region responsible for the sham rage of the decorticate cat was undertaken by Bard and the results were reported in 1928. The experimental procedure adopted was that of ablation of varying amounts of brain-stem after removal of the cerebral cortices. In a series of forty-six successful acute experiments the sham rage occurred regularly after ablation of corpora striata and the rostral half of the diencephalon. It appeared in typical form after still more caudal truncations of the brain-stem. For example, sham rage of maximal intensity occurred when there remained above the midbrain only a thin caudal segment of diencephalon. This consisted, ventrally, of the distal portion of the hypothalamus and, dorsally, of a correspondingly small amount of thalamus, metathalamus, and epithalamus. That the dorsal portion of this region is not essentially concerned in the activity was shown by the results of other experiments in which the sections passed ventrally and rostrally from the anterior colliculi. In these animals there remained of the diencephalon only the greater part of the hypothalamus and very small ventro-caudal fractions of the thalamus. When the brain-stem was truncated at the caudal extremity of the diencephalon or through the cranial portion of the mesencephalon (Figure 3), the sham rage invariably failed to develop. Such animals exhibited decerebrate rigidity and remained quiet during the hours of survival.

From these results the conclusion was drawn that the discharge of nervous impulses which evokes this extraordinary motor activity of the acute decorticate preparation is conditioned by central mechanisms which lie within an area comprising the caudal half of the hypothalamus and the most ventral and most caudal fractions of the corresponding segment of the thalamus. From the point of view of localization the experimental facts justified a less conservative statement. Anatomical considerations make it improbable that the small remnants of certain thalamic nuclei left in some of the active animals were of any functional significance. Consequently it may be stated with assurance that the sham rage depends on the caudal hypothalamus. Certain theoretical writers (Harlow and

Stagner, 1932), ignoring obvious anatomical facts, have been incautious in claiming that the thalamus is involved in these activities.

Important parts of the central arrangements for the expression of rage are of course located below the diencephalon. Certain individual elements of the entire reaction may be induced in the spinal animal, and still more in bulbo-spinal or midbrain preparations. Decerebrate cats which Bazett and Penfield (1922) were able to keep alive for periods of time varying from several days to three weeks exhibited a certain "pseudaffective" activity. This consisted of such isolated items of behavior as biting, clawing, and waving of the tail; it never attained a general affective state and was typically brought forth by a stimulus connected with some habitual mode of response. Recently Keller (1932) has reported the occurrence of rage responses in cats which he succeeded in maintaining for as long as 18 to 20 days after decerebration. The specific reactions were somewhat more readily elicited after cutting through the middle and lower portions of the midbrain than after high mesencephalic transections. This "rage" was evidenced by spitting, growling, tail-waving, pawing (scratching?), and signs of sympathetic discharge. Rather slight disturbances sufficed to provoke the reactions. The protocols published by Keller give no indication that his animals ever exhibited at any one time more than a few of the activities which constitute the full expression of rage seen in decorticate or hypothalamic cats. It appears that the full capacity of expression is not present unless the hypothalamic region is intact. The very fact that there is such a tremendous contrast in behavior between hypothalamic and decerebrate cats in the acute state is sufficient evidence that the diencephalic mechanism adds a prepotent factor for the expression of rage. Even were it argued that the inactivity of acute decerebrate preparations is due to some sort of "shock" there remains the fact that such "shock" is absent in hypothalamic animals.

The central source of the vigorous sympathetic activity which accompanies strong emotional excitement is a matter of primary importance in any consideration of the neural basis of emotional expression. A central representation of the sympathetic can be discerned in the medulla oblongata (Bard, 1929). We may regard as sympathetic centers the well-established bulbar vasoconstrictor center, the center for the reflex secretion of adrenin located by Cannon and Rapport (1921b) in the upper part of the medulla, and the neural mechanism concerned in reflex hyperglycemia which Brooks (1931) has delimited in this same part of the brain. Although sympathetic activity may be induced in the chronic spinal animal by nociceptive stimuli and even by hypoglycemia (Brooks, 1933, 1934), it is practically certain that the tonic and most of the reflex sympathetic responses of intact animals are dependent upon the medulla oblongata. There is available no good evidence that such activities require suprabulbar levels of integration. Nevertheless it is now thoroughly established that there is a hypothalamic representation of the sympathetic. Karplus and Kreidl (1909, 1910, 1911, 1918, 1927) have observed that local stimulation of the hypothalamus in narcotized animals causes various sympathetic discharges, and Houssay and Molinelli (1925) reported that similar stimulation induces medulliadrenal secretion. Beattie, Brow, and Long (1930) have shown that the very same part of the hypothalamus which is necessary for sham rage is the source of the sympathetic impulses responsible for the cardiac extrasystoles occurring under chloroform anaesthesia. The thalamus apparently lacks any similar sympathetic representation (Karplus and Kreidl, 1909, 1910, 1911, 1918, 1927; Ranson and Magoun, 1933; Sachs, 1911). What is the significance of the fact that sympathetic discharges may be induced by local stimulation of the hypothalamic region? It seems to the writer that a likely explanation of this fact may be derived from Cannon's concept of the emergency function of the sympathetic. This implies a dominant central mechanism responsible for the sympathetic activity characteristic of emergency states. Conspicuous among the latter are emotional excitement and exposure to cold. The actual existence of such a center and its hypothalamic location are supported not only by the work on sham rage, but by the various lines of work which have delimited the part of the brain essential for maintaining a constant body temperature in the face of environmental cold (Bazett, Alpers, and Erb, 1933; Keller and Hare, 1932).

As has already been pointed out, several physiologists have reported that signs of anger can be elicited in dogs and cats during prolonged survival periods following decortication (Goltz, 1892; Rothmann, 1923; Dusser de Barenne, 1920; Schaltenbrand and Cobb, 1931). These writers, however, were not particularly concerned with this aspect of behavior and did not devote much attention to it. Therefore it seemed worth while to reinvestigate the matter and to determine more precisely, if possible, the conditions under which a display of anger can be evoked in such animals. It seemed especially desirable to compare at first hand the chronic with the acute preparation. Altogether the writer has prepared and studied during long survival periods four cats and three dogs in which the least extensive cerebral ablation has been bilateral removal of the neocortex, i.e., all cortex except that belonging to the rhinencephalon. The general behavior of these animals and detailed descriptions of the modes of emotional expression displayed by them are given elsewhere (Bard, 1934). The brain of each has been serially sectioned and the exact extent of the removal thus ascertained. The four cats differed considerably in respect to the extent of forebrain ablated and a report correlating the anatomical with the physiological differences will soon appear (Bard and Rioch).

The first animal of this series was cat 103. She was kept for twenty-eight months after the second and final intracranial operation. Serial sections of the brain have shown that the entire neocortex, the lateral parts of the dorsal thalami, the rostro-lateral portions of the caudate nuclei, and most of the rhinencephalon on one side had been cut away. The greater part of the striatum, the entire hypothalamus and the mesencephalon were uninjured. In cat 313 a similar ablation was carried out, but with somewhat less involvement of rhinencephalon and with very little damage to the thalamus. This animal remained in excellent health for six weeks and then suddenly succumbed to an acute respiratory infection. Cat 244 was subjected to a somewhat greater removal of cerebral tissue than were cats 103 and 313. The greater part of the striatum, much of the rhinencephalon and almost all of the thalamus had been extirpated, but the hypothalamus remained intact. With the brain in this condition she remained in good health for eleven months and was finally sacrificed for the neuro-anatomical study. The fourth cat, No. 228, survived thirteen months and was to all intents and purposes a hypothalamic preparation. The rhinencephalon had been wholly removed or disconnected except for a small fragment of septum and tuberculum olfactorium on one side, the striatum had been ablated and apart from the hypothalamus there remained of the diencephalon only the habenular ganglia and a little of the most medial portion of the dorsal thalamus. Two dogs were subjected to essentially the same cerebral removal as cat 313 and were kept for three and four months, respectively. Another dog was maintained for eleven weeks after removal of all cortex, striatum, and most of the diencephalon above the hypothalamus.

Each of the four "decorticate" cats exhibited definite signs of anger when stimulated in various ways. Pinching the tip of the tail or the loose skin of the flank evoked a stereotyped reaction consisting of lowering the head, raising the back, retraction of ears, loud growling, hissing, biting, alternate striking movements of the forelegs with claws unsheathed, turning to one side or the other, erection of hair, pupillo-dilatation, retraction of nictitating membranes, widening of the palpebral spaces, cardiac acceleration, and, occasionally, sweating from the toe-pads. This reaction varied from the display of rage seen in normal cats in being undirected. Although the striking was not incoordinate and the biting quite energetic, both were first directed to the region just beneath the jaws. As the head was turned the attack was usually shifted to the animal's own flank, hip, or hindleg but without reference to the point of stimulation. Thus the experimenter's hand could be applied with impunity. It is significant that the animal never made any attempt to escape or move away during the stimulation. The response never outlasted the stimulus; "after-discharge" was minimal. It was always safe immediately upon stopping the effective stimulation to place one's finger against the animal's mouth. The ease with which the rage reaction could be induced in each cat varied from time to time and in general it was impossible to correlate these changes with any definite condition or circumstance. At times merely rolling the tip of the tail gently between thumb and forefinger sufficed to evoke a violent reaction. At other times a strong pinch was required. Occasionally the full response occurred when the cat was brushed or merely lifted. When the animal was tied on its back in precisely the same manner as were the cats of the earlier experiments (Bard, 1928), the reaction induced was in every detail precisely the same as that described as sham rage. In order the better to appraise this behavior a large number of normal cats were subjected to this form of restraint. The responses obtained in vigorous normal animals differed in no essential way from the sham rage of acutely or chronically decorticate and hypothalamic cats. Although the typical rage reaction of cats 103 and 313 showed certain fluctuations in the ease with which it could be evoked, it failed to undergo any progressive change in threshold or intensity. During the third, fourth, and fifth weeks of her survival cat 228 exhibited signs of the most extreme fury on the slightest disturbance, but from the sixth to the tenth weeks a diminution in the intensity and a rise in the threshold of the response were observed. Thereafter it could always be evoked, but only by strong nociceptive stimulation. Rage reactions were always less readily induced by ordinary manipulations in 244 than in any of the other cats. This animal, however, was peculiar in that she struck out with vigor, hissed and spat when attacked by other cats or when such an attack was mimicked by tapping her on the face with one's finger.

Each of the dogs showed signs of anger when disturbed in certain ways. The responses were essentially the same as those described by Goltz and Rothmann. They were so readily provoked in one of the dogs without neocortex that an attendant, used to ill-tempered animals, expressed his unwillingness to continue handling the animal. In the course of experiments on the temperature control of these dogs it was found that subjecting them to warm environmental temperatures diminished their tendency to display signs of anger whereas exposure to cold had the opposite effect.

On the basis of the foregoing account it may be stated with some assurance that the pattern of response which constitutes the *expression* of anger in certain mammals depends on a central mechanism that is situated subcortically. The results obtained in acute experiments on cats showed that this neural mechanism is located in the base of the diencephalon, a phylogenetically ancient part of the brain, common to all members of the vertebrate series. The more recent observation that typical signs of rage can be elicited in dogs and cats during long periods of survival following removal of nearly all cerebral tissue above the hypothalamus supports the earlier findings. The survival experiments also afford a more substantial basis for a discussion of the nature of the central processes which underlie the expression of this emotion in normal animals.

In 1884 the English neurologist, Hughlings Jackson, made a suggestion that has received much support in recent years, especially in the writings of Head (1920, 1921). It was to the effect that the nervous system is organized in such a way that the primitive reactions of the older parts are prevented from playing a dominant rôle in behavior by the inhibitory influence of higher levels. Thus the cerebral cortex normally holds in check those activities of the lower, more archaic centers which would seriously interfere with its more discriminative reactions. The expression of strong emotional excitement is just this sort of activity. On the basis of the doctrine of Jackson, its occurrence after removal of the cortex may be regarded as a "release phenomenon" due to the freeing of a subcortical mechanism from cortical restraint. It will be profitable to examine, in the light of the available evidence, the probability of this explanation.

The excessiveness and easy elicitation of the sham rage exhibited by freshly decorticated cats indicate that the central mechanisms involved are overactive and hyperexcitable, a state certainly suggestive of release from higher control. However, in acute experiments the possibility of excitation from some sort of "irritation" cannot be wholly excluded. Nevertheless the fact that sham rage develops in the same form after cutting through the forebrain at any subcortical level above the caudal diencephalon makes it most improbable that direct irritation from injury is a significant factor in its genesis. It is certain that any tendency of long-surviving animals to react excessively must be attributed to some sort of release. The seven chronic preparations described above were observed and studied before operation for periods of time sufficient to obtain an excellent knowledge of the general nature and individual traits of each. Thus there is a firm basis for stating that after decortication the tendency of cat 103 to react to any one of several rage stimuli (tying on board, pinching tail, handling roughly) was, as a rule, definitely greater than before operation. During the fourth and fifth weeks of her survival cat 228 displayed anger excessively under conditions which had proved wholly ineffective as rage stimuli before the cerebral ablation. The gradual regression of the rage reaction in this animal is of interest, but it does not seem possible to account for it on the basis of any known fact. The rage response evokable after operation was somewhat more violent and more easily provoked in 313 than in any of the other cats. This may possibly be related to the extraordinary wildness and intractability that characterized this animal before operation. However, the difference between the rage reactions of 103 and 313 in the decorticate state becomes trivial when compared to the very great contrast in disposition exhibited by the two animals through long pre-operative observation periods. After operation the three dogs showed a greater tendency to display anger in response to mildly nociceptive stimuli. Cat 244 was the only animal of the series that failed indubitably to show such a change. The results of these two sets of studies favor the idea that decortication leads to a release of the subcortical rage mechanism from an inhibitory influence. The fact that the chronic preparations reacted in general less excessively than did the animals of the acute experiments suggests the operation of other factors than release. The possibility of the presence of "irritation" as a factor in the acute experiments has been discussed. It is not unlikely that in the case of continued survival without cortex and other higher centers release of the hypothalamic mechanism is coupled with and modified by some lowering of its excitability.

If a behavior pattern such as that of rage can be elicited after removal of cerebral cortex it may be supposed that the display of other primitive forms of emotional excitement may also be evoked in the absence of this highest and newest part of the brain. No evidence that such is the case had been given in the earlier reports of surviving decorticate animals, and one of the main objectives in the preparation of the four cats described above was the exploration of this question. It was therefore a matter of much interest to find that the first of the decorticate cats, No. 103, reacted to certain loud noises by exhibiting signs of fear. On the eleventh postoperative day it happened, quite by chance, that this animal was exposed to the sound made by the escape of steam under high pressure. The moment the noise was heard the cat abruptly retracted and lowered its head, crouched, mewed, and then dashed off running rapidly in a slinking manner with head, chest, belly, and tail close to the floor. After blindly colliding with several objects in her path, she came to rest in a corner, where she crouched mewing plaintively with eyes and pupils wide and the hair of back and tail erected. This reaction was frequently obtained in 103 during her long period of survival and it was easily evoked in 313. Cat 244 also responded in a similar, but somewhat less intense, fashion. Loud noises proved to be the only agents capable of inducing a fear reaction in these animals. After much experimentation it was found that the most effective stimulus was the loud blast o   a bugle or police whistle. No frank signs of fear could ever be evoked in cat 228. This animal differed also from the others in failing to respond to certain sounds of low intensity. A low whistle or scraping and clicking noises caused 103, 313, or 244 to turn the head and prick up the ears so that a listening attitude was assumed.

When normal cats were subjected to the blast of a bugle or the sound of escaping steam the majority reacted in very much the same way as did decorticate cats 103, 313, and 244. A few merely crouched with head retracted, eyes wide, and mewed as if frightened and bewildered. Others at once dashed off precipitately and made wild attempts to escape as if possessed by the most profound terror. Such observations lead to the conviction that it is correct to describe the similar behavior of the decorticate animals as an exhibition of fear or terror. It is a specific form of activity that cannot possibly be confused with any other mode of response. The element of escape which was completely lacking in the rage responses of these same animals was a most prominent feature of their fear reaction. Conversely, the element of attack which characterized their exhibitions of anger formed no part of the fear response. While these observations show that fear may be displayed in cats after removal of neocortex and much of the diencephalon, they fail to delimit the subcortical region responsible for the activity. Its failure to occur in cat 228 is of some interest in this connection. This fact may lead at first sight to the supposition that some part of the forebrain above the hypothalamus is essential for the elicitation of a fear reaction, but when one considers that the effective stimuli were auditory a more cogent explanation comes to mind. In cat 228, the medial geniculate bodies were removed, whereas these important parts of the central auditory apparatus remained intact in cats 103 and 313; in cat 244, where the fear reaction was somewhat less pronounced, one medial geniculate had been extensively damaged.

It would be of great interest to know whether a full display of sexual excitement could occur in animals without cerebral cortex. Of the ten or twelve dogs and cats that have been reported as surviving for long periods without cortex, cat 103 (a mature female) has been the only one that exhibited any evidence of this type of emotional behavior. During the second month following the final cerebral operation and again in the sixth month of survival it was noted that mechanical stimulation of the genitalia evoked elevation of the pelvis and tail and treading movements of the hindlegs. This response was sometimes followed by rolling, head-rubbing, and the assumption of a playful attitude. Considerable observation has shown that such behavior is an invariable accompaniment of oestrus in normal female cats and that it becomes accentuated when a male is present. Cat 103 attracted males and yielded a vaginal smear typical of oestrus only when this behavior could be induced. When she became the object of the attentions of a sexually excited male cat, 103 failed to respond to their preliminary advances except to show the usual signs of anger in response to rough treatment. When, on three occasions, intromission actually occurred in spite of her failure to cooperate, she displayed the same reaction that was induced by artificial mechanical stimulation. Thus a behavior pattern which constitutes a part of the elaborate courtship behavior of the normal oestrous female was evoked only by direct sexual stimulation. No very definite conclusions as to the central management of sexual behavior can be drawn from this isolated experience. The observations have had their chief value in suggesting that further analysis may definitely reveal a subcortical locus for the essential neural organization involved in this important mode of emotional expression.

Many years ago Bekhterev (1887) reported signs of pleasure in freshly decorticated animals, purring in cats and tail-wagging in dogs, and he stated that these responses disappeared after removing the thalamus. On the other hand, Goltz's dog never gave any evidence of joy or pleasure and Rothmann's animal was also apparently incapable of this sort of behavior. The same was true of the three dogs prepared by the writer; petting never induced tail-wagging or other signs of enjoyment. On many occasions persistent attempts were made to evoke signs of pleasure in each of the four cats prepared by the writer. Stroking them gently or rubbing their heads never induced such signs. Cat 244 was heard to purr on one occasion. Although the conditions under which this occurred (lying unrestrained on a soft surface with thermocouples applied to the flank) were many times repeated they invariably failed to induce it. None of the other cats ever purred when made comfortable and gently petted. On several occasions Schaltenbrand and Cobb heard purring in their cat without neocortex and this leaves no doubt that such animals may purr. It is, however, very doubtful that purring in itself is a sign of pleasure or contentment. Normal cats purr under several quite different circumstances and it is not uncommon to hear it in animals that are definitely agitated and restless; indeed, it sometimes occurs in cats that are showing signs of anger. In the light of these facts it seems fair to say that there is at hand no evidence that typical signs of pleasure can be evoked in dogs and cats after removal of cerebral cortex.

Before dismissing the subject of emotional expression in animals, it may be of some service to stress certain features of the results that have been obtained. In the first place, it cannot too strongly be emphasized that in his experimental work the physiologist (as distinguished from the student of subjective experiences) considers emotions as behavior patterns. When Cannon and Britton (1925) first described the remarkable activity of acutely decorticate cats they identified it as an expression of rage. Bard (1928), in reporting his subsequent study of these preparations, concluded that "this behavior simulates the expression of anger as seen in the normal cat and is best described as sham rage." Both Cannon and Bard have employed the term "sham rage" to indicate that they were dealing with an *expression* of this emotion and to suggest the very great probability that decortication profoundly modifies the capacity for subjectively experiencing emotion.[4] The propriety of designating this activity of decorticate animals as a display of rage has been questioned by Harlow and Stagner (1932). These writers maintain that it really represents "excitement" and they suggest that the activities of the sham rage "would characterize the emotion of 'fear' as adequately as they would the emotion of 'rage.'" But Bard (1928) had pointed out that anyone who has ever tied an unruly cat to an animal board will agree that the sham rage closely resembles the behavior of the infuriated normal animal. It is doubtless impossible to determine whether a cat standing up to an attacking or threatening dog is subjectively *experiencing* rage or fear or a mixture of both, but on the supposition that different things should have different names it can be asserted that a normal cat is capable of *displaying* both rage and fear. When a cat reacts by spitting and aggressive biting and clawing, it is necessary to call it one thing. When this same cat dashes off in a furtive or precipitate manner, mewing plaintively, and tremblingly goes to cover on the first opportunity, it is proper to designate this as something else. General usage leads one to call the former an expression of anger, the latter a display of fear or terror. This distinction is also applicable to long-surviving decorticate animals, for it is now known that they are capable of showing not only sham rage, but an entirely different reaction pattern that very closely resembles the exhibition of fear evokable in normal animals of the same species. In view of the available facts, it can scarcely be denied that emotions, as patterns of response, do exist. These facts also dispose of the contention (Harlow and Stagner, 1933) that the specificity of an emotion is dependent upon cognitive processes whose anatomical seat is in the cerebral cortex. It is now established that specifically different forms of emotional behavior are evokable after removal of cerebral cortex.

---

[4] Since "sham" implies something false or counterfeit, while "quasi-" means "as if," or "having some resemblance," it would doubtless have been more accurate to use the expression "quasi-rage."

When we turn to the experience of the clinic, we find a mass of evidence to show that there is subcortical management of several types of emotional expression. This has recently been presented in some detail by Cannon (1927, 1928b). It consists of examples of emotional overactivity and of emotional paralysis. In the former there are generally good reasons to suspect removal of cortical control; in the latter there are usually signs of subcortical impairment of function.

First of all are certain phenomena associated with anaesthesia. The general anaesthetics, such as ether, chloroform, and nitrous oxide, together with alcohol, are drugs which act as depressants, not as excitants (Cushny, 1928). All parts of the central nervous system, however, are not equally sensitive to their action. Indeed they are useful in surgery because they first depress the cortical processes associated with consciousness, next reflexes in general, and, last of all, the bulbar centers concerned with respiration and other essential functions. Accordingly they may be used to produce insensibility and muscular relaxation without endangering life. When any one of these agents is administered the stage of relatively deep surgical anaesthesia is preceded by a primary stage of imperfect consciousness and a secondary stage of excitement. During the excitement stage there may be the most remarkable emotional display; the patient is likely to weep and groan, sing joyously, laugh uproariously, or exhibit all the aggressive signs of rage. While such emotional behavior is going on, the surgeon may—as is sometimes necessary—perform an operation of considerable extent and gravity, and yet later the patient, when wholly conscious, will testify that he was not at all aware of what was happening. It is clear that in such cases vigorous emotional behavior occurs in the absence of emotional consciousness. This means that, although the cerebral cortex is narcotized and inactive, lower centers, themselves not depressed, act in much the same way as after surgical decortication. The anaesthetic functionally decorticates, lessens or destroys for a time cortical inhibition of lower centers, and so releases them to carry out their characteristic motor activities.

In further support of a subcortical origin of various kinds of emotional behavior in human beings are many findings of clinical neurology. When a destructive lesion interrupts the voluntary motor path from the cortex, paralysis of willed movement may not be attended by any impairment of emotional expression. The deficiency is most often unilateral, but may be bilateral. Such patients are incapable of moving one or both sides of the face, but when a sad or joyous situation develops, the muscles of facial expression go into action to give both sides of the face an expression of sadness or gaiety (Wilson, 1924, 1929). In single or double hemiplegia with partial or complete facial paralysis or, more commonly, in "pseudobulbar palsy," a condition involving volitional facial weakness, there may be fits of exaggerated, forced, uncontrollable laughing or crying brought on inevitably and with extreme facility by almost any stimulus. A number of such cases have been described and discussed at length by Kinnier Wilson (1924, 1929). Two will serve as typical examples. One, a young pseudobulbar patient, had suffered a complete loss of all voluntary facial movement so that he could not voluntarily close his eyes, elevate and retract the corners of his mouth, close or open his mouth, bite, swallow, utter a vocal sound or cough.   In contrast to this paralysis of voluntary movement was the preservation of emotional movements of laughing; he went off into rounds of laughter on the slightest provocation so that his existence was one long roar of laughter.   Another of Wilson's patients, a woman, became peculiarly lachrymose after a stroke had produced a right hemiplegia with aphasia, the least emotional stimulus threw her into a fit of crying with copious tears so that bout after bout of weeping succeeded one another through the day.   In such cases as these the over-reaction may be confined to either laughing or crying, or both modes of expression may occur at different times in the same individual.   Uncontrollable pathological laughing or crying are typically allowed by lesions of the voluntary paths from the cortex to the medulla and spinal cord, and Wilson states that "the more severe the volitional facio-respiratory paralysis, the more exaggerated is involuntary innervation of the same mechanism." This fact suggests that interruption of the voluntary cortical control leads to unbalanced activity in a separate neural apparatus which is the source of the emotional behavior and which under normal conditions is held in check by cortical activity.

Because the lesions associated with pathological laughing and crying most often involve cortico-thalamic fibers it has been supposed that the abnormality is the result of freeing the thalamus from a cortical check. Brissaud long ago asserted that integrity of the thalamus is essential for the appearance of spasmodic uncontrolled laughter and weeping, but Wilson (1924, 1929) objects to this view for the reason that they may occur when the thalamus itself is grossly diseased.   Nevertheless, there is evidence to show that when the base of the thalamic region, the part essential for the rage-reaction, is the site of a morbid condition there is typically a loss of emotional expression.   This fact is mentioned by Wilson, but it is interpreted by him as due to the interruption of fibers of cortical origin which he believes are "the routes taken by emotional impulses to modify the facio-respiratory synkinesis in the direction either of laughter or the reverse."   For the existence of such paths in the brain-stem, especially in the midbrain, Wilson presents good evidence, both clinical and physiological, but his assumption that they are of cortical origin is not convincing, for, as he himself admits, no case of emotional paralysis originating in a cortical lesion has yet been recorded.   On the other hand, lesions which separate the cortex from lower levels are commonly followed by exaggerated emotional activity.   It is more in accord with the evidence at hand to think in terms of a subcortical organization for emotional expression located or centered in the under part of the thalamus, connected by efferent paths with the primary motor nuclei of medulla and spinal cord, and normally subject to cortical restraint.

The occurrence of emotional paralysis with retention of volitional normality is another datum of clinical experience which bears upon the present discussion. There are patients who can voluntarily move both sides of the face in a normal symmetrical manner, yet one side remains motionless whenever they laugh in fun, weep in sorrow, or make a grimace in pain. The lesions provocative of this effect are, as far as the writer has been able to determine, invariably subcortical. Kirilzev (1891) has described a man with emotional paralysis of the right side of the face in whom autopsy disclosed a tumor in the center of the left thalamus. Wilson (1924, 1929) reports three similar cases; in one there was a tumor of the subthalamic region on one side; and in the other two there were lesions in the midbrain. More complete loss of emotional expression is sometimes seen when the ventral part of the diencephalon is involved in a pathological process. Fulton and Bailey (1929) have pointed out that among the symptoms of tumors of this region is a curious emotional negativism; for example, one of their patients appeared to be devoid of all emotional expression, exhibited a "fatuous serenity of mind with complete failure to appreciate the gravity of his own physical condition." Also, in cases of "narcolepsy" with disease of the region of the third ventricle the expression and the feeling of emotion may be quite absent; such patients meet jibes and insults with utter indifference and give no evidence of affective response when some tragic happening is called to mind. All these instances of impairment of emotional expression can be reasonably accounted for on the basis of a defect in the subcortical mechanism suggested above.

The foregoing observations, physiological, clinical, and pathological, point to the diencephalon as the region in which resides the neural organization for the expression of various emotional states. It also follows from the same evidence that inhibitory cortical influences normally prevent the primitive activities from dominating behavior. The subcortical processes are at all times ready to seize control of the motor reactions and when the cortical check is released they do so promptly and with elemental vigor. Thus while the behavior attending the primitive emotions is certainly not due to a nervous discharge of cortical origin, we must ascribe to the cortex an important rôle in the production of such behavior. As an efferent projection system the cerebral cortex apparently has a negative function in regard to these activities. Furthermore, as the neural basis for the conditioned responses of the higher mammals (Pavlov, 1927), the cortex greatly increases the number of circumstances which are capable of acting as emotional stimuli. By means of the cortex the inborn, stereotyped, emotional reactions, like the secretion of saliva and other simple reflexes, become, as the result of experience, conditioned responses. When conditioned stimuli evoke emotional responses we may suppose, on the basis of the argument just developed, that they do so by releasing the cortical check.

THEORY OF EMOTION

The term emotion, as it is reasonably employed, implies two things: a way of acting and a way of feeling. The foregoing account has been limited to a consideration of the nature and the neural basis of the bodily changes in emotion. It would, however, be a truncated and incomplete treatment of the subject that did not mention the relation of these physiological phenomena to emotion as a mode of feeling. The nature of that relation constitutes a problem of psychological importance, and it may be approached with advantage from the point of view of this chapter.

A cross-section of contemporary psychological literature reveals a fairly widespread tendency to accept as a solution of this problem the familiar theory of the emotions which is associated with the names of William James and C. G. Lange.

The James-Lange Theory. Broadly stated, this theory holds that consciousness of the bodily disturbances is the essential element in emotional consciousness. Contrary to the popular conception which regards emotional display as the sequence of emotional consciousness, it insists that the bodily manifestations of emotion must be interposed between the perception of the exciting fact and the occurrence of the mental state termed emotional. Expressed in terms of neural happenings, the theory is that the emotional stimulus (an object or a thought) evokes a motor discharge to effector organs whereupon afferent impulses course back from the reacting organs and throw into action the cerebral processes which underlie emotional feeling. Such is the core of the hypothesis put forward by James, first in 1884 (see James and Lange, 1922), and re-explained by him ten years later (1894). As regards the source of the afferent impulses which transform the "object-simply-apprehended" to the "object-emotionally-felt," James assumed that they arise generally from somatic and visceral effectors. Always, however, he was inclined to attribute greater importance to the backflow from the viscera. Lange, who in 1885 independently announced a similar theory, elaborated it almost entirely on the basis of changes in the circulatory system. According to him (see James and Lange, 1922, p. 73) stimulation of the vasomotor center by whatever arouses the emotions is the "root of the causes of the affections, however else they may be constituted, and is fundamental to the physiological phenomena which are the essential components of the affections." Common to both James and Lange was the tendency to limit their theory to the explanation of the "coarser" emotions, fear, anger, joy, and sorrow.

The arguments advanced by the original sponsors of the theory were not based on any crucial experimental tests. Lange enumerated the symptoms of the major emotions, claimed that they are all referable to vascular changes, and distinguished between one emotion and another on the basis of different bodily accompaniments. He pointed out that physiological effects attended by emotion may be induced by a variety of causes (wine, hashish, certain mushrooms, opium, a cold shower) which, he thought, are "utterly independent of disturbances of the mind." In addition he argued (p. 66) that abstraction of the bodily symptoms from a frightened individual leaves nothing of his fear—"let his pulse beat calmly, his look be firm, his color normal, his movements quick and sure, his speech strong, his thought clear; and what remains of his fear?" This same speculative argument was one of the chief lines of evidence cited by James in support of his contention. He urged (p. 102) as the vital point of his whole theory this introspective consideration: *"If we fancy some strong emotion, and then try to abstract from our consciousness of it all the feelings of its bodily symptoms, we find we have nothing left behind,* no 'mind-stuff' out of which the emotion can be constituted, and that a cold and neutral state of intellectual perception is all that remains." In further support of his theory James mentioned certain experiences in which bodily effects appear to be antecedent to the arousal of an emotion or an emotional idea; he summoned the testimony of fellow psychologists and of actors that sometimes, at least, voluntary mimicry of emotional behavior is attended by the appropriate affect.

Experimental and Observational Tests of the James-Lange Theory. Since the time when the James-Lange theory was developed, physiological experimentation and neurological observation have provided a number of objective facts which bear directly upon it and give considerable insight as to its validity. These we shall consider.

1. First of all, there are the numerous events occurring in the viscera during great emotional excitement. According to James, they play a major rôle in giving to consciousness an emotional hue. According to Lange, emotion is wholly the product of vascular changes. Pertinent to these assumptions are the following experimental facts.

When the visceral processes which typically occur in emotion cannot occur, emotional behavior is not altered. The first proof of this was obtained by Sherrington (1906), who sectioned the cervical spinal cord and vagus nerves in a number of dogs, thereby destroying all connection of the brain with the viscera of abdomen and thorax and separating the vasomotor center from all vasomotor nerves except the tiny vasodilator components of the seventh and ninth cranial pairs. As previously mentioned, Cannon, Lewis, and Britton (1927; see also Cannon, Newton, Bright, Menkin, and Moore, 1929) have kept cats in a healthy state for many months after removal of the entire sympathetic division of the autonomic system, the division which in fear and rage operates to produce the visceral changes typical of those emotions. These operations, which removed surgically the sensations from the viscera to which Lange attributed the whole and James the major part of the felt emotion, had no effect upon the emotional responses of the parts which remained capable of reacting. Cannon reports (1927) that in the sympathectomized cats "all superficial signs of rage were manifested in the presence of a barking dog— hissing, growling, retraction of the ears, showing of the teeth, lifting of the paw to strike—*except* erection of the hairs." In Sherrington's dogs, reduction of the field of perception to the head, neck, and a small portion of the forelimbs with practically total visceral paralysis and anaesthesia produced no lessening of their emotional character. In anger, joy, disgust, and fear the innervated effectors reacted as before. These experiments demonstrate clearly that, if the operated animals experienced any emotional feeling, that feeling was not subsequent to or in any way dependent upon visceral changes. To that extent they contradict the James-

Lange theory. It has been argued, however, that such experiments have little or no bearing upon the theory because the animals' consciousness may have been modified under the experimental conditions, that in fact the marked emotional display might not have been accompanied by any emotional feeling. But, as Sherrington has remarked, it is difficult to think that the perception initiating the wrathful expression should bring in sequel angry conduct and yet have been impotent to produce "angry feeling." It may be added here, in anticipation of later consideration, that there have been human cases (Dana, 1921) in which elimination of the entire sympathetic system (and all of the somatic system below the neck as well) failed in any way to alter the emotional *feelings* of the patient.

If the emotions are the consequences of the visceral aspects of emotional behavior, we should expect them to follow these changes whenever and however they are produced. But this is not the case. We have already seen that secretion or injection of adrenin evokes all the visceral changes characteristic of and common to fear, rage, and other strong emotional excitement. But Marañon and others (see Cannon, 1927) have reported that injections of this substance into normal human beings in amounts sufficient to evoke these changes did not produce an emotional experience. They merely gave rise to coldly perceived sensations of palpitation, of diffuse arterial throbbing, of oppression in the chest, of trembling, of chilliness, of nervousness. In certain cases these sensations were coldly reminiscent of previous emotional experiences in which such changes had occurred; the subjects described their feelings by such remarks as, "I feel as if afraid," "as if moved," "as if I had a great fright yet am calm."

Pertinent in this same connection is Cannon's criticism (1927) of the James-Lange theory that the same visceral changes occur in such different emotional states as fear and rage and in such non-emotional states as exposure to cold, hypoglycemia, asphyxia, and strong muscular exercise. All of these states rouse the entire sympathetic system to activity and so affect in a stereotyped way the viscera which are under sympathico-adrenal influence. As Cannon states, the responses in the viscera are too uniform to offer a satisfactory means of distinguishing states which, in man at least, are very different in subjective quality. Physiological evidence thus completely refutes the assumption made by Lange (see James and Lange, 1922, p. 62) that the difference between the different emotions is to be explained by a difference in vasomotor reactions. James, at least in the final expression of his views (1894) did not expressly attempt to differentiate emotions on the basis of different bodily changes, and it would not be fair to employ this argument against his theory. He did, however, greatly emphasize the importance of visceral factors in the total reaction, which, he claimed, is the essential cause of any affective state. For example, when it was objected that laughing from tickling, and shivering from cold, give rise to mere local bodily perceptions, not to real mirth or an emotion of fright, he answered that in no such instance is "the reproduction of an emotional diffusive wave complete. Visceral factors, hard to localize, are left out; and these seem to be the most essential ones of all. I have said that where they also from any inward cause, are added, we have the emotion; and then the subject is seized with objectless or pathological dread, grief, or rage as the case may be." In complete refutation of this is the demonstration (Cannon, Querido, Britton, and Bright, 1927) that with shivering from cold alone there occur the very same visceral changes as occur in actual fright, and that the more intense the shivering the more intense the visceral changes.   In this non-emotional state and in others (e.g., running) the *total reaction,* including the visceral reaction, is the same as in fright and yet there is a notable absence of the emotion which the theory of James demands.

2.   Supporters of James's theory cannot escape the logic of the evidence that visceral factors are inadequate to explain the genesis of emotion by affirming that sensations of the positions and tensions and movements of skeletal muscle constitute the felt emotion and vary to make the differentia of emotion. The following facts will show how untenable is such an assumption.

In those cases of pathological laughing and crying described by Kinnier Wilson (1924, 1929) and already mentioned in this chapter, the apparent, visible emotion by no means always corresponds to the patient's real feelings. Indeed these patients, whose emotional feelings are quite normal, suffer greatly in mind from the contradictory expression of their real feelings. Laughing uproariously they may feel sad, weeping profusely they may feel hilarious. Such cases are numerous, interesting, and convincing. "With all the outward appearances of mirth and hilariousness, and with concomitant activity of visceral mechanisms," writes Wilson, "the individual may not only not feel happy, but his state of mind may be in patent conflict with the apparent emotion." "It is clear," Wilson continues, "that the James-Lange hypothesis must be materially modified if it is to be brought into line with observations such as have here been recorded, with no complete fusion between peripheral and cerebral components."

Other clinical evidence of a lack of parallelism between psychical and somatic elements in emotion is available. Wilson has pointed out the frequency of cases of facial emotional paralysis in which the patient readily feels and is acutely conscious of experiencing normal emotional states in response to the usual stimuli. There may be a mask-like expression behind which is experienced the full play of the emotions. A patient thus suffering from complete absence of facial expressional movement "was very sensitive on this point, and termed it his greatest misfortune that he was forced to be joyful or sad without making any demonstration to his fellow-creatures." But still more significant is the presence of normal emotional feelings in patients suffering from total or nearly total immobility of the skeletal musculature. Such is the condition in advanced stages of paralysis agitans with rigidity, in terminal arthritis deformans, in the terminal stages of tabes, and in certain forms of progressive muscular atrophy. Dana (1921) remarks that in his experience such patients have normal subjective emotional reactions. This neurologist also reports the case of a woman who, as the result of a fracture of the neck, suffered complete paralysis of the skeletal musculature of trunk and all four extremities with complete loss of cutaneous and deep sensibility from the neck down. She lived for nearly a year without change in personality or character, showed and felt emotions of grief, joy, displeasure, and affection. It may be added that the possibility of an emotional discharge of sympathetic impulses was eliminated.   Such cases are not uncommon.   We may say with Dana that it is difficult to understand, on the theory of James, why there is no change in them emotionally.

The clinical studies of Head (1920) have thrown much light upon the conditions underlying the production of feeling-tone.   He has described and studied many cases of unilateral lesions of the thalamus, in which the characteristic symptom is "a tendency to react excessively to all potentially affective stimuli."   The thalamus, it must be understood, is the great sensory ganglion of the brain-stem; it receives and forwards all sensory impulses (except olfactory) destined for the cerebral cortex.   Thalamic lesions may therefore cause deficiencies in sensation.   But they also have the effect just noted.   This is explained by Head as due to the fact—and there is adequate evidence for it—that a part of the thalamus, "the essential center of the thalamus," has the ability to add to affective experience, that this function is normally under the inhibitory influence of the cortex and, when released from cortical control by a lesion which interrupts cortico-thalamic fibers, induces an excessive affective response to certain stimuli. Under such circumstances, pin-pricks, painful pressure, immoderate heat or cold, all produce far keener discomfort when applied to the body on the side of the lesion; also agreeable stimuli, such as moderate warmth, may evoke intense pleasure when applied to the damaged side.   Again, these cases have an excessive sensory reaction to ordinary emotional stimuli.   A woman, very appreciative of certain kinds of music before her illness, found that while ordinary sounds left her cold any music capable of stirring her emotions induced disturbing sensations over the afflicted side of the body.   Another patient had to keep away from church because the singing of hymns evoked unbearable agony on the damaged side of the body.   These cases show that the feeling-tone of any sensation is a product of thalamic activity.   Now it is highly significant, as Cannon (1927) has pointed out, that in these patients "sensations which underlie the appreciation of posture are entirely lacking in feeling-tone."   Hence, the afferent impulses from skeletal muscles which adherents of James's theory have relied upon to provide the extra-visceral part of felt emotion are the very ones which lack the quality to serve the purpose.

The real and essential quality of an emotion is to be found neither in sensory returns from the viscera nor in those from skeletal muscle.   Furthermore, the fact that in non-emotional states (exposure to cold, muscular exercise) bodily activity as a whole is the same as in states rich in emotional feeling (fright, anger) makes it very difficult indeed to attribute the emotion to the total reaction.   The theory of a peripheral source of emotional experience is thus opposed by overwhelming experimental evidence.   The most that can be said for it is that bodily reverberations may add slightly to, and so reinforce, the central processes which under-lie emotional consciousness, and that visceral changes may, by a process of association, lead to a calm, non-emotional recall of previous emotional experiences.

A Theory of Emotion Based on Diencephalic Processes. As we have seen, every relevant experimental fact points away from the periphery and directly toward the brain as the site of the processes which determine whether or not a stimulus shall give rise to emotional feeling. What is the nature and the locus of these all-important central processes?

Cannon (1927, 1931) and also Dana (1921) have proposed the theory that emotion results from the action and reaction of the cerebral cortex and the diencephalon. This theory, unlike the James-Lange theory, has considerable experimental support and takes into account anatomical and physiological facts ignored by the older view. First of all, there is the evidence that at the base of the diencephalon are located the neural patterns responsible for emotional behavior, mechanisms capable of independent discharge but normally held in check by the cerebral cortex. At the same time the cerebral cortex is the immediate site of emotional consciousness, and, as we have seen, emotional experience and emotional expression may be dissociated by disease or surgical intervention. But we know that thalamic processes are a source of affective experience, that bodily sensations such as are sometimes associated with emotion may be thalamic in origin. Well-established anatomical facts show that, with the possible exception of the olfactory,[5] all sensory impulses are interrupted at the thalamic level before gaining the cerebral cortex, and Head's (1920) studies suggest how there may be regrouping of corticopetal impulses in the thalamus. Cannon's theory has its basis in these facts and it proposes that, at the same time that the diencephalon discharges downward the motor impulses which produce the emotional behavior, it discharges upward to the cortex impulses which throw into action the processes which underlie emotional consciousness.

The neural events which, on this new theory, occur in emotion are outlined in Figure 4. The sensory impulses set up by an emotional stimulus start from R and, following path 1, reach the thalamus where they may directly excite the (hypothalamic) mechanisms involved in emotional expression and so cause a downward discharge of definite pattern to effector organs by path 2. Or, after undergoing regrouping, the afferent impulses may pass on by path 1' to the cerebral cortex where they may arouse conditioned responses which, in turn, excite the efferent diencephalic mechanisms by means of a release of cortical inhibition (inactivation of path 3). Thus the downward discharge of impulses from the motor part of the diencephalon may be provoked either by sensory im-

---

[5]Although olfactory impulses reach the cortex from the reflex olfactory area without passing through the diencephalon proper, there are indirect paths from this area to the thalamus through the mamillo-thalamic tract and the habenular connections (Herrick, 1931).

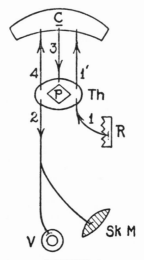

FIGURE 4

DIAGRAM OF THE CONNECTIONS IN THE THALAMIC THEORY

R, receptor; C, cerebral cortex; V, viscus; $Sk\ M$, skeletal muscle; Th, thalamus; P, pattern. The connecting lines represent nerve paths, with the direction of impulses indicated in each instance. The cortico-thalamic path 3 is inhibitory in function.

(From W. B. Cannon's "Again the James-Lange and the Thalamic Theories of Emotion," *Psychol. Rev.*, 1931.)

pulses to the thalamus or by a release of cortical inhibition or by a combination of both events. Coincident with the downward discharge there occurs an upward discharge of impulses over path 4. On reaching the cortex these impulses transform the "object-simply-apprehended" to the "object-emotionally-felt." From this it is clear that Cannon's theory is in perfect accord with the view of James that emotion is a *quale* added to simple perception. But, while James attributed the "object-emotionally-felt" to the feeling of bodily changes, Cannon considers that *"the peculiar quality of the emotion is added to simple sensation when thalamic processes are aroused,"* or, in terms of Figure 4, when the cortex is affected by a diencephalic discharge over path 4.

It is important to note that Cannon has not suggested that the diencephalon is the "seat of the emotions," in the sense that this subcortical station contains the neural mechanisms underlying emotional consciousness as well as those which discharge the motor impulses that produce emotional expression. Failure to comprehend this point which was plainly expressed in Cannon's original presentation has led Newman, Perkins, and Wheeler (1930) to misunderstand and so to criticize the "thalamic theory." In their critique, which Cannon has recently answered (1931), these writers exhibit an inability to discriminate between emotional *be-*

havior and emotional *experience;* they disregard the force of the evidence that one of these two aspects of emotion may occur independently of the other; and they most erroneously ascribe to Cannon the view that the thalamus exercises a discriminative function. In fact, Cannon specifically stated (1927, p. 123) that the diencephalic patterned processes, like glandular and muscular responses, can be controlled by processes in the cerebral cortex—processes conditioned by all sorts of previous impressions. When an originally indifferent stimulus becomes an emotional stimulus, that is to say, when it acquires the property of eliciting diencephalic discharge, it does so by virtue of the discriminative powers of the cortex. The latter organ, as indicated in Figure 4, receives sensory impulses from R over paths 1 and 1' and controls the reaction patterns in the diencephalon over the inhibitory path 3. Ordinarily this path holds the lower level in check. Unconditioned emotional stimuli, if adequate, are capable of directly exciting diencephalic discharge in spite of cortical inhibition, a case in point being the elicitation of rage in a normal cat by restraint. But when the emotional stimulus is a conditioned one such as perception of a person or animal who has repeatedly subjected the cat to this experience, the cortex exercises its discriminative function by releasing the diencephalic rage mechanism. In the case of decorticate animals and lightly anaesthetized persons not only may the unconditioned rage reaction occur, but, because of the absence of cortical inhibition, it tends to be excessive and more readily evokable.

Cannon (1927) has pointed out how well the new theory fits all the known facts. It accounts for the coincidence of the bodily changes and the emotional experience and so explains how James and Lange could reasonably make the suggestion which they did. It explains how the assumption of an attitude does sometimes *help* to establish the emotional state which the attitude expresses, for then the normal cortical inhibition of the lower neurons with reference to that attitude is abolished so that they are already released when a real emotional stimulus acts. On this theory are readily explained the cases of unilateral release of the thalamus from cortical control with accompanying ipsilateral intensification of emotional tone. But, as Cannon has urged, such cases present an insurmountable obstacle to the James-Lange theory, for the viscera cannot function by halves, these patients do not engage in one-sided expression of their emotions, and the impulses sent back from the disturbed periphery are bilateral; the unsymmetrical feeling is due to the organ which is functioning unsymmetrically—the diencephalon. When disease has made the expression of emotion impossible by destroying the motor innervation from the diencephalon, there may remain, as we have already seen, the possibility of emotional feeling. That feeling must be central in origin, and on the proposed theory it is occasioned by afferent impulses from an intact thalamus. But when the diencephalon is widely involved in a morbid process, as in the cases of Fulton and Bailey, both the expression and the feeling disappear together.

The greatest service this new theory can do is to divert the experimental study of the emotions from the periphery to the brain.

BIBLIOGRAPHY

ALVAREZ, W. C. 1929. Ways in which emotion can affect the digestive tract. *J. Amer. Med. Asso.*, **92**, 1231-1237.

BAINBRIDGE, F. A. 1931. The physiology of muscular exercise. (3rd ed., rev. by Bock and Dill.) London & New York: Longmans, Green. Pp. viii+272.

BARD, P. 1928. A diencephalic mechanism for the expression of rage with special reference to the sympathetic nervous system. *Amer. J. Physiol.*, **84**, 490-515.

————. 1929. The central representation of the sympathetic system as indicated by certain physiologic observations. *Arch. Neur. & Psychiat.*, **22**, 230-246.

————. 1934. On emotional expression after decortication with some remarks on certain theoretical views. *Psychol. Rev.* (July and September).

BAZETT, H. C., ALPERS, B. J., & ERB, W. H. 1933. Hypothalamus and temperature control. *Arch. Neur. & Psychiat.*, **30**, 728-748.

BAZETT, H. C., & PENFIELD, W. G. 1922. A study of the Sherrington decerebrate animal in the chronic as well as the acute condition. *Brain*, **45**, 185-265.

BEATTIE, J., BROW, G. R., & LONG, C. N. H. 1930. Physiological and anatomical evidence for the existence of nerve tracts connecting the hypothalamus with spinal sympathetic centres. *Proc. Roy. Soc. London*, **106B**, 253-275.

BEKHTEREV, V. 1887. Die Bedeutung der Sehügel auf Grund von experimentellen und pathologischen Daten. *Virchow's Arch. f. pathol. Anat.*, **110**, 322-365.

BICKEL, A., & SASAKI, K. 1905. Experimentelle Untersuchungen über den Einfluss von Affekten auf die Magensaftsekretion. *Dtsch. med. Woch.*, **31**, 1829.

BRITTON, S. W. 1928. The prepotency of medulliadrenal influence in emotional hyperglycemia. *Amer. J. Physiol.*, **86**, 340-352.

BROOKS, C. M. 1931. A delimitation of the central nervous mechanism involved in reflex hyperglycemia. *Amer. J. Physiol.*, **99**, 64-76.

————. 1933. Reflex activation of the sympathetic system in the spinal cat. *Amer. J. Physiol.*, **106**, 251-266.

————. 1934. The resistance of surviving spinal animals to hypoglycemia induced by insulin. *Amer. J. Physiol.*, **107**, 577-583.

BULATAO, E., & CANNON, W. B. 1925. The rôle of the adrenal medulla in pseudaffective hyperglycemia. *Amer. J. Physiol.*, **72**, 295-313.

CAMPOS, F. A. DE M., CANNON, W. B., LUNDIN, H., & WALKER, T. T. 1929. Some conditions affecting the capacity for prolonged muscular work. *Amer. J. Physiol.*, **87**, 680-701.

CANNON, W. B. 1911. The mechanical factors of digestion. London: Arnold. Pp. xi+227.

————. 1919. The isolated heart as an indicator of adrenal secretion induced by pain, asphyxia and excitement. *Amer. J. Physiol.*, **50**, 399-432.

————. 1927. The James-Lange theory of emotions: a critical examination and an alternative theory. *Amer. J. Psychol.*, **39**, 106-124.

————. 1928a. Die Notfallsfunktionen des sympathico-adrenalen Systems. *Ergeb. d. Physiol.*, **27**, 380-406.

————. 1928b. Neural organization for emotional expression. In *Feelings and emotions: the Wittenberg symposium*, ed. by M. L. Reymert. Worcester, Mass.: Clark Univ. Press. Pp. 257-269.

————. 1929. Bodily changes in pain, hunger, fear and rage. (2nd ed.) New York: Appleton. Pp. xvi+404.

————. 1931. Again the James-Lange and the thalamic theories of emotion. *Psychol. Rev.*, **38**, 281-295.

————. 1933. Chemical mediators of autonomic nerve impulses. *Science*, **78**, 43-48.

CANNON, W. B., & BACQ, Z. M. 1931. A hormone produced by sympathetic action on smooth muscle. *Amer. J. Physiol.*, **96**, 392-412.

CANNON, W. B., & BRITTON, S. W. 1925. Pseudaffective medulliadrenal secretion. *Amer. J. Physiol.*, **72**, 283-294.

―――. 1927. The influence of motion and emotion on medulliadrenal secretion. *Amer. J. Physiol.*, **79**, 433-465.

CANNON, W. B., LEWIS, J. T., & BRITTON, S. W. 1926. A lasting preparation of the denervated heart for detecting internal secretion, with evidence for accessory accelerator fibers from the thoracic sympathetic chain. *Amer. J. Physiol.*, **77**, 326-352.

―――. 1927. The dispensability of the sympathetic division of the autonomic nervous system. *Boston Med. & Surg. J.*, **197**, 514-515.

CANNON, W. B., McIVER, M. A., & BLISS, S. W. 1924. A sympathetic and adrenal mechanism for mobilizing sugar in hypoglycemia. *Amer. J. Physiol.*, **69**, 46-66.

CANNON, W. B., NEWTON, H. F., BRIGHT, E. M., MENKIN, V., & MOORE, R. M. 1928. Some aspects of the physiology of animals surviving complete exclusion of sympathetic nerve impulses. *Amer. J. Physiol.*, **89**, 84-107.

CANNON, W. B., QUERIDO, A., BRITTON, S. W., & BRIGHT, E. M. 1927. The rôle of adrenal secretion in the chemical control of body temperature. *Amer. J. Physiol.*, **79**, 466-507.

CANNON, W. B., & RAPPORT, D. 1921a. Further observations on the denervated heart in relation to adrenal secretion. *Amer. J. Physiol.*, **58**, 308-337.

―――. 1921b. The reflex center for adrenal secretion and its response to excitatory and inhibitory influences. *Amer. J. Physiol.*, **58**, 338-352.

CANNON, W. B., & ROSENBLUETH, A. 1933. Sympathin E and sympathin I. *Amer. J. Physiol.*, **104**, 557-574.

CUSHNY, A. R. 1928. Pharmacology and therapeutics. (9th ed., rev. by C. W. Edmunds & J. A. Gunn.) Philadelphia: Lea & Febiger. Pp. x+743.

DANA, C. L. 1921. The anatomic seat of the emotions: a discussion of the James-Lange theory. *Arch. Neur. & Psychiat.*, **6**, 634-639.

DUMAS, G. 1928. Le choc émotionnel (réactions glandulaires et musculaires). *J. de psychol.*, **25**, 130-164.

DUSSER DE BARENNE, J. G. 1920. Récherches expérimentales sur les fonctions du système nerveux central, faites en particulier sur deux chats dont le neopallium a été enlevé. *Arch. néerl. de physiol.*, **4**, 31-123.

ELLIOTT, T. R. 1912. The control of the suprarenal glands by the splanchnic nerves. *J. Physiol.*, **44**, 374-409.

―――. 1913. The innervation of the adrenal glands. *J. Physiol.*, **46**, 285-290.

FREEMAN, N. E., PHILLIPS, R. A., & CANNON, W. B. 1931. An unsuccessful attempt to demonstrate humoral action of "vagus substance" in the circulating blood. *Amer. J. Physiol.*, **98**, 435-440.

FULTON, J. F. 1926. Muscular contraction and the reflex control of movement. Baltimore, Md.: Williams & Wilkins. Pp. xv+644.

FULTON, J. F., & BAILEY, P. 1929. Tumors in the region of the third ventricle: their diagnosis and relation to pathological sleep. *J. Nerv. & Ment. Dis.*, **69**, 1-24, 145-164, 261-277.

GASKELL, W. H. 1920. The involuntary nervous system. London & New York: Longmans, Green, 1920. Pp. viii+178.

GOLTZ, F. 1892. Der Hund ohne Grosshirn. *Pflüg. Arch. f. d. ges. Physiol.*, **51**, 570-614.

HARLOW, H. F., & STAGNER, R. 1932. Psychology of feelings and emotions: I. Theory of feelings. *Psychol. Rev.*, **39**, 570-589.

————. 1933. Psychology of feelings and emotions: II. Theory of emotions. *Psychol. Rev.*, **40**, 184-195.

HEAD, H. 1920. Studies in neurology: Vol. 2. London: Oxford Univ. Press. Pp. viii+333-862.

————. 1921. Release of function in the nervous system. *Proc. Roy. Soc. London*, **92B**, 184-209.

HERRICK, C. J. 1931. An introduction to neurology. (5th ed.) Philadelphia: Saunders. Pp. 417.

HOUSSAY, B. A., & MOLINELLI, E. A. 1925. Centre adrénalino-sécréteur hypothalamique. *C. r. Soc. de biol.*, **93**, 1454-1455.

IZQUIERDO, J. J., & CANNON, W. B. 1928. Emotional polycythemia in relation to sympathetic and medulliadrenal action on the spleen. *Amer. J. Physiol.*, **84**, 545-562.

JAMES, W. 1894. The physical basis of the emotions. *Psychol. Rev.*, **1**, 516-529.

JAMES, W., & LANGE, G. C. 1922. The emotions. Baltimore, Md.: Williams & Wilkins. Pp. 135.

KARPLUS, J. P., & KREIDL, A. 1909. Gehirn und Sympathicus. *Pflüg. Arch. f. d. ges. Physiol.*, **129**, 138-144.

————. 1910. Gehirn und Sympathicus. *Pflüg. Arch. f. d. ges. Physiol.*, **135**, 401-416.

————. 1911. Gehirn und Sympathicus. *Pflüg. Arch. f. d. ges. Physiol.*, **143**, 109-127.

————. 1918. Gehirn und Sympathicus. *Pflüg. Arch f. d. ges. Physiol.*, **171**, 192-200.

————. 1927. Gehirn und Sympathicus. *Pflüg. Arch. f. d. ges. Physiol.*, **215**, 667-670.

KELLER, A. D. 1932. Autonomic discharges elicited by physiological stimuli in midbrain preparations. *Amer. J. Physiol.*, **100**, 576-586.

KELLER, A. D., & HARE, W. K. 1932. The hypothalamus and heat regulation. *Proc. Soc. Exper. Biol. & Med.*, **92**, 1069-1070.

KIRILZEV, S. 1891. [Cases of affection of the optic thalamus.] (Russian.) Reviewed in *Neur. Zentbl.*, **10**, 310.

KODAMA, S. 1923. Effect of stimulation of the sensory nerves upon the rate of liberation of epinephrine from the suprarenal glands. *Tohoku J. Exper. Med.*, **4**, 166-242.

LANGLEY, J. N. 1900. The sympathetic and other related systems of nerves. In Vol. 2 of *Text-book of physiology*, by E. A. Schäfer. London: Pentland. Pp. 616-696.

————. 1903. Das sympathische und verwandte nervöse Systeme der Wirbeltiere (autonomes nervöses System). *Ergeb. d. Physiol.*, **2**, 818-872.

————. 1921. The autonomic nervous system: Pt. 1. Cambridge, England: Heffer. Pp. viii+80.

MAGNUS, R. 1924. Körperstellung. Berlin: Springer. Pp. viii+740.

NEWMAN, E. B., PERKINS, F. T., & WHEELER, R. H. 1930. Cannon's theory of emotion: a critique. *Psychol. Rev.*, **37**, 305-326.

NEWTON, H. F., ZWEMER, R. L., & CANNON, W. B. 1931. The mystery of emotional acceleration of the denervated heart after exclusion of known humoral accelerators. *Amer. J. Physiol.*, **96**, 377-391.

PAVLOV, I. P. 1910. The work of the digestive glands: lectures. (Trans. by W. H. Thompson.) (2nd ed.) London: Griffin. Pp. 266.

————. 1927. Conditioned reflexes: an investigation of the physiological activity of the cerebral cortex. (Trans. and ed. by G. V. Anrep.) London: Oxford Univ. Press. Pp. xvi+430.

RANSON, S. W., & MAGOUN, H. W. 1933. Respiratory and pupillary reactions induced by stimulation of the hypothalamus. *Arch. Neur. & Psychiat.*, **29**, 1179-1194.

ROSENBLUETH, A., & CANNON, W. B. 1932. Some effects of sympathin on the nictitating membrane. *Amer. J. Physiol.*, **99**, 398-407.

ROTHMANN, H. 1923. Zusammenfassender Bericht über den Rothmannschen grosshirnlosen Hund nach klinischer und anatomischer Untersuchungen. *Zsch. f. d. ges. Neur. u. Psychiat.*, **87**, 247-313.

SACHS, E. 1911. On the relation of the optic thalamus to respiration, circulation, temperature and the spleen. *J. Exper. Med.*, **14**, 408-432.

SATAKÉ, Y., WATANABÉ, M., & SUGAWARA, T. 1927. Effect of fasting and sensory stimulation upon the rate of epinephrine output from the suprarenal gland in dogs. *Tohoku J. Exper. Med.*, **9**, 1-40.

SCHAFER, E. S. 1924. The endocrine organs: Pt. 1. (2nd ed.) London & New York: Longmans, Green. Pp. ix+175.

SCHALTENBRAND, G., & COBB, S. 1931. Clinical and anatomical studies on two cats without neocortex. *Brain*, **53**, 449-491.

SCHIFF, M. 1896. Moritz Schiff's gesammelte Beiträge zur Physiologie: Vol. 3. Lausanne: Benda.

SHERRINGTON, C. S. 1906. The integrative action of the nervous system. New Haven, Conn.; Yale Univ. Press. Pp. xvi+411.

SOURY, J. 1899. Le système nerveux central. Paris: Carré & Naud. Pp. x+1863.

STEWART, G. N. 1922. The significance of the suprarenal glands in relation to the vital processes. In Vol. 2 of *Endocrinology and metabolism*. New York: Appleton. Pp. 127-168.

SUGAWARA, T., WATANABÉ, M., & SAITO, S. 1926. Effect of stimulation of the sensory nerves on the rate of liberation of epinephrine from the suprarenal glands. *Tohoku J. Exper. Med.*, **7**, 1-79.

WIGGERS, C. J. 1923. Circulation in health and disease. (2nd. ed.) Philadelphia: Lea & Febiger. Pp. viii+662.

WILSON, S. A. K. 1924. Pathological laughing and crying. *J. Neur. & Psychopathol.*, **4**, 299-333.

―――――. 1929. Modern problems in neurology. New York: Wood. Pp. 364.

WOODWORTH, R. S., & SHERRINGTON, C. S. 1904. A pseudaffective reflex and its spinal path. *J. Physiol.*, **31**, 234-243.

CHAPTER 7

EMOTION: II. THE EXPRESSIONS
OF EMOTION

CARNEY LANDIS

New York State Psychiatric Institute

Emotion: The sum total of the experiences during any period in which marked bodily changes of "feeling," "startle," or "upset" take place.

Feeling: (1) Experience less vivid than emotion. (2) The report of vaguely perceived kinaesthetic and organic sensations. (3) A general attitude which favors either positive or negative reactions to possible future stimuli or situations.

Startle: Poorly coordinated responses elicited by stimuli not reacted to by the organism in its immediate past and which occur suddenly. The term will be used to denote the behavior usually called "surprise," "start," or "shock" but without the mental connotations of these words.

Upset: The condition of an organism brought about by a series of stimuli which cannot be reacted to adequately, with consequent dissociation of neural function and of various behavior patterns which are usually integrated.

Expression: Any change in an organism which may be said to be a criterion of, accompaniment of, or part of, a reaction system. This change must be noted by a second organism or by some recording or measuring instrument before it may be truly considered as an expression.

Affect or Affective Experience: A general term used to denote any variety of emotional experience or emotional concomitant.

Three methods have been available for the experimental investigation of emotion: (1) the study of the expressions which accompany—or are—the emotion, (2) descriptive and introspective reports of the experiential phenomena of "mental life" which are characterized by feeling, and (3) the investigation of the action of the nervous system and of the endocrine glands. Of these methods, one may say that the first has furnished the greater mass of factual material, the second is the earliest historically but has been the least productive, while the last is the more fundamental since it is from neuro-endocrine physiology that psychology must draw many of its ultimate explanations of emotion.

The major portion of this chapter will be given over to the direct consideration and evaluation of our present knowledge concerning the expressions of emotion in the narrow sense of the term. The material which is available on the description of affective processes of mental life will be considered briefly under the heading of "Feeling." The neuro-humoral basis of emotion has been taken up in Chapter 6 and will be discussed in the present chapter only when it may be considered as a part of the expressive mechanisms.

CRITERIA

How do we recognize an emotion when we see it? What are the marks which characterize one expression as "emotional" and another as "language"? Is such recognition innate or acquired? What are the valid criteria of emotion or of the expressions of emotion? Can any reaction which is reported to have been pleasant or unpleasant be classified as emotional or as an affective experience? Is emotion an entity of itself, either in the sense of a pattern or series of patterns of physiological functions of a specific variety, or in the sense that it is a unique experience of mental life? Anyone who gives the matter some thought can easily add a dozen or more such questions which should have some sort of answer in the systematization of our knowledge on this subject. Many such questions have been answered by experiments. The answer to others depends at present upon rational deduction. Still others have not as yet found a satisfactory answer.

The behavior of the human infant indicates that the recognition of emotional expression is not present at birth but develops very rapidly, as if there were some innate tendency awaiting only maturation and directional stimuli. The development of language habits from the random verbalizations of the infant is probably very closely analogous to the development of the ability to recognize and to use expressions of emotion. This seems to be less and less true as one goes down the animal scale. Lower animal forms do not seem to react differentially to expressions but only to the direct application of stimuli of a nocuous or benign character.

Socially, the recognition of expressions of emotion is clearly of an acquired nature. This acquisition is in the nature of a language mechanism. That is, the recognition is learned just as verbal speech is learned. Some individuals become quite adept at one or the other; others do not. The expressions themselves, so far as the facial responses are concerned, are *usually* learned responses. Just as one learns to say "Ouch" or "Oh" in response to injury or surprise, so the expression accompanying the verbalization is usually a learned response. The entire question of distinction of acquired expression from native or innate expression of emotion is one which is not clearly defined or definable.

The expressions called emotional are diverse and include any portion of the body which is capable of reacting or having part in a reaction. Some of the more common reactions which have been considered expressions of emotion are facial expressions, blushing or flushing, certain patterns of bodily movement, certain types of verbal responses, laughing and crying, changes in the secretion of sweat, blood pressure, blood volume, respiration, changes in the activity of the gastro-intestinal system, variations in metabolism, changes in the balance between the secretions of the endocrine glands, variations in balance between portions of the nervous system, electrical responses of the skin, and so forth.

FACIAL EXPRESSION AND VOCALIZATION

Historical.[1] The earliest systematic study of facial expression is that of physiognomy. Physiognomy was originally a twofold science: (1) a mode of discriminating or predicting character by the outward appearance, and (2) a means of classifying form and feature. The first of these uses is usually considered as outside of the scope of modern science. The first systematic treatise on the subject is that of Aristotle, who considered the method, the general signs of character, the particular appearances characteristic of the dispositions, of strength and weakness, of genius and stupidity, etc. The practice of physiognomy was one of the foremost branches of intellectual interest through all the Dark and Middle Ages. Treatises showing shrewd observation mixed with mysticism and pious teaching are to be found in the extant literature of those days. Physiognomical speculation is best characterized by the works of Lavater (1879). He attempted to mix piety with character observation and shrewd deductions as to the relationship existing between physique (physiognomy) and character or personality. His observations, though interesting, are of no scientific importance.

It remained for Darwin to furnish an hypothesis and systematization on which it has been possible to carry out experimental work. In 1873 Darwin formulated three principles for the systematic explanation of most, if not all, of the expressive gestures involuntarily used in emotion by man and the lower animals. These principles are as follows:

1. *The Principle of the Serviceable Associated Habits.* Complex movements which may, under certain circumstances, be directly or indirectly useful are retained after the use has passed. The peculiar "pawing" movements of the cat's forefeet when it is pleased are relics of the purposeful use of the same movements to start or increase the flow of milk from the mammary glands of the mother. Such movements were associated with a pleasurable and satisfied feeling and tend to recur when such a feeling recurs. Wundt considers that this is but a special case of Darwin's third principle (*q.v.*).

2. *The Principle of Antithesis.* Darwin states:

> Every movement which we have voluntarily performed throughout our lives has required the action of certain muscles; and when we have performed a directly opposite movement, an opposite set of muscles has been habitually brought into play. . . . So when actions of one kind have become firmly associated with any sensation or emotion, it appears natural that the actions of a directly opposite kind, though of no use, should be unconsciously performed through habit and association under the influence of a directly opposite sensation or emotion.

Thus, impotence is expressed by raised eyebrows, shrugged shoulders, and open palms; these being antithetical to the frowning brow, thrown-back shoulders, and the clenched fists, symbolic of rage and power.

3. *The Principle of the Direct Action of the Nervous System.* The

---

[1]Modified, in part, from Titchener (1920).

sudden release of a large amount of nervous energy in startle demands unusual outlets from the central nervous system. This overflow takes place according to the innate connections within the brain. The results are shown in a general disturbance of organic functions due to the exciting or inhibitory effects of this irradiation of energy. By this principle are explained such phenomena as the muscular tremor in fear or excitement and such movements as the clapping of the hands in joy.

Wundt (1903), like Darwin, has three principles of systematization:

1. *The Principle of Direct Change in Innervation.* This is but a different wording of Darwin's third principle, involving the hereditary transmission over certain nervous connections, as in the reflex of weeping. The transmission of a characteristic family physiognomy or general expressive attitude is very common; and we invariably argue from the physical similarity to a similarity of mood, even though there may be no direct possibility of imitation of the parents by the children.

2. *The Principle of the Association of Analogous Sensations* of similar feeling-tone which mutually reinforce. This process forms the basis of the most characteristic of all emotional expressions, the "mimetic movements." These are physiologically conditioned by reflex movements in and about the facial sense-organs; thus the expression which stands for "bitter" is an arrangement of the parts of the buccal cavity most sensitive to bitter in such a way as to prevent their excessive stimulation by the unpleasant taste. The "sweet" expression, on the contrary, is that calculated to favor the continued stimulation of the tip of the tongue, the part most sensitive to sweet substances. By virtue of the second principle, these reactions have come to appear in response not only to an actually bitter taste, but also to an emotional condition which possesses the same general feeling-tone. A wry face may denote a mental as well as a physical pain.

3. *The Principle of the Connection of Movement with Sense Ideas* explains facial expressions and gestures which are not included under the two previous principles. Here belong movements of the arms and hands, the clenching of the fists in anger, and also certain facial expressions such as the curling of the lip in scorn and the staring eyes of surprise. The principle is closely allied to Darwin's first. It is not to be thought that any complex expression of emotion must be explained by a single principle. Such phenomena as laughing and weeping demand the use of all three principles for their elucidation.

James (1890) proposed five principles: (1) The weakened repetition of movements which formerly were of utility to the subject. This is equivalent to Darwin's first proposition. (2) The principle of reacting similarly to analogous-feeling stimuli. This is identical with Wundt's second principle. (3) The principle of weakened repetition of movements which under other conditions were physiologically necessary effects. The respiratory disturbances of anger and fear, e.g., may be considered as "organic reminiscences of the blowings of the man making a series of combative efforts, of the pantings of one in precipitate flight." (4) The principle of the mechanically determined idiopathic effects of the stimulus, i.e., the physiological overflow of nervous energy through the easiest drainage channels (cf. Wundt's first and Darwin's third law). (5) The principle of the mechanical perpetuation of emotional reactions which may be called accidental as far as their origin goes. For some of our emotional reactions no plausible reason can be conceived. "In fact, in an organism as complex as the nervous system there must be many such reactions, incidental to others evolved for utility's sake, which would never themselves have been evolved independently for any utility they might possess."

In conclusion, it may be said that no one of these explanatory series of principles is logically complete. There is need of further observation, and perhaps for the construction of a new set of principles upon the basis of the psychology of action rather than emotion.

It might be well to note here that there is a very pertinent criticism of Darwin's, Wundt's, or James's descriptions of expressions of emotion which are based on folk psychology or the study of the various races of mankind. The reports on which these principles are based were made for the most part by individuals trained in the habits of our Western culture; that is to say, their methods of observation and perception as well as of interpretation were those of Western European culture, and hence the expressions would be reported and interpreted in Western terms.

Anatomy and Physiology. In 1806, Sir Charles Bell published the first edition of his *Anatomy and Philosophy of Expression.* This treatise provided the first basis for the scientific investigation of facial expression. Bell developed the notion that the expressive reactions of the face were dependent upon the anatomical relationships of the facial muscles so that expression was limited in its scope by the anatomical structure. His ideas of the nature of emotion and the expressions of emotion are forerunners of Darwin and of James in that he insists on the bodily expression as a basic fact of emotion and takes up in detail the changes in respiration, circulation, and the like, which have been the subject of so much subsequent experimental investigation. Duchenne in 1862 published *Mécanisme de la Physionomie Humaine.* This work is basic for the physiological study of facial expression. Duchenne's method was that of stimulating each muscle or muscle group of the face directly by means of a galvanic current, so obtaining expressions, many of which had been viewed as complicated responses. The resulting reactions were photographed and, from the examination of the pictures, the thesis was developed that expression depends primarily upon the activity of single muscles.

Frappa (1902) has formulated an opposing view to that of Duchenne which has been very interestingly developed by Dumas (1923, pp. 606-732). Frappa's contention was that facial expression may be reduced to three fundamental expressions, namely, astonishment, grief, and joy. From these three expressions he believed that one could synthetically build up most, if not all, other facial expressions. Dumas has reworked the hypothesis of Frappa and shown in a most suggestive fashion that the three elementary expressions are easily explained in terms of direct neural function. The expression of startle (astonishment) Dumas considers to be due to the sudden tonic contraction of facial muscles and particularly of the masseters and the orbicular muscles of the eyes, giving rise to the expression termed "surprise." The expression of joy is explained by the raising of the tonicity of the entire body, including that of the face. Hence joy may be said to be the pattern of heightened facial tonus. Grief is considered as the opposite of the tension of joy; that is, the facial muscles are relaxed and the balance of forces between the stronger (heavier) muscles as compared to the weaker muscles results in the expression called grief.

The evolution and comparative anatomical development of facial expression has been compiled by Huber (1931). He has investigated the anatomy of facial musculature throughout the main lines of the developing animal forms, showing how possible expressive mechanisms have developed. The rôle played by each muscle group and its functional relationship to other groups is demonstrated. The work illustrates how complicated these expressive reactions are and the futility of relating expressions to single muscles, as Duchenne attempted to do. From a psychological point of view Huber's work is unsatisfactory, but it does demand a reformulation of psychological views.

Interpretation of Facial Expression. One may find, not only in the older literature but also in very recent texts of psychology, elaborate systematic classifications of expression or of emotion. (Usually the distinction between expression and emotion is a vague one at the best.) These classifications or dictionaries are of value in calling attention to the diversity of reactions of the face. Indeed, they seem to indicate that the face is second only to the vocal mechanism in its ability to give finely differentiated reactions. It remains to be seen whether or not such an assumption is based upon fact.

The acquisition of the ability to interpret facial expression has been studied by Gates (1925). She exhibited a series of posed photographs which depicted the traditional expressions of emotions to groups of children of different age levels. The children were asked to name the expression portrayed by each photograph. She found that the success which a child has in assigning such a name is closely correlated with his age but that at best the interpretative process was far from perfect. In general, the experiment shows that this perceptual discrimination of differences in facial expression is a learned social response of the individual.

The work upon the interpretation of photographs which had been posed as expressions of emotions was initiated by Miss Feleky (1914). She posed for a series of pictures which she hoped would run the entire range of expression and which various judges would agree were typical expressions of this or that emotion or emotional situation. She found that the expressions of disgust, sneering, and breathless interest were judged correctly more often than any others, while those of suspicion, religion, anger, fear, hate, and rage were judged very poorly. Several years later Langfeld (1918) tried a similar experiment making use of an artist's sketches of posed emotional expressions. He found that laughter could usually be interpreted correctly; that fear and anger were confused; that surprise and suspicion were confused; and that the contempt-scorn group was judged more correctly than any other expression. His subjects reported that the use of kinaesthetic imitation and imagination of the situation aided in the labeling of the photographs. A check on the reliability of this experiment was obtained in a second study in which positive and negative suggestions were given to the judges. Individual suggestibility of different subjects was found to color the results, but in general it was shown that positive suggestion was a distinct aid, while negative suggestion interfered markedly with all judgments, indicating that each judge had a clear sense of distrust of his own judgment. Ruckmick, Allport, Guilford, and others have carried out somewhat similar experiments and have obtained essentially the same general results.

During the past five years four experiments have been reported on the question of the interpretation or judgment of facial expression. Each of these experiments has been conducted from an independent viewpoint and the comparison of the results obtained is quite interesting. Frois-Wittmann (1930) posed for a series of photographs which he felt depicted various emotional expressions. From these photographs he constructed drawings of various portions of the face combined in various ways. These synthetic expressions, together with the photographs, were presented to different groups of students who were asked to name the emotion or feeling portrayed. He analyzed the results in an entirely new fashion. The various characterizations were tabulated for modal usage and for secondary or tertiary modes. In this way he was able to show the relationship existing between various names assigned and the relation of these name groups to the various groupings of musclar involvement. He concludes from this work that, while most of the possible muscular involvements were present in practically all of the expressions, there was, nevertheless, a unique and distinctive pattern of these involvements for each modal "judged expression." There were frequent disagreements between the judgments of the face and of its separate features, and also between the judgments of the separate features; but analysis of the individual pictures indicated that those elements that were in agreement combined to characterize the expression of the whole face to which the elements in disagreement became assimilated. He found that the significance of a given muscular involvement was not constant but was relative to the rest of the pattern.

Making use of the Feleky photographs, Kanner (1931) made a study of the spontaneous judgments or names which would be assigned as appropriate for the expression. He compiled a very interesting analysis of the semantic and etymological derivation of the words which are used in description of the emotions or emotional expressions. The names which his judges assigned were classified and compared on the basis of this compilation. Such a procedure seemed to show that there is a possibility of certain common factors which might be interpreted as rather vague and ill-defined patterns of response. He also devotes some attention to the fact that the interpretation of the expression depends upon a wide variety of factors which have not been sufficiently considered in previous studies.

Landis (1929) presented a group of students with photographs of facial expression which had been taken under conditions which were characterized by the person who had been photographed as emotional and to which that person had been able to assign a verbal report which characterized his feeling at the approximate time the picture was taken. Landis gave the judges a list of possible emotions which might be portrayed and a list of situations which might give rise to these expressions. The judges were asked to assign to each photograph the best name for the emotion portrayed and the name of a situation which they thought would give rise to this expression. His results show that it is practically impossible to name correctly a photograph taken in an emotional situation, either as to the emotion being experienced by the subject or to the situation which might give rise to the expression. It is to be emphasized that he was using actual photographs obtained in emotional situations and not posed photographs.

Approaching the problem of expression from the standpoint of the *Gestalttheorie*, Arnheim (1928) made use of portraits and of silhouettes which he asked subjects to give characterological ratings. In part of his experiments he limited this rating by suggesting various possible answers. In other experiments he allowed the subject to judge without suggestion of any sort. Arnheim found marked individual differences in the way in which various subjects interpreted the material. Errors were often due to wrong attitudes, extraneous criteria, consideration of only one part of the object without realizing its relationship to the whole, and to certain ambiguities in the questions which were addressed to the judges. Allowing for these mistakes, Arnheim feels that this type of experiment is easy for the person who judges from his impressions and is not hampered by preconceived theories or directions. The free description of character or expression (not limited by directing or suggestive questions) gives more descriptive and correct results than when judgments were hedged about with directive material. In general, his work indicated that facial expression is estimated not on the basis of any single trait or feature but on the basis of the entire configuration or *gestalt*. Very frequently the altering of a single portion of a silhouette led the judge to report an entirely different estimate without even noticing that most of the features were identical to those of a previous judgment. The interpretation of the expression did not seem to depend on the analyzable features of the face but almost always was based on the face in its entirety.

These new experiments constitute a distinct advance in our knowledge in this field. In the first place, the interpretation of expression, whether that expression is "social" or "emotional," depends almost entirely upon the entire configuration. Presenting a photograph showing only the face, and asking for judgment or description of the face, is after all an almost wholly artificial procedure. Arnheim showed that when he furnished, along with his portraits, samples of writing or lists of literary productions such material added to the completeness of the description. The notion that there are patterns of facial reactions in the social expressions of emotion or feeling receives partial substantiation in the work of Frois-Wittmann and of Kanner. The patterns are not clear-cut or exact and they are partially dependent on patterns of language, but there is evidence to support the common-sense belief that such facial arrangements do exist. The patterns are only partially analyzable and are perceived better on an impressionistic basis than on the basis of a careful study. Personally, I believe that the results of Guilford's (1929) study, which showed an increase in the ability to read expressions from photographs after practice or training, were probably due to the remembering of names which were said to be correct and which were told to the subject during the learning process rather than to an increase in descriptive accuracy. Lastly, there is no evidence so far which would indicate that the expressions used in situations of stress, which are characterized as emotional, are to any great extent related to the social expressions which have been studied by various writers. These social expressions may, and probably do, possess certain patterns. It still remains to be demonstrated that such patterns of reaction of facial muscles occur in emotion and if they do occur that they agree with the social expressions of emotion. The work of Landis seems to demonstrate this point so far as static photographs are concerned. He has pointed out that a different conclusion might be found if use were made of motion pictures, but unfortunately the work of Sherman fails to give any very marked support to this hope.

The study of emotional expressions in real situations of everyday life has never been satisfactorily carried out under controlled conditions. Mantegazza (1904) has published vivid descriptions of the behavior of criminals on the way to execution, maniacal lunatics, and other individuals under the influence of intense emotion. His descriptions were thoroughly qualitative and follow the traditional literary lines of description. It is theoretically possible to make a study of the expressive reactions of a group who have been cinematographed during some situation of high affective value, but the research still waits the doing.

McKenzie (1905) has made some very interesting studies of facial expression of athletes during strenuous competition and after partial collapse from such competition. He bases his work on photographs which were reproduced in sculpture. The expressions are marked by extreme tonicity of the face in strenuous situations and in collapse and by the blankness of lowered muscular tonus.

Experimental Studies of Facial Expression. Landis (1924a, 1924b) has conducted several experimental studies of facial expression. In the first of these he was chiefly interested in the recording and analyzing of the expressions of persons subjected to a controlled series of situations of a more or less emotional nature. The expressions were recorded both by photograph and cinematograph. The first of the studies showed that there was a great deal of variability in the expressions obtained. So long as the expressions were those which accompanied a mild degree of stimulation, they closely approximated the reactions traditionally considered appropriate to the situation. When several of the subjects who had been very expressive in the original situations were asked to return and to endeavor to reproduce the expression which they believed that they had given in the original situations, it was found, in general, that these attempts resulted in the purely traditional expressions rather than those which were actually obtained in the more severe of the emotional situations.

A second study by Landis repeated in part the first experiment. The situations were made more intense and real, so that there was little doubt that true emotion was elicited. About twelve hundred photographs of facial expressions of twenty-five subjects were recorded by means of a camera capable of following fairly rapid facial reactions. Records were obtained of blood pressure and of the respiratory ratio during the entire series of situations. The stimulation evoked in practically every subject emotional disturbance, while certain subjects showed signs of complete upset.

These photographs were analyzed by a semi-objective determination of the amount of movement shown by the principal groups of facial muscles. The emotional expressiveness was determined by an estimate of the amount of movement of facial muscles and in terms of the subjective significance which the facial patterns conveyed to the investigator. It was found that each individual tended to use certain muscles or muscle groups (expressions) in practically all of his expressive reactions. There were marked individual variations in the expressive reactions so produced. In no situation did the contraction of a muscle, group of muscles, or expression occur frequently enough to be considered significant. That is, there was no expression typical of any situation in this experiment. Nor was any expression typically associated with any verbal report of feeling or emotion given in this experiment. Some degree of smiling was the most common facial reaction, occurring in 34 per cent of the photographs. Asymmetrical expressions almost never occurred as emotional expressions. The men in this experiment used more facial reactions than the women.

When certain of the subjects were later recalled and asked to endeavor to reproduce the feelings or emotions (centrally aroused emotion) which they experienced in the original situation it was found that no expression or pattern of response characterized even these imagined situations or experiences.

Ranking the amount of facial movement which accompanied the various emotions named in the verbal reports revealed that pain, surprise, anger, exasperation, crying, disgust, sex, and revolting gave decreasing amounts of expressive movements in the order named. That each subject had two or three facial patterns which he used in all situations and which constituted the vast majority of that individual's expressiveness is an interesting point bearing on a general theory of emotion.

The emotional responses of infants have been studied by Sherman (1928). He used four types of stimulation: hunger, dropping, restraint, and pain. When motion pictures of these reactions were shown to students, he found that from twelve to twenty-five different emotions were named as appropriate titles for the pictures. When nurses and medical students were shown three types of infant reactions resulting from dropping, restraint, or pain, without seeing the actual stimulation, the nurses named seven emotions and the medical students eight. If the pictures were accompanied by a knowledge of the actual stimulation the resultant reaction was judged with a great deal more unanimity than under any other conditions. The basis of judgment stated by the observers indicates for the most part that the differentiation was strongly influenced by the knowledge of the stimulus. This was further shown by an additional experiment in which the stimuli were attached in the motion pictures to reactions elicited by other stimuli. The interpretation of these falsified pictures indicated that the stimulus preceding the reaction shown was usually the deciding factor in the name given to the reaction.

Sherman's work indicates clearly that no reliance can be placed upon the judgments of either trained or untrained observers of the expressive reactions of the infant. If, as Watson (1924) and others have stated, anger, fear, and love are the three innate patterns of emotional response, then Sherman should have found a large percentage of agreement among the judges in the naming of reactions. Whether the reaction was named rage, fear, or love is of little import, but the judgments should fall into three clearly marked groups. This was not found. Sherman's work shows that the differentiations of the responses of the infant are differentiations made when the stimulating conditions are known, and are accurate only when those conditions are known.

The experimental investigations of the facial expressions of emotion of the adult or the bodily activity of the infant indicate that there is no pattern of expression (except smiling) which may be said to characterize any situation or emotion of any one individual or group of individuals. Practically all of the current theories of emotion demand that we should find such patterns, if not in the voluntary musculature, then in the visceral responses of the individual.

Vocal Expression. The significance of the variation in vocal expression as a concomitant or part of emotion is older phylogenetically than is facial expression. Darwin classifies most of the vocalization of animals as emotional. The practical significance of variations in speech conveying emotional meaning, which may or may not agree with the words, is common knowledge. There is surprisingly little experimental work available which classifies this behavior or explains the phenomena. Sherman's (1928) experiment, in which a group of observers was presented with the cries of infants stimulated by hunger, dropping, restraint, or pricking with a needle, is of interest in this connection. These observers named twelve different emotions which showed very little relationship between the name given and the qualitative nature of the stimuli. When a group of students heard only the cries of the infants, about 20 per cent of the judgments attributed the crying to colic. On the other hand, when a similar group of observers was presented with motion pictures of the reactions resulting from similar stimuli, not one judgment of colic was made. Evidently, the crying was associated in the minds of the observers with the organic processes of the infant rather than with the emotions. The intensity and the duration of the cries were the determining factors in judgments of the observers. The more intense the stimulating conditions the sharper was the ensuing cry and the longer was its duration.

Gates (1927) has studied the development of the ability in school children of various age groups to interpret correctly the auditory element of expression. Phonographic records were made of the recitation of the alphabet in tones of happiness, unhappiness, anger, fear, surprise, etc. When this record was given before 627 children the following results were obtained: ". . . . (2) an increase in the capacity for understanding with age, grade, and school experience; (3) a superiority in this test of the more intelligent over the less intelligent school children; . . . . (5) differences in the ease of interpretation of the types of auditory stimuli."

Seashore (1928), by means of phonophotography, has analyzed the peculiar attributes of music or speech which are regarded as expressive of emotion and finds that the presence of vibrato (defined as a synchronous oscillation of pitch and of intensity at a rate of from five to eight per second) in artistic singing and in speech gives the element which we commonly term emotional.

Laughing and Crying. The development of smiling and laughter in the infant has been studied by Washburn (1929). She finds that smiling is shown from a very early age by most children. Smiling without specific stimulation was seen very rarely; the response seems almost always to be elicited by or in the presence of other people. Smiling, by the end of the first year, was a learned or conditioned response to a very marked extent indicating that in most instances the smile is of the character of the communicative, adaptive, social response rather than a purely expressive one.

Miss Washburn found that laughing, unlike smiling, appeared much later in the child's life, usually after the twentieth week. Laughter was always the more stereotyped behavior throughout the first year of life. Individual differences between children were found to depend mainly upon the *frequency* of smiling or laughter rather than on the form of the behavior. In general, the work indicates that, in origin, smiling and laughter are not always different degrees of the same behavior pattern. It seems that laughter is an expressive emotional pattern response even at its first appearance. Smiling is either a social or an emotional expression depending upon circumstances.

The treatment which Dumas has given to the problems of laughter and of crying is illuminating and will be followed in part in the discussion of this subject. There are, according to Dumas (1923), five major problems in connection with laughter: the problem of its physiological mechanism, the problem of *"le rire de la joie,"* the problem of *"le rire du comique,"* the problem of the connection between mental state and its outward expression, and the problem of laughter as a social phenomenon. The physiological mechanism for laughter consists of fifteen facial muscles, which are used in smiling, the respiratory muscles, the vocal mechanism, and, in extreme cases, other muscles throughout the body.

There is a fundamental difference between the joyful laugh and the comic laugh. The joyful laugh is a sort of bubbling-over of good humor, very commonly shown by children. It is usually seen when some restraint is suddenly removed, as when children come out of school, when there is some sudden good fortune, or when old friends meet after a long separation. The laughter caused by tickling is probably to be classed along with these.

The comic laugh, on the other hand, is always a laugh *at* some joke or ludicrous situation, and it may represent an entirely different attitude from that which produces the joyful laugh. The nature and cause of this attitude has been a problem for philosophers ever since Aristotle. The question, "Why are things funny?" is as difficult as the question, "Why are things beautiful?" According to Aristotle, laughter is due to the sudden feeling of triumph which comes with the sudden perception of a superiority in us, by comparison with the inferiority of others or our own former inferiority. When another person slips on a banana peel, or sits down on a non-existent chair, or commits a social blunder, we laugh because of the instinctive feeling that, "*I* didn't do that!" Hobbes restated the same general idea when he said that laughter is due to the "degradation of some person or interest possessing a certain dignity." Examples of this are the dog in church, the wedding procession spattered with mud, or the fit of sneezing in the middle of a proposal of marriage. For Kant, laughter was due to the sudden relief of tension or expectation. We laugh because of relief of tension when a clown runs toward a horse as if to leap in the saddle at one bound but stops short to flick a microscopic speck of dust off the bridle. For Schopenhauer, humor consisted in the sudden perception of a discord between reality and our idea or representation of reality. We laugh at a monkey or a cartoon because it is such a pitiful imitation of a man. According to Bergson, humor consists in the fact that, in place of an intelligent and well-adapted reaction, some individual makes an unintelligent and poorly adapted reaction to a situation. Humor is an infinite variation on the theme *"du mécanique plaqué sur le vivant."* The customs officer who asked the shipwrecked sailor if he had anything to declare, the short man who stooped to go through the high doorway, the pompous man who slipped on a banana peel, are all examples of this.

The fourth problem connected with laughter is that of finding the connection between the mental state (sum total of implicit and explicit responses?) and outward expression. Given the feeling that a certain thing *is* funny, why should we express that feeling by working the muscles of the face? This is largely an unsolved problem and necessarily depends on the actual nature of the mental state. Spencer explains laughter as an outlet of surplus energy. This agrees with the theories of Hobbes and Kant but not very well with the others. Dumas suggests that when there is a sudden contrast or contradiction, especially when the contrast is a descent from the greater to the less, the nervous energy stored up in the first case finds an unexpected outlet through laughter.

With regard to the social aspect of laughter, Dumas calls attention to its contagious nature. We laugh far more easily in a group than when alone. Laughter, like facial expression, has become a kind of language. Sometimes we laugh merely to show others that we understand the joke. At other times it is a communication of real good will and the spirit of fun; usually, perhaps, both. We sometimes laugh for the pure joy of laughing. For instance, in certain situations the slightest stimulus will start us off and prolong the laughter out of all reason, as the contagious giggling of the school child or of a maniacal patient.

Freud (1917) has advanced a theory of wit and of laughter which accounts for some of the difficulties of the connection between the muscular activity of laughter and the mental content of comedy. He states the theory as follows: "A fore-conscious thought is left for a moment in the unconscious elaboration and the results are grasped by the conscious perception. Wit seeks to draw a small amount of pressure from the free and unencumbered activities of our psychological apparatus and later to seize this pressure as incidental gain." The pressure of wit originates in an economy of expenditure of inhibition, the comic from an economy of expenditure in thought, and humor from an economy of expenditure of feeling. Freud evidently considers the expressions themselves as native reaction patterns since he fails to raise the question. His theory is concerned only with the mental content.

The question of tears involves four problems: physiological, psychological, psychophysiological, and social. The physiological question is, as in the case of laughter, comparatively simple. The lachrymal glands, situated over the outer corners of the eyes, send their lubricating fluid over the eyeballs through four or five large, and eight to ten small, canals. These glands function continuously when the eyes are open, since the action of the air on the eyeballs stimulates them to reflex action.

Tears (abnormal secretion of the lachrymal fluid) are produced in physical pain, grief, anger, extreme joy, and excess laughter. The common element in the psychological situation seems to be physical stress. Tears, in the infant, probably occur as a sort of by-product of the general bodily excitation.

Tears, like facial expression and laughter, are used as language. Infants very early learn that crying often gets them what they want. Though the process is difficult to manage voluntarily, because it is originally reflex, it can be done. It is interesting to speculate whether other reflex glandular activities, such as the production of saliva or gastric juice, might have become language mechanisms if only they had been visible from the outside.

Borgquist (1906) made a study of grief and crying by means of a questionnaire, scattered physiological data, and references from literature. He concluded that crying, in the last analysis, was a reaction which comes at the end of a period of stress where there has been strong effort and exhausted nervous energy. It is essentially a breaking-down of adaptive mechanisms which are no longer adequate to meet environmental conditions. There are clearly two groups of symptoms which accompany different moments of the crying act. The first are those active movements of "calling," as represented by the vocalization of the infant or child. The second group includes the facial expression, sobbing, tears, etc., which may be interpreted as withdrawing movements going back to a primitive rejection of food.

Lund (1930, pp. 130-157) observed the situations which brought about tears in both normal and abnormal individuals. He concluded:

> Tears, when affectively produced, are indicative of a mixed emotional state. Neither sorrow, dejection, joy nor elation, when occurring in pure form, is very effective, if at all, in producing the discharge. Typically, it appears when a depressing or otherwise unpleasant situation gains a redeeming feature or when a period of tension with unpleasant stimulation is followed by pleasant or alleviating stimulation.

This viewpoint is essentially the same as that of Borgquist except that it demands a *realization* of the relief. It is obvious that neither theory is a complete one as many varieties of crying are left unexplained by either theory.

The Relation of Facial Expression to Emotion. The investigations, together with the rational deductions which have been considered thus far, lead one to the conclusion that facial expression is a more or less variable *part* of emotional experience. The presence or absence of pattern of expression from the voluntary musculature of the face adds to or detracts from the entire emotional experience but is only one element in a group of forces and not a very important element at that. The important elements in emotional expression are the situation and the level of activity of the body. Three patterns of facial expression—surprise, joy, and depression—result from the condition of the facial musculature as direct responses to the stress of the situation. The particular character of the expression is, to the best of our present knowledge, dependent on the survival of primitive connections within the nervous system. It is possible that early in animal evolution the baring of the teeth and the opening of the mouth in periods of emergency was of survival value and that this particular connection has persisted. Still another possible explanation lies in the fact that the nuclei of the seventh or facial nerves are located in the midbrain in close approximation to the centers of organization of affective response. This proximity might conceivably lead to the use of the face as an overflow mechanism in the draining-off of nervous energy expended in affective experience.

BODILY ACTIVITY AND EMOTION

The question of the activity of the entire body in affective experience is an exceedingly complicated one. The analysis of behavior in the adaptive activity of the organism brought about by an emotional situation shows that it is so highly complicated that any attempt to make a simple or orderly behavior classification can meet with but little success. Carr

(1917) has pointed out that the bodily responses in emotion should be considered under three heads: (1) the *act*, which refers to the processes of adaptation to the objective situation, (2) the *emotion*, which refers to those activities which increase the effectiveness of the act, and (3) the remaining processes, which constitute the *by-products* of the emotion or the act. He goes on to show that there is no coordinate fourth group of processes which may be termed expressive activities or expressive responses of emotion for the body as a whole.

Even though there are no well-marked patterns of bodily responses in the adult human, it seems plausible that such responses might be found in animals or in the infant. Darwin's studies, which have been mentioned above, imply that there are well-marked emotional pattern responses in animals. Subsequent work of the various comparative psychologists shows that these total responses are almost as variable in the intact animal as in the adult human being. Emotional responses are limited only by the mechanical limits of activity of the animal.

Several years ago Watson (1924) reported the results of his studies concerning the emotional responses in the newborn infant. He stated that there were three well-defined emotional patterns—rage, fear, and love. The names which he gives to these patterns are his own labels. (Cf. Sherman's work, 1928.) The patterns of response which Watson described he believed to be innate and adequate, in the evolutionary sense, to the situation. It is probable that it would be equally easy to define and limit three other patterns of response which might be regularly elicited by appropriate stimuli and which would have as great inherent worth as those to which Watson has called attention. The main point is that the appearance of true patterns of expression in the human adult or infant or in higher animal forms is a matter of extreme doubt.

The work of Freud and the psychoanalysts suggests that in abnormal behavior there may be more or less well-defined bodily patterns of emotional expression. These, according to Freud, are for the most part symbolic or mimetic of repressed desires or wishes. The responses represent the acting-out of "un-live-out-able" wishes. In the inescapable kinship of the human race the sameness in activity of all members of the race will appear in these mimetic or symbolic pattern responses, which are most clearly defined in neurotic individuals. These findings are all based on clinical observation and, until they have been subjected to controlled experimental verification, their significance for experimental psychology is questionable.

Visceral Responses

Circulation, Blood, and Heart

a. *Blood volume.*[2] Following the theoretical and clinical suggestion of Lange that the core of emotional experience was to be found in the changes of blood distribution throughout the body, variations in blood volume during affective experience have been extensively studied. Some modi-

---

[2]See Eng (1925) for technical details and diagrams.

fication of the Mosso plethysmograph, an instrument for determining changes in the volume-flow of blood in any particular member or locality of the body, has been most frequently employed in this work. More than twenty experiments which were reported between 1879 and 1925 and which made use of the plethysmograph for analysis of the variations in blood volume in emotion have been critically studied and analyzed by Robins (1919). The plethysmograph does not lend itself to experimentation where the situation is intense or where the stimuli are apt to evoke marked voluntary bodily activity. Hence these experiments have been chiefly directed towards the correlation between pleasantness, unpleasantness, or milder affective experiences and blood-volume changes. Most of these experiments report an increase in the blood volume of the periphery of the body during pleasantness and a decrease during unpleasantness. However, certain experiments reporting contrary results to this general claim have been so well conducted as to leave the point in doubt. In general, there is little hope of accurate differentiation of pleasantness, unpleasantness, or of other affective experience on the basis of blood-volume changes in the body. Miss Eng (1925) has recently reported an elaborate study of the emotional life of the child in terms of plethysmographic records. Her work, in the main, confirms the indefiniteness of all of the previous findings. There was no more of a volume pattern in the emotional response of the child than there was for the adult. The "spontaneous" emotional reactions in children last longer and are stronger than those of the adult but are no more definite in their blood-volume pattern. Her work failed to confirm any of the standard psychological theories of feeling or emotion.

Weber (1910) carried on an experimental investigation of the changes in blood volume of the entire body. For this work he used the "balanced board of Mosso." He found that during pleasantness, sleep, or ideas of movement, there was a general flow of the blood to the periphery of the body. In most other situations there was a draining of the blood to the viscera and interior of the body. The chief criticism of the work of Weber is that for the most part his situations were artificial. He hypnotized the subject and suggested the desired emotional reaction. The question of the physiology and psychology of hypnotism and of the validity of expression of emotion during hypnotism is even more obscure than is the waking expression of emotion.

b. *Blood pressure*.[3] The use of measurements of blood pressure as an expression of emotion grew out of the work on blood volume. This work makes use of the sphygmomanometer, an instrument for the indirect determination of arterial blood pressure. The measurements are usually made on the upper arm and expressed in terms of pressure in millimeters of mercury. Marston (1917) used the sphygmomanometer for the distinguishing of emotional responses, particularly the differentiation of truth and falsehood. His work on the expression of emotion other than deception is inconclusive, particularly in light of more recent work. Landis

---

[3]See Landis (1924b) and Landis and Gullette (1925) for technical details.

and Gullette (1925) studied the changes in systolic blood pressure which accompany emotional experiences. This investigation revealed no pattern of blood-pressure response to any situation or with any reported feeling or emotion. A single exception was noted in the case of the vascular response to the unexpected explosion of a firecracker. In this situation most subjects exhibited a sharp rise in systolic blood pressure followed by an equally rapid fall to the original level. Blatz (1925) has reported a similar finding in such situations. In a control experiment Landis and Gullette found that when blood-pressure measurements were taken at approximately fifteen-second intervals, over a period of from one to four hours, during which the subject was passively reading material of a non-emotional nature, there were almost as great variations in blood pressure as were found during the emotional situations. Landis, Gullette, and Jacobsen (1925) made a statistical analysis of the correlation between the amount and variability of blood-pressure changes with seventeen other objective and subjective measures of emotional response which they had at hand for a group of twenty-four subjects. These correlations indicate that blood-pressure responses are negatively correlated (not significantly) with other emotional expressions.

Marston's (1917, 1924) work has called a great deal of attention to the use of blood pressure in the differential diagnosis of truth and falsehood. He claims that an increase of 8 mm. to 12 mm. of pressure in response to a question is sufficient to indicate that the subject was lying. The blood-pressure change during truth is that of a slowly decreasing general level. His determinations were made by taking one or two readings of systolic pressure before a question was asked and again immediately after the question was answered, the difference in pressure being the basis of diagnosis. Larson (1923) has carried on this notion with modified technique. He used an adaptation of the Erlanger method for graphic recording of blood pressure. His studies were made in prisons and in police courts where the factor of truth or of falsehood was undoubtedly very real in the life of the subject. In general, his results indicate that blood-pressure determinations can be used as a mild variety of the "third degree" for detecting falsehood. The technique is neither accurate nor controllable to a place where one is safe in reporting an unqualified diagnosis in absence of other supporting evidence.

Brunswick (1924) has made use of the Erlanger and Festerling (1912) method of recording blood pressure during a series of emotional situations in the laboratory. His work shows that blood pressure does not furnish a differential pattern of emotional expression. Landis (1926) has studied by the Erlanger method blood-pressure changes in pronounced upset. No pattern of response was found other than the gradual decrease of pulse pressure (systolic pressure minus diastolic pressure) which is comparable to the vascular change in "surgical shock."

Recently, Chappell (1929) has investigated blood-pressure changes in deception and has criticized the work of the earlier investigators, particularly that of Landis and Gullette. He found that blood pressure might be used to detect deception experimentally when the deception situation gave rise to excitement. However, a "deception curve" might be obtained under conditions other than those of deception, as when the subjects had been told that their intelligence was being measured. Consciousness of deception as such was not found to affect blood pressure; the rise, when occurring, being due to excitement. Bryan (1930) has repeated Chappell's work. She points out that the results which Chappell obtained were due to the way in which he conducted his experiments. What Chappell did was to establish a correlation between consciousness of deception and blood-pressure rises by correlating these rises with the behavior reactions of lying, while neglecting to correlate lying with the consciousness of deception. As she shows, his logical generalizations from his results are fallacious. In general, she found that blood pressure gives an accuracy of differentiation between truth and falsehood of 69 per cent, which is not sufficiently accurate to be of any diagnostic value.

In all probability, the rises in blood pressure which have been attributed to deception are due, as Chappell as well as others have pointed out, to the factor of general excitement. The blood-pressure rises which are attributed to emotion are to be explained similarly. In so far as general or undifferentiated excitement is an emotional experience just that far is blood pressure an expressive reaction of emotion. No experimental work has yet been produced indicating any other relationship than this.

c. *Blood changes.* It has been suggested that the change in the pH of the blood might be considered as an expression of emotion (pH is a chemical symbol used to denote the ratio of free acid hydrogen ions to free alkali hydroxyl ions in a solution). The normal pH of the blood is 7.2 as compared to 7.0 which represents a neutral solution; that is, the blood is slightly alkaline. Certain investigators have stated that the pH of the blood changes from 7.2 to as much as 7.7 during emotion. This change is usually attributed to the accumulation of carbon dioxide in the blood stream brought about by the increased metabolism of emotion. The studies of this acid-base ratio in the blood as expressions of emotion have not been overly successful. More significant results have been claimed for the use of the pH of saliva, which affords an indirect measure of changes in the blood. Starr (1922) has reported that in emotionalized or psychopathic subjects there is an increase in alkalinity of the saliva during emotional disturbance which is greater than the normal variations due to psychological reactions of everyday life. Renshaw (1925) was unable to confirm Starr's claims.

Another variable factor in the constitution of the blood is the presence of glycogen (blood sugar), which, as Cannon (1929) has demonstrated, is increased during emotional stress. The kidneys constitute a mechanism which normally and automatically maintains a constant level of sugar concentration in the blood. When this level is exceeded, due to an excess secretion of sugar by the liver, the excess appears in the urine. Studies made on both men and animals in periods of emotional stress demonstrate this glycosuria.

Mann (1925) has shown that there is a change in the amount of sugar in the blood stream following the ingestion of a glucose meal. He presents curves showing the increase and decrease of this blood-sugar level in normal people and comparable curves for psychopathic patients who were suffering from definite emotional disturbances, e.g., acute depression, euphoria, mania, etc. These curves show a persistent hyperglycemia in stuporous and melancholic patients, whereas there is a hypoglycemia in the euphoric individual.

d. Heart reactions. Even though the vasomotor control of the circulation fails to show a pattern of response, the reaction of the heart itself might furnish some expressive pattern during emotion. Landis and Slight (1929) made an electrocardiographic study of cardiac activity in response to a sudden stimulus. They occasionally found pronounced deviation from normal cardiac activity, but the appearance of this divergency was more closely related to the temporal correlation between the time of stimulation and the point in the cardiac cycle at which the stimulation took place than to any other factor. A study by Blatz (1925) has given essentially the same findings. Blatz was particularly interested in the pulse rate and found a "pattern" of pulse rate in response to surprise but no other change of importance.

Respiratory Reactions. While no theory basing emotion on respiration has gained any great amount of attention, the changes in the rate, depth, or pattern of respiration in response to emotional stimuli have long been noted and studied. Experimental work upon respiration in relation to affective experience is, on the whole, rather unsatisfactory. Dumas (1923), following Sikorsky, has tried to make a case for respiratory function as diagnostic of mood in the psychotic individual. It seems possible that at certain times and in certain cases such diagnostic patterns may occur. However, prolonged studies of the same individual, who has been suffering from, say, acute depression, indicate that, although there may be a slowing-down of the respiratory rate, there is no general pattern in his breathing. Miss Feleky (1916) attempted to correlate various respiratory expressions, viz., respiratory work, respiratory volume, inspiration-expiration ratio, with the facial expression and bodily activity during an imagined emotional experience. Her findings are interesting but are reported as being based on one experiment on each of six subjects for each imagined "emotion." In view of the small number of cases and the limitation of imagination, little significance may be attached to the point of "pattern" upon which she insisted, at least so far as pattern in real emotion is concerned. Indeed, certain of her differential findings, when subjected to statistical analysis, show that the differences are not statistically significant, as, for example, those between disgust and pleasure, anger and pain, pleasure and anger, etc.

Landis (1926) reports that breathing in pronounced upset showed marked respiratory effort which slowly decreased; and, as the upset progressed, the respiration became more and more shallow. Blatz (1925) found that, if startle occurred during expiration, the respiratory wave was at once changed to inspiration; whereas, if it occurred in inspiration, no change was noted. Skaggs (1926) confirmed this. Landis and Slight (1929) did not obtain such a change.

In the detection of falsehood special use has been made of the inspiration-expiration ratio (I/E). Benussi (1924) first investigated this function and claimed 100-per-cent certainty in the diagnosis of the truth or falsity of the verbal response of a subject in highly artificial situations. Benussi claimed that the I/E ratio of the three or five breaths before telling the truth was greater than the I/E ratio of the three or five breaths after telling the truth. The ratio before lying was less than the ratio after lying. Benussi stated that it was possible to detect falsehood even when the subject was attempting to breathe regularly, keeping in time with the beating of a metronome. He also found that imagining a falsehood gave no significant breathing changes. Burtt (1921) repeated, in part, Benussi's experiments, making use of an instrument which gave the I/E ratios directly. He found that he could diagnose falsehood from truth 20 per cent better by this method than would be possible by chance. (He further confirmed this by making use of a jury whose findings were no more accurate than one would expect to obtain by chance.) Landis and Wiley (1926) attempted to determine the lower limit of actuality or reality in a deception situation which would give diagnostic respiratory or circulatory symptoms. Their situations were artificial, and no attempt was made to make the situation emotional or vivid. They found that respiratory changes (I/E) as a diagnostic symptom were 6 per cent better than chance. While no one has been able to confirm Benussi's sweeping claims, it is evident that some factor is operating in the deception situation which does, to a certain extent, influence respiration. Landis and Wiley have advanced the theory that this change is a tendency to prolong expiration and to shorten inspiration; that is, a tendency to a gasping sort of breathing in deception but not in truth.

Considerable investigation has been directed toward the relationship between respiratory pattern or respiratory function and feeling (pleasantness or unpleasantness). Much of this has been done to check the tridimensional theory of Wundt. Drozyński (1911), in an analysis of the I/E ratio in relation to pleasantness and unpleasantness, found a tendency for the ratio to increase in pleasantness and excitement and to decrease in unpleasantness. Rehwoldt (1911), in a similar study, confirms most of the findings of Drozyński. For the most part careful research has failed to bring evidence which does more than show that the respiratory functions are variable by-products of affective experience whose connection to the experiential content of pleasantness or unpleasantness is dubious or variable.

The findings concerning respiration as an expression of emotion may be summarized as follows: (1) Respiration does not vary directly with emotional excitement. (2) Certain respiratory patterns are diagnostic of certain situations. Startle and possibly deception are situations for which the experimental evidence is positive. (3) Simple pleasantness and unpleasantness probably are accompanied by respiratory changes which may influence the content of the experience. (4) Respiration is undoubtedly a factor in emotion but has not yet been shown to be a differential expression of emotion.

Metabolic Rate. Metabolic rate refers to the sum of a series of energy changes within the organism. These changes may be either the accumulation of energy (anabolism) or the depletion of energy (catabolism) within the body. It is, of course, obvious that in emotional disturbance there is a marked change in the energy transformation and output. The earlier studies of the relationship between metabolism and affective experience were made upon the insane. The aspect of these experiments which is of interest here is the attempt to relate metabolic rate to the general mood or prevailing affective tone of the patient. The studies are so conflicting that the results do not indicate anything more startling than that the depressed or melancholic individual has a lowered metabolic rate, while the excited or euphoric patient shows an increased rate. Graff and Mayer (1923) attempted to find the effect of emotion upon metabolism by use of hypnosis in which emotional reactions were suggested. They state that in one case they found as high as a 25-per-cent increase in oxygen consumption when the subject was told that he had an incurable cancer, while the same subject showed only 4-per-cent increase when he was told that he had been left a large sum of money. Their experiments were not adequately controlled and lack verification.

Miss Totten (1925) was the first to attempt to study metabolism as an expression of emotion. She recorded muscular movements, abdominal respiration, pulse rate, and oxygen consumption with fourteen subjects who were subjected to a series of emotional situations. She found in six subjects an increase of from 5 to 20 per cent in oxygen consumption. In the remaining eight subjects there was no change worth noting. Her explanation for the increased metabolic rates was that an increased volume and ventilation of the lungs occurred. This increase was attributed to the relaxation of the bronchioles by the adrenalin liberated during the emotion.

The effect of pronounced upset upon metabolism was the subject of an experiment by Landis (1925). He made determinations of the basal metabolic rate daily for a period of three weeks, thus obtaining an average rate and the range of rates for each of three subjects. The subjects were then required to go without food for forty-eight hours, without sleep for thirty-six hours, and were then submitted to moderately intense electrical stimulation. At the end of this "starvation-insomnia period" it was found that anticipation before stimulation was characterized by a very marked increase in metabolism. This increase amounted to 16 per cent, 29 per cent, and 48 per cent, respectively, for the three subjects. When the actual stimulation was started, the metabolism dropped rapidly and at the end of six or eight minutes was practically normal. The metabolic rate during the hour after the stimulation was not significantly different from normal, nor for the succeeding three or four days did it show significant deviation. In the same paper Landis reports that the emotional experience aroused by listening to phonographic music did not cause any significant change in metabolic rate.

It is doubtful that the metabolic rate is an expression of any mood or temperament. Unpleasant or nocuous stimuli usually are accompanied by a transient increase in metabolism, while extreme upset is marked by a sharp increase followed by a decrease which is almost as rapid as the primary increase. Several causes have been suggested to account for the increase in metabolism during emotion: (1) an increase in the secretion of adrenalin or of thyroxin with consequent increase in release and consumption of glycogen; (2) an increased muscular tonicity or incomplete muscular relaxation of the voluntary muscles of the body; (3) relaxation of the bronchioles with consequent absorption of more oxygen; and (4) an increased metabolism of the central nervous system. The evidence for any one of these suggested causes is incomplete. More experimental work is needed before one will be able to say with any degree of certainty which explanation is correct or the proportion of the change which is to be attributed to any one of the factors.

Gastro-intestinal Activity. It is common knowledge that affective situations frequently lead to disturbances in gastro-intestinal activity. The nausea and disturbances of digestion accompanying emotional upset have been known and remarked upon by psychologists for many years. James developed his famous theory of emotions on the hypothesis that the perception of the visceral changes constituted the differentia of emotion from other mental experience.

The work of Pavlov (1902) has demonstrated that the mere presence of food in the mouth is sufficient to call out what he calls "psychic secretion," even when no food has entered or can enter the stomach. It has also been shown that this secretion is altered by emotional stimulation. Cannon (1929) found essentially the same facts for humans that Pavlov had demonstrated with animals. He notes that salivary and gastric secretion are inhibited in the angry dog or in the frightened cat. The activity of the smooth muscles composing the gastro-intestinal tract is markedly changed during affective experience. If an animal is given a bismuth meal and the progress of the food through the intestinal tract followed fluoroscopically, it may be demonstrated that unpleasant or nocuous stimuli lead to inhibition of the orderly process of digestion. It may also be shown that intense excitement of a pleasant nature will inhibit digestion while mild pleasantness will tend to facilitate activity.

Brunswick (1924) has conducted a very interesting experiment upon the effect of emotional stimuli on the gastro-intestinal activity of the human being. He studied by means of gastric, duodenal, and rectal balloons gastro-intestinal activity during emotional situations. The situations were such as to bring about emotional disturbances in most of his ten subjects. He found that there was a loss or decrease of gastro-intestinal tone when the subject reported that he had experienced fear, envy, disappointment, irritation, pain, and unpleasantness; while distress, surprise, and startle usually went with increased tonus. Amusement, delight, admiration, appreciation, or disappointment were never associated with gastro-intestinal change; while with fear, relief, and envy the intestinal records were contradictory. In all of his work it was obvious that specific changes in gastro-intestinal tonus were related to mild pleasantness or unpleasantness and to nothing more. He found no gastro-intestinal pattern reactions which would furnish a basis for James's theory of emotion. James's theory also depends upon the temporal relationship between the feeling and the visceral change. This visceral change should take place and, subsequently, the sensory qualities should be perceived and labeled as emotion or feeling. Brunswick's evidence on this point is contradictory. Some of his subjects showed the necessary temporal sequence; others failed to demonstrate it.

In Landis' (1926) experiment, where the subjects went without food or sleep for two days, records were taken of respiration, blood pressure, gastric contractions, rectal contractions, and metabolism. The stimulation at the end of the period produced emotional upset. The effect of this situation was to bring about a cessation of gastro-intestinal activity both of the stomach and the rectum. The effect of the stimulation upon blood pressure, respiration, and metabolism has been described above. According to the James-Lange theory there should be different patterns or sequences in the visceral and metabolic reactions during the upset of each subject, since each of the three reported entirely different emotional experiences. The similarity of the reactions of the three and the haphazard sequence of the physiological relationships may be best interpreted by assuming that there was a disturbance in the usual physiological integration, and that the reactions were merely those of random, chance occurrence, or of the selective balance of autonomic nervous functions peculiar to each individual.

From these studies of visceral reactions it will be seen that metabolism, gastro-intestinal activity, respiratory activity, and circulatory activity are all intimately interconnected. It seems that excitement, startle, or mild facilitation of activity creates a favorable balance so that visceral activity is facilitated. Nocuous, strong, or pronounced stimulation of any variety, or "intense emotional experience" all tend to interfere with the complicated integration of visceral function. The visceral responses are, to the best of our present knowledge, mediated over the autonomic nervous system or through the action of hormones acting directly on the organs. The disturbance in emotion lacks pattern in the sense that essentially the same pattern should be shown by all individuals. What is found, then, is an individual rather than a common pattern. A man experiences an emotion, and every time he experiences it about the same organic reactions take place, but there is no evidence of similar reactions in any other individual under similar conditions, or, indeed, from one period in the same man's life to some other period separated by months or years.

The Rôle of the Endocrine Glands in the Expression of Emotion

The relationship between the endocrine glands and emotion has been the subject of a great deal of experimental investigation. The interrelationship between the activities of these glands and the autonomic nervous system is one of the most abstruse and complicated problems which face the physiologist. It is a matter of biochemical and biophysical balance in which there are some eight or ten variables in relation to an autonomic nervous system of control, the fundamental action of which is only imperfectly understood. We may state in advance that certain internal secretions have a marked rôle in emotion. Others may be involved, but we are unable to state specifically the effect of their activity. Still other internal secretions probably have no part in affective experience.

Adrenal Glands. The work of Cannon (1929) and his collaborators on the importance of the adrenal glands in emotion constitutes a brilliant chapter in physiological psychology. A detailed discussion of Cannon's work is given in Chapter 6. In order to complete the picture which we are endeavoring to give of the expressions of emotion, certain factors concerning adrenal function should be pointed out.

The physiological effects of adrenalin may be summarized as follows: (1) increases the tremor in voluntary muscle; (2) causes relaxation of smooth muscle; (3) counteracts fatigue in voluntary muscle by affecting the myoneural junction; (4) alters blood distribution by its inhibition of the sympathetic division of the autonomic nervous system, so changing the volume distribution of blood of the body; (5) alters blood pressure by direct action on the cardiac muscle and on the contraction of the arteries; (6) hastens the rate of clotting of the blood; (7) relaxes the bronchioles; (8) causes the liver to release into the blood stream glycogen available for muscular work. All of these physiological changes brought about by the action of adrenalin are, after a fashion, emergency reactions which enable an organism to meet situations which demand quick and probably prolonged discharge of energy. No one of the reactions offers a pattern which could be considered as a differential expression of any of the "emotions," but the reactions are all of a sort which fit under our definition of emotion.

The doctrine which has been advanced by Marañon (1924) is frequently cited as evidence of the relationship between adrenalin and emotion. Marañon subcutaneously injected various patients with 1 to 1½ cc. of 1 to 1000 adrenalin. He reported that the patients characterized their experience as a "cold emotion." That is, they reported that they were organically stirred up without having an external reference or a situation to account for the experience. Recently, Landis and Hunt (1932) reviewed the literature on which Marañon based his conclusions and found that the original protocols state clearly that in some cases a true emotion may be aroused by the injection of adrenalin. Marañon does not attribute this "true emotion" to the simple organic syndrome of adrenalin but states that it is due to hyperthyroidism, "predisposition," or "raised emotional level" of the patient. Cantril and Hunt (1932) injected adrenalin into a group of subjects who had had some training in introspection. The reports of these subjects indicated clearly that in some instances the mere existence of the organic syndrome set up by adrenalin was accepted as furnishing a complete and satisfying subjective emotional experience. Landis and Hunt (1932) conducted a similar experiment with psychopathological patients. Their results were in line with those of Cantril and Hunt. In general, they found that the injection of sufficient amounts of adrenalin would reproduce roughly the organic picture usually characterized as emotion. There was considerable variation, both quantitatively and qualitatively, within the specific details of the reaction. The production of the adrenalin syndrome gave results differing from subject to subject. Certain individuals reported merely the perception of the organic condition. Others reported an associated emotional content, saying that they felt "as if afraid," or "as if in great joy," etc. In a few cases a complete emotion was aroused and this emotion seemed both satisfying and genuine. Landis and Hunt feel that adrenalin furnishes an interesting and suggestive approach to certain of the problems of emotional experience. Their work needs to be enlarged in its scope and to be carried out with more direct reference to emotional states which have been set up before the injection of adrenalin or while the adrenalin effect is present. This avenue of approach is very promising.

Thyroid Gland. The internal secretion of the thyroid gland is known as thyroxin. Since we have no direct chemical or physiological test for the presence of thyroxin in the blood stream, most of our knowledge concerning its action comes from indirect or clinical evidence. There is no experimental work showing whether the secretion of thyroxin is accelerated in an emotional situation. It is probable that such acceleration does take place, since emotion is expressed through the sympathetic nervous system and the thyroid gland is innervated and stimulated through this system, and since adrenalin stimulates both the activity of the sympathetic nervous system and of the thyroid gland. Although the experimental evidence is meager, the clinical evidence is rather clear. In hyperthyroidism or in exophthalmic goiter we find a marked emotional instability in the patient. Such individuals over-react to emergency situations or to nocuous stimuli and seem to be in a state of heightened tension and irritability most of the time. In hypothyroidism or myxedema we find a paucity of emotional expressions and responses. The patient is stolid, stuporous, and sluggish. The level of emotional reaction, mood, or temperament, whether excited or depressed, is somehow at least partially a function of the presence of thyroxin in the blood stream.

The Pituitary Body. This small two-lobed gland at the base of the brain has at least two internal secretions, tethelin and pituitrin. Uno (1922) has shown that prolonged emotional stimulation in rats brings about changes in the size and chemical constitution of the pituitary gland. The exact nature of these changes is not clear. Our evidence from clinical medicine concerning the pituitary and emotion is meager. The physiological action of pituitrin is somewhat similar to that of adrenalin or thyroxin while tethelin is probably concerned chiefly in bodily growth.

The Gonads. The internal secretions of the sex glands go by various names at present, since their chemical composition is a matter of great research interest. The absence or deficiency of these internal secretions is quite marked and fairly well understood, especially from studies which have been made upon eunuchs or eunuchoidal individuals. The hyperfunction is equally marked in the development and expression of sexual passion or lust, particularly in satyriasis or nymphomania.

Summary of Endocrine Action in Emotion. The progress of biochemical research on the composition and physiological action of these endocrine secretions is making such rapid progress and is such a matter of dispute and controversy because of the variation in the results obtained by various workers that conclusions are not warranted. With the exception of the adrenalin effects, there seems to be little agreement concerning the action of any one of these agents on the entire and intact organism. Very evidently they do play some rôle in emotional experience, but the matter is not clearly understood at present and we can only wait until the evidence is more generally agreed upon.

THE RÔLE OF THE NERVOUS SYSTEM IN THE EXPRESSION OF EMOTION

The Peripheral Nervous System and Spinal Cord. The external expressions of emotion are mediated over the peripheral nervous system. There is no evidence that the peripheral nervous system is anything more than the connecting linkage between the central control and the expressions of the emotion. In spinal animal preparations certain of the integrated reflex patterns are sometimes spoken of as pseudo-expressions of emotion. The struggling or scratching which results from the painful pinching of the leg of a spinal dog is an example of this. In the human subject where the spinal cord has been severed we find these same varieties of reflex coordination.

The Midbrain and Thalamus. This most complex region of the central nervous system is of particular and peculiar interest, since most evidence goes to show that it is here that the expressions of emotion are organized, integrated, and controlled. This area acts as a relay station for all sensory impulses passing on to the cerebrum. It contains many of the nuclei in which are centered the control of the vegetative activity of the body. The nucleus of the facial nerve is in this region. The neurology and physiology of this area have been discussed in Chapter 6. For the purpose of the present chapter it is necessary only to show how this system acts in the organization of expressive emotional responses. The integrity of the emotional life of the individual, the facility of expression, the range of emotional experience, are all, somehow, functions of the intimate connections of this old brain center. It is just possible that the occurrence of facial expression in emotional experience is due to the fact that the nucleus of the facial nerve lies in the thalamic region in close anatomical approximation to other organization points for responses controlled over the autonomic nervous system. The probable neural scheme in the central organization of emotional expression is somewhat as follows: Sensory nervous impulses passing upward on their course to the cerebrum relay in the thalamus. The impulse may then pass in either of two major directions: (1) to the cerebrum, where it enters into sensory, perceptual, and voluntary motor activity; or (2) part of the impulse may be diverted at the level of the thalamus and initiate muscular activity from these centers. This latter activity constitutes the emotional background of reactions or reaction systems.

The Cerebrum. For the purposes of the present discussion the cerebrum is an organ of voluntary and learned expression and of the inhibition or control of expressive reactions. All of the voluntary expressions of the face, the gestures, and the voluntary bodily activity with which we knowingly convey our emotional reactions are functions of the cerebrum. The question of the development and socialization of expression is one which falls more properly into the field of learning. We have rather arbitrarily considered that the true expression of emotion is an unlearned and a more or less involuntary matter, since the treatment of expression as a form of learned response would lead us far afield from emotional expression.

The Autonomic Nervous System. In view of the extended treatment of this topic in Chapter 6, the treatment of the subject here will be very brief. All smooth or visceral muscular reactions are innervated over the autonomic system. All organization, all pattern of response, all of the temporal relationships which may be considered as visceral expressions of emotion are therefore somehow integrated by the autonomic system. There is, as has been shown by Cannon (1929) and his co-workers, a functional balance between the sympathetic division and the cranial and sacral divisions of this system. Such physiological patterns as are shown by the autonomic responses are attributed to the balance between these divisions. Mild pleasure (absence of pain or strong stimulation) is shown by a predominance of cranial and sacral function; while marked unpleasantness, upset, or violent emotion shows a predominant activity of the sympathetic division. The entire mechanism is reflex in nature. It is so balanced that any portion of the visceral response which becomes predominant will quickly and effectively find compensation elsewhere in the system in all normal circumstances.

The Properties of Nervous Conduction. Lapicque (1911) has developed a systematic explanation of neural activity based on the time-energy relations of the activity of functional tissue. He calls this characteristic stimulation value of living matter "chronaxie." Stimuli usually give rise to impulses which follow neural pathways in which the neurons are isochronous (have the same chronaxie). If the stimulation is strong or persists, the neural impulses which result will follow not only the isochronous pathways but will also be forced into heterochronous paths. Lapicque suggests that the taking-over of nervous impulses from isochronous to heterochronous paths furnishes the neural basis for the experience of unpleasantness. The more intense the heterochronicity of the neural system, the more intense the unpleasantness of the emotional experience. Pleasantness is regarded as the absence of unpleasantness.

The problem of the nature of feeling (pleasantness or unpleasantness) is one which has long baffled physiologists and psychologists. The suggestion of Lapicque represents only one of many theories which have been advanced to furnish a physical basis for affective experience. A broader theory, which has gained some attention, is based on the probability that the autonomic nervous system contains sensory as well as motor fibers. These sensory fibers carry impulses from smooth muscles and glands which are reported in midbrain centers merely as coordinated or incoordinated activity. Coordination is then identified with perceptual pleasantness and incoordination with unpleasantness.

THE ELECTRICAL EXPRESSIONS OF EMOTION[4]

The phenomenon usually termed "psychogalvanic reflex" was first called to the attention of the scientific world by Vigouroux, Féré, and Tarchanoff. Vigouroux, in 1879, reported a study of the variations in the resistance of the human body and mentioned changes in resistance which are due to the *"sensibilité"* of the subject. Féré (1888) called specific attention to the relationship between affective experience and variations in the resistance of the body. In 1890, Tarchanoff reported a study of the relationship between mental activity and the galvanic phenomenon of the skin. His work apparently grew out of duBois-Reymond's earlier investigation and was an attempt to establish the physiological basis for such bodily electrical responses.

The notion advanced first by Féré that the electrical response was an expression of emotion has been of a great deal of interest to psychologists and has led to many investigations. Veraguth (1909), who named this phenomenon the psychogalvanic reflex, and Binswanger (1918) seem to have been the first to hold that the reflex was specific to emotion. Binswanger's work was part of the "Diagnostic Association Studies" of Jung and the Zurich Psychoanalytic School. He maintained that, although the reflex occurs as a response elicited by a variety of stimuli, the mental processes involved may always be grouped under the concept of emotion. F. Peterson (1907) was probably the first to hold that the amount of galvanometric deflection is directly proportional to the strength of the emotion. Waller is responsible for persuading the majority of the scientific world interested in the phenomenon that it is specific to emotion. This he did largely through numerous demonstrations and papers given before scientific meetings in Great Britain, Belgium, and France. Wechsler (1925) was the first experimenter who investigated the problem of specificity of the reflex to emotion. Landis (1930*b*) has shown that Wechsler's conclusion, viz., that the response is specific to emotion, was not borne out either by his experiment or by his own logical analysis of his results.

---

[4] See Landis and DeWick (1929), and Landis (1932) for full bibliographical citations on this subject.

Radecki in 1911 and Abramowski in 1913 were the first to question the assumption that the galvanic reflex is associated *only* with emotion. These investigators believed that the mental processes known as volition were more commonly associated with the reflex than was emotion. This notion has been followed up in the work of Aveling and his associates. They hold that the reflex is the correlate of conation and shows itself in affective experience only when the conative process is present. Other psychological investigators have held that the reflex follows every sensory stimulation, that it comes only in periods of stress, that it always accompanies the appearance of unconscious processes in behavior, that it is correlated with the complex oretic process, that it occurs in only purely ideational processes, etc., etc. Indeed, a survey of the literature shows that psychologists have identified this electrical reaction with almost every conceivable mental process and with only the most questionable of evidence to back their claims.

When we turn to the work of the anatomists, we find that Schilf and Schuberth demonstrated in 1922 that the electrical response occurred only when the autonomic nervous connections between effector and receptor were intact. Foà and Peserico (1923), using cats for experimental material, found that the effector side of the response depended on the autonomic fibers following peripheral motor nerves; that the control center is localized in the corpora quadrigemina and in the apex of the calamus scriptorius; that peripheral stimulation starts impulses which traverse any sensory path which leads to the bulbar region, out of which the impulse giving rise to the response passes to connect with the autonomic system.

The anatomical work has been summarized as follows by Wang (1930):

> From these physiological findings we know that when a receptor organ is stimulated, nerve-impulses are set up in its afferent nerves; that these nerve-impulses may be transmitted first to the cortical sweat area and then therefrom to the preganglionic sudo-motor neurones in the spinal cord; that these nerve-impulses may be conducted first to the vegetative center in the tuber cinereum and then from there to the preganglionic sudo-motor neurones; that these nerve-impulses may be directly sent to the preganglionic sudo-motor neurones in the cord; that the nerve-impulses conducted by the preganglionic neurones activate the post-ganglionic sudo-motor neurones in the sympathetic ganglia, which in turn transmit them to the sweat glands; that when the sweat glands are excited by these nerve-impulses and begin to secrete, the galvanic skin reflex appears.

It has been demonstrated by Gildemeister (1922-23) that the apparent change in resistance of the body is in reality a change in either the amount or the rate of polarization. He has also demonstrated that the apparent electrical output of the body is to be explained in terms of polarization. Since polarization is the important factor in the response, he has carried out very elaborate studies on the nature, rate, and factors affecting polarization in the skin and in the living tissue. His results show that the alterations of polarization, usually called the psychogalvanic reflex, are dependent in the living organism upon the integrity of the autonomic nerve supply, and that the rate and duration of the reflex are a function of the sympathetic nervous control. Careful physiological investigations have shown that these electrical responses of the skin are general autonomic responses which are associated with the pupillary reflex, various vasomotor changes, changes in the cardiac rate, contraction of pilo-motor musculature, respiratory variations, increased muscular tension, etc. Darrow has shown in a series of critical experiments that there is a one-to-one relationship between this electrical response and variation in skin temperature. There is good reason to believe that the response is part of the temperature regulation of the skin and that its appearance is to be correlated with variations in skin temperature.

Most of the psychological studies have followed the uncritical conclusion of Veraguth and Binswanger, who assumed that these electrical responses were associated with some psychological category, usually emotion. It is, of course, possible to set up an experiment in which the situation is designed to bring out emotion, volition, conation, etc., and to measure these electrical responses during these situations. It is then usually concluded that the responses are associated with the mental function or functions usually assigned as appropriate to that situation. In a similar way, one could probably demonstrate that the salivary reflex is a measure of intelligence, or that the number of closures of the palpebral fissure is a measure of ideation.

Recently, several critical psychological investigations have been conducted from the introspective standpoint, trying to determine the conscious content associated with the appearance of these electrical variations. The most satisfactory is that of Abel, who shows that sudden checks in comprehension are most usually reported at the time of the appearance of the response, although there is considerable variation in the conscious content at these particular instants.

In so far as the expression of emotion is organized and integrated through midbrain centers, these electrical responses may be regarded as one of the expressions of emotion. It is equally clear that every bodily activity or mental function other than emotion, which is integrated in these same midbrain areas, may and probably does give rise to these responses. The use of these phenomena in psychological work should be interpreted in the light of the functional activity of the autonomic nervous system. If emotion is to be inseparably linked and totally identified with autonomic responses, then only would one be correct in saying that these electrical changes are specific to emotion. Undoubtedly, the electrical changes are valid measures of changes in balance in the autonomic nervous system and may so be used. Other psychological work which presupposes that the emotion and these responses are inseparably connected has found no real experimental verification.

EMOTION AND FEELINGS

The word "feeling" has at least three accepted usages: (1) a term referring to the experience of pleasantness and unpleasantness; (2) a description of an experience which is less vivid than emotion; and (3) the report of vaguely perceived sensations which do not have clear perceptual quality. These differences in usage are sufficient reason why the entire subject of feeling is so unsettled, both from the point of view of the psychologist and the physiologist. One can never be quite sure whether the investigator is referring to the experiential qualities of pleasantness and unpleasantness, to emotional experience, or to a sensation. We shall endeavor in this chapter to restrict our treatment of the subject to the phenomena of pleasantness, unpleasantness, and vaguely perceived emotion.

The older experimental psychology, particularly that of Wundt and of Titchener (1908), held that feeling is one of the three basic elements of mental life. Feeling in the Wundtian system is marked by quality (pleasantness or unpleasantness), intensity, and duration, but lacks clearness. Wundt also taught that feeling was tridimensional in quality. These dimensions are tension-relaxation, excitement-depression, and pleasantness-unpleasantness. Most attempts to verify Wundt's hypothesis have been unsuccessful. It has been impossible to identify the tension, excitement, etc., with pulse, breathing, or any other physiological correlate.

Physiological studies should, it seems, be able to furnish some clue to the nature of feeling or to its relation to emotion. Following the lead of Lange, various experimenters have tried to associate pleasantness and unpleasantness with the volume distribution of blood within the body. The results of these experiments are very conflicting and have failed to give us any real insight into the matter. Other theorists have hypothesized that pleasantness and unpleasantness were to be identified with facilitation and inhibition in neural activity. Facilitation was supposed to carry pleasantness with it as an induced phenomenon; inhibition, to carry unpleasantness. Unfortunately, there is no neurological substantiation of this theory. Other psychologists have maintained that unpleasantness equals mild pain, while pleasantness equals the absence of pain. This is an attractive notion but one which has defied thus far either affirmation or negation. The work of Head (1920) on the protopathic and epicritic elements of sensation is regarded by some as a basis for assuming that pleasantness and unpleasantness might be derived from the sensory qualities of experience. The work of Nafe (1924), concerning the psychological or experiential basis of feeling, has presented some very interesting points. His method is a variation from the usual introspective routine. In place of attempting to describe a feeling in dynamic terms, Nafe established the feeling process and then, after cutting it off short, obtained as complete an introspective report as possible concerning the feeling. His subjects finally came to a description which identified pleasantness with "bright pressure," which was described as kinaesthetic sensation from the region of the upper chest and shoulders. Unpleasantness was described as a "dull pressure" and associated with a pulling-down sensation in the region of the diaphragm. He concluded that sensory experience may be either affective or non-affective, but, if pleasantness or unpleasantness was present, there was an addition or complete change in the experience. Qualitatively, the affective increment was either a bright or a dull pressure. Pleasantness and unpleasantness were found inherently weak and mild, though they have a certain pattern of density. Pleasantness came on gradually while unpleasantness appeared at full strength and at high intensity, passing over to emotion, while pleasantness, as such, never did. Pleasantness and unpleasantness never appeared in isolation but always accompanied the sensory components, although they were not organic sensations or the perception of organic sensations.

Young (1927) attempted to check Nafe's findings. With one of Nafe's original observers he obtained reports of pressures, but his other observers' reports failed to duplicate Nafe's results. He denied Nafe's identification of pleasantness and unpleasantness with bright and dull pressure and concluded that Nafe's results were a product of the general laboratory atmosphere of Cornell. Hunt (1931a, 1931b) has again repeated Nafe's experiment with certain modifications in method. He concludes that affection is accompanied by bright and dull pressure. In his second article he found that the pleasantness of an emotion is no more intense than that of a purely affective situation, while the unpleasantness experienced in an emotion may be much more intense than that experienced in an affective reaction.

From the relevant literature certain conclusions concerning the relation of feeling and emotion as expressive reactions may be drawn: (1) Feeling is certainly not a simple, easily identified mental experience. (2) Feeling has never been successfully identified with any specific physiological occurrence or pattern of reactions. (3) Feeling may be either (a) the protopathic-epicritic element of sensation, (b) facilitation or inhibition in neural activity, (c) presence or absence of pain, (d) presence of reactions governed by the autonomic nervous system, (e) the energy balance of the organism at any particular time, or (f) a derived experience based on thalamic neural integration. (4) Psychologically, feeling, in the sense of pleasantness or unpleasantness, appears as a unique experience but one which may be the product or by-product of many other experiential processes.

The expressions of feeling are more difficult to systematize than are the expressions of emotion. For the most part this is due to the fact that feeling is less clear than emotion and that the expressions of feeling are even more a matter of socialized response than are the expressions of emotion. Practically all of the expressions which are usually attributed to emotion should be termed expressions of socialized feeling. The entire subject of the development of feeling as a social reaction is one which has only recently had the benefit of the experimental method. Murphy and Murphy (1931) have shown that it is a most promising field for real scientific advance.

Anhedonia

When James first announced his famous theory of emotion, he stated that confirmatory evidence would probably be found in certain pathological conditions in which there was a decrease or lack of visceral sensation. This condition has been termed "anhedonia." In 1905, D'Allonnes described a case of anhedonia coupled with disorders of the time sense. This patient complained of an utter lack of the *feeling* of emotion while displaying all outward expressions of emotion. She suffered from complete thermal, visceral, and pain anaesthesia. Myerson (1918) has reported a similar case of a young woman of cyclothymic temperament, who was suffering from "nervous prostration" as the result of an unrequited love affair. Following the affair, she retained all the outward expressions of nervousness and emotion, such as crying, blushing, and laughter, but protested that she had a complete lack of all "feeling." She reported that there was a total absence of hunger, thirst, fatigue, desire for sleep, joy, and fear. She would jump and scream at a sudden noise but denied all feeling of emotion.

Each of these cases presents an interesting study of hysteria, and in the opinion of the writer should be considered as such. Other clinical case histories of complete cutaneous analgesia show no such lack of emotion or feeling. The explanation of such cases of anhedonia should be made in terms of dissociated functional habit systems, which are more easily discussed today in the terms of psychoanalysis than in the terms of physiological psychology.

Conclusions

The Relation between Emotion and Its Expressions. Many classifications and schematic diagrams of the interrelationship existing between the emotions or the expressions of emotion are to be found in the psychological and philosophical literature. In the present consideration of this subject the factor of classification, or of the naming, or of an attempt to name, the emotional expressions has been neglected. This has been done because it seemed that it was more worth while to adopt an experimental attitude, to study first the behavior, the physiology, the experimental literature on emotion rather than to begin by hanging tags on events or phenomena not understood. It is doubtful that the appending of a classification would add particularly to the present treatment.

The descriptions which have been given of the expressions of emotion indicate that emotion, *per se,* is a unique physiological system of reactions for which the general boundary lines and landmarks have been determined, leaving the more intimate topography for future study. The expressions which we have studied—facial reactions, vascular reactions, respiration, gastro-intestinal reactions, etc.—are all of them outstanding landmarks on our map. To carry the analogy further, these reactions are the innate factors, the geographical or geological formations which are to be modified by the weathering action of the environment, thus more clearly defining those types of behavior which have been traditionally classified as emotions.

The question of nature *versus* nurture is as marked in emotion as in any other type of human behavior. It is customary to speak of emotion as a natural reaction, one which is little varied by experience. Certainly this is a very inexact concept. What the natural emotional life of an individual might be like is an unknown territory. Emotional life is modified more rigorously in the growth and education of an individual than perhaps any other variety of human experience. The reason for the statement so frequently made that emotion is a natural reaction, unmodified by learning, is that emotional reactions occur in such large units of physiological disturbance that they frequently swamp the mental life of the individual.

Psychology and physiology are essentially on common ground when dealing with the problems of emotion. The psychologist talks glibly about the rôle of the endocrines or the autonomic nervous system in emotion, while the physiologist is quite as careless in his remarks concerning the effect of the psyche, psychic life, or mind upon the factors which he calls emotional. Certainly a closer *liaison* between investigators in this field would make the work of one more intelligible to the other and would facilitate greatly our knowledge concerning these unique types of biological reactions which do play such an important rôle in human behavior.

The Expressions of Emotion. It is apparent that certain of the expressions of emotion are innate. Some of the purposeful interpretations of expression are very interesting. The notion that some of the expressions of emotion are due to the survival of emergency reaction patterns is attractive. The idea that many of the expressions are survivals of racial habits formerly useful is intriguing. There are, however, many expressions which do not fall into any evolutionary or teleological classification, as, for instance, laughter and crying. Another puzzling feature of this study is that of the way in which racial cultures or social factors modify and form expression. If, as some theorists have believed, certain expressions are mimetic of either past experiences of the individual or, more particularly, of past experiences of the race, then we must have a variety of neural function or an inheritance of modified nervous functioning which has not been hitherto described. It is safer to say that the major expressions of emotion are survivals of earlier biological and physiological functional relationships within the species, and that for the most part the shadings of expression shown by the adult are the result of learning or training.

The question of expression as a language mechanism is one which deserves more attention than it has received. We have mentioned before that vocal reactions often have emotional connotations which are not conveyed by the words themselves. The change in tones of the voice, the alteration in timbre, the occurrence of the vibrato, all serve as emotional expressions, most of which are learned, some of which seem to be native. The same is true for facial expression. The language of gesture, which has been largely neglected in modern psychology, certainly will add interesting side-lights to our knowledge of the subject. The question of "expression," in the sense in which it is used by the artist or the actor, is another which deserves the attention of the physiological psychologist. We know that certain gestures, certain varieties of reaction occurring in appropriate situations, are almost without exception interpreted as emotional. Why? The answer is not easy. There is no experimental evidence. The answer, when given, will modify many of our present concepts concerning the nature of aesthetics and of the nature of socialized emotional expression.

Future Lines of Development in Experimentation with Emotion. There have been pointed out, throughout this chapter, places in which further experimental evidence would be desirable. It remains only to consider briefly points which will probably be of importance in verifying or changing our viewpoints on this subject. The most important line of future research is that of the nature of the relation existing between emotion and learning in the broadest sense of each term. The acquisition of ability to interpret the expressions of emotion, the acquisition of facility of expression, the understanding of the probable underlying mechanisms of habit formation, will all of them be certain to modify our present concepts. Another main line of future development will come most probably from the study of the physiology of the central nervous system and of the autonomic nervous system with relation to their action in the control, organization, integration, and modification of emotion. The extremely rapid progress in endocrinology and in the biochemistry of body fluids may be expected to change our present concepts concerning the visceral organization of emotion and probably of the basic nature of personality. If mood, attitude, and the like are founded in the chemistry of the body, as has been postulated for centuries, it seems possible that we may be approaching some solution or verification of the hypothesis. In addition to these three lines, it is very possible that the new phenomenology of the *Gestalttheorie* will modify our concept of emotion just as the theory has modified the formulation of the field of perception. These reformulations may be descriptive or psychological, in the strictest sense of the word, but, as Arnheim's experiments have indicated, the new viewpoint and descriptive method is certain to lead to an advance in our knowledge.

It has been stated in texts of psychology and of physiology for many years that the problems of emotion defied the experimental method. True, this statement has not always been made explicitly, but certainly this notion is implicit in all too many of our modern texts. It is to be hoped that the picture given here of the expressions of emotion or of the availability of emotion as an experimental field in both physiology and psychology may bring about a change in this attitude.

BIBLIOGRAPHY

ABEL, T. M. 1930. Attitudes and the galvanic skin reflex. *J. Exper. Psychol.,* **13**, 47-60.

ABRAMOWSKI, E. 1913. Recherches expérimentales sur la volonté. *J. de psychol.,* **10**, 491-508.

ARNHEIM, R. 1928. Untersuchungen zur Lehre von der Gestalt: IV. Experimentell-psychologische Untersuchungen zum Ausdrucksproblem. *Psychol. Forsch.,* **11**, 2-132.

AVELING, F. 1929. The psychogalvanic phenomenon. *Proc. & Papers 9th Int. Cong. Psychol.*, New Haven, 63-65.

BENUSSI, V. 1914. Die Atmungssymptome der Lüge. *Arch. f. d. ges. Psychol.*, **31**, 244-273.

BINSWANGER, L. 1918. On the psychogalvanic phenomenon in association experiments. Chap. 12 of *Studies in word association*, by C. G. Jung. London: Heinemann. Pp. 446-530.

BLATZ, W. E. 1925. The cardiac, respiratory and electrical phenomena involved in the emotion of fear. *J. Exper. Psychol.*, **8**, 109-132.

BORGQUIST, A. 1906. Crying. *Amer. J. Psychol.*, **17**, 149-205.

BRUNSWICK, D. 1924. The effects of emotional stimuli on the gastro-intestinal tone. *J. Comp. Psychol.*, **4**, 19-79, 225-287.

BRYAN, A. I. 1930. Blood pressure deception changes and their use as an index of personality. M.A. thesis, Columbia Univ.

BURTT, H. E. 1921. The inspiration-expiration ratios during truth and falsehood. *J. Exper. Psychol.*, **4**, 1-23.

CANNON, W. B. 1929. Bodily changes in pain, hunger, fear and rage. (2nd ed.) New York: Appleton. Pp. xvi + 404.

CANTRIL, H., & HUNT, W. A. 1932. Emotional effects produced by the injection of adrenalin. *Amer. J. Psychol.*, **44**, 300-307.

CARR, H. 1917. Relation between emotion and its expression. *Psychol. Rev.*, **24**, 369-375.

CHAPPELL, M. N. 1929. Blood pressure changes in deception. *Arch. Psychol.*, **17**, No. 105. Pp. 39.

D'ALLONNES, G. R. 1905. Le rôle des sensations dans les émotions et dans la perception de la durée. *Rev. phil.*, **60**, 592-623.

DARWIN, C. 1873. Expression of emotion in man and animals. New York: Appleton. Pp. vi + 374.

DROZYŃSKI, L. 1911. Atmungs- und Pulssymptome rhythmischer Gefühle. *Psychol. Stud.*, **7**, 83-140.

DUMAS, G. 1923. Traité de psychologie. Vol. 1. Paris: Alcan. Pp. 967.

ENG, H. 1925. The emotional life of the child. London: Oxford Univ. Press. Pp. vi + 243.

ERLANGER, J., & FESTERLING, E. G. 1912. Respiratory waves of blood pressure, with an investigation of a method for making continuous blood pressure records in man. *J. Exper. Med.*, **15**, 370-389.

FELEKY, A. M. 1914. The expression of emotions. *Psychol. Rev.*, **21**, 33-41.

———. 1916. The influence of emotions on respiration. *J. Exper. Psychol.*, **1**, 218-241.

FÉRÉ, C. 1888. Note sur les modifications de la résistance électrique sous l'influence des excitations sensorielles et des émotions. *C. r. Soc. de biol.*, **5**, 217-219.

FOÀ, C., & PESERICO, E. 1923. Le vie del reflesso neurogalvanico. *Arch. di fisiol.*, **21**, 119-130.

FRAPPA, J. 1902. Les expressions de la physionomie humaine. Paris: Schmid. Pp. 140.

FREUD, S. 1917. Wit and its relation to the unconscious. (Trans. by A. A. Brill.) London: Allen & Unwin; New York: Moffat, Yard. Pp. vii + 388

FROIS-WITTMANN, J. 1930. The judgment of facial expression. *J. Exper. Psychol.*, **13**, 113-151.

GATES, G. S. 1925. A test of ability to interpret facial expressions. *Psychol. Bull.*, **22**, 120.

———. 1927. The role for the auditory element in the interpretation of emotion. *Psychol. Bull.*, **24**, 175.

GILDEMEISTER, M. 1922-23. Der galvanische Hautreflex als Teilerscheinung eines allgemeinen autonomen Reflexes. *Pflüg. Arch. f. d. ges. Physiol.*, **197**, 432-436.

GRAFF, F., & MAYER, L. 1923. Ueber den Einfluss der Affekte auf den Gesamtstoffwechsel. *Zsch. f. d. ges. Neur. u. Psychiat.*, **86**, 245-253.

GUILFORD, J. P. 1929. An experiment in learning to read facial expressions. *J. Abn. & Soc. Psychol.*, **24**, 191-202.

HEAD, H. 1920. Studies in neurology. (2 vols.) London: Oxford Univ. Press. Pp. ix + 329; viii + 862.

HUBER, E. 1931. Evolution of facial musculature and facial expression. Baltimore, Md.: Johns Hopkins Press. Pp. xii + 184.

HUNT, W. A. 1931a. The relation of bright and dull pressure to affectivity. *Amer. J. Psychol.*, **43**, 87-92.

————. 1931b. The pressure correlate of emotion. *Amer. J. Psychol.*, **43**, 600-605.

JAMES, W. 1890. The principles of psychology. Vol. 2. New York: Holt. Pp. vi + 704.

KANNER, L. 1931. Judging emotions from facial expressions. *Psychol. Monog.*, **41**, No. 186. Pp. 94.

LANDIS, C. 1924a. Studies of emotional reactions: I. A preliminary study of facial expression. *J. Exper. Psychol.*, **7**, 325-341.

————. 1924b. Studies of emotional reactions: II. General behavior and facial expression. *J. Comp. Psychol.*, **4**, 447-509.

————. 1925. Studies of emotional reactions: IV. Metabolic rate. *Amer. J. Physiol.*, **74**, 188-203.

————. 1926. Studies of emotional reactions: V. Severe emotional upset. *J. Comp. Psychol.*, **6**, 221-242.

————. 1929. The interpretation of facial expression in emotion. *J. Gen. Psychol.*, **2**, 59-72.

————. 1930a. Blood pressure changes in deception. A reply. *J. Comp. Psychol.*, **10**, 437-439.

————. 1930b. Psychology and the psychogalvanic reflex. *Psychol. Rev.*, **37**, 381-398.

————. 1932. Electrical phenomena of the skin (galvanic skin response). *Psychol. Bull.*, **29**, 693-752.

LANDIS, C., & DEWICK, H. N. 1929. The electrical phenomena of the skin (psychogalvanic reflex). *Psychol. Bull.*, **26**, 64-119.

LANDIS, C., & GULLETTE, R. 1925. Studies of emotional reactions: III. Systolic blood pressure and inspiration-expiration ratios. *J. Comp. Psychol.*, **5**, 221-253.

LANDIS, C., GULLETTE, R., & JACOBSEN, C. 1925. Criteria of emotionality. *Ped. Sem.*, **32**, 209-234.

LANDIS, C., & HUNT, W. A. 1932. Adrenalin and emotion. *J. Exper. Psychol.*, **39**, 467-485.

LANDIS, C., & SLIGHT, D. 1929. Studies of emotional reactions: VI. Cardiac responses. *J. Gen. Psychol.*, **2**, 413-420.

LANDIS, C., & WILEY, L. E. 1926. Changes of blood pressure and respiration during deception. *J. Comp. Psychol.*, **6**, 1-19.

LANGFELD, H. S. 1918. The judgment of emotion by facial expression. *J. Abn. Psychol.*, **13**, 172-184.

LAPICQUE, L. 1911. Essai d'une nouvelle théorie physiologique de l'émotion. *J. de psychol.*, **8**, 1-8.

LARSON, J. A. 1923. The cardio-pneumo-psychogram in deception. *J. Exper. Psychol.*, **6**, 420-454.

LAVATER, J. C. 1789. Essays on physiognomy. (1st Eng. ed.) London: Murray. Pp. 274.

LUND, F. H. 1930. Emotions of men. New York: McGraw-Hill. Pp. 350.

MANN, S. A. 1925. Blood sugar studies in mental disorders. *J. Ment. Sci.*, **71**, 284-305.

MANTEGAZZA, P. 1904. Physiognomy and expression. (3rd ed.) New York: Scribner's. Pp. x+327.

MARAÑON, G. 1924. Contribution à l'étude de l'action émotive de l'adrenaline. *Rev. fr. d'endocrinol.*, **2**, 301-325.

MARSTON, W. M. 1917. Systolic blood pressure symptoms of deception. *J. Exper. Psychol.*, **2**, 117-163.

————. 1924. A theory of emotions and affection based upon systolic blood pressure studies. *Amer. J. Psychol.*, **35**, 469-506.

McKENZIE, R. T. 1905. The facial expression of violent effort, breathlessness, and fatigue. *J. Anat. & Physiol.*, **40**, 51-55.

MURPHY, G., & MURPHY, L. B. 1931. Experimental social psychology. New York: Harpers. Pp. xi+709.

MYERSON, A. 1918. A case of altered emotions bearing on the Lange-James theory. *J. Abn. Psychol.*, **13**, 239-249.

NAFE, J. P. 1924. An experimental study of affective qualities. *Amer. J. Psychol.*, **35**, 507-544.

PAVLOV, I. P. 1902. The work of the digestive glands. (Trans. by W. H. Thompson.) London: Griffin. Pp. xii+196.

PETERSON, F. 1907. The galvanometer as a measurer of emotions. *Brit. Med. J.*, **2**, 804-806.

RADECKI, W. 1911. Recherches expérimentales sur les phénomènes psycho-électriques. *Arch. de psychol.*, **11**, 209-293.

REHWOLDT, F. 1911. Ueber respiratorische Affektsymptome. *Psychol. Stud.*, **7**, 141-195.

RENSHAW, S. 1925. Apparatus and experiments on the postural stability component in human behavior. Ph.D. dissertation, Ohio State Univ.

ROBINS, S. D. 1919. A plethysmographic study of shock and stammering. *Amer. J. Physiol.*, **48**, 285-330.

SCHILF, E., & SCHUBERTH, A. 1922. Ueber das sogennante psychogalvanische Reflexphänomen beim Frosch und seine Beziehung zum vegetativen Nervensystem. *Pflüg. Arch. f. d. ges. Physiol.*, **195**, 75-95.

SEASHORE, C. E. 1928. Phonophotography as a new approach to the psychology of emotion. Chap. 16 in *Feelings and emotions: the Wittenberg symposium*, ed. by M. L. Reymert. Worcester, Mass.: Clark Univ. Press. Pp. 206-211.

SHERMAN, M. 1928. The differentiation of emotional responses in infants: I and II. *J. Comp. Psychol.*, **7**, 265-284, 335-351.

SKAGGS, E. B. 1926. Changes in pulse, breathing and steadiness under conditions of startledness and excited expectancy. *J. Comp. Psychol.*, **6**, 303-318.

STARR, H. E. 1922. The hydrogen ion concentration of mixed saliva considered as an index of fatigue and of emotional excitation, and applied to a study of the metabolic etiology of stammering. *Amer. J. Psychol.*, **33**, 394-418.

TARCHANOFF, J. 1890. Ueber die galvanischen Erscheinungen in der Haut des Menschen bei Reizungen der Sinnesorgane und bei verschiedenen Formen der psychischen Thätigkeit. *Pflüg. Arch. f. d. ges. Physiol.*, **46**, 46-55.

TITCHENER, E. B. 1908. Lectures on the elementary psychology of feeling and attention. New York: Macmillan. Pp. ix+404.

————. 1920. Expression, expressive movements. In Vol. 8 of *The new international encyclopedia.* (2nd ed.) New York: Dodd, Mead. Pp. 285-286.

TOTTEN, E. 1925. Oxygen consumption during emotional stimulation. *Comp. Psychol. Monog.,* **3**, No. 13. Pp. 79.

UNO, T. 1922. Effect of general excitement and fighting on some of the ductless glands of male albino rats. *Amer. J. Physiol.,* **61**, 203-214.

VERAGUTH, O. 1909. Das psychogalvanische Reflexphänomen. Berlin: Karger. Pp. 187.

VIGOUROUX, R. 1879. Sur le rôle de la résistance électrique des tissus dans l'électrodiagnostic. *C. r. Soc. de biol.,* **31**, 336-339.

WANG, G. H. 1930. Galvanic skin reflex and the measurement of emotions. Canton, China: Sun Yatsen Univ. Press. Pp. 28.

WASHBURN, R. W. 1929. A study of smiling and laughing in infants in the first year of life. *Genet. Psychol. Monog.,* **6**, 403-537.

WATSON, J. B. 1924. Behaviorism. New York: Norton. Pp. 248.

WEBER, E. 1910. Der Einfluss psychischer Vorgänge auf den Körper. Berlin: Springer. Pp. 426.

WECHSLER, D. 1925. The measurement of emotional reactions: researches on the psychogalvanic reflex. *Arch. Psychol.,* **12**, No. 76. Pp. 181.

WUNDT, W. 1903. Grundzüge der physiologischen Psychologie. Vol. 3. (5th ed.) Leipzig: Engelmann. Pp. ix+796.

YOUNG, P. T. 1927. Studies in affective psychology: III. The 'trained' observer in affective psychology. *Amer. J. Psychol.,* **38**, 175-185.

CHAPTER 8

LEARNING: I. THE FACTOR OF MATURATION

CALVIN P. STONE

Stanford University

The early literature of animal behavior is replete with accounts of "instinctive" responses so perfectly executed as often to pass the bounds of credulity. "Many of the performances of the lower animals," observes Wesley Mills (1898), "if accomplished by men, would be regarded as indicating the possession of marvellous genius." As everyone knows, it is the genetic history of these marvelous aptitudes that has provided one of the most baffling problems with which students of comparative psychology have been confronted since the time of Aristotle, the patron saint, if not the father, of genetic psychology.

Early theorists shrewdly observed that if real progress was to be made in understanding the genesis of such performances it was necessary to find examples in which opportunities for learning, either by repeated individual attempts or through observation and imitation of other living creatures, were, as far as possible, excluded. They believed that the study of such examples would explain the acquisition of many life-preserving and life-perpetuating responses observed by them to appear in animals under appropriate conditions of age and motivation without benefit of specific training, as that term was commonly understood. Perhaps no example satisfies their quest more fully than that of the Yucca moth, as described by Lloyd Morgan (1896).

> The silvery, straw-colored insects emerge from their chrysalis cases just when the large, yellowish-white, bell-shaped flowers of the yucca open, each for a single night. From the anthers of one of these flowers the female moth collects the golden pollen, and kneads the adhesive material into a little pellet, which she holds beneath her head by means of the greatly enlarged bristly palps. Thus laden, she flies off and seeks another flower. Having found one, she pierces with the sharp lancets of her ovipositor the tissue of the pistil, lays her eggs among the ovules, and then, darting to the top of the stigma, stuffs the fertilizing pollen-pellet into its funnel-shaped opening.
>
> Now, the visits of the moth are necessary to the plant. It has been experimentally proved that, in the absence of the insects, no pollen can get to the stigma to fertilize the ovules. And the fertilization of the ovules is necessary to the larvae, which in four or five days are hatched from the insect's eggs. It has been ascertained that they feed exclusively on the developing ovules, and in the absence of fertilization the ovules would not develop. Each grub consumes some twenty ovules, and there may be three or four such grubs. But the ovary contains some two-hundred ovules. Of these, therefore, say, a hundred are sacrificed to the grubs of that moth, through whose instrumentality alone the remaining hundred can be fertilized and come to maturity.

Morgan proceeds to say, in substance, that these activities are performed but once in the lifetime of the individual Yucca moth. Hence, the parent never has an opportunity to learn by imitation or from success or failure what acts really must be performed that this sequence of biological phenomena may take place, involving as it does both development and perpetuation of plant and animal species.

Another example, quoted from Herrick (1924), further illustrates the kinds of data sought in ancient times. It concerns the common mason wasp, that familiar mud-dauber whose handiwork ofttimes appears on attic rafters, on the nether framework of bridges, and tucked away in hundreds of out-of-the-way places.

> These insects lay their eggs in hollow cylinders about an inch long skilfully fabricated of mud which is manipulated into the desired form. Before the chamber is sealed with the last daub of mud, spiders are captured and so stung as to paralyze the animals (usually without killing them), an egg is laid on a crippled spider, and the chamber is crammed full of the unfortunate victims, which are then entombed by closing the opening. The mud dries into a prison cell with firm but porous walls. In a few days the eggs hatch, the larvae devour the meat so bountifully supplied, and when sufficiently mature dig their way out to freedom. . . . The mother wasp apparently has no understanding of what she does nor why. She never sees her offspring and can have no intelligent prevision of these requirements. (p. 147)

Similar instances, collected by the hundreds, gave rise to the commonly accepted belief that insects acquire highly specialized behavioral mechanisms during their pupal stages and that without benefit of practice these become serviceably mature near the time of the final molt.

What the naturalists found to be true of insects also appeared to hold equally well in certain spheres of behavioral development in the higher animals. Hence, bit by bit, the conceptual groundwork of what today is known as the *maturational hypothesis* of behavioral development was laid in the minds of naturalists.[1] According to the modern version of this hypothesis, *certain behavior mechanisms are organized in animals during the pre-adult phases of life by virtue of the same or of similar endogenous regulatory agencies as those accounting for characteristic changes of the ovum prior to fertilization, segmentation of the fertilized egg, gastrulation, histogenesis, organogenesis, and many other phases of somatic growth.*

DEVELOPMENTAL SCHEDULES IN THE FETUS AND NEWBORN

An excellent foundation for descriptive studies of unlearned behavior was laid by anatomists and embryologists[2] during the past one hundred years through detailed analyses of structural and functional development

---

[1]An historical résumé of the instinct doctrine provides an excellent foundation for the more objective studies of ontogenetic development made by the eighteenth- and nineteenth-century naturalists. See especially the work of Wilm (1925).

[2]All aspects of this subject pertinent to the present chapter have been ably treated by Needham (1932) in his recent three-volume work.

in diverse forms of animals. Their researches convincingly demonstrated that structural development is orderly, that differentiation of organs and their subsequent mass development goes on with definite temporal intervals, and that schedules of development are highly stereotyped in members of the same species. One healthy individual is found to be the prototype of all members of the species. These early observers, particularly those who were physiologically minded, also observed that behavioral growth followed laws that are remarkably similar to those describing somatic growth. This discovery was one of capital importance for psychology because it suggested the possibility of describing stages of ontogenetic development in terms of the animal's repertoire of responses or in terms of the deftness or precision with which a given response might be executed. In this lies the germ of all subsequent attempts at describing mental, physiological, and developmental ages in terms of behavior. What has just been said in the abstract now can be repeated in the concrete by referring to selected examples of developmental schedules of various laboratory animals.

1. *Fetal Guinea Pigs, 45-68 Days of Age.* As early as 1885, William Preyer, a distinguished comparative embryologist, attempted to chart the developmental schedule of the fetal guinea pig. His study is one of the most instructive of its time and has stimulated much research of similar nature on several species of animals. Our present summary will be taken from a study by Avery (1928). The latter determined the age of conception of each mother with only a few hours of experimental error. Then, by caesarian section, unborn young of known fetal ages were removed from mothers in order to provide suitable materials for systematic observations. In Figure 1 will be found a graphical representation of the incidence of many gross bodily responses, which are so arranged in the figure as to stress the age factor in the developmental schedule, but also to permit one to observe that behavioral development proceeds simultanously along many fronts.

A few gasps for breath are made by fetuses of 45 to 50 days' gestation but irregular breathing appears in those of 50 to 60 days. Regular and continuous breathing is found after the sixty-fourth day. On the forty-fifth day, or earlier, a mild electrical stimulus evokes respiratory gasps after spontaneous gasps have ceased. By the forty-eighth day, kicking or withdrawal responses follow upon pinching the skin of either foot. On the fiftieth day, the first spontaneous kicking movements were observed. Eyelids were open between the fifty-fifth and fifty-seventh days. On the fifty-seventh day, kicking responses to pin-pricks and also eyelid reflexes to air blown on the cornea were noted.

Vocal responses were observed on the fifty-eighth day and scratch reflexes with the forepaws came on the fifty-ninth day. On the sixtieth, the pig crawled and rolled from back to side or over to the haunches and gave a twitch of the ear to tones and noises. On the sixty-first day, responses to olfactory stimuli and spontaneous scratch responses appeared. On the sixty-third, the pigs could stand and walk, and on the sixty-fourth,

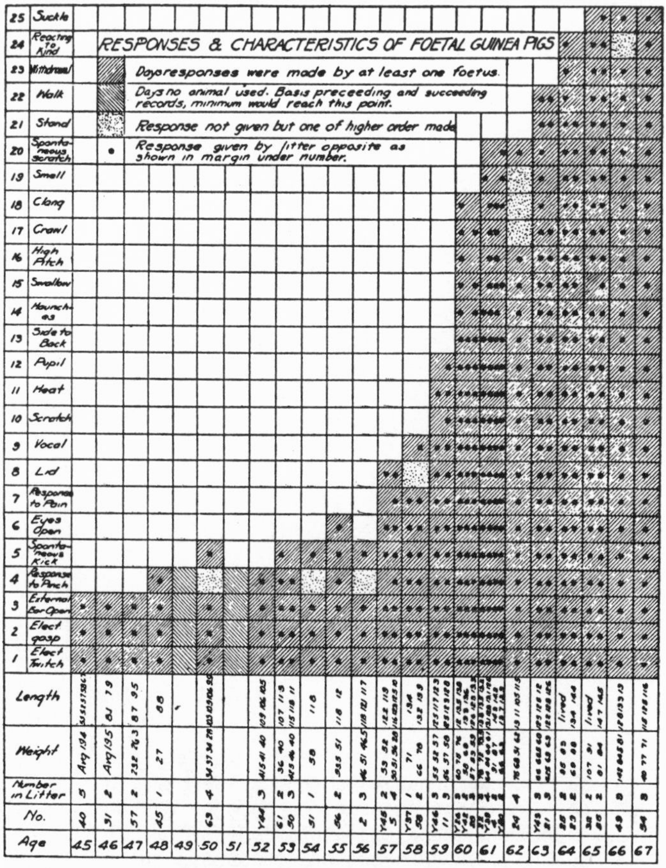

FIGURE 1

DEVELOPMENTAL SCHEDULE OF RESPONSES IN FETAL GUINEA PIGS
The fetuses were delivered by caesarian section after known periods of gestation
and were systematically observed under standard conditions.
[After Avery (1928); redrawn from Figure 4, p. 301.]

fear, social responses, and sucking were elicitable. On the sixty-seventh
day, nosing of objects, and chewing of shavings, paper, and alfalfa hay
were noticed. Birth usually occurred on the sixty-seventh or sixty-eighth
day.

To test the degree to which fetuses of 63 days or older use their ability
to orient with respect to gravity while *in utero,* radiograms of pregnant
females held in various positions were made (e.g., back down, back up,
on right side, and on left side). The results consistently showed that
the fetuses did not shift their positions in response to shifts of the mother.

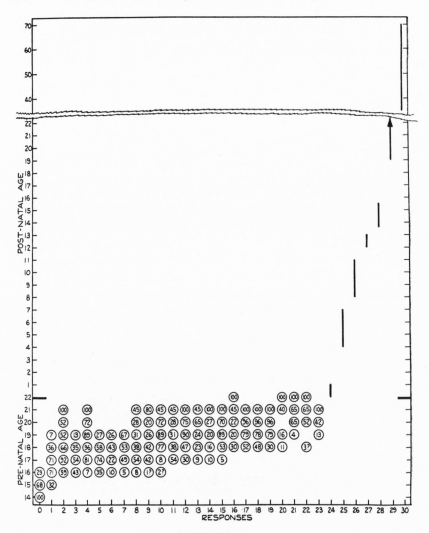

FIGURE 2

GROWTH OF RESPONSES IN PRE- AND POSTNATAL ALBINO RATS

Data for the prenatal period, 14 to 22 days, are based on the extensive observations of Angulo y González (1932), who observed the following numbers of fetuses
of the ages 14 to 21 days, respectively: 59, 63, 150, 93, 70, 90, 98, 20. (Gestation
period, 22 days.)   Data for the postnatal period are based on observations by
Small (1899) and the present author.   The numbers enclosed by circles indicate
the percentage of each age group displaying the response indicatd by the code
numbers on the abscissa.   Vertical lines at the right of the diagram indicate the
approximate age ranges at which postnatal responses, indicated by code numbers

at the bottom of the diagram, are first manifested. Percentages for each age can be given only for the reproductive responses, and these vary somewhat according to the diet used. Numbers at the bottom of the diagram refer to the following responses:

0—non-motile
1—lateral flexion of trunk
2—lateral flexion of trunk with movement of forelimbs
3—lateral flexion of rump
4—extension of the head
5—extension of head with opening of mouth
6—extension of head with opening of mouth and protrusion of tongue
7—lateral flexion of rump with movements of hind limbs
8—ventroflexion of the trunk and rump
9—independent movement of the forelimbs
10—maintained contractions
11—contraction of the abdominal muscles
12—extension of the rump
13—attempts to assume *"the optimum physiological posture"*

14—independent movement of the hind limbs
15—extension of the head and rump with kicking of hind limbs
16—independent opening of the mouth
17—independent extension of the hands
18—independent flexion of the hands
19—specific reflexes
20—movement of tail
21—independent movement of the feet
22—independent movement of the tongue
23—independent closing of the mouth
24—rolls from back to belly
25—crawls rapidly
26—washes face; sitting on haunches
27—response to noises
28—eyes opening
29—eats solid foods
30—initial sexual responses

For a discussion of the fact that some of the early responses are not found in the older fetuses, see the original paper by Angulo y González (1932).

In one series of radiographs in which the mother was shifted at 5-minute intervals, during a 30-minute period, radiograms being made before each shift, the young kept their original positions in the uterine tubes throughout the half hour. But when they were removed from the mother, an hour or so later, each rolled to its feet immediately after delivery and returned to that posture when put upon side or back. From lack of adequate extroceptive stimuli, it would seem, guinea pigs do not exercise their ability to orient in space prior to the end of the gestation period although they are capable of so doing at least four or five days before the time of normal birth.

Up to the present time experimentalists have not determined beyond doubt that learning, in the accepted meaning of that term, cannot go on during the intra-uterine period of life. However, in the guinea pig, conditions of intra-uterine life are such as to minimize the opportunity for complex habit formation. Therefore, most biologists infer that the same intrinsic factors which regulate somatic and functional development are responsible for the schedule of behavioral growth found in the fetal guinea pig.

2. *Fetal and Postnatal Rats.* Taking the work of Angulo y González (1932) as our source of information, we have constructed a chart of the rat's developmental schedule up to the time of birth. Other studies have provided data for the period of postnatal development. Referring to Figure 2, the reader will see that the growth of response ability in the fetus is very gradual. Apparently the general wave of behavioral

development prior to birth continues without marked change during the first two or three months of postnatal life. Individual differences in rate of development for different fetuses are clearly suggested by the study of Angulo y González, although he was unable to study representative animals by the longitudinal rather than by the cross-sectional method. The individual differences pertain to temporal spacing of responses rather than to their sequential arrangement. The latter is common to all members of the species and can be changed experimentally only with great difficulty, and, when changed, whether experimentally or occurring spontaneously, the individual is an ill-formed, pathological specimen.

3. *Behavior of Pouch-young Opossums.* The very intriguing study of pouch-young opossums, as reported by Hartman (1923) and Langworthy (1928), is a fruitful sequel to the pioneer studies of Preyer and Avery on the guinea pig, and that of Angulo y González on the rat. The opossum deserves consideration in this connection because its first weeks of postnatal life correspond roughly to well-known stages of intra-uterine

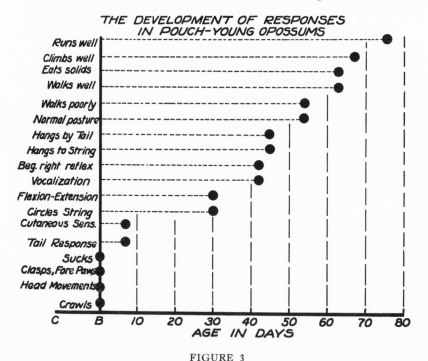

FIGURE 3

DEVELOPMENTAL SCHEDULE OF RESPONSES IN POUCH-YOUNG OPOSSUMS

The age-response determinations are only approximations which may be expected to vary in either direction with further observations. *C*—conception; *B*—birth. [Constructed from the data of Langworthy (1928).]

development of many other mammals, since the gestation period, 12 to 14 days, is extremely short. Thereafter, attached to a nipple in the mother's pouch, its extra-uterine development continues for about two months in a very protected and relatively stable environment.

Certain points of the developmental schedule of the opossum, as briefly described hereafter, are graphically illustrated in Figure 3. As to behavioral characteristics, Langworthy observed that at birth the opossum sucks, crawls with its forelegs, clasps small objects such as hair or thread with its claws, and moves its head from side to side in great sweeping movements. It responds to cutaneous stimuli, particularly those applied in the region of its face. It cannot right itself when placed on its side nor can it perform any of the more complex locomotor and defensive movements exhibited by fetal guinea pigs of 60 days, and by newborn kittens, puppies, calves, and hundreds of other well-known wild and domestic animals.

At one week of age the opossum is still poorly developed. The forelegs beat in such a manner as to insure progression if the claws catch onto solid objects, but the hind legs are more or less useless. The tail is prehensile but unable to support the animal's weight. The cutaneous receptors are functional, as evidenced by responsiveness to thermal and tactile stimuli; at this time the animal will crawl toward warm and away from cold objects. Eyes are not open; ears are non-functional; there is no evidence that the vestibular apparatus is functioning, for the animal cannot right itself.

At one month of age the young opossum continually lies on its side because of inability to right itself; now the hind legs move more than at the end of the first week, but hind-limb and forelimb movements are not well coordinated. It can grasp a suspended thread with the foreclaws but it only circles the thread rather than climbs up.

Near the end of six weeks all previously displayed responses have become more precise and vigorous than when previously seen and some new ones are in evidence. Imperfect righting reflexes are first manifested at this age; if put on its feet, the animal may take two or three steps before falling upon its side. Vocalizations now can be elicited. At the age of 46 days, the animal supports its weight by its tail. By the fifty-fourth day it no longer lies continually on its side but sometimes assumes the normal bodily posture of mammals. Now it crawls fairly well, but with sprawled-out legs; as yet it walks poorly. It barely climbs a rope at this stage. At approximately nine weeks the young can walk without difficulty and support its own weight. Also it eats solid foods. It can climb and run well at or near the tenth week, when in many respects its proclivities for coordinated responses and self-maintenance are grossly similar to those of the newborn guinea pig.

4. *Fetal and Newborn Rabbits.* The rabbit, having a gestation period of only 30 days, occupies a mid-position between the opossum and the guinea pig as to motor development at birth (Kao, 1927). From three to four days before the end of the gestation period, the fetus, if removed,

will display respiratory responses in various stages of functional maturity and completeness.   At the same time it will move its body and trunk in response to cutaneous stimuli of all kinds.   Within a day or two of birth it is capable of righting itself, making progression movements, and sucking from the mother's nipple.   All of these responses are somewhat weaker than similar responses elicited from full-term newborn, as might be expected, since they come from young that are examined at the earlier age, in which functional maturity is less advanced.   A day or two of further maturation, however (*no practice in response*, so far as known), makes the difference between the relatively weak response of the fetus of 28 days and the newborn of 30 days' gestation.

Figure 4 illustrates the age at which other responses appear in the postnatal life of the rabbit.   In this figure, small bars on either side of the average for the group indicate the lowest and the highest ages at which the specific responses manifested themselves in this study.   From

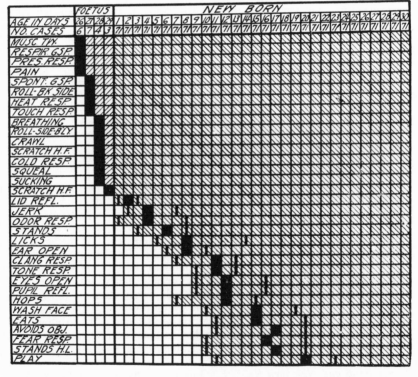

FIGURE 4
DEVELOPMENTAL SCHEDULE OF RESPONSES IN FETAL AND NEWBORN RABBITS
[After Kao (1927).]

the data at hand Kao (1927) could have computed the standard deviation of each distribution of ages, as is done when one wishes to describe an array of data from the standpoint of central tendency and variability. This was not done by Kao, however, owing to certain inaccuracies of his methods which led him to believe that more complete statistical treatment of his data was unwarranted. The fact that it has not yet been done for any laboratory animal, excepting man, indicates the relatively undeveloped status of quantitative research on the ontogenesis of animal behavior. Beyond a doubt, quantitative work will be indispensable for the analysis and weighting of the controllable factors which give rise to individual differences in maturational rate within each species.

5. *Developmental Schedules in Man.* Recently, comprehensive studies of fetal and postnatal development in man have been made by Minkowski (1922), Peiper (1928), Blanton (1917), Gesell (1925), Bühler (1930), Shirley (1931a, 1931b), Halverson (1931), Castner (1932), and numerous others (cf. Murchison, 1933). These investigations have laid a stable foundation for the belief that *man's developmental schedules, whether physical, intellectual, emotional, or volitional, requiring a much greater fraction of the total life-span than any other mammal for their completion, probably differentiate him more clearly from the higher animals, including the orang-utan, chimpanzee, and gorilla, than any of his well-known structural characteristics—better, we may say, than the fluid tissues, osseous skeleton, form of the hands, or the postures assumed by these animals when at rest or in motion.*

6. *Common Factors in, and Characteristics of, Maturational Development.* Some of the more obvious, but none the less illuminating, generalizations derived from comparative studies of developmental schedules and the extra-organic conditions under which they come into being are the following:

a. Structural and behavioral maturative processes appear to be inseparable in every stage of ontogenetic development. The anlagen of the most fundamental behavioral patterns are laid down in the central nervous system at a relatively early stage of embryonal and fetal development, and primarily under the regulatory control of endogenous factors; these anlagen continue their development until functionally mature stages are reached, under the guidance of the same or similar controls (Coghill, 1926; Herrick, 1924).

b. No practice whatever is required to initiate the first embryonal movements, so far as can be determined at the present time; and subsequent development, in the sense of individuation of responses, goes on without practice or tuition both in mobile and in immobile zones of the organism's body until the adult stage of physical growth is reached (perhaps even beyond that).

c. Serviceable maturity in fundamental action systems usually is attained just before the latter are required by the organisms for maintaining a properly regulated internal and external environment for its own further development and maintenance or for that of its progeny.

d. Those kinds of development which ordinarily are called learning or habit formation appear to be secondary elaborations or extensions of maturational development; they serve the purpose of making each individual of the species a more integral part of its personal and momentarily changing inner and outer environment.

HEREDITARY MECHANISMS: THE PRIMARY REGULATORS OF MATURATION

The primary or basic regulators of maturational development are endogenous in the sense that they are determined by hereditary mechanisms. (See Chapter 2.) The laws of heredity, particularly the modern genic theory, have brought into biological science an understanding that has prompted and greatly facilitated the minute analysis of different physical constitutions. And these same laws now provide us with conceptual tools for building up and tearing down at will diverse behavioral mechanisms.

1. *Learned Responses Are Not Transmitted as Heritable Characters.* At the outset a word should be said concerning the heritability of learned responses. Although animals of the same species ofttimes develop similar habits as a result of interacting with similar situations of a common habitat, these habits are not transmitted from one generation to another as heritable characters. Like scar tissues, muscles hypertrophied by special exercises, pock-marks on the face, elongated necks of African beauties, dwarfed feet of Chinese women, or hundreds of other accidental and intentional modifications of the soma, habits leave no permanent imprint, figuratively speaking, on the germ plasm. Moreover, scientists are still looking (probably in vain) for unequivocal evidence that training of any kind in one or in many generations produces more easily educated animals in subsequent generations, *unless the effects of that training are such as to select for breeding the more educable and to discard those having the lesser aptitude for learning.*[3] In keeping with this same generalization is the commonly accepted belief that the *ancestral habits* of the dim past did not in some way become the innate responses of present-day animals, as one time was believed by such eminent scientists as Lamarck, Darwin, and Romanes.

2. *Control of Maturational Trends by Selective Breeding.* The most effective way to influence maturational development along desired lines and to give reasonable assurance of its effects' being perpetuated in successive generations is the well-known method of selective mating of parental stock. This method was used by ancient peoples to enhance the highly prized behavioral characteristics of animals they wished to domesticate, as well as to weaken or eliminate the less desirable characteristics.[4]

---

[3]Probably the most noteworthy test of the Lamarckian hypothesis in recent years is that of McDougall (see Chapter 2). His finding of confirmatory evidence is weakened, however, according to many critics, by what they consider to be defects in methodology.

[4]Scientific manuals setting forth the differential features of various breeds of cattle, horses, swine, sheep, dogs, poultry, etc., usually cite characteristic behavioral differences as well as morphological differences. These differences are found under similar conditions of husbandry and presumably are determined by constitutional factors.

The following experiments will illustrate the results that can be obtained by such methods.

 a. Modification of temperamental traits in rats. In the laboratory it is relatively easy to vary such temperamental traits as wildness and savageness in rats by selectively mating parents in whom, prior to taming or systematic handling, the desired strengths of these traits were manifested (Stone, Darrow, Landis, and Heath, 1932; Yerkes, 1913). To illustrate, three groups of rats were reared in the same laboratory room until the age of 100 days and, up to that time, were not subjected to any taming influences whatever, beyond those necessitated by feeding and cleaning of cages. The groups consisted of 10 descendants of wild brown rats, 17 domestic albinos, and 70 half-breeds resulting from crossing wild brown males and domestic albinos. When all had reached the age of 100 days they were removed from the home cages daily to be rated, under various experimental conditions, for degrees of wildness and savageness. The differences between means of the three groups on each of the ten days of rating were statistically significant. The sigmas of the distributions, however, were quite similar as to magnitude. Although one finds some overlapping of scores of wild and half-breeds and also of albinos and half-breeds, there is no overlapping at all between scores of albinos and the wild strain. On the whole, the obtained differences in temperamental traits are clean-cut and unequivocal. Moreover, they are such as any competent observer might be expected to obtain upon repeating the experiment. Therefore, although the experiment is by no means crucial for determining what specific intra-organic factors gave rise to the temperamental differences in the three strains, we are probably safe in assuming that the primary controls were hereditary.

Supporting this supposition are the results of another experiment in which the fertilized eggs of a wild brown rat were transferred to the uterine tubes of a domestic albino, following the method of Nicholas (1933). There, adjacent to albinos, these young of a wild strain developed and eventually were reared by the albino mother. Despite the fact that all nutrients obtained by the embryos were from a common supply and that all young were reared under identical conditions after birth, the two strains exhibited the expected somatic and behavioral characteristics of their progenitors. In view of these findings, one is justified in assuming that the temperamental traits of different strains of rats, *when obviously not the product of different living-conditions,* are the product of maturational development, the latter being regulated by endogenous factors inherent in the germ plasm or developing in the embryo as a part of the total hereditary mechanism.

As a corollary to the foregoing data, I presume that one may add that experimental methods now available make it possible to vary through selective breeding many other temperamental traits in rats, such as persistency, aggressiveness, submissiveness, daring, laziness, excitability, docility, etc. Rats, because of their short life-spans and wide variations in temperamental traits should be ideal subjects on which to lay the experimental foundations for a proper physiological approach to the study of personality in man, a field of research that, to date, is difficult of approach because in the majority of instances genetic and environmental factors cannot be accurately determined, controlled, or systematically varied.

b. Speed and pattern of locomotion in horses. In keeping with the foregoing example are the heritable differences in speed and stamina which sportsmen have produced in horses by selective breeding. Without citing evidence from the stud books, we are justified in claiming that "class" among race horses is determined primarily by constitutional differences in the germ plasms which preside over their maturational development. It is an established fact that carriage horses, coach horses, plough horses, or hunters rarely develop speed, in the turf-man's sense of that term, irre- spective of their opportunities; also, the "get" of common "platers" seldom acquire the speed and stamina required of "stake" horses; finally only the parent stock belonging to strains which, when properly trained, have reached the top-flight in speed and endurance consistently transmit through successive generations the potentiality of developing speedy loco- motion. (The training, of course, serves no function beyond that of revealing to the breeders what sires and what dams have the constitutional bases of speed. Some brood mares, from good lines, are never raced at all.)

In this same connection, a word may be said concerning patterns of locomotion. Among standard bred horses there are the pacers and the trotters. Although all can execute the trotting movement, only cer- tain strains, purified by selective breeding, execute the pacing motion as a natural, unlearned mode of locomotion. Pacing is handed down in pre- dictable manner when pacers and trotters are crossed. Also it may make its appearance in the hybrid mule. It is a phenomenon no less striking to the eye than meaningful to the scientist to observe a high-spirited mule, prancing about with head erect, ears pointed forward, and finally moving off with a graceful pacing motion. This rare animal, the product of a jack and a standard bred pacing mare, is a rarity merely because the ordinary mule is bred for behavioral characteristics other than grace and speed of locomotion.

c. Inherited behavior characteristics in dogs. Incidental to his studies on the genetics and endocrine factors underlying somatic constitu- tions in dogs, Stockard (1931) made many noteworthy observations on the transmission of behavior patterns in hybrids. Discussing the short- legged, F_1, hybrids obtained by crossing a short–bent-legged basset hound and a normal, wild-type, long-legged German shepherd, he says:

> The short-legged, F_1, hybrids all have the long drooping ears of the hound and never the erect ears of the shepherd, and the voice or bark is also more hound-like than shepherd-like. When these hybrid pups are reared by a shepherd mother and have never seen a basset hound, they will, when put on the field for the first time, scent with their noses down and bark as they run, behaving as their hound father would do, acting in a manner entirely unlike the reactions of their shepherd mother with whom they have always associated. Thus

their hunting instincts are as truly inherited as leg-lengths or hair color, being probably associated with acuteness of smell, and are not, in this case at least, developed as a conditioned reflex. (pp. 228-229)

Other observations on postures in standing, sitting, lying, etc., leave no doubt as to the facts concerning the transmission of behavior patterns as units or as mosaics in hybrid dogs. To be sure, all of these distinctive patterns of behavior come to full expression only through process of growth or development, but, granting that training may alter them somewhat, they are in no proper sense to be accredited to any of the known methods of learning.

d. Genetic nature of the time of attainment of puberty. Puberty denotes a stage of development in which the individual attains the ability to elaborate functional gametes and also the ability and willingness to play the appropriate rôle in sexual congress. Although these several abilities are not perfectly coordinated in time, the discrepancies are small and may be neglected for our present consideration (Stone, 1924). Our momentary interest is that of pointing out the fact that the attainment of puberty relatively early or relatively late by mice and rats is hereditary in nature, as clearly demonstrated by recent experiments.

Using mice, Crew (1931) made a crucial test of this point in the following manner. One hundred five female albino mice and 60 female descendants of a colored strain were subjected to the same conditions of husbandry in early life. All were examined daily for evidence of the attainment of puberty as indicated by vaginal smears or by mating. The average age of first oestrus was found to be 39 days in the case of the albino strain and 52 days in the case of the colored. Although there is some overlapping of ages, as shown in Figure 5, the differences between means is sufficiently large to indicate that it is statistically significant. In view of the fact that all of the individuals were subjected to a "constant optimum temperature and optimum population density, excellent food and general care" and yet the average ages of puberty of the

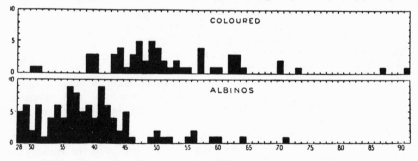

FIGURE 5

AGE OF FIRST OESTRUS IN A STRAIN OF COLORED MICE (UPPER) AND A STRAIN OF ALBINO MICE (LOWER)

[After Crew (1931).]

two groups differed so greatly, Crew concluded that the rate of maturative changes underlying the total phenomena of puberty were genetically
determined and that "relatively early and relatively late attainment of
puberty are hereditary characters."

Working with albino rats, the author has arrived at conclusions
similar to those of Crew. After determining the age of puberty, as
measured by the age of first copulation in males and first ovulation in
females, he bred males and females that were approximately two sigmas
above the average and likewise males and females that were two sigmas
below the average for the respective sexes. By repeating this process in
successive generations, two strains of albino rats were produced, the one
with relatively early and the other with relatively late ages of pubescence.
In the F_6 generation, the average for age of pubescence in the early group
is approximately 42 days and that for the late group is in the neighborhood
of 58 days. The amount of overlapping is roughly similar to that found
by Crew in his genetically different strains of mice. Future experiments
involving hybridization of these two groups may throw important light on
the mechanism of heredity underlying the development of early and
late puberty. No doubt this can be accomplished in part by experimental analyses of some of the supplementary regulators of maturational
development, particularly the endocrines.

SECONDARY REGULATORS OF MATURATIONAL DEVELOPMENT

On both experimental and inferential grounds it is usually claimed
that at the outset of individual life genes are the primary regulators of
development. There is little precise information as to the manner of
their action, but it is usually assumed that they become effective through
their influence on the reactions, or metabolism, of certain parts of the
organism while it is still an undifferentiated mass. The result of this
influence appears to be that supplementary regulators, the *organizers* of
experimental embryologists, are formed, and these take up the task of
controlling histogenesis and organogenesis. Some of them appear to be
more generalized as to the scope of their influence than others and
control cellular processes at considerable distances in a manner somewhat
analogous to the endocrines. Others have a very circumscribed area to
control and act only for a short period of time. The net result of their
regulation is that all members of a species of animals achieve similar
structural development and that characteristic temporal and sequential
relationships (the developmental schedules) may be observed as these
are attained.

1. *Neural Patterns; the Counterparts of Behavior Patterns.* An
introduction to the nature of developmental mechanics in the embryo can
be had by considering certain aspects of structural patterning which go on
in the nervous system. The work of Coghill (1929) and Herrick
(1924), among others, has greatly illuminated this very intricate problem. Although their work is confined chiefly to relatively simple forms
of animal life, such as amphibian and piscian species, the work of other

investigators who have dealt with mammals indicates that Coghill and Herrick have revealed principles of neuromuscular patterning which are common to all vertebrate forms.

The following quotation from Coghill (1926) indicates his conclusion as to how the neural counterparts of behavior patterns arise in the early stages of amphibian development:

> The growth of the nervous system, insofar as it has been definitely correlated with the development of the behavior pattern, demonstrates that fractional patterns (reflexes) arise by a process of individuation within a primarily integrated total pattern, and that the latter does not arise by an integration of independent reflexes. The form of the behavior pattern in Amblystoma up to and including locomotion is determined by specific neural counterparts that acquire their specificity in functional value through laws of growth in the nervous system. There is evidence also that mechanisms that condition the performance of such a behavior pattern as locomotion in mammals are determined in the same manner. It is important, therefore, to know how far growth, in the sense of the differentiation of new functional parts of cells, is projected into the life-history of the vertebrate, for so long as it continues it must participate in the function of the nervous system as a whole and, therefore, in the development of the behavior pattern. (p. 136)

In further discussions of the locomotor system, he says that the neuromuscular mechanism is laid down before the first stages of mobility are reached in the Amblystoma.

The same, in substance, is true of the special sense-organs concerned with equilibrium. From the very beginning they respond selectively to forces or stimuli of the intra- and extra-organic environment. Further he says:

> The central relation of the neurones of the postural mechanism must therefore be determined without reference to the peripheral stimulation of the sense organs concerned. . . . The pre-sensory growth of the cerebral mechanism may accordingly be regarded as determining what the attitude of the individual as a whole shall be toward the environment before the organism can take cognizance physiologically of its environment. (Coghill, 1930, pp. 641-642)

Coghill also speculated somewhat on the possible effects of experience, in the form of extraneural excitation, on the functional development of action systems. Relevant to this point he says:

> In the counterpart of the form of the pattern, as already explained, the specificity is fixed by the relations into which the elements grow. In the counterpart of experience, on the other hand, specificity of function is established by interaction of growth and excitation, that is to say, the excitation fixes upon the growing terminals of neurones its own mode of activation. In the conditioning mechanism in general, as in the case of the Rohon-Beard cell, according to this hypothesis, laws of growth determine the structural relation of conductors, but their specific sensitivity is fixed by the mode of excitation.
> In the motor mechanism of *Amblystoma* we see structural counterparts of attitudes which are released into action of definite form

> in appropriate situations. It is possible that in the conditioning
> mechanisms, also, situations organize themselves into definite struc-
> tural counterparts through the interaction of growth and excitation.
> (Coghill, 1929, p. 105)

The point is one of capital importance and should be subjected to
many crucial tests in the laboratory for it pertains to the age-old question as to whether maturative processes and learning processes are
essentially one and the same in fundamental nature, differing only with
respect to arbitrary distinctions, made for good and sufficient practical
reasons, that are based on the kinds or loci of extraneural excitations.
Perhaps a beginning has already been made in subjecting the above
hypothesis to the experimental test by such work as that of Carmichael
(1926, 1927, 1928), in which some of the factors which do not appear
to determine specific types of behavior are brought to light. He brought
eggs of the frog (*Rana*) and salamander (*Amblystoma punctatum*) into
the laboratory to develop under conditions suitable for observation. A
number of embryos in their early head- and tail-bud stages were divided
into control and experimental groups. The controls were allowed to
develop in tap water, a satisfactory medium for normal growth and
activity. The experimental group, on the other hand, was put into a
chloretone solution of just sufficient concentration to keep the developing larvae in a state of anaesthesia without injuring the developing organs.
At well-known stages in the development of these larvae the controls
began to respond to tactile stimulation along the skin of the body. Some
hours afterward the more complex swimming movements were elicited.
Stimuli applied to the anaesthetized individuals, however, did not evoke
the least motor response, hence there is no reason for supposing that
movements were at any time present in the anaesthetized young while
they passed from the non-motile to the free-swimming stage of their
developmental life. The net result of this series of experiments was to
demonstrate that *Amblystoma* developing to the free-swimming age in
the anaesthetizing solution swim just as soon as the narcosis wears off
and that those kept in a dark and vibration-free room show no handicaps
or retardation in swimming as compared with the normal controls reared
in the ordinary environment.

By experimental methods Carmichael produced an artificial resting
stage in the amphibian larvae which from the standpoint of immobility
roughly resembled the pupal stage of an insect's natural development.
And, as in the case of the insect, there appeared in the amphibian larvae
the same action systems and aptitudes for response as displayed by
unhampered young of the same age and racial stock. An experiment of
this kind does not tell us just what factors of the environment are
essential to the acquisition of swimming responses, but it does afford
us an opportunity for observing with what facility abilities to respond
may be attained without the complicating factors of tuition and practice.

2. *Endocrines Supplementing Genic Control.* The scope of regulatory influence exerted on maturative processes by the endocrines is still

imperfectly known, but evidence of various kinds warrants our placing them in the list of secondary controls. Even the final development of the neuroblasts, particularly those of the cortex which play a rôle so important in human learning, is not immune from this type of regulation. Witness, for example, the underdeveloped condition of the cretin's brain, that of the Mongolian idiot, and, in certain instances, the victim of Froelich's syndrome.

a. Gonadic determination of sexual behavior. Endocrine influence in producing sexual dimorphism in the insects seems to be lacking or of negligible importance; the same can be said, also, for sexual behavior. But in the higher animals, such as the birds and mammals, they are of the utmost importance (Allen, 1932). The genes determine what the endocrines shall be and also when they shall assume their respective functions in the individual, but these powerful agents are necessary to bring to full somatic expression what is latent in the chromosomes.

Gonadic influences on sexual behavior are no less certain than their influence on the growth of secondary characters and the accessory sexual apparatus. Crowing, strutting, and fighting by a cock-like poulard, produced by castrating a typical female chick one day of age, is now a commonplace among experimental embryologists, as was the same behavior some years ago when brought about by gonadal transplantation (Allen, 1932). So also is eunuchoid behavior, including the total failure of the sexual "instincts" in birds and mammals which are castrated in early life.

When mammals are deprived of the anterior hypophysis or ovaries prior to puberty, the congenital sexual responses never appear without restorative therapy; likewise oestrual phenomena disappear if deprivation of the anterior hypophyseal or ovarian secretion comes after sexual maturity has been attained.

b. Premature pubescence. Acceleration of the age of puberty was accomplished by Smith (1927), who injected fresh anterior hypophyseal tissue subcutaneously into young animals. To illustrate, when into young rats or mice of 15 days a daily subcutaneous injection of one pituitary body was made, puberty praecox followed within a week or less. It appeared about 10 to 15 days earlier than is the case with normal controls. From the standpoint of accelerating puberty in young females, similar results may be obtained by injecting the active hormone from the ovarian follicles (Allen and Doisy, 1923).

Similar to the foregoing, but possibly complicated by additional factors, are the instances of puberty praecox in man. In Figure 6 is shown the Toledo Giant, a case completely reported elsewhere (McClure and Goldberg, 1932). This boy weighed 81 pounds at the age of 5½ years and at this same age had attained a height of 49 inches. Possessing great strength, the boy took particular delight in demonstrating his muscular development by lifting adult men and women. As is usually the case, his mental age was not accelerated, and, for the most part, his psychological outlook, except when obviously disturbed by adventitious factors,

FIGURE 6

PUBERTY PRAECOX

C. K. (middle), age 6 years 1 month, with brother, age 9 years 9 months, and sister, age 11 years 0 months. His height is slightly over 4 ft. 1 in. and his weight is about 81 pounds, or 30 pounds more than the average child of his age and height. Mental age is 6 years and 0 months. Has great muscular development and strength; sexual development like that of a 14-year-old boy.

[After McClure and Goldberg (1932).]

such as those brought about by vicious exploitation of such cases in public, was more in keeping with his chronological age than with his somatic development. Such cases are of particular interest because they show that premature release of growth-promoting hormones brings about a profound disturbance in the normal schedule of developmental processes.

c. *Hastening metamorphosis in amphibia.* Somewhat similar to the *dissociated* type of development in the case of puberty praecox is that of premature metamorphosis in amphibian larvae. The following example, quoted from Jennings (1930), will illustrate the point:

> In that group of the Amphibia which includes the toads and frogs, at a certain period the tail and gills are lost, legs develop, there is an internal and external transformation, and the tadpole metamorphoses into the four-legged frog or toad. What brings about this metamorphosis? J. F. Gudernatsch [1912] found that if very young tadpoles are fed pieces of the thyroid gland, they quickly metamorphose into frogs, even though as yet extremely small. In this way frogs as small as flies were produced. Tadpoles of the bull-frog, that usually do not metamorphose till two or three years old, were thus caused to metamorphose during the first season of their existence, and within two weeks of the time that the feeding of thyroid was begun. . . . The thyroid gland produces an inner secretion or hormone, that contains iodine, and that passes into the blood and so circulates through the body. The iodine that it contains is united with certain organic compounds, and some of the effects of its secretions are not producible by iodine alone; this is particularly true of its effects in higher animals. The thyroid, like other parts of the body, develops gradually, and in the early stages of its development it does not produce its secretion. But at a certain period it begins to produce its characteristic secretion, and to pour it into the blood. And as a result the tadpole transforms into the frog or toad. (pp. 113-114)

Although Jennings is speaking chiefly of the structural transformations these organisms undergo, it is important for our present interests to recall that to a great extent *structural metamorphosis goes hand in hand with behavioral metamorphosis in these same amphibian forms.* Jennings goes on to say:

> The effect of the thyroid hormone thus differs greatly in different animals. The cells in different species have different constitutions, diverse genes; and they react diversely to the same hormone; just as diverse parts of the same individual react diversely to the same hormone. The effect produced depends as much on the constitution of the cells acted on as it does on the nature of the hormone. (p. 117)

3. *Nutrition: Its Influence on Behavioral Maturation.* One needs only to be reminded of the profound influences exerted by the food supply upon the rate of maturational development as applied to somatic structures. That its influence may also be expressed in the determination of behavioral development is readily demonstrated by such experiments as the following.

a. *Synthetic queens in the bee family.* One of the most important duties of the workers of the bee hive is feeding the young, for the queen pays no attention to their nutritive requirements. The egg hatches in about three days; then at the bottom of the cell there lies a little white grub—the bee in its *larval state*. These wormlike larvae are so helpless that the workers have to force food into their mouths. The first food that they receive is the special "bee-jelly," a predigested substance forced out from the stomachs of the workers. After about three days the larvae which are to develop into workers are given "bee-bread," a mixture of honey and pollen, whereas the potential queens are fed only the "bee-jelly" throughout the feeding stage of the larval state. A larger cell also is provided for the queens than that permitted to the workers, but aside from this no known difference, except that of the food supplied during the larval stage, may be said to be responsible for the structural and behavioral differences of workers and queens.

Should accident befall the developing queens, adult workers meet this emergency by enlarging certain cells containing worker larvae and by beginning to feed these larvae the diet of "bee-jelly." Thenceforth the trend of development changes, provided that maturation has not already proceeded too far. The worker larvae ultimately develop into queen bees and, in the most perfect cases, are very similar to those which were developing into queens from the very beginning. Not only do they have the primary and secondary characters of normal queens, and thus differ markedly from the workers, but also they assume the reproductive functions of the queen rather than engage in the diverse routine activities of the workers.

b. Accelerating or retarding the time of puberty. It is interesting to note that puberty in female rats can be retarded as to age of appearance, held in a state of dormancy subject to later revival, or totally suppressed throughout the lifetime of the individual by effective control of the diet (Evans and Bishop, 1922). Similar experiments with the male are less varied and extensive, yet they clearly suggest that the same can be done with it. In 1924 and 1925 the author reported a series of experiments on male rats in which, by quantitative restriction of a standard diet, their body weights were held at maintenance for 20 consecutive days. As a result the age of puberty as determined by the copulatory test was delayed on the average from 16 to 23 days in groups undergoing chronic inanition for 20 days, beginning at the ages of 20, 30, and 45 days. As a rule, the earlier the stunting the greater the retardation in age of puberty.

The primary effect of inanition is suppression of the growth or functions of the gonads. This, in turn, deprives other endocrine glands and the nervous system of a hormone which is necessary to their normal functioning in reproductive phenomena. As a rule, the ill effects of inanition are readily corrected by realimentation.

4. Synchronized Development Paves the Way for Complex and Compound Native Responses. Through secondary regulation of maturative development serviceable maturity may be attained in functionally related action systems at approximately the same time. For instance, the newborn opossum attains serviceable maturity of the forelimb progression mechanism and the musculocutaneous system of the head region at the same time, and both of them are required at birth to reestablish connection with the maternal food supply which was broken off temporarily with the severance of the umbilical cord. Also, in the chick, quail, and turkey, pecking and locomotor mechanisms mature simultaneously, but the flying-mechanism is functionally immature for many days after hatching. Well known also are the coordinated eye and head movements appearing in the human infant soon after birth, and the eye and hand coordinations which make their appearance when the child normally begins to take in solid foods. Apparently these and thousands of other synchronizations which might be cited are primarily the product of intra-organically regulated development. A hierarchy of primary and secondary regulators determines when and in what zones of the body metabolic processes will be accelerated, thereby giving rise to correlated patterns of behavioral development.

DEPENDENT AND INTERDEPENDENT RELATIONSHIPS BETWEEN MATURATION AND LEARNING IN POSTNATAL LIFE

Ability of the organism to extend or to elaborate its course of development by training appears to come only after certain stages of maturative development have been achieved, presumably some time after the motility stage has been reached. As a consequence, learning may begin in different regions of the body at different times, because certain zones precede others in their maturative development; for the same reason, learning rate in the young may vary greatly in different zones of the body.

Such experiments as the following provide us with satisfactory evidence for the foregoing statements, but, taken alone, cannot be made the basis of widespread generalizations embracing different behavior mechanisms in different species of animals.

1. *Behavioral Development When Practice Is Controlled.* The one-day-old squab cannot stand, walk, or fly. Its head droops to one side. Eyelids are closed most of the time, but they open when the squab is suddenly stimulated, as by tilting of the body. At 5 days of age the squab holds its head erect, but not yet does it "fixate" objects, although the eyes are open. When about 10 days old it fixates objects of the optical field, as it is moved from place to place. At 20 days, the squab can stand but walks very unsteadily. As yet it cannot fly and is still fed by the parents. Around the age of 35 days it begins to feed itself, to walk well, and to fly short distances. Before the age of 3 months all of the usual cage activities except those pertaining to reproductive phenomena are well developed and the bird is a relatively independent creature. Our present purpose in reporting the foregoing data is that of giving the reader a foundation for the experiment by Stoltenberg and Fearing (1929) which had as its object the correlation of structural development, particularly that of the vestibular apparatus, with ability to modify reflex responses under standardized experimental situations.[5]

---

[5]These data on squabs were taken from an unpublished paper an abstract of which was read at the International Congress of Psychology, Yale University, 1929 (see Stoltenberg and Fearing, 1929). I am indebted to Miss Stoltenberg for permission to use a copy of this paper while preparing the present report.

Stoltenberg rotated birds on a turn-table at the ages of 5, 10, 20, 35, and 90-120 days. Each bird was subjected to rotation 10 different times with the direction of turning alternated on successive trials. A trial consisted of 10 turns of the table completed in a 20-second period. Successive trials followed at intervals of about 2 minutes and the experiment as a whole lasted from 25 to 30 minutes for each individual. From 14 to 16 birds were experimented upon in each of the five age groups, and from these averages were computed.

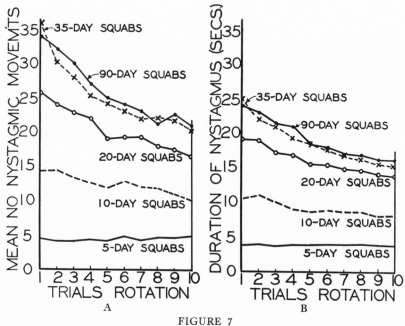

FIGURE 7

AVERAGE NUMBER AND AVERAGE DURATION (SECONDS) OF NYSTAGMIC MOVEMENTS
MADE BY SQUABS OF VARIOUS AGES

Each observation followed 10 rotations on a turn-table. An interval of 2 minutes was allowed between trials. During rotation the pigeons were so anchored to the turn-table that only head movements were possible.

[Unpublished data from Stoltenberg (1929).]

In Figure 7A is shown the average number of nystagmic movements made by each of the five groups after each of the 10 trials. The mean lengths of time during which nystagmic movements took place in each post-rotational interval are shown in Figure 7B. It may be noted that up to 35 days, the approximate time at which squabs leave the nests, there is an age increase in both the number of movements and the duration of time during which they were made. Also, excepting the 5-day-old birds, in which little change was observed, there is a decrease in the frequency and the duration of nystagmus. For our present interest it is important to note that the decrement with successive trials increases with age up to the time the squabs leave the nest (35 days) but not thereafter. Tables 1 and 2 provide numerical data showing this differential modifiability with age. Records of the first and second rotations have been taken as representative measures of the unmodified reflex, as studied under the present conditions, and, likewise, those of the ninth and tenth are taken as a fair measure of the phenomenon at the end of the 10 trials.

TABLE 1

AVERAGE NUMBER OF POST-ROTATIONAL NYSTAGMIC MOVEMENTS IN
DIFFERENT AGE GROUPS OF SQUABS
From 14 to 16 birds were in each group.

| Rotations | Age of groups (days) | | | | |
	5	10	20	35	90-120
1 and 2	4.29	14.35	24.89	33.20	32.95
9 and 10	4.65	10.53	17.33	20.97	21.85
Decrease	— .36	3.82	7.56	12.23	11.10
Percentage decrease	—8.40	26.60	30.30	36.90	33.80

TABLE 2

AVERAGE OF THE TIME INTERVALS IN WHICH POST-ROTATIONAL NYSTAGMIC MOVE-
MENTS WERE OBSERVED IN DIFFERENT AGE GROUPS OF SQUABS
From 14 to 16 birds were in each group.

| Rotations | Age of groups (days) | | | | |
	5	10	20	35	90-120
1 and 2	3.66	10.75	19.11	23.59	23.56
9 and 10	3.67	8.07	13.68	16.20	17.13
Decrease	— .01	2.68	5.43	7.39	6.43
Percentage decrease	— .27	25.80	28.40	31.40	27.30

As yet the analysis of factors thought to be responsible for this differential effect of rotation within the early ages herein studied has not been reported, but it may be expected that correlated studies of nystagmic movements and the developing vestibular apparatus will throw much light upon this important question. Little weight can be placed upon the supposition that pre-experimental practice can account for the difference shown by the birds because opportunity for practice is relatively meager in the nestling squab.

By way of further illustration let us consider a cluster of responses which makes its initial appearance in the adolescent period. In 1926, I reported an experiment on the initial copulatory response of 21 female rats which had been reared in isolation from the age of 20 days. Heterosexual (but not autosexual) stimulation of erogenous zones thus was prevented, and opportunities for motor and thigmotactic responses involved in lying together in cages, pursuit, pseudo-combat, and playful wrestling were reduced to a minimum. In short, the female's experience was so restricted that training in the novel elements of heterosexual behavior and playful rehearsal of the copulatory act as a whole were out of the question; yet in no way was the physiological development, as measured by somatic growth, interfered with in the least observable degree. Fortunately, for this experiment a trained observer may detect the presence of the receptive phase of oestrus with a fair degree of accuracy relying on external cues and without the necessity of any form of breeding test or instrumental examination of the female.

Of the 21 cases, one became receptive only during the daytime and for that reason was not tested under the standard, night-time conditions set up for all. One of the other 20 females failed to copulate on her initial test night, but 10 days later, when subjected to the second test, responded within 10 seconds after being put with the male. *Some of the females responded appropriately to the first mounting,* but the majority of them gave a typical sexual response only after two or three mountings of the male, the latter following in rapid succession. Had the experimenter been aided by more refined methods of ascertaining precisely what stage of the oestrous cycle each young female was in before placing her with the male, there is little reason to doubt that complete responsiveness would have been obtained in the majority of instances at the first mounting by the male. Therefore, making only a small concession to faulty experimental methods, its seems proper to conclude from the foregoing experiment that the action systems displayed in this native heterosexual response are integrated primarily by endogenous factors which control sexual maturation. Stimuli of the external environment call them out only after necessary maturative stages have been passed.

In this same connection attention may be directed to experiments on the chick. Bird (1926) has repeated and greatly extended the earlier experiments of Shepard and Breed (1913) on the improvement of feeding reactions in chicks of various ages and with varying amounts of practice at different ages. Especially important are the elaborate controls of the experimental situations and the numbers of animals subjected to the tests. Among the more important of his conclusions bearing on our present interests are the following:

> The most rapid increase in accuracy of swallowing grains occurs during the three initial practice days, whether these three days immediately succeed the time of hatching or come after a period of artificial delay. A part of the increase is attributed to general physiological development, which occurs during the first few days of postnatal development, which occurs during the first few days of postnatal life, irrespective of practice in pecking. Delayed practice is followed by accuracy of swallowing which at the initial test is no greater than that observed in one day old animals.

Another independent investigation on the accuracy of pecking has been reported by Moseley (1925). She verified the data of Shepard and Breed on the relatively complete development of the pecking response at the time the young emerge from the shell, but found a decrease in the rate of improvement of the pecking response in chicks fed artificially for various periods of time after hatching. The latter is contrary to Shepard and Breed's findings. Moseley believed that learning, in the accepted sense of that term, accounts primarily for increased accuracy in seizing objects, whereas striking and swallowing are more nearly unlearned responses.

The unique experiment of Gesell and Thompson (1929), performed on a pair of identical twins, throws the relative contributions of maturation and training into relief somewhat better than similarly conceived experiments on the lower animals. Using twins which seemed ideally equated at the outset, T serving as experimental subject and C as control, they gave to subject T a daily training course in stair-climbing and cube manipulation for a period of 6 weeks, beginning at the age of 46 weeks. The control was restrained from practice in these special activities during this time, but was tested at the end of the training series to determine the nature and the level of its performances in the acts which subject T had practiced. In addition, C was given a two-weeks training course in stair-climbing at the age of 53 weeks to determine the relative ability of Twins T and C to profit from training at different ages and different maturative stages. Experimental subject T required much assistance at stair-climbing at the outset, but "after four weeks of training (age 50 weeks) she climbed the staircase with avidity and without assistance. At 52 weeks she climbed the staircase in 26 seconds." The control twin, "at the age of 53 weeks, without any previous training, climbed the same staircase unaided in 45 seconds. After 2 weeks of training, at the age of 55 weeks, Twin C climbed the stairs in 10 seconds" (p. 116). The authors conclude that superiority of the control in stair-climbing at the age of 55 weeks, and with only one third as much practice as given to the experimental twin, must be ascribed to the maturity advantage which three weeks of aging affords.

The following quotation indicates the comparative results of cube behavior.

> A day-by-day analysis of this cube behavior showed a trend toward daily changes and increments in prehension, manipulation, and exploitation. At the close of the training period, however, the cube behavior patterns of Twin C were highly similar to those of Twin T. It was impossible to demonstrate any significant influence of training upon the cube behavior patterns of Twin T. . . . The similarity in patterns of cube behavior was confirmed by a time-space cinema analysis of the prehensory reactions to cubes under experimental conditions at 42, 52, 63, and 79 weeks of age. (p. 117)

Numerous other experiments, semi-crucial in nature, have been performed on children in recent years to determine various relationships between maturative processes·and ability to profit from specific kinds and amounts of training. The literature of this subject, however, is more properly the province of another author of the present volume (see Chapter 11.)

2. *Rate of Learning in Relation to Chronological Age in Different Species.* Although space does not permit our developing the point, we may

state that the age of maximal rate of educability is not attained at the same points of the total life-course in different species of animals. In this respect it is like the individual action systems which develop with characteristic tempo and sequence in individuals of the same species but whose tempo and sequence may vary widely from species to species. As will be discussed elsewhere (Chapter 11), maximal learning ability in white rats for typical maze and light discrimination problems seems to be attained when they are from 1 to 3 months of age, or at a fraction of the rat's life-span corresponding roughly to 3 or 4 years of age in children. Moreover, most of the familiar animals about us attain their intellectual and motor maturity very precociously, as compared with man. This is a meaningful fact if we but recall that the lower animals begin to shift for themselves much earlier than the offspring of man. Maximal learning ability seems to be attained, as a general rule, near the time each animal takes up an independent existence or one that is relatively free from paternal provisions or guardianship.

Individual differences in developmental rate within a species are well known. Some types of these may be attributed to differences in intra-organic and others to extra-organic regulation, as has been clearly established by numerous studies of mental development in man (National Society for the Study of Education, 1928; Murchison, 1933).

3. *Learning, or Secondary Elaboration of Maturative Development.* That some optimal amount of practice or use of an immature action system, *per se*, accelerates (possibly retards?) maturational rate in the higher animals is quite generally believed by trainers and teachers. But, so far as known by the author, no crucial evidence supporting this hypothesis has been forthcoming. What seems to be more in line with all of the scattered information on development is the supposition that learned responses neither accelerate nor retard maturative development except as they affect the general metabolic processes upon which somatic growth and maintenance depend; at all times, the products of maturative development determine where in the body and at what rates organization and reorganization by the process of learning may take place.

Subscribing to the foregoing point of view does not entail valuation of the learned and the unlearned responses; when both are observed in nature, both appear to be indispensable to the life or well-being of the organism. Through maturative development many of the basic life adjustments of each individual to the forces of its native habitat are made; through learning, as here defined, these adjustments are refined, extended, and individualized.

BIBLIOGRAPHY

ALLEN, E. 1932. Sex and internal secretions. Baltimore, Md.: Williams & Wilkins. Pp. xxii+951.

ALLEN, E., & DOISY, E. A. 1923. An ovarian hormone. *J. Amer. Med. Asso.,* **81**, 819-821.

ANGULO Y GONZÁLEZ, A. W. 1932. The prenatal development of behavior in the albino rat. *J. Comp. Neur.,* **55**, 395-442.

AVERY, G. T. 1928. Responses of foetal guinea pigs prematurely delivered. *Genet. Psychol. Monog.*, **3**, 247-331.

BIRD, C. 1926. The effect of maturation upon the pecking instincts of chicks. *Ped. Sem.*, **33**, 212-234.

BLANTON, M. G. 1917. The behavior of the human infant during the first thirty days of life. *Psychol. Rev.*, **24**, 456-483.

BÜHLER, C. 1930. The first year of life. [Trans. by P. Greenberg and R. Ripin from the following three German publications: Bühler, C., & Hetzer, H. Inventar der Verhaltungsweisen des ersten Lebensjahres. (*Quell. u. Stud. z. Jugendk.*, No. 5.) Jena: Fischer, 1927. Pp. 125-250. Hetzer, H., & Wolf, K. Babytests. *Zsch. f. Psychol.*, 1928, **107**, 62-104. Hetzer, H., & Koller, L. Vier Testreihen für das zweite Lebensjahr. *Zsch. f. Psychol.*, 1930, **117**, 257-306.] New York: Day. Pp. x+281.

CARMICHAEL, L. 1926. The development of behavior in vertebrates experimentally removed from the influence of external stimulation. *Psychol. Rev.*, **33**, 51-58.

————. 1927. A further study of the development of behavior in vertebrates experimentally removed from the influence of external stimulation. *Psychol. Rev.*, **34**, 34-47.

————. 1928. A further experimental study of the development of behavior. *Psychol. Rev.*, **35**, 253-260.

CASTNER, B. M. 1932. The development of fine prehension in infancy. *Genet. Psychol. Monog.*, **12**, 105-193.

COGHILL, G. E. 1926. Correlated anatomical and physiological studies of the growth of the nervous system in amphibia: VI. The mechanism of integration in *Amblystoma punctatum*. *J. Comp. Neur.*, **41**, 95-152.

————. 1929. Anatomy and the problem of behavior. New York: Macmillan; Cambridge, England: Univ. Press. Pp. xii+113.

————. 1930. The structural basis of the integration of behavior. *Proc. Nat. Acad. Sci.*, **16**, 637-643.

CREW, F. A. E. 1931. Puberty and maturity. *Proc. 2nd Int. Cong. Sex Res.*, 1-19.

EVANS, H. M., & BISHOP, K. S. 1922. On the relation between fertility and nutrition: II. The ovulation rhythm in the rat on inadequate nutritional regimes. *J. Metab. Res.*, **1**, 335-357.

GESELL, A. 1925. The mental growth of the preschool child. New York: Macmillan. Pp. x+447.

————. 1929. Maturation and infant behavior pattern. *Psychol. Rev.*, **36**, 307-319.

GESELL, A., & THOMPSON, H. 1929. Learning and growth in identical infant twins: an experimental study by the method of co-twin control. *Genet. Psychol. Monog.*, **6**, 1-124.

GUDERNATSCH, J. F. 1912. Feeding experiments on tadpoles. *Arch. f. Entwickmech.*, **35**, 457-483.

HALVERSON, H. M. 1931. An experimental study of prehension in infants by means of systematic cinema records. *Genet. Psychol. Monog.*, **10**, 107-286.

HARTMAN, C. G. 1922. Breeding habits, development, and birth of the opossum. *Ann. Rep. Smithsonian Instit. for 1921*, Publ. 2675, 347-363.

HERRICK, C. J. 1924. Neurological foundations of animal behavior. New York: Holt. Pp. xii+334.

JENNINGS, H. S. 1930. The biological basis of human nature. New York: Norton. Pp. xviii+384.

KAO, HAN. 1927. Notes on the congenital behavior of rabbits. M.A. thesis, Stanford Univ.

LANGWORTHY, O. R. 1928. The behavior of pouch-young opossums correlated with the myelinization of tracts in the nervous system. *J. Comp. Neur.*, **46**, 201-248.

McCLURE, W. E., & GOLDBERG, B. 1932. A clinical study of "Toledo's Strong Boy." *J. Abn. & Soc. Psychol.*, **27**, 159-167.

MILLS, W. 1898. The nature and development of animal intelligence. New York: Macmillan. Pp. xii+307.

MINKOWSKI, M. 1922. Ueber frühzeitige Bewegungen, Reflexe und muskuläre Reaktionen beim menschlichen Fötus und ihre Beziehungen zum fötalen Nerven- und Muskelsystem. *Schweiz. med. Woch.*, **52**, 721-724, 751-754.

MORGAN, C. L. 1896. Habit and instinct. London: Arnold. Pp. 351.

MOSELEY, D. 1925. The accuracy of the pecking response in chicks. *J. Comp. Psychol.*, **5**, 75-97.

MURCHISON, C. [Ed.] 1933. A handbook of child psychology. (2nd ed., rev.) Worcester, Mass.: Clark Univ. Press; London: Oxford Univ. Press. Pp. xii+956.

NATIONAL SOCIETY FOR THE STUDY OF EDUCATION. 1928. Nature and nurture: Parts I and II. (*27th Yrbk. Nat. Soc. Stud. Educ.*) Bloomington, Ill.: Pub. School Publ. Co. Pp. 645; 393.

NEEDHAM, J. 1932. Chemical embryology. (3 vols.) Cambridge, England: Univ. Press. Pp. xxi+1-613; xiv+615-1253; xiv+1255-2021.

NICHOLAS, J. S. 1933. Development of transplanted rat eggs. *Proc. Soc. Exper. Biol. & Med.*, **30**, 1111-1113.

PEIPER, A. 1928. Die Hirntätigkeit des Säuglings. *Ergeb. d. inn. Med. u. Kinderhk.*, **33**, 504-605.

PREYER, W. 1885. Specielle Physiologie des Embryo. Untersuchungen über die Lebenserscheinungen vor der Geburt. Leipzig: Grieben. Pp. 644.

SHEPARD, J. F., & BREED, F. S. 1913. Maturation and use in the development of an instinct. *J. Anim. Behav.*, **3**, 274-285.

SHIRLEY, M. M. 1931*a*. The first two years, a study of twenty-five babies: I. Postural and locomotor development. Minneapolis: Univ. Minn. Press. Pp. xvi+227.

———. 1931*b*. The sequential method for the study of maturing behavioɪ patterns. *Psychol. Rev.*, **38**, 507-528.

SMALL, W. S. 1899. Notes on the psychic development of the young white rat. *Amer. J. Psychol.*, **11**, 80-100.

SMITH, P. E. 1927. The induction of precocious sexual maturity by pituitary homeo-transplants. *Amer. J. Physiol.*, **80**, 114-125.

STOCKARD, C. R. 1931. The physical basis of personality. New York: Norton. Pp. 320.

STOLTENBERG, C. S., & FEARING, F. S. 1929. Development of post-rotational head nystagmus in squabs. *Proc. 9th Int. Cong. Psychol.*, New Haven, 414. (Abstract of unpublished manuscript, Department of Anatomy, Sanford University.)

STONE, C. P. 1924*a*. The awakening of copulatory ability in the male albino rat. *Amer. J. Physiol.*, **68**, 407-424.

———. 1924*b*. Delay in the awakening of copulatory ability in the male albino rat incurred by defective diets: I. Quantitative deficiency. *J. Comp. Psychol.*, **4**, 195-224.

———. 1925. Delay in the awakening of copulatory ability in the male albino rat incurred by defective diets: II. Qualitative deficiency. *J. Comp. Psychol.*, **5**, 177-203.

————. 1926. The initial copulatory response of female rats reared in isolation from the age of twenty days to the age of puberty. *J. Comp. Psychol.,* **6,** 73-83.

STONE, C. P., DARROW, C. W., LANDIS, C., & HEATH, L. L. 1932. Studies in the dynamics of behavior, ed. by K. S. Lashley. Chicago: Univ. Chicago Press. Pp. xiv+332.

WILM, E. C. 1925. The theories of instinct. New Haven, Conn.: Yale Univ. Press. Pp. xiv+188.

YERKES, R. M. 1913. Heredity of savageness and wildness in rats. *J. Anim. Behav.,* **3,** 286-296.

CHAPTER 9

LEARNING: II. THE FACTOR OF THE CONDITIONED REFLEX[1]

CLARK L. HULL

Yale University

INTRODUCTION

In one sense the conditioned reflex is not a new discovery. Indeed, it is nothing more than a special case of association by contiguity, which principle has been recognized since the time of Plato[2] and Aristotle.[3] Until recently, however, the major emphasis of association theory has been upon the association of "ideas," though most writers on the subject have recognized the fact that associations could be set up between sensory stimulations and motor reactions. Thus John Locke (1690) tells of the man who learned to dance in a room where there happened to stand an old trunk, only to find that he could not dance in a normal manner anywhere else unless a trunk of similar appearance was present.

During the two and one-half centuries since the beginning of the English association movement there has been a slow but fairly constant tendency for associationism to stress more and more the aspect of physical reaction. This has reached its logical limit in the behavioristic psychology of America, which, despite its migration to another continent and its general repudiation by present-day English psychologists, is a genuine and perfectly natural evolution of English associationism.[4]

The first strictly experimental observation concerning the conditioned motor reflex appears to have been made by Twitmyer in 1902, at the University of Pennsylvania, as an incident in an experiment directed to an entirely different end. His experimental procedure was so arranged that frequently a bell sounded shortly before the familiar knee-jerk was evoked by a blow struck on the patellar tendon. It happened that on one occasion following numerous paired stimulations of this sort the bell sounded without the usual blow. The experimenter noted with some surprise that the knee-jerk took place apparently the same as if the blow had been given. Further investigation confirmed the paradoxical results thus accidentally observed. Moreover, careful questioning elicited reports from the subjects that the reactions thus executed were quite non-voluntary and unin-

---

[1] The writer is greatly indebted to Dr. S. A. Switzer for assistance in the preparation of this summary.

[2] Plato, *Phaedo*, secs. 73-76 .

[3] Aristotle, *De anima*, Book II, chap. 12; Book III, chaps. 2-4.

[4] The extreme slowness with which the reactive aspect of associationism came to be recognized may doubtless be attributed in large part to religious influences, particularly the *odium theologicum* which has ever been directed against anything which savors too much of the physical, i.e., of materialism.

tentional. Twitmyer followed up these chance observations with a series of systematic experiments on six subjects by means of which the genuineness of the phenomenon was proved. These results established further the facts that the conditioned reactions could be evoked after from 30 to 230 paired stimulations, that the reactions following the bell alone tended clearly to be weaker than those resulting from the blow, and that, in general, various collateral conditions such as motor tonicity, sensory stimulation, etc., influenced the two types of reaction in a substantially similar manner. He even saw the possibility of differentiating the two forms of reaction by a determination of their respective latencies (p. 36), an experiment which was to take place "in the near future." Apparently this plan was never carried out. Instead, this extremely promising beginning was buried in a privately printed thesis mainly concerned with a very different subject, and with a title giving no hint of its exceedingly significant findings.

A still earlier experimental observation of conditioning, in this case a spontaneous secretional one, suffered a somewhat similar fate. As long ago as 1852, Bidder and Schmidt reported that "the offering of food to a hungry dog is sufficient to cause a flow of gastric juice from the empty stomach." This observation, while also fully substantiated experimentally, was so far in advance of its time that no attention was paid to it until the decade preceding 1897. During the latter period, Ivan P. Pavlov, the famous Russian physiologist, while investigating the digestive secretions, encountered an exactly similar manifestation. The secretions thus obtained were at first called "psychic" reactions, to distinguish them from the ordinary physiological secretions resulting from the presence of food in the stomach.

Pavlov's methods of investigating the digestive processes are noteworthy because of their bearing on the procedures which he later employed in studying the physiology of the nervous system. In general, they depended upon surgical operations whereby the various digestive secretions might be diverted from their normal course in such a manner as to flow from the surface of the body, where they might be collected, measured, and analyzed. Thus, by means of a delicate operation, he was able, without disturbing either the nerve or blood supply, to segregate approximately a tenth of the interior of a dog's stomach from the main portion. Moreover, he succeeded in so joining the lips of a perforation in this small artificial stomach to the skin outside the dog's abdomen that the two grew together, leaving a permanent fistula or opening. Through this fistula the gastric secretions could then be studied with relative ease and quite uncomplicated by admixture of food materials.

In some animals the main portion of the stomach was also connected with the outside world by means of a second fistula. This latter opening was so placed that food eaten and swallowed by the animal in a normal manner would presently fall through it and drop upon the experimental table. Through this fistula it was also possible to introduce food into the stomach without the dog's knowledge, which enabled Pavlov to study the process of digestion uncomplicated by the usual psychic secretion. In some cases the esophagus of the dog was also cut and the two open ends grown to the skin on the outside of the neck. This last arrangement permitted what is known as sham feeding: The food when swallowed would pass out through the skin of the neck and fall on the experimental table instead of into the stomach.

By utilizing these various experimental preparations in an ingenious manner, Pavlov was able to show that the "psychic" secretion is an essential component of the normal digestive process. The total amount of gastric secretion for the first four hours after a normal feeding of meat is represented by graph *A* of Figure 1. Graph *B* shows the amount secreted

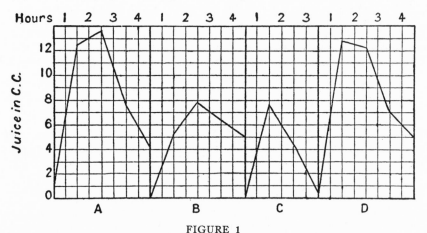

FIGURE 1

PAVLOV'S GRAPHS PORTRAYING HIS EXPERIMENTAL ISOLATION OF THE PHYSIOLOGICAL
AND THE "PSYCHIC" COMPONENTS OF THE NORMAL GASTRIC SECRETION
A, ordinary curve of gastric secretion (200 **gms. flesh**)
B, curve from direct introduction of food (150 gms. flesh)
C, sham feeding with same
D, summation of *B* and *C*
(From Pavlov, 1910, p. 101.)

during a similar period when the meat was placed in the stomach without the dog's knowledge. It will be observed that in this graph the total amount of secretion at each hour appears to be distinctly reduced, especially that of the first. The absence of the psychic component is thus plainly evident. Graph *C* shows the amount of hourly gastric secretion which resulted from a mere sham feeding. The secretion under these latter conditions must, of course, be purely "psychic." While less in aggregate amount, this secretion is characterized by a perceptibly larger amount during the first hour than resulted when the food was placed in the stomach. Indeed, the "psychic" secretion is reported as normally beginning about five minutes after the sham feeding, whereas the secretion initiated by the mere presence of the meat in the stomach is stated to have begun only after a delay of twenty-five minutes. Finally, graph D represents a summation of the values shown in graphs B and C, i.e., it represents a kind of arithmetical synthesis of what might be expected to be a normal secretion on the assumption that the two components thus experimentally isolated are combined in the normal secretional process. It will be seen that this synthesis bears a striking resemblance to the normal secretion shown in graph A. Pavlov regarded this as an *experimentum crucis*.

The above results are still more striking when viewed in the light of a control experiment involving the sham feeding of clean quartz pebbles carried out on a dog which had obligingly learned to eat them like ordinary food. No gastric secretion whatever was observed under such circumstances.

Pavlov early observed that the so-called "psychic" secretions differed from the regular physiological secretions in being dependent upon a considerable number of *conditions* or attendant circumstances, particularly the previous history of the animal. This led him to state that the psychic secretions were *conditional* reflexes, whereas the physiological secretions were *unconditional* reflexes. From this has grown up the somewhat illogical custom in English-speaking countries of calling such reactions *conditioned* reflexes. From many points of view the practice of Vladimir Bechterev, a Russian psychiatrist who was a contemporary and rival of Pavlov in this field, is to be preferred. He called such reactions *association* reflexes.

Since about 1904, when he received the Nobel prize in medicine for his work on the digestive glands, Pavlov has devoted the energies of himself and a large number of his students almost exclusively to the investigation of the physiology of the nervous system. His subjects have been dogs, and the tool employed has been the conditioned reflex. The reaction utilized has been almost exclusively that of salivary secretion as contrasted with the motor response employed by Bechterev (1913). One or more of the salivary ducts has been diverted so that the saliva could flow through a fistula outside the dog's mouth. The fistula for the parotid gland is on the cheek, that of the submaxillary gland under the dog's chin. Because of its favorable location the former has been the more widely employed. The saliva was collected by means of a specially constructed celluloid funnel or glass bulb cemented tightly over the fistula. In the early days a slender graduated glass vial was suspended from the bulb by a wire in such a way that the saliva would flow into it as secreted. Sometimes the experiment was so arranged that the drops would fall on a small platform so delicately poised that it would be actuated by the impact of each drop in such a way as to make a special mark on the smoked paper of a moving kymograph. Thus there was obtained an objective and detailed record of the progress of secretion. Figure 2 shows a drawing of this experimental arrangement.

As Pavlov's experimental work progressed, however, it was discovered that the conditioned reflex is an extremely delicate phenomenon which is susceptible to disturbance by the most minute of uncontrolled stimulations.

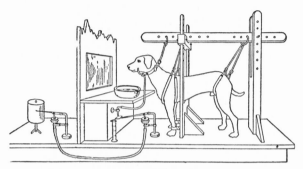

FIGURE 2
DIAGRAMMATIC REPRESENTATION OF AN EARLY APPARATUS ARRANGEMENT EMPLOYED
IN CONDITIONING THE ALIMENTARY SALIVARY REFLEX
(From Yerkes and Morgulis, 1909.)

As a result, an elaborate laboratory was finally built which protected the animals from substantially all stimulations except those specifically employed in the experiment. To this end the animal occupied one room and the experimenter with his apparatus controls occupied another. This is

FIGURE 3
VIEWS SHOWING THE MORE RECENT EXPERIMENTAL ARRANGEMENT EMPLOYED IN
PAVLOV'S LABORATORY FOR CONDITIONING THE SALIVARY REACTION
The left view shows the experimenter's room and the right view shows the animal's room. In the former, note the elaborate system of controls before the experimenter. By means of connections between these and the apparatus in the animal's room, the various stimuli are administered without the stimulus complications which would result from the presence and activity of the experimenter's body.
(From Pavlov, 1927.)

illustrated by Figure 3.   The animal is viewed through a periscope, and all stimulations are administered mechanically.

Another improvement has been introduced—a precise method of measuring the flow of saliva. This is based on the principle of the movement of a colored liquid along a graduated glass capillary tube by the pressure of the secreted saliva within the closed tubular system. This can be made delicate enough to register one-tenth of a drop. In some cases a special electrical device recorded on smoked paper (p. 388) (Anrep, 1920, p. 372) the progress of the secretion in drops of small and uniform size (.01 cc.). Such a record is reproduced in Figure 4.

FIGURE 4
A SMOKED-PAPER RECORD OF THE DROPS OF SALIVA OBTAINED ON ONE OF THE
30-SECOND TESTS OF THE STRENGTH OF THE CONDITIONING TENDENCY
OBTAINED BY ANREP WHILE CONDITIONING A DOG TO A
TONE OF 637.5 VIBRATIONS PER SECOND
A special combination of air currents and electrical contacts insured that each vertical mark represents a drop of saliva of exactly .01 cc. The first stroke beneath the line represents the beginning of the tone; the second, the termination of the 30-second period; and the third, the giving of the biscuit powder.
(From Anrep, 1920.)

Basic in the conditioning process is what is known as the *unconditioned reaction*.   This is regarded as innate or unlearned.   The stimulus which evokes this reaction is called the *unconditioned stimulus*.   Pavlov, despite the fact that he employs only salivary reactions, has utilized two distinct unconditioned reflexes.   The most frequently used one is what he calls the alimentary reaction, a relatively viscous secretion containing much mucin which aids the swallowing process by lubrication.   This type of secretion normally follows the presence in the mouth of meat powder, biscuit powder, and indeed almost any food substance.   The second reaction is a profuse flow of relatively thin, watery saliva following the unconditioned stimulus of dilute acid placed in the mouth.

The stimulus which acquires a new reaction in the conditioning process is called the *conditioned stimulus*.   Examples of conditioned stimuli frequently employed by Pavlov and his pupils include the sound of a bell, the tone of a tuning fork, and the flash of a light.

TWO TYPICAL CONDITIONED-REFLEX EXPERIMENTS

A Conditioned Secretional Reaction.   An example of a simple conditioning experiment characteristic of the Russian work is seen in an investigation reported by Anrep (1920).   A tuning fork of 637.5 vibrations per second was first sounded for five seconds. Two or three seconds after the termination of the tone a plate containing a measured portion of powdered biscuit was automatically moved forward within reach of the animal's mouth. When the dog had finished eating, the plate was mechanically withdrawn behind the screen. Such paired stimulations were given at intervals of from 5 to 35 minutes. Each experimental occasion lasted from one to two hours, during which period on the average only about three stimulations were given. Occasionally during the process, in order to test the progress of the conditioning, the tone would be sounded continuously for 30 seconds and the flow of saliva recorded graphically (Figure 4), after which the biscuit powder would be given as usual.

The results of the tests throughout one typical experiment are shown in Table 1. Naturally the test at the first combined stimulation showed

TABLE 1

RECORD OF THE ACQUISITION OF A CONDITIONED SALIVARY REFLEX BY ANREP'S DOG
No. 4

(From Anrep, 1920.)

Working days	Number of com- bined stimulations	Strength of reflex in number of drops secreted in 30 seconds	Latent period
1	1	0	—
3	10	6	18
7	20	20	8
10	30	60	2
13	40	62	1
16	50	59	2

no secretion. By the tenth reinforcement, however, 6 drops of saliva were secreted, but the secretion did not begin until the tone had sounded eighteen seconds. By the twentieth reinforcement, 20 drops were secreted with a latency of eight seconds, and by the thirtieth paired stimulation the conditioned reaction appears to have been fully established with a total flow of 60 drops.

It is especially to be noted that, from the thirtieth paired stimulation on, the salivation commenced only *one* or *two* seconds after the beginning of the tone, whereas during the regular conditioning process the biscuit powder was not presented until *seven* or *eight* seconds after the beginning of the tone. This means, of course, that the conditioning process not only resulted in the acquisition by the conditioned stimulus of the power to evoke in the organism a new adaptive reaction, but that, as an essential characteristic of its adaptiveness, *the reaction precedes or anticipates the situation originally giving rise to it.* We shall have occasion to refer to this phenomenon and its significance later (p. 433).

A Conditioned Motor Reaction. A second conditioned-reaction experiment on the dog, but in this case involving a motor reflex and typifying the more precise American approach, is seen in an unpublished investigation by Hilgard and Marquis. The reaction conditioned is the reflex wink to a sudden puff of air directed against the right eyeball. Naturally, the head of the animal must be held practically rigid in order to be certain that the movements recorded shall be those of the lid rather than of the head or of the body as a whole. In order to accomplish this, the body of the animal, except for the head, is enclosed in a box. The head itself is held rigidly, as shown in Figure 5. Light but rather stiff strips of paper

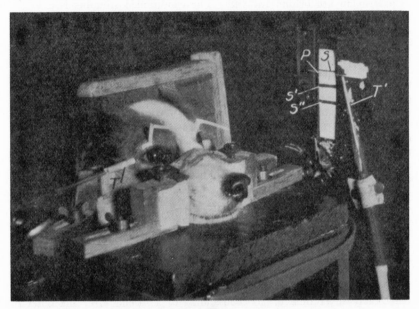

FIGURE 5

A PORTION OF THE APPARATUS ARRANGEMENT EMPLOYED BY HILGARD AND MARQUIS IN THEIR INVESTIGATION OF THE CONDITIONED LID REACTION IN THE DOG

The animal's head is held rigidly to the top of the box containing his body by wooden brackets padded with thick pieces of porous rubber. The unconditioned stimulus, a puff of air to the right eye, is delivered by the tube T. A "Y" in the tube leading to T ends in a tapering glass tube T'. This ends just beneath the strip of paper P, which casts across the vertical lens of the Dodge photochronograph the shadow S. The two artificial eyelashes attached to the dog's lids are in such a position with respect to the source of illumination that they cast across the slit of the recording apparatus the shadows S' and S''. Fine threads, 1 millimeter apart, are stretched across the slit of the apparatus; these cast the additional shadows which appear as white horizontal lines on the records shown in Figure 6. The white vertical lines are produced by momentary interruptions of the light source caused by successive spokes of a rimless wheel revolving at a constant speed such that one spoke passed every 5 thousandths of a second. Every tenth spoke has an extra width which causes the wider white lines seen in the records. In order to enable the latter to be read from left to right, it was necessary to invert them in Figure 6 so that the "puff" shadow appears at the bottom instead of at the top.

(Reproduced by permission of Hilgard and Marquis)

about one and one-half inches long are attached somewhat like artificial eyelashes to the respective upper lids of the dog by means of an adhesive. The animal is then placed in such a position that these strips of paper are in line with a beam of light which is projected into the slit of the Dodge photochronograph.[5] This instrument is so constructed that shadows such as those made by the artificial eyelashes are recorded as broad white lines on a piece of photographically sensitive paper (Figure 6) which is made to pass in an arc behind the slit. The conditioned stimulus is a bright light flashed directly into the eye of the dog. The beginning of this stimulus in indicated by the dark band at the top of the record. Each experimental session lasts approximately 60 minutes, during which time 65 stimulations are normally administered.

The various stages of the conditioning process are revealed in a remarkably perfect manner by the photographic records secured by this experimental procedure. Three records chosen at characteristic points in the process are reproduced as Figure 6. They are to be read from left to right. The vertical lines on the record mark off periods of 5 thousandths of a second each. Record A shows the reaction of the lid to the conditioned and the unconditioned stimuli respectively at the beginning of the conditioning process. It should be noticed at the outset that the so-called conditioned stimulus (the light) is not really a neutral stimulus, as a less sensitive recording system might have permitted one to suppose, but causes a slight reflex of its own which appears at the point R_L. A count of the vertical time lines of this record shows that the light reflex took place 85 thousandths of a second after the beginning of the light, which is a normal latency. Passing now to the right of the record, it will be observed that the puff of air gave rise to a relatively large movement of the right eyelid (R_P), but to practically no movement of the left one. A count based on the vertical time lines shows that this reaction took place in the remarkably short time of 20 thousandths of a second after the onset of the puff stimulus.

After numerous such paired stimulations as those shown in record A, the dog was found to give reactions like those shown in record B. In this record we find both lids still showing slight unconditioned reactions to the light, and the right lid, particularly, showing a vigorous reaction to the puff of air. There is, however, the new phenomenon of an anticipatory lid reaction (CR) substantially resembling that of the true reflex but beginning some 190 thousandths of a second preceding the puff itself. This is the conditioned reaction.

Passing now to record C of Figure 6, we may observe the final phase of the conditioned reflex. Here we still find the slight reflex movement to light at 90 thousandths of a second, which is followed by the conditioned reaction (CR), as in record B, after a further interval of 80 thousandths

---

[5]This instrument (Dodge, 1926) is essentially a heavy compound pendulum mounted behind a screen provided with a narrow slit. A piece of sensitized paper attached to the bob of the pendulum records all lights and shadows playing on the slit as the bob swings by in its arc-shaped excursion.

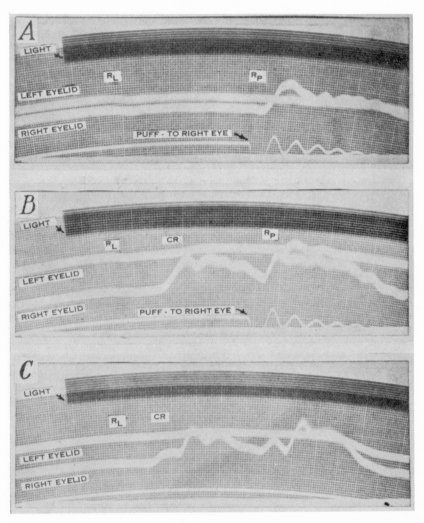

FIGURE 6

RECORDS SHOWING CHARACTERISTIC STAGES IN THE PROCESS OF CONDITIONING THE
EYELID REACTIONS OF A DOG TO LIGHT

A, paired stimulations at the outset of the conditioning process

B, paired stimulations after conditioning has taken place, showing both the conditioned reaction (CR) and the unconditioned reaction (reaction to puff of air, Rp)

C, the conditioned reaction uncomplicated by reinforcement, i.e., the unconditioned reaction to puff of air against the right eyeball

(Reproduced with the permisson of Hilgard and Marquis)

of a second. This time, however, the conditioned reaction appears by itself, uncomplicated by the unconditioned reaction to the puff of air.

In addition to showing the details of the conditioning process in a peculiarly complete and perfect manner, the records reproduced as Figure 6 illustrate two important principles involved in the development of conditioned reactions. The first is that the conditioned stimulus does not necessarily lose its unconditioned tendency when, during the process of conditioning, it acquires a new excitatory tendency. This is shown in records *B* and *C* by the fact that the light reflex appears to be quite as vigorous as in record *A* (Hilgard, 1931, p. 38), which was taken preceding the conditioning process. This is important in the light of Pavlov's apparent belief to the contrary (1927, pp. 29 ff.).

The second observation is that, despite the great dissimilarity between the process involved in the Anrep experiment and that of the present one, the tendency of the conditioned reaction to anticipate the unconditioned stimulus is again apparent. In the present experiment, however, the biological significance of this anticipation is peculiarly evident. The puff of air on the right eyeball may be regarded essentially as an injurious stimulus. The conditioned lid closure as shown in record *B* anticipates the onset of this nocuous stimulus in such a way that the lid is closed more than a tenth of a second before the puff of air takes place. The significance of this primitive automatic adaptive mechanism thus effectively demonstrated can hardly be overestimated. It will be discussed later (p. 433).

REACTIONS WHICH HAVE BEEN CONDITIONED

The Knee-Jerk. All of the experimental work on conditioning the knee-jerk appears to have utilized human subjects. The pioneer study by Twitmyer has already been mentioned (p. 382). Other studies in this field have been reported by Shevalev (1926), Cornil and Goldenfoun (1930), Schlosberg (1928), Switzer (1930), and Wendt (1930).

Wendt's study is the most elaborate of those performed up to the present time. Two stimulus hammers were permitted to fall in succession: first, one hammer fell on the left tendon and, after a period varying around a fifth of a second, another hammer fell on the right tendon. The reaction was recorded mechanically on smoked paper by a lever system which was actuated by the thickening of the quadriceps muscle, the one chiefly involved in this reaction. Typical tracings of the knee-jerks obtained in this way previous to conditioning are shown in record *A*, Figure 7. This record is to be read from left to right. The lower tracing is from the thickening of the left quadriceps; the upper, that from the right quadriceps. The wavy line between is the tracing made by a stylus attached to one tine of a tuning fork vibrating 50 times per second. Just at the left of the rise in each muscle-thickening curve may be seen a small sharp notch. This marks the point at which the hammer hit the tendon.

After a considerable number of stimulations, the right quadriceps usually began to show conditioned reactions partially superposed on, and following,

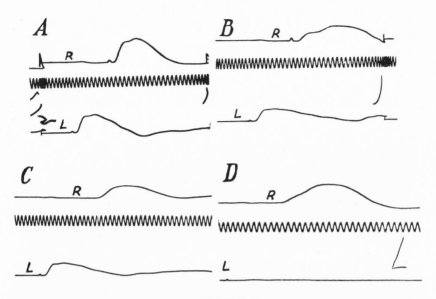

FIGURE 7

RECORDS OF QUADRICEPS MUSCLE THICKENINGS PREVIOUS TO AND AFTER THE PROCESS
OF CONDITIONING THE KNEE-JERK OF THE RIGHT LEG TO A BLOW ON THE
PATELLAR TENDON OF THE LEFT LEG

The wavy line in the middle of the record is the tracing from a 50-vibration
tuning fork. The tracing above this is of the right leg; that below is of the left.
The impact of the hammer on the tendon is shown by a small notch shortly
preceding the reflex thickening of the muscle in six of the eight tracings. Record
A represents the unconditioned reaction to the blows on the respective tendons
before conditioning took place, and records *B*, *C*, and *D* show the conditioned
reaction on the right leg under various circumstances.
(From Wendt, 1930.)

the unconditioned reaction. Such a combined reaction appears as the two
waves in the upper tracing of record *B;* the first wave is the unconditioned reaction, the second the conditioned reaction. The upper tracing
of record *C* shows a thickening but without the usual preceding notch,
which thus marks it clearly as a conditioned reaction; the stimulus was
the blow delivered to, and possibly in part the reaction of, the other leg.
A careful comparison of the contour of this reaction with that of the true
reflexes reveals a qualitative difference. Wendt reports that the type of
contour characteristic of conditioned reactions is also characteristic of
voluntary kicks.

Lastly, it may be observed that the unconditioned reaction natural to the
conditioned stimulus, the kick of the left leg, has not been lost in the
conditioning process since it is present with considerable amplitude in
records *B* and *C*. The conditioned reaction may be evoked, however, in
cases where the unconditioned reaction to the conditioned stimulus is

almost entirely lacking, as is illustrated by record D. The blow delivered against the left tendon is indicated in this record only by the small notch at the extreme lower left-hand corner, but hardly a trace of an unconditioned reaction to it is discernible.

The Plantar Reflex. Shipley (1932) has recently reported the conditioning of the plantar reflex in man. This reflex involves a flexion both of ankle and of toes. The normal stimulus evoking the reflex is the slow movement under pressure of a blunt point along the sole of the foot over a path indicated by the arrows in part C of Figure 8. The reactions were

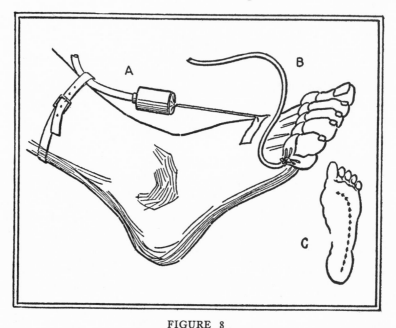

FIGURE 8
DRAWING SHOWING *A*, ANKLE-MOVEMENT RECORDER; *B*, TOE-MOVEMENT RECORDER;
AND *C*, PATH OF STIMULATION
(After Shipley, 1932.)

recorded automatically by pneumatic pressure transmitted to Marey tambours connected with the receiving devices pictured at A and B, respectively, in Figure 8. A characteristic record from such an experiment is reproduced as Figure 9. Shipley reports that, of ten subjects used in the investigation, seven showed conditioned toe movements. Three of these showed, in addition, conditioned ankle reactions. Three subjects showed no conditioned tendencies whatever. In some cases the conditioned reactions appeared as a movement in a direction opposite that characteristic of the unconditioned reflex.

The Abdominal Reflex. The abdominal reflex is evoked by a stimula-

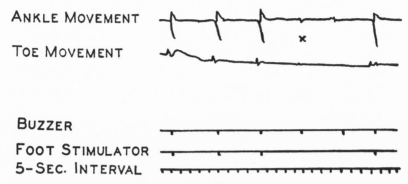

ANKLE MOVEMENT

TOE MOVEMENT

BUZZER

FOOT STIMULATOR

5-SEC. INTERVAL

FIGURE 9

REPRODUCTION OF TYPICAL RECORD SHOWING CONDITIONED PLANTAR REACTION
Ankle flexion is represented by downward, and toe flexion by upward
movement.
(After Shipley, 1932.)

tion very much like that described for the plantar reflex except that it is
applied to the abdomen a little to one side of the umbilicus. The total
reaction to this stimulus is somewhat complex. The component usually
referred to as the abdominal reflex is a homolateral deviation of the linea
alba and the umbilicus. In addition to this, however, there also results
a slight but characteristic shrinking movement which consists of a simultaneous withdrawal and tensing of the abdominal muscles. A preliminary
attempt was made to condition this reflex by Robert R. Sears and Donald
G. Marquis, in the writer's laboratory, but no report of the experiment
has as yet been published. The subject lay on his back with the abdominal
region exposed. The abdominal movements were recorded on a kymograph
by mechanical markers connected with three threads which, in turn, were
attached by adhesive tape to a single spot of skin on the region in question.
The course of the threads from their common point of attachment was
varied in each case in such a way that each mediated a record in a different dimension—dorsoventral, longitudinal, and transverse. The conditioned stimulus was a buzzer. Three subjects were employed. No conditioning of the specific lateral abdominal reflex was observed, though after
over a hundred paired stimulations the dorsoventral or shrinking component
showed a slight conditioning in one subject.

The Achilles Reflex. An extensive attempt was made by Garvey
(1932a) to condition this reflex to the sound of a buzzer. The unconditioned stimulus was the sharp tap of an automatic hammer falling
pendulum-wise against the Achilles tendon. Reactions were recorded on
the smoked paper of a kymograph by a mechanical marker which communicated by means of a stout thread with the toe of the subject's shoe.
In some cases the buzzer preceded the hammer by a brief interval; in some
cases it coincided with the hammer. Twelve subjects were used. With

some of the subjects five hundred or more paired stimuli were employed. Only four or five conditioned reactions were obtained in the entire investigation. The results thus showed scarcely any evidence of ordinary conditioning. So far as the present evidence goes, the Achilles reflex appears to be one of the most difficult to condition of any investigated.

Reflex Withdrawal from a Painful Stimulus. The reflex withdrawal of a portion of the body from the source of a painful stimulus, usually an electric shock, has been very widely used in conditioning experiments. This was the basic procedure long employed by Bechterev and his students and is probably the most frequently used of any one method in America. With animals it has been customary to press one of the feet to a metal plate or grill by means of a spring attachment. The grill is wired in circuit with an induction coil in such a way as to deliver a shock to the member in question, which causes the foot to lift. A cord usually extends from the animal's foot to a marker in contact with the smoked paper of a kymograph in such a way that any movement of the foot is automatically recorded. This general experimental procedure has also been employed by Watson (1916) with the dog and extensively by Liddell (Liddell and Anderson, 1928, 1931) with sheep and several of the other domestic animals.

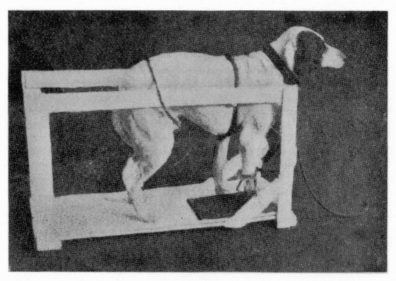

FIGURE 10

A DOG WITH RIGHT FOREPAW ON AN ELECTRIC GRILL AS IN EXPERIMENTS WHERE MOTOR REACTIONS ARE CONDITIONED

When shocked, the foot lifts. Suitable cords attached to the foot record the movements automatically on the smoked paper of a moving kymograph. Note the pneumograph around the dog's chest.

(From Watson, 1916.)

With human subjects the shock has usually been delivered to the end of one or more of the fingers. The most widely used recording device is that invented by Watson (1924). The heel of the hand rests on a broad electrode (Figure 11), and the tip of the finger on another. When the

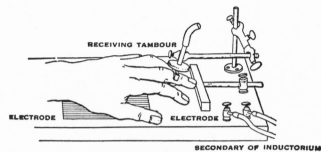

FIGURE 11

DRAWING OF WATSON'S APPARATUS FOR CONDITIONING THE REFLEX WITHDRAWAL
OF THE HAND TO THE ELECTRIC SHOCK
(From Watson, 1924.)

shock is received the finger jerks away from the electrode. This act, through the saddle resting upon the finger and connected with the receiving tambour, sets up a disturbance in the air pressure of the recording system, which causes a corresponding movement of the recording tambour. A record of a complete conditioning process involving the withdrawal from a nocuous stimulus is shown in Figure 12. In this record, R represents

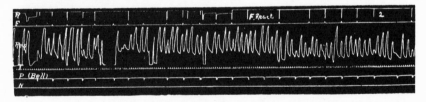

FIGURE 12

A RECORD OF THE PROCESS OF CONDITIONING THE FINGER-WITHDRAWAL REACTION
AND BREATHING DISTURBANCES, AS EVOKED BY AN ELECTRIC SHOCK,
TO THE SOUND OF A BELL
For explanation see text.
(From Watson, 1916.)

the finger movement, F represents the occasions when the induction shock (unconditioned stimulus) was delivered, and P (*bell*) indicates when the bell (conditioned stimulus) was sounded. It will be observed that the shock accompanied the bell on the first 13 occasions. On the fourteenth, however, the bell was given but no shock was delivered. It will be noted that on this occasion a finger movement took place, as is indicated by characteristic downward deviation of the upper line. This is the first conditioned reflex elicited. The fifteenth bell was also unaccompanied by a shock, but this failed to evoke a reaction. The same is true of the seventeenth. The twenty-second bell, however, was also unaccompanied by a shock, but this time the finger was withdrawn.[6]

This general procedure has also been employed by Hamel (1919), Scott (1930), Wolfle (1930, 1932), Shipley (1929, 1933), Garvey (1932b, 1933), Switzer (1933), and others. Garvey has made the technique somewhat more sensitive by having the first two fingers of the hand each depress a flat steel spring about a quarter of an inch. The springs are placed side by side and constitute the electrodes. As usual, they are wired in circuit with an inductorium. To one of the springs is attached a thread which communicates with a sensitive marker in contact with the smoked paper of a kymograph. Since the spring follows in detail any movement of the end of the finger, however slight, the subject's behavior in this respect is recorded with precision (Figure 22).

The Reflex Wink. The reflex closure of the eyelid has been found to condition very readily, both with man and the dog. The technique employed by Hilgard and Marquis in conditioning this reaction in the dog has already been given in considerable detail (pp. 389 ff.). The more important investigations which have studied the conditioning of this reflex have been performed by Cason (1922b), Switzer (1930), Hilgard (1931), and Shipley (1933). All of the latter studies have been performed on human subjects. Cason employed an electric shock as his unconditioned stimulus; Switzer and Shipley used a mechanical tap on the lower eyelid; and Hilgard used the sound of a sharp blow on a sounding-box placed close to the subject's ear. Cason, in his pioneering study, secured objective indication of lid closure by having an electric circuit closed automatically by the movement of the eyelid. This circuit closure controlled the action of a Bergstrom chronoscope which yielded rough measures of the reaction latencies. Switzer secured tracings of the lid movements of his subjects by means of a silk thread cemented to the eyelid; this communicated with a delicate glass lever in contact with the smoked paper of a kymograph. Hilgard recorded the lid movements of his human subjects by means of an artificial eyelash and the Dodge pendulum-photochronograph, in a manner substantially like that described above in the case of the conditioning of the dog (p. 390).

The Pupillary Reflex. The conditioning of the pupillary reflex was first proposed and performed by Watson (1916). He reports a preliminary investigation in which a bell was used as the conditioned stimulus and a very strong light as the unconditioned stimulus. In the short time which he had available for training subjects he found two out of four individuals who, after 15 or 20 minutes of training, showed a small conditioned constriction of the pupil in about 75 per cent of the stimulations.

---

[6]The conspicuous undulatory line in the middle of the record is a respiratory tracing or pneumogram. For a discussion of this reaction, see pp. 401 ff. under the head of *Disturbances in the Amplitude and Rhythm of Breathing.*

The next study, a much more elaborate one, was performed by Cason in 1922. In general, the technique of Cason was substantially like that of Watson, with the exception that he had a special apparatus for measuring the diameter of the pupil. Cason found it possible to condition the constriction, and probably the dilation, of the pupil to an electric shock, the sound of a bell, and the sound of a telephone receiver. Cason reports that in one experiment he conditioned the iris to contract at the telephone sound and to dilate at the sound of a bell. In another the process was reversed: the iris was conditioned to contract in response to the bell stimulus and to dilate at the stimulus from the telephone receiver.

The most extensive investigation in this field is that reported by Hudgins (1933). In this latter study the pupil of the subject was observed through a specially constructed telescope containing vertical hairs which were susceptible of lateral adjustment by means of a thumb screw. The experimenter continuously adjusted this apparatus so that the two hairs appeared exactly to coincide at all times with the respective sides of the pupil. To the cylinder of the thumb screw was attached a thread which, when the screw was turned, actuated a marker in contact with the smoked paper of a kymograph. In this way was secured a graphic record of all the changes which took place in the horizontal diameter of the pupil throughout the experiment.

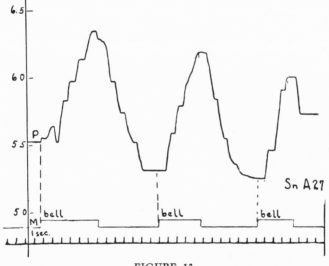

FIGURE 13

KYMOGRAM OF PUPILLARY RESPONSE TO THE BELL STIMULUS BEFORE TRAINING

P, tracing of pupillary changes. The vertical broken lines connect simultaneous points on the tracings P and M. A rise in the tracing P indicates dilation; a fall, contraction. The test light was on continuously during the record. M, tracing of signal magnet. The upper levels of M indicate the presence of the bell sound; the lower levels, the presence of the test light alone. Time in seconds; ordinate in millimeters.

(From Hudgins, 1933, p. 15.)

A record of the spontaneous or unconditioned reactions to the bell stimulus is reproduced as Figure 13.   An examination of this figure will show that the natural (unconditioned) reaction to the bell stimulus is a dilation of the pupil amounting to nearly a millimeter.   In order to secure clear evidence of a conditioned reaction under these circumstances it is obviously necessary that the action to be conditioned must be a movement in a direction opposite to that originally evoked by the bell; that is, in order to be distinguishable from the unconditioned reaction to the conditioned stimulus, the conditioned reaction must be a *constriction* of the pupil.   A constriction of the iris is easily produced by using as an unconditioned stimulus the flash of a strong light.   Hudgins found that after from 125 to 225 paired stimulations of this kind the tendency to dilation at the sound of the bell had practically ceased and in its place had appeared a very definite and clearly marked constriction with at least 12 of his 13 subjects so trained.

A record of a typical conditioned constriction is shown as Figure 14. It is noteworthy that a remnant of the original dilational tendency manifests itself as a slight rise in the tracing at the very outset of the reaction. Hudgins states that this appeared in nearly every record.   The latency of the conditioned reaction is found to be much greater than that of the unconditioned reaction to light, and the rate of conditioned contraction,

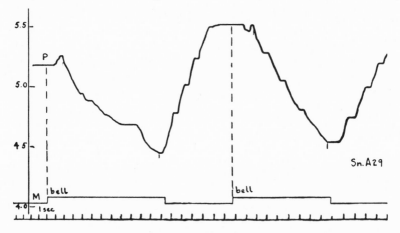

FIGURE 14

KYMOGRAM OF CONDITIONED PUPILLARY RESPONSE TO BELL STIMULUS

P, tracing of the pupillary changes. Broken lines connect simultaneous points on *P* and *M*. Two seconds after the bell rings the pupil begins to constrict. There is a slight dilation immediately following the stimulus.   When the bell ceases to ring dilation of the pupil follows.   *M*, tracing of the signal magnet. The rise of the tracing represents the incidence of the bell stimulus; the tracing falls when the bell ceases to ring. The scale at the left is a projection of the millimeter scale of the micrometer.   Time in seconds.

(From Hudgins, 1933, p. 17.)

once it gets under way, is distinctly slower. It is of interest that when the bell stops ringing the pupil promptly returns approximately to its former size, just as if a light had been removed.

One of the most striking phenomena brought out by the Hudgins experiment relates to the stimuli which were able to acquire the power to evoke this reaction. In addition to the bell, by an ingenious experimental procedure it was proved that pupillary constriction could be conditioned to a spoken nonsense syllable from the experimenter, to the experimenter's command to "contract," to the gripping of a dynamometer by the subject himself, to the subject's repeating aloud the words "contract" and "relax," to his whispering these words, and, finally, to a mere subvocal repetition of the words! Certain important theoretical implications of these results, as to the nature of what are ordinarily called voluntary reactions, will be mentioned later (p. 440). Hudgins' work has recently been criticized by Steckle and Renshaw (1934).

Disturbances in the Amplitude and Rhythm of Breathing. A reaction under semi-voluntary control which is readily conditioned and which has been used quite often in conditioning experiments is that of certain changes in respiration. This technique has proved effective with both human and animal subjects (Figure 24). Automatic records of the rhythmic breathing activities, usually on smoked paper, are obtained by means of one or another of the devices built for the purpose and called pneumographs (Figure 10).

The electric shock applied to the tip of the finger, as employed in the conditioning of the finger retraction described above (p. 397), is the most convenient and common unconditioned stimulus for the evocation of respiratory disturbances. This stimulus usually produces two fairly dis-

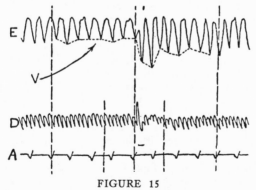

FIGURE 15

RESPIRATION AND PULSE TRACINGS SHOWING TYPICAL REACTIONS TO A PAINFUL STIMULUS

The stimulus was applied at the point marked by the middle vertical line. *E*, respiration; *D*, pulse; *A*, time in 5-second intervals. For further explanation, see text.

(After Sears, 1932.)

tinct changes in the breathing reaction, both of which prove susceptible to conditioning. They may be understood by referring to the conventional record reproduced in Figure 15. It will be observed that during a period of 20 seconds preceding the stimulus, the breathing was moderate in amplitude and fairly regular. After the stimulation, however, the depth of breathing was increased very markedly for a period of at least 20 seconds. In addition, the contour of the line connecting the lower points of the tracing had greatly increased in irregularity.

Figure 24 is taken from Watson's early experiment, where, as evidence that conditioning had taken place, it was sufficient to observe the increase in amplitude and the irregularity in rhythm merely by inspection. The quantification of conditioned breathing reactions was introduced by Scott, both as to amplitude and variability. Scott (1930) employed the laborious method of directly measuring the amplitude of each inspiration by means of a fiftieth-inch scale. By the time Garvey had performed his study, however, the linear oscillometer (Hull, 1929b) was available. The oscillating line of a pneumogram may be traced with the stylus of this instrument, which will summate automatically and with precision all of the breathing movements within any given period of time. This is usually from 10 to 20 seconds. Thus, in the respiration record produced in Figure 15, the total oscillation during the 20 seconds previous to stimulation amounts to 85 oscillometer units, whereas that following the stimulation amounts to 165 such units. The magnitude of the reaction may conveniently be expressed by the ratio of the score after stimulation divided by that before. In this case the ratio is 1.94. Garvey (1933) has utilized a second method, that of simple subtraction. By the latter procedure the score would be 80 oscillometer units.

The matter of variability was determined by Scott by computing the mean variation of the amplitude of the several inspirations taking place within a period of fifteen seconds before and after the stimulus and dividing the latter by the former. A positive reaction will be indicated by a ratio above unity. A distinctly different and probably more significant function of the variability may be secured by running the oscillometer tracer along the line connecting the lower points of the pneumogram (dotted line, Figure 15). It is evident that if the breathing is regular these points will be in a straight line and the oscillometer will register zero, whereas the more the amplitude of each successive breath differs from the one preceding it, the more the line connecting the successive points will itself oscillate, and the greater will be the amount registered on the instrument. Thus the broken line connecting the lower points of the pneumogram shown in Figure 15 yields only four oscillometer units for the 20 seconds preceding stimulation, whereas that for the 20 seconds following stimulation measures nineteen such units. The difference or index of magnitude of the reaction in this case accordingly amounts to 16. This latter method of measurement was employed on a large scale by Garvey (1933). The general indication seems to be that the variability index is a more significant measure of the reaction to strong stimuli both of an unconditioned and of a conditioned sort than any other which can be secured from tracings of the breathing reaction.

One possible defect of the breathing reaction for purposes of conditioning experimentation is that, owing to the extreme sensitivity of the reaction, most stimuli tend to evoke it previous to the conditioning process. This may be seen by an examination of Figure 16, reproduced from

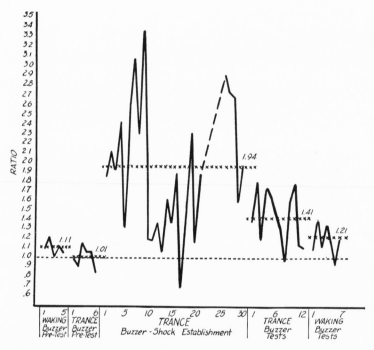

FIGURE 16

COMPOSITE GRAPH SHOWING RESPIRATORY REACTION TO STIMULATION PRECEDING CONDITIONING (BUZZER PRE-TEST), DURING THE PROCESS OF CONDITIONING (ESTABLISHMENT) AND FOLLOWING CONDITIONING (BUZZER TESTS)

The graph is based on ratios obtained by dividing respiratory amplitude during the 15 seconds following stimulation by that during the 15 seconds preceding stimulation.

(After Scott, 1930.)

Scott's pioneer study in this field. It will be observed that of the two periods of stimulation by the buzzer preceding the conditioning process, one, at least, showed an appreciable tendency to produce the response. In such cases conditioning can manifest itself only by an increase in the extent of the reaction which actually appears. However, the method has the advantage of permitting measurements of experimental extinction below zero, which would be indicated by ratios below unity (p. 439).

Disturbances in the Amplitude and Rhythm of the Pulse. The reaction of the vasomotor system in response to an electric shock or other painful stimulation is characteristic. A graphic record of this action is secured on smoked paper under favorable circumstances by means of the Meek-Erlanger recording sphygmomanometer. A typical reaction of this kind is shown in tracing *D* of Figure 15. The painful stimulus was applied at the point indicated by the middle vertical line. It will be observed that the pulse beat preceding this was rather full and extremely regular, whereas immediately following the stimulation there was a marked irregularity of the reaction which was accompanied by a distinct diminution in its amplitude. This reaction thus affords two measures, just as was the case with breathing. The amplitude change, on the sphygmomanometer, however, is exactly the opposite to that of breathing; that is, where the breathing shows an *increase* in amplitude following the stimulation, the pulse under these particular conditions tends to show a *decrease*. Thus the measurement of the total oscillation of the pulse record reproduced as Figure 15 for the 7 seconds preceding stimulation yielded 37 oscillometer units, whereas the 7 seconds following stimulation yielded only 33. The variability index, however, is of the same general nature as that presented by breathing. The tracing of a line connecting the lower points of the pulse beat in this case yielded a score of only 1 oscillometer unit prior to stimulation, whereas that following the stimulation yielded a score of 5. The conditioning of this reaction has been carried out in a preliminary way by Scott (1930), and by Shipley (1929).

Vasomotor Constriction. The typical vasomotor reaction to any strong or startling stimulus is a constriction of the blood vessels which results in a small but measurable reduction in volume of portions of the body, such as the hand. This reaction is usually studied with the aid of an instrument called the plethysmograph. This device takes various forms, but generally consists of a relatively inelastic chamber filled with warm water in which the hand or the arm of the subject is placed. As the total volume of the hand shrinks, the water in the system falls and this is recorded by the stylus of an ordinary pneumatic tambour on the smoked paper of a moving kymograph. Cytovitch and Folkman (1917) report the conditioning of this reaction on ten human subjects. The unconditioned stimulus was cold applied to the skin. The conditioned stimuli employed were various: the sounding of a tuning fork, a note sounded on a fife, and the vibration of an electric buzzer. It is reported that after 25 paired stimulations the conditioned stimuli were able to evoke the vascular constrictions. These writers also report an unpublished study by Dr. Tchaly, in which this reaction, produced by an induction shock as an unconditioned stimulus, was successfully conditioned.

The Galvanic Skin Reaction. This reaction has been known for a long time, though it is one not ordinarily suspected by the naïve subject because it cannot be observed except with the aid of special apparatus.

There are several methods of observing and recording this response, no two of which appear to yield exactly comparable results. One of the simplest, and at the same time one of the best, methods of observing the galvanic skin reaction is to bind two polished silver coins (quarter dollars) to the hand, one on the back and the other on the palm. To these coins should be soldered wires which connect with a sensitive D'Arsonval galvanometer. A beam of light is reflected from the mirror in the galvanometer either upon the aperture of a special camera or upon a simple translucent screen. When the subject is stimulated, particularly by means of an electric shock, the minute differences in potential developed at the electrodes, presumably through the action of the sweat glands in the hand, produce a movement of the mirror of the galvanometer. This causes a beam of light (which appears as a luminous spot) to move in a lateral direction. In case this moves along the slit-like aperture of a special camera provided with a moving photographic film, the course of the spot of light will be photographically recorded and will constitute a graphic history of the electrical changes in the subject's hand. A simpler method of securing a graphic record of the galvanic changes as shown by the movement of the spot of light is to have mounted on the screen a sliding point which may be continuously adjusted by the experimenter so as to coincide exactly with the spot of light. By means of a simple series of pulleys, a thread connected with the slider communicates with a vertical recording device which, in turn, traces on the smoked paper of a moving kymograph a faithful record of the electrical changes being investigated. A typical record secured in this way is reproduced as Figure 17.

The first attempt to condition this reaction seems to have been made by Watson in 1915 (1916, p. 99), though his effort resulted in failure apparently because of the insensitivity of his galvanometer. The reaction has been successfully conditioned by Golla (1921), Freeman (1930), Scott (1930), Jones (1928, 1931), Switzer (1933), Bass and Hull (1934), and others. Jones has employed it to excellent advantage in an investigation of the conditioned reflex in young children. The reaction suffers from the same general disadvantage as the breathing reaction considered above—namely, that owing to its extreme sensitivity it is evoked to a certain extent by almost any stimulus of even moderate intensity. This defect, however, is largely obviated by employing very weak stimuli. The reaction has the decided advantage that the naïve subject is completely unaware of its existence, and the sophisticated subject cannot tell whether it is operating or not. No doubt in part as the result of these circumstances, the reaction is not under voluntary control and subjects are therefore unable voluntarily to inhibit its appearance as they seem frequently to do in the case of such conditioned reactions as the finger withdrawal.

Rise in Pitch of the Voice. Taylor (1933) has recently discovered that one of the effects of receiving an electric shock is to increase the pitch of vocalization taking place at the time the shock is delivered, or

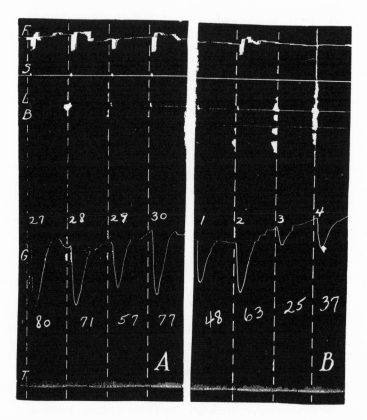

FIGURE 17

PORTIONS OF THE FINGER-WITHDRAWAL AND GALVANIC-SKIN-REACTION RECORDS OF
SWITZER'S SUBJECT NO. 5

Record *A*, last four reinforcements in the conditioning series. Record *B*, first
four stimulations of the experimental-extinction series. *F*, finger reaction; *S*,
shock to tip of finger; *L*, light; *B*, buzzer; *G*, galvanic reaction; *T*, time in
seconds. The numbers above the galvanic tracing represent the ordinals of the
reinforcement and experimental-extinction series respectively; those beneath are
the total oscillation of the galvanic line for the period of 38.5 seconds between
the successive stimulations as marked off by the dashed perpendicular lines. Note
the unstable nature of the conditioned finger reaction in comparison with the
regularity of the appearance of the galvanic.

(After Switzer, 1933.)

soon after.   He has shown, for example, that, if a subject speaks the
word *sat* at the moment of receiving a rapid series of induction shocks on
the wrist, the vocalization will be at a pitch averaging, for eight male
subjects, some 27 vibrations per second higher than normal. He
attempted to condition this reaction to light.   Placed before the subject

were two small flashlight bulbs exactly alike but 3 inches apart. Sometimes one would glow, and sometimes the other. The subject was instructed to pronounce the word *sat* when either bulb became luminous. Whenever the right-hand bulb became luminous the subject received a shock as he was saying the word, whereas no shock was given when the response was made to the left-hand light. About 20 reinforcements of the right-hand light were interspersed among about 80 unreinforced stimulations of the left-hand light and with occasional presentations of the right-hand light without reinforcement to test for the presence of conditioning. It was found that every one of the eight subjects showed a mean increase in pitch of the responses given to the right-hand light over those given to the left, though in a number of cases this increase was slight. The subjects as a whole showed an average conditioned increase of four vibrations per second, which value was found to have satisfactory statistical reliability.

The Fetal "Kicking" Reaction. An attempt has been made by Ray (1932) to condition the kicking reactions of a fetus. The mother, a trained psychologist, lay on her back. Three two-inch tambours of special design were placed diaphragm-down at the following points against her abdomen: one over the fetus' shoulder, one close to the base of its spine, and the third approximately over the knees. The tambour was light enough to ride up and down with the mother's respiratory movements, but heavy enough for the more sudden movements of the abdominal wall made to the kicks of the fetus to move the diaphragm before overcoming the inertia of the receiving tambour and thus communicate a pressure to the recording tambour. The unconditioned stimulus was a very loud sound resembling an explosion, whereas the conditioned stimulus was a mechanical vibration against the maternal abdomen at a point within the triangle formed by the three tambours. There is some reason to believe that conditioning took place under these circumstances, though the writer refrains from asserting this because of the failure of an attempted preliminary control experiment designed to establish the significant neutrality of the vibratory stimulus previous to the conditioning process.

Food-Taking Reactions of Newborn Infants. This problem has been investigated by Mrs. Marquis (1931). The subjects in the experimental group were eight newborn babies. For the first ten days of their lives these children received milk freshly pumped from their own mothers' breasts, but given them only from bottles, under experimental conditions. The feeding took place six times per day. On each occasion an electric buzzer was sounded for five seconds preceding the insertion of the nipple into the child's mouth, and again for five seconds after he had begun to suck. Occasionally the feeding was interrupted for a brief interval and the conditioning procedure just described was repeated in detail upon the resumption of the feeding. The more specifically feeding reactions displayed by these children were the opening of the mouth and sucking movements made by the lips and tongue. Both types of movements were recorded pneumatically by means of a balloon-type capsule fastened beneath the infant's chin, which communicated with a Marey recording tambour. It was found that seven of the eight infants developed definite conditioned food-taking reactions. The time of appearance of these reactions varied somewhat from subject to subject, but in general the conditioning process required only from three to six days. The conditioned mouth-opening reaction usually appeared about the fourth day, and the conditioned sucking movements usually appeared on the fifth day.

The Food-Taking Reactions of Children from Three to Six Years of Age. The experimental work in this field has been performed largely by Krasnogorski (1909, 1913, 1926), one of Pavlov's pupils, and later by Mateer (1918), in America. Krasnogorski took his point of departure from the salivary experiments of Pavlov. Since salivary fistulas could not be produced in children, he attempted to measure the amount of secretion indirectly by counting the movements made in the course of swallowing the accumulation. Later he placed the membrane of a Marey tambour over the thyroid cartilage on the throat, and in this way was able to secure automatic records both of the process of swallowing and of the characteristic anticipatory mouth opening. The unconditioned stimulus usually employed was the placing of chocolate or honey in the child's mouth. Various conditioned stimuli were used, such as the ringing of an electric bell, the sounding of a reed pipe, and the stroking of the skin with a brush. He experimented for the most part on children ranging from three to six years of age, but also reports results on younger children. In general, he found that children condition more readily with increasing age. He also made some observations on the phenomenon known as experimental extinction and on that known as conditioned inhibition.

Mateer, while taking her point of departure from the work of Krasnogorski, proceeded largely according to the clinical methods characteristic of American testing psychologists. She compared the conditionability and experimental extinction tendencies of normal and feebleminded children of different ages and intelligence quotients. She recorded the children's reactions in substantially the manner employed by Krasnogorski, but simplified the conditioning stimulus so that it became the mere pushing-down of the bandage over the child's eyes. Typical kymograph records showing the reaction of a normal child before conditioning and afterwards are reproduced in Figure 18. In general, Mateer confirmed Krasnogorski's findings that older children condition more readily than younger, up to about five years of age, and that normal children condition more readily than feebleminded children. With normals, conditioning took place within from three to nine trials. Seventy per cent of the normals retained the reaction for twenty-four hours. Experimental extinction tended to be more rapid among the older children, but much slower with the feebleminded.

Gastric Secretion. We have already referred above (p. 383) to Bidder

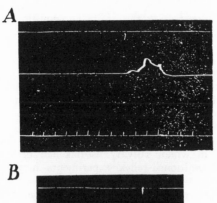

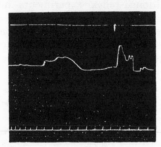

FIGURE 18
RECORDS OF THE FOOD-TAKING REACTIONS OF A 61-MONTHS-OLD GIRL

Record *A* shows the reaction of the child in the process of being fed; record *B*, the response at the third trial. The latter shows an anticipatory conditioned food-taking reaction previous to feeding, which is followed by the reaction when actually fed. The mark on the upper line shows the point at which feeding took place. The middle line records movements of chin and throat, and the lower line records time in seconds.

(From Mateer, 1918.)

and Schmidt's (1852) and Pavlov's (1910) observations on the psychic secretion of gastric juice in dogs. These conditionings appear in all cases to have been of spontaneous or accidental origin, resulting from the natural incidents associated with eating. Bogen (1907), however, reports a genuinely experimental gastric conditioning of a child. It seems that a boy three and one-half years of age developed a stenosis of the esophagus from accidentally drinking lye. In order to prevent starvation, a gastric fistula was produced through which food could be introduced directly into the stomach. This fistula permitted the observations of purely conditioned secretions. The psychic secretion observed by Bidder and Schmidt and by Pavlov was confirmed when the child was given a sham feeding of milk or meat. Following this, the attempt was made to condition the gastric secretion experimentally. On 40 occasions a trumpet was blown while the child was being fed. The trumpet was then blown on 10 occasions during which no food was given. Of the 10 latter trials, 7 are reported as having yielded an appreciable gastric secretion, thus demonstrating the arbitrary conditioning of this reaction.

Salivation. We have already sketched above the methods of conditioning salivary secretion which have been employed on dogs by Pavlov and his pupils. This constitutes a great portion of the studies in the conditioned-reflex field, and it is by means of these experiments, for the most part, that the fundamental laws of the conditioned reflex have been discovered (pp. 424 ff.). A number of attempts have been made, however, to condition the salivary reaction in man. Obviously, the surgical methods employed in dogs are impossible here. Two techniques have been used to escape this difficulty. It happens that a number of persons have been found in whom salivary fistulas had been produced by accidental means. Conditioned-reflex experiments may be carried out on such subjects by very much the same procedures as have been employed by the Pavlovian investigators with dogs. A second method was made available by Lashley's invention, in 1916, of the salivary suction disk (Figure 19). This consists of two concentric chambers (*A* and *B*), the

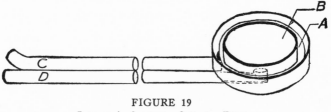

FIGURE 19
LASHLEY'S SALIVARY SUCTION DISK
For explanation see text.
(From Watson, 1924, p. 30.)

inner one of which is placed against the cheek over the opening of Stenson's duct where it pours the parotid secretion into the mouth. Suction is applied to tube *C*, which exhausts the air from the outer chamber (*A*), thus sealing the apparatus tightly to the cheek. The saliva then collects in chamber *B*, and ultimately passes out of the mouth and into the recording apparatus through tube *D*.

In general, the human salivary reaction has proved exceedingly difficult to condition. For example. Brunacci (1910) and Richter and Wada (1924) report complete failure to condition this response. Zebrowski (1905), however, reports some indications of an increased secretion when his subjects observed the food being brought to them. Glev and Mendelsohn (1915) also reported a secretion at the sight of food, but failed to secure evidence of a conditioned salivary reaction to an electric light and to a bell after 40 paired stimulations. Lashley (1916) observed a psychic secretion when his subject held candy in his hand, and an increased secretion when the food was brought near the mouth. Krasnogorski (1926) reports with juvenile subjects successful conditioning of this reaction to a bell, an electric light, and a metronome. Lastly, Winsor (1929), while able to elicit the naturally acquired psychic secretions resulting from the sight of food, reports a practical failure to establish arbitrary conditioned salivary reactions to either food or the injection into the mouth of two cc. of orange juice. Upon the whole, the indication appears to be that with the possible exception of the Achilles reflex (p. 395) the salivary reaction is one of the most difficult of all reflexes to condition in the adult human subject.

Vomiting. Among the complex phenomena which result from the injection of morphine in the dog is nausea with its prominent components of profuse salivation and vomiting which are followed by sleep if the dose is large enough. Pavlov (1927, p. 35) states that Krylov found with dogs, after five or six daily injections of morphine, that the mere sight of the experimenter opening the box containing the syringe or, if this failed, the preparation of the skin and the injection of some harmless fluid "were in themselves adequate to produce all these symptoms— nausea, secretion of saliva, vomiting, and sleep." Collins and Tatum (1925), incidental to a study of chronic morphinism in eight dogs and a cat, confirm the results of Krylov. Finally, the conditioning of this reaction was carried out by Kleitman and Crisler (1927) in an elaborate quantitative study. Their procedure was to place dogs in a stock for periods varying from 15 minutes to 2 hours, at the end of which time morphine was injected into the animal's back. Salivary secretions were collected from a simple fistula of the submaxillary ducts. In addition to showing profuse salivation, most of their animals at one time or another showed retching tendencies, together with actual vomiting, as soon as placed in the stock, i.e., *preceding* the injection of the morphine. These animals also showed marked panting reactions both before and after the injection. Several of the animals also occasionally showed distinct anticipatory tendencies to drowsiness and sleep.

Defecation and Urination. Bachrach and Morin (1932) report a successful attempt to condition the reflex of defecation in the kitten. The unconditioned stimulus was an enema of lukewarm water. The conditioned stimulus was a musical tone sounded on a reed pipe. The tone was sounded simultaneously with the entrance of the cannula and continued throughout the injection of the water. The conditioned reflex thus obtained is reported to have been weak and unstable.

No specific experimental attempt to condition the micturition reflex has been found, though certain observations seem to indicate very strongly that it could be conditioned without serious difficulty. It has long been a practice in hospitals where the nervous control of the sphincter of the bladder has been somewhat disturbed to aid the patient in voluntary urination by placing him near a tap of running water. The conditioning mechanism in this situation is obviously the association between the sound of splashing water and the act of urination throughout the preceding life of the patient.

Diuresis. Conditioned diuresis, or the secretion of urine, as distinguished from the voiding of it (micturition), has been investigated a number of times. Bykow and Alexejew-Berkmann (1930) employed as their unconditioned stimulus the rectal injection of water. They report in one investigation evidence of a conditioned diuresis after 15 injections, and in another investigation the same result after 16 injections. Grossman (1929) reports positive results after daily experiments for a week. Marx (1931*b*), however, repeated Bykow and Alexejew-Berkmann's experiment but failed to obtain any evidence of the conditioned diuresis after twenty injections.

In a second experiment (1931*a*) Marx attempted to condition diuresis in dogs by sounding a mouth organ, after which the dog was given a pan containing 400 cc. of a mixture of milk and water. The tone was sounded four times while the dog was drinking. Previous to this procedure the dogs were catheterized and three hours after their drinking they were again catheterized. On occasional experimental days the above procedure was varied by the single circumstance that the dogs were given no water whatever after the auditory stimulations, but were catheterized three hours later the same as usual. Of four dogs employed, three never showed any clear signs of conditioned diuresis. In a fourth dog, however, the conditioned diuresis suddenly appeared at the end of five months of continuous training followed by an interruption of three weeks, during which no experimentation took place. These results are summarized in Figure 20. The quantity of urine secreted under the conditioned-reflex

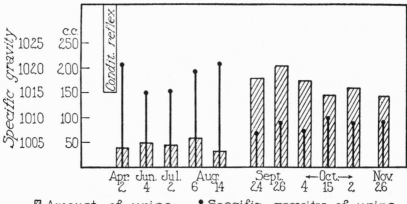

☒ Amount of urine   ↑ Specific gravity of urine

FIGURE 20

DIAGRAM SHOWING THE OUTPUT OF URINE OF A DOG TO A CONDITIONED STIMULUS
COMPLEX OVER A PERIOD OF MONTHS DURING WHICH THE TRAINING
WAS CONTINUED

The sudden rise at the sixth month followed a three weeks' interruption of the training. It is likely that this period of rest permitted the internal inhibition associated with the conditioning process, even when all stimulations are reinforced, to disappear. This hypothesis is supported by the fact that the yield on subsequent months gradually declined.

(From Marx, 1931*a*, p. 358.)

conditions was approximately the same as that obtained as the result of water-drinking in this dog.

Marx (1926) has reported another significant investigation which, while not specifically a conditioned-reflex experiment, probably reflects the results of spontaneous conditioning. It was suggested to subjects in the hypnotic state that they were drinking large quantities of water. The results indicated that under such conditions subjects show a change in their water metabolism substantially like that produced when water in large quantities has actually been drunk.

The experimental work in this field, while not entirely consistent, seems to indicate rather definitely that the secretional activity of the kidneys is susceptible to conditioning.

Defensive Blood Reactions Related to Immunity. Proceeding on the analogy of Pavlov's conditioned secretional experiments, a number of investigations have been made on the possibility of conditioning in a similar manner certain important defensive blood reactions related to immunity. The unconditioned stimuli in these experiments are various toxic substances, such as tetanus toxin, diphtheria antigen, cholera and typhoid bacteria (previously killed by heat), and serum from such animals as the horse, sheep, dog, cat, and man, which have been injected into the body of the organism. The defensive blood reactions vary more or less with the type of injection, but in general they are characterized by changes in the blood count, particularly an increase in the leucocytes, and in certain cases by significant agglutination reactions. The conditioned stimuli vary from the mere external incidents characteristic of the act of making the injection, such as was the case in the morphine experiment of Kleitman and Crisler (p. 411), to the administration of a specific stimulus such as the sound of a trumpet, the application to the ear or the abdomen of the animal of a metal plate heated to about 60° C., the scratching of the ear with a metal instrument, or the application of an electric shock.

This work appears to have been initiated in 1926 through an investigation by Metalnikov and Chorine, who reported the finding of conditioned internal defense reactions to such stimuli as scratching, heat, and sound. They report confirmation of their investigations by Vygodchikoff and Barykine and by Podkopaeff and Saatchian (1929). In successive articles, Metalnikov and Chorine (1928a, 1928b) report positive results from heated cholera cultures injected into the ear once a day for from 15 to 30 successive days in association with the sound of a trumpet or the scratching of the ear. Nicolau and Antinescu-Dimitriv (1929a, 1929b, 1929c) report positive results with the same general technique. While these studies sometimes contained efforts at control squads, the reports are so fragmentary and the controls usually so inadequate that they are not entirely convincing.

An excellent study by Ostrovskaya (1930) reports what appears to be a very well-controlled investigation, in which he gave to 43 guinea pigs peritoneal injections of boullion antigen every day for a period of three weeks. Associated with these injections were the application of heat to the skin with 27 animals, scratching of the skin with 7 animals, and electric stimulation to the ear with 9 animals. The leucocytic formula of the peritoneal exudate was determined before the injection and at various periods following. After a period of from 10 to 15 days of rest the conditioned stimulation alone was given and the exudate again examined as before. It was found that 67 per cent of the experimental group gave positive leucocytic reactions with the conditioned stimulus alone. A control group of 44 animals received the conditioned stimulus without their having had an opportunity for conditioning to be set up. Of these animals, 22 per cent showed the characteristic leucocytic defense reaction. These latter results indicate clearly that the conditioned stimuli were not really neutral at the beginning of the experiment. This naturally throws serious doubt on the outcome of previous investigations in this field. Ostrovskaya reports, however, that one of the conditioned stimuli (the scratching of the skin) proved itself to be very neutral in the control group, and it is largely upon this fact that he bases his continued belief in the genuineness of the conditioning tendency. He also carried out an experiment on the agglutination reaction in 10 rabbits, with which were run 11 control animals. Both groups yielded the agglutination reaction, though Ostrovskaya believes that the reaction to the conditioned stimulus in the experimental group was distinguishable as being more stable than that observed in the control group.

Ramon (1929) has attacked the specific immunity aspect of the above investigations on the basis of a series of experiments in horses which had been injected for many months with diphtheria antigen. This normally causes the animals to develop in their blood diphtheria antitoxin. It was found that these animals showed a marked diminution in this antitoxin when the injections of diphtheria antigen were replaced by systematic injections of tetanus toxin. Ramon argues that if the conditioning of immunity reaction could take place it would have done so during the repeated injections of diphtheria antigen and that the conditioned stimuli, consisting of the forceful means of restraint employed when the injections occurred, together with the prick of the needle of the syringe containing the diphtheria antigen, should have continued to evoke the generation of diphtheria antitoxin during the injection of tetanus toxin after the actual injection of diphtheria antigen had ceased.

One of the most convincing of the investigations in this field is that conducted by Smith and Salinger (1933). Their unconditioned reaction was the anaphylactic response to peritoneal injections of sera from various animals. Their experimental animals were guinea pigs. The conditioned stimulus employed by them in some cases was the application of heat to the ear of the animal, and in some cases the ringing of a very loud electric bell for one minute. The blood reaction which they investigated was the increase in the white blood cells that are susceptible to staining by eosin. The gross motor responses of the animals to the injections consisted of coughing, labored breathing, scratching of the nose

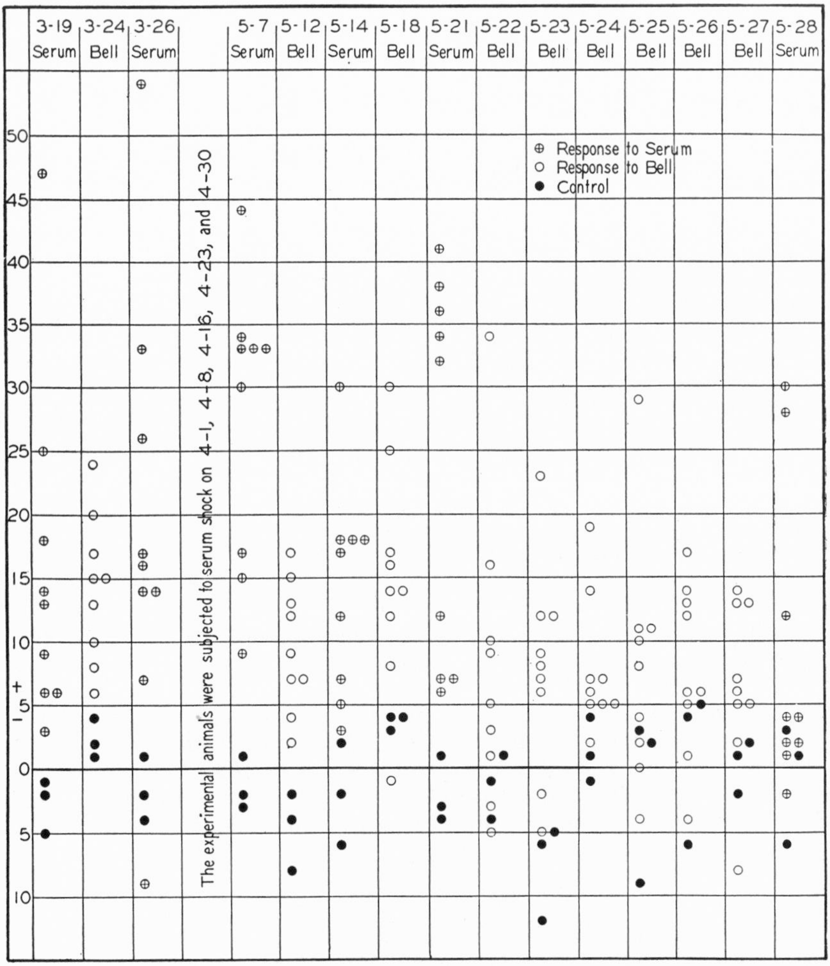

FIGURE 21

SMITH AND SALINGER'S CHART SHOWING THE PERCENTAGE OF INCREASE IN THE
NUMBER OF WHITE BLOOD CELLS OF THE TYPE WHICH STAIN WITH EOSIN
(EOSINOPHILS) 30 MINUTES AFTER (A) A PERITONEAL SERUM INJECTION
ACCOMPANIED BY THE RINGING OF A BELL AND (B) AFTER THE
RINGING OF THE BELL ALONE

It may be seen that the three control animals yield scores consistently near
zero, whereas the experimental animals as a group run consistently above zero,
on every bell-only stimulation, which indicates a positive conditioning of this
physiological defense reaction.

(Redrawn from Smith and Salinger, 1933.)

involuntary voiding, a ruffling of the hair on the back of the neck, and in some cases complete prostration.

In general, it was found that after repeated combinations of the conditioned stimulus with the injection the former alone would produce a form of external behavior strikingly resembling the behavior pattern characteristic of the injection itself, with the exception that the conditioned reaction manifested itself in fewer animals and in a distinctly slighter degree on those that did show it. There seems to be no question, however, about the genuineness of the conditioned motor reactions on those animals which showed it. Nevertheless these authors place their chief dependence on the blood reactions obtained from smears taken 30 minutes after the two types of stimulations. A typical group of nine experimental animals and three control animals will serve to illustrate their findings. The results from these animals are exhibited in the chart reproduced as Figure 21. An examination of this chart shows that, while not all the experimental animals showed the anaphylactic blood reaction, many of them showed this in a very marked degree and the experimental animals as a group are clearly distinguished from the control animals.

It must be admitted that there is still an appreciable degree of uncertainty in this field of conditioned-reflex experimentation. The evidence, however, appears to support the belief that certain leucocytic reactions and even agglutination reactions may easily be evoked in some animals by ordinary stimuli without any conditioning whatever, but that the leucocytic reaction, at least, may be markedly strengthened by association with an unconditioned physiological stimulus of great potency. Individual animals show marked differences in their susceptibility to this form of conditioning, though this type of idiosyncrasy has long been a commonplace of all kinds of conditioning and offers no obstacle to crediting the results of the experiments. Just what bearing these results may have upon the psychic nature of disease and immunity to disease in general remains to be seen.

STIMULI WHICH HAVE BEEN CONDITIONED

A great variety of stimuli in practically all sensory fields have proved themselves susceptible of conditioning. Among the visual stimuli which have been thus employed may be mentioned ordinary electric lights, colored lights, and series of gray papers. A variety of visually perceived figures such as ellipses and T-shaped objects (Pavlov, 1927, p. 134) have been utilized in discrimination experiments with dogs. A favorite visual stimulus in the Russian laboratories has been a "rotating object."

Many different sounds have been used as conditioned stimuli. Among these may be mentioned tones from tuning forks and oscillators of various frequencies yielding relatively pure tones (Pavlov, 1927; Anrep, 1920). Other laboratory sounds of varying pitch have been produced by Stern's tone-variator, whistles, reed pipes, organ pipes, trumpets, bells, and the piano. Among the less musical sounds which have been used are toy horns, automobile hooters, electric buzzers, bubbling water, and the ticking of metronomes set to beat at various rates. Lastly, there may be mentioned the conditioning by Hudgins (1933) of the specific words *contract* and *relax,* as spoken by the experimenter.

Among the tactual stimuli which have been employed are simple cutaneous contact, vibratory contacts, and stroking with a brush. Thermal stimuli of various degrees of heat and cold have frequently been employed by the Russians. The odors of vanilla and camphor have been occasionally used. Electric stimulation has usually been confined to induction shocks of various intensities.

By an ingenious experimental arrangement, Hudgins (1933) was able to condition the proprioceptive stimuli arising from the subject's own vocal apparatus in such a way as to evoke the hitherto non-voluntary constriction of the iris when the subject whispered certain words, and even when he merely spoke them to himself subvocally, or "thought" them. This experiment is of considerable significance because it probably lays bare the essential mechanism of what has been known to the classical psychologists as voluntary action, or will. This latter interpretation is perhaps strengthened by the fact that, according to Hudgins, reactions conditioned to such stimuli appear to be relatively immune to experimental extinction, one of the most conspicuous characteristics differentiating voluntary reactions from ordinary conditioned reflexes (see p. 401).

In addition to the above list of stimuli representative of the ordinary sensory fields, there may be mentioned a number of somewhat miscellaneous modes of stimulation which have proved to be susceptible of conditioning. Pavlov has shown (1927, p. 38) that changes in intensity of stimuli and the termination of stimuli (1929, p. 39) may be conditioned as well as the beginnings of stimuli. Moreover, Pavlov describes somewhat astonishing results in which specific time intervals appear to be the critical component of conditioned stimulus combinations (1927, p. 41). That time intervals as such may become conditioned has recently been confirmed in the writer's laboratory. Human subjects were stimulated by an electric induction shock on the tips of the fingers regularly every 38.5 seconds for 30 times, after which the stimulus was discontinued. A typical record of the outcome is shown in Figure 22. There it may be seen that, despite the interruption of the stimulus sequence, the galvanic reaction continued to take place ($X, Y,$ and Z) at about the proper interval for three times in succession.

Pavlov and his pupils have experimented rather extensively on the conditioning of temporal stimulus patterns with dogs. For example, on one occasion (1927, p. 146) Pavlov reports the conditioning of the salivary reaction to the stimulus sequence: a light flash, a cutaneous stimulation, and the sound of bubbling water, applied in the order named. The reaction was effectively differentiated from the same stimuli applied in a reverse sequence. A second stimulus pattern employed was a hissing sound, a high tone, a low tone, and a buzzer, in the order given; this was effectively differentiated from the presentation of the same stimuli

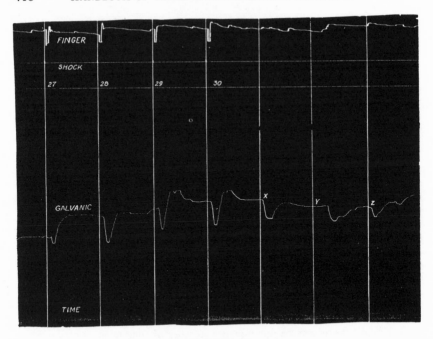

FIGURE 22

RECORD SHOWING TEMPORAL CONDITIONING

The tracing shows the reactions to the last four of 30 induction shocks
delivered at 38.5-second intervals. Conditioned galvanic reactions to the
temporal interval appear at X, Y, and Z. The vertical lines have been drawn
to show points of simultaneity on the several tracings.

in the order: hissing sound, low tone, high tone, and buzzer. Other
patterns of a simultaneous nature have also been conditioned, one of
the simplest being the presentation of a conditioned stimulus in conjunction with a second stimulus known as the conditioned inhibitor. It
was found that such a combination could be effectively differentiated by
dogs from the conditioned stimulus not so accompanied. There is
reason to believe that vigorous application of the principles involved in
the conditioning of compound stimuli both as stimulus complexes and
stimulus patterns (Hull, 1931, p. 500) may throw considerable light on
processes much higher in the scale of mammalian adjustment.

CONDITIONING AS A FUNCTION OF STIMULATION SEQUENCE

Temporal Contiguity of Conditioned and Unconditioned Stimuli.
The principle or "law" of contiguity has long been recognized by the
association psychologists. This principle is stated by Bain (see Warren,
1921, p. 107) as follows: "Actions, sensations, and states of feeling
occurring together or in close succession tend to grow together or cohere

in such a way that when any one of them is afterward presented to the mind the others are apt to be brought up in ideas." The relationship thus grasped from general observation has been subjected to precise experimental investigation on the strictly motor level by the workers in conditioned reflexes.

Formerly, Pavlov made the positive statement (1927, pp. 27 ff.) that conditioned reflexes could be established if the conditioned stimulus preceded the unconditioned stimulus (and the reaction) or was simultaneous with it, but not in case the unconditioned stimulus (and the reaction) preceded. It will be observed that the first sequence mentioned above is that according to which all reactions must function; in the actual performance of a conditioned reaction the conditioned stimulus must precede the response. For this reason this conditioning sequence is called *forward* conditioning. But when the conditioned stimulus follows the response to which it is to be conditioned, the sequence in the conditioning process is necessarily the reverse of the order of functioning. It has therefore come to be called *backward* conditioning. Pavlov's emphatic denial of the possibility of backward conditioning has led to a considerable amount of confusion. It is true that in this same work he has seemed in a later but rather obscure passage (1927, pp. 393 ff.) to retract this view. Moreover, he (1928, p. 381) stated explicitly in his Croonian lecture that conditioned reflexes may be set up when the unconditioned stimulus precedes the conditioned one, though even then he was of the opinion that in the resulting conditioning the reflexes were "insignificant and evanescent," and were associated with an excessive amount of internal inhibition (pp. 436 ff.). Unfortunately, this revised view has attracted much less attention than the earlier one (Evans, 1930, p. 340).

In 1929 Switzer attacked experimentally the problem of backward conditioning in man, employing the lid reflex as his major reacting mechanism and the knee-jerk and the galvanic skin reaction as collateral mechanisms. In the case of the eyelid reaction, the unconditioned stimulus was a sharp tap of a padded stick against the lower eyelid. This was delivered at periods of 2 seconds, 1 second, .75 second, and .5 second *preceding* the sound of a buzzer. Under these conditions all of the subjects at the three shortest intervals yielded at least three successive conditioned lid reactions, and two of the four subjects at 2 seconds yielded positive results. Many of the conditioned reflexes thus obtained proved to be sufficiently stable to resist the experimental extinction resulting from a number of successive unreinforced stimulations. This removed all question concerning the possibility of establishing relatively stable conditioned reflexes in a backward direction.

More recently two systematic investigations with human subjects of the relative readiness of conditioning as a function of the temporal relationships of the two stimuli (*a*) when the conditioned stimulus precedes, (*b*) when the two stimuli coincide in time, and (*c*) when the unconditioned stimulus precedes, have been reported by Wolfle (1930, 1932).

The first investigation is typical. The unconditioned reaction was the reflex withdrawal of the finger from a shock, and the conditioned stimulus was the sound of a buzzer. Ten subjects were tested with the stimuli given simultaneously and at each of the following intervals: where the unconditioned stimulus preceded the conditioned stimulus by .25 and .5 second (backward), and where the conditioned stimulus preceded the unconditioned one by .25, .5, .75, 1.0, 1.25, and 1.50 seconds (forward). The percentage of conditionings reported from each group of ten subjects is shown in Figure 23. This significant figure confirms definitely a number

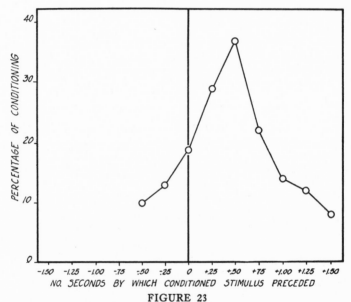

FIGURE 23

COMPOSITE GRAPH SHOWING THE RELATIVE CONDITIONABILITY OF REFLEX HAND WITHDRAWAL FROM SHOCK WHERE THE CONDITIONED STIMULUS PRECEDES AND FOLLOWS THE UNCONDITIONED STIMULUS BY VARIOUS INTERVALS

Note the marked gradient sloping each way from the optimal interval of +.5 second.

(After Wolfle, 1930.)

of observations (Hilgard, 1931; Schlosberg, 1928) indicating that the conditioned stimulus preceding the unconditioned one by about a half second is especially favorable for conditioning to take place. It is particularly noteworthy, however, that, in proportion as this optimal point is departed from in either direction, the facility of conditioning is progressively diminished. There is thus revealed a double gradient sloping downward from the optimal point in both the forward and backward directions. It will be surprising if these facts do not prove ultimately to have important implications for the understanding of the higher processes of learning and adjustment.

Delayed Conditioned Reflexes. In some cases the conditioned stimulus when given prior to the unconditioned one may be prolonged for seconds and even many minutes. The unconditioned stimulus is administered during the continuation of the conditioned stimulus, but near the end. (Figure 23A.) There is a tendency when the interval between the be-

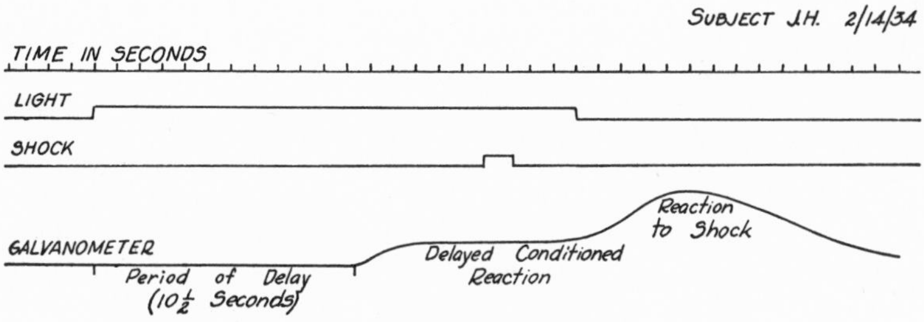

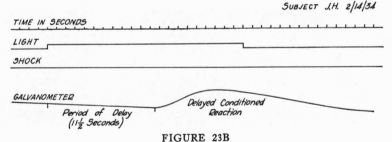

SUBJECT J.H. 2/14/34

FIGURE 23A

TRANSCRIPTION OF THE EXPERIMENTAL RECORD OF THE THIRTY-SIXTH REINFORCEMENT OF THE DELAYED CONDITIONED REFLEX OF SUBJECT J. H.
(Reproduced by permission of Dr. S. A. Switzer.)

ginning of the conditioned stimulus and the administration of the unconditioned stimulus is large for the conditioned reaction similarly to be delayed; that is, not to take place until an appreciable time after the beginning of the conditioned stimulus, but still some time before its termination. (Figure 23B.) Such reflexes are known as *delayed condi-*

SUBJECT J.H. 2/14/34

FIGURE 23B

TRANSCRIPTION OF THE EXPERIMENTAL RECORD OF AN UNREINFORCED CONDITIONED REACTION OF SUBJECT J. H. SHORTLY AFTER THE REINFORCEMENT SHOWN IN FIGURE 23A
(Reproduced by permission of Dr. S. A. Switzer.)

tioned reflexes. They have been studied to a considerable extent by the Russian reflexologists with the aid of canine subjects. One of the most significant claims emerging from this mass of investigation is that known as the "inhibition of delay" (p. 444). However, the specifically inhibitory characteristics of this period of delay have not yet been definitely proved.

Trace Conditioned Reflexes. In some cases instead of the conditioned stimulus' persisting until the unconditioned stimulus is delivered, as in the setting-up of delayed conditioned reflexes, the conditioned stimulus is terminated after a brief period and the interval between that and the administration of the unconditioned stimulus is filled with no particular stimulation. Under such circumstances it is possible to set up conditioned reflexes which do not take place until some considerable time after the termination of the conditioned stimulus. In such cases it is naturally assumed that the reaction is evoked not by the conditioned stimulus itself, because objectively that has long since ceased, but by some *trace* left by it. Therefore such conditioned reactions are known as *trace conditioned reflexes.* These reactions also have been studied to a considerable extent by the Russian reflexologists, and more recently in the United States.

Secondary Conditioned Reflexes. If a conditioned reflex has been established by the ordinary procedures of temporal contiguity it is possible to set up secondary conditioned reflexes without the new conditioned stimulus' ever being associated with the unconditioned stimulus, but merely with the original or primary conditioned stimulus (and its newly acquired reaction). A reaction tendency thus acquired is called a *second-order conditioned reflex.* An experiment on a human subject reported by Watson will serve to illustrate the process (Figure 24). A reflex withdrawal of the hand was conditioned to a bell by associating it with a shock. Then a light was given in conjunction with the bell (and the finger retraction) a number of times, after which the light was given alone. The light was then found also to have acquired the capacity to evoke a weak finger retraction. The reaction in question was accordingly a second-order conditioned reflex.

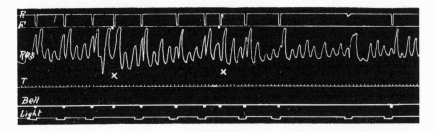

FIGURE 24

RECORD OF THE SETTING-UP OF A SECONDARY CONDITIONED REFLEX WITH A
HUMAN SUBJECT

R, finger reaction to shock; *F*, shock; *Res*, respiration; *T*, time. The conditioned reaction of finger withdrawal to a bell had previously been set up in the usual way. This record shows its transfer to a light by associating the light with the bell. In order to prevent experimental extinction of the primary conditioned reaction to the bell, this is reinforced by the shock at the two points marked with *X*. Near the end of the record the light is given alone and it evokes a weak finger reaction and a marked respiratory reaction. These constitute a secondary conditioned reflex.

(After Watson, 1916.)

Attempts were made repeatedly (1927, p. 34) in Pavlov's laboratory to establish still another transfer giving rise to a third-order conditioned reflex. This failed with the salivary reaction but succeeded in an experiment conducted by Dr. Foursikov employing a strong defensive motor reaction. The unconditioned stimulus in this case was a shock to the forepaw of a dog, which produced a defensive lifting of the foot. The primary conditioned stimulus was the mechanical stimulation of the skin of the hind paw. After repeated combinations of this pair of stimuli, the dog would react to the stimulation of the hind paw by a lifting of the front paw. This was the primary conditioned reflex. Next the sound of bubbling water was given in combination with the mechanical stimulation of the hind paw, after which the dog would lift his front paw to the sound of bubbling water. This was the second-order conditioned reflex. Finally, a tone of 760 double vibrations per second was given in combination with the sound of bubbling water, and the tone also acquired the capacity to evoke the lifting of the front paw. This was a third-order conditioned reflex. Dr. Foursikov, by appropriate reinforcement to prevent experimental extinction, endeavored for over a year to extend the series to a fourth-order conditioning, but entirely without success. It is significant that the latent period of these conditioned reflexes increased progressively from the first to the third order. Coincidentally there was a parallel weakening of the reaction itself.

From certain points of view the transfer of a reaction from one stimulus to another indefinitely appears to be characteristic of human voluntary reaction. For this reason the psychology of secondary conditioned reflexes is of special significance, particularly where human subjects are concerned. Unfortunately, little work involving the ordinary higher-order conditioning of human subjects appears to have been reported.

Shipley's Indirect Conditioning Technique. A procedure distinctly different from the above, but one which seems to bring about the same final results as the Pavlovian technique of secondary conditioning, has been developed by Shipley (1933). This resembles the one just described in that the conditioned stimulus which finally evokes the secondary conditioned reaction has never been associated with the unconditioned stimulus. It differs from the ordinary secondary-conditioning technique in that the conditioned stimulus *has never been associated with the reaction which it finally evokes.* One of Shipley's experiments will illustrate the point. He first associated a flash of light with a mechanical tap on the lower eyelid. This presumably served to set up a primary conditioned tendency for the flash to evoke the eyelid reaction. The next step was to associate the tap on the eyelid with a shock on the finger, which presumably established a primary conditioned tendency for the blow to evoke finger withdrawal. When these conditioning procedures had been accomplished the flash of light was given alone. It was found that 9 subjects out of 15, or 60 per cent, reacted with an involuntary finger withdrawal even though the flash had never been associated either with the shock or the finger retraction.

The Chain Conditioned Reflex of Miller and Konorski. A second type of conditioned reflex which appears to be in some sense a chain-reaction sequence has recently been investigated by Miller and Konorski (1928*a*, 1928*b*) and by Konorski and Miller (1930*a*, 1930*b*). A typical experimental arrangement is as follows: A stimulus (*A*), such as a note of a piano, will be followed by the lifting of the dog's front paw. The lifting of the paw may be brought about either by a reflex stimulation or by a passive movement on the part of the dog. In the latter case the paw is lifted mechanically. The complex of proprioceptive stimuli incidental to the lifting is called the stimulus (*B*). This is followed by what is called the *absolute stimulus* (*R*). The latter may be either the giving of food or some nocuous stimulus such as striking the animal or blowing into its ear. In the case where food is given (reward) it is found that after a number of repetitions the tone of the piano will cause both the lifting of the foot and the salivation, but in case of punishment the piano stimulus is not followed by the lifting of the foot. The promising suggestion is made by these authors that all possible stimuli may be divided into two classes on the basis of this criterion.

The above result, where the lifting of the foot was originally a genuine reflex retraction, appears rather clearly as a chain reflex. Both links of the chain were set up at practically the same time. This latter characteristic at once throws these results, superficially at least, into the form of sequential or rote learning. In addition to simple chaining there is the further indication of a possible development of a trace conditioned reflex (from the piano note to the salivary reaction) with the ultimate manifestation of remote excitatory tendencies such as were demonstrated by Ebbinghaus (1913). In cases where the lifting of the paw was a purely passive movement, however, the interpretation appears not to be so simple. Here, superficial appearances would seem to indicate kinship to serial reactions of the maze type with the typical food reward at the termination or goal. This latter circumstance, as is well known, serves in some way to fixate the stimulus-response relationships not only at the point of reinforcement but also, to a lesser degree, at points remote from the goal. The gradient of the fixation tendencies apparently follows a logarithmic law (Hull, 1932). These suggested relationships serve to indicate that the Miller-Konorksi conditioned reflex may offer distinct potentialities in the direction of a new and possibly more effective experimental approach to the problems of serial learning.

GENERAL CHARACTERISTICS OR PROPERTIES OF CONDITIONED REFLEXES

So far in this account we have been largely concerned with what stimuli and, particularly, what reactions may become joined by the conditioning process. We turn now to the still more important matter of the properties characteristic of conditioned reflexes in general.

The Rate-of-Acquisition Curve of Conditioned Reflexes. For a long time one of the fundamental questions concerning any learning process has been that of the shape of the curve of acquisition. Despite the great num-

ber of studies involving the establishment of conditioned reflexes, there
is as yet comparatively little evidence on this important matter. This is
because most conditioning procedures are able to measure the strength of
the conditioning tendency only on those occasions when the unconditioned
stimulus is omitted. This of necessity yields only fragmentary results
at best. Moreover, every test so made complicates and distorts the process to considerable but unknown degrees by injecting into it the irrelevant factor of periodic experimental extinction which necessarily results
from the conditioned stimulus' not receiving reinforcement. Fortunately,
there are available two investigations which do not suffer from this defect:
that of Kleitman and Crisler (1927), and that of Hilgard (1931).

Kleitman and Crisler's investigation has already been described (p. 411).
The conditioned reactions of their dogs were always anticipatory in nature, which permitted their being measured without interrupting the conditioning process. The records from four of their animals have been
judged sufficiently comparable to permit of their combination into an
equally weighted composite Vincent graph (Figure 25). It will be observed that this curve begins at a relatively slow rate, which is progressively
accelerated until about midway in the process, after which the rate of increase remains fairly constant. Ultimately, of course, there must gradually come in any such learning process a time when no more gain is possible, at which point the curve will become horizontal. Consequently,
we may be confident that these animals would have shown this effect had

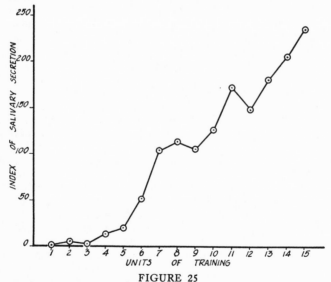

FIGURE 25

EQUALLY WEIGHTED COMPOSITE VINCENT CURVE OF THE ACQUISITION OF THE
SALIVARY REFLEX FROM FOUR DOGS
(Derived from published data of Kleitman and Crisler, 1927.)

the training been sufficiently protracted. This means that the curve of acquisition of this conditioned reaction, if complete, would present a distinctly S-shaped appearance.

Hilgard's technique and that of Hilgard and Marquis described above (pp. 389 ff.) also permit clear measurements of the progress of conditioning without interruption of the conditioning process. Hilgard (1933b) has published learning curves based on the conditioned lid reactions from two human subjects. Both subjects definitely confirm the existence of an initial period of positive acceleration shown by Kleitman and Crisler's salivary data. The failure of one of them to show the phase of negative acceleration is evidently due, just as was the case with Kleitman and Crisler's dogs, to the interruption of the process of training before it had reached its natural limit.

Finally, there may be added to this accumulation of evidence a recently published graph (Wendt, 1930, p. 43) of the rate of conditioning of the knee-jerk. This also shows unmistakable evidence of the initial period of positive acceleration.

It will be noted that the initial portion of conditioned-reflex acquisition curves differs radically from that of the conventional curves of learning often given in works on psychology (Perrin, 1932, p. 250), which begin with a maximal steepness and proceed by negative acceleration to approach a horizontal. There is some reason to believe, however, that curves of the latter type really represent only the final portions of the learning process—that in such cases the subject really comes to the experiment with a considerable portion of the activity already learned. On the other hand, it seems likely that the S-shaped curve is characteristic of a complete learning process. It has been shown in a number of experimental situations, notably by Thurstone (1919), Hull (1920), and Wolfle (1931), that complex and difficult learning processes characteristically begin with a period of positive acceleration exactly as manifested in the above graphs of conditioned-reflex learning and end with a period of negative acceleration. Kleitman and Crisler (1927) have emphasized the resemblance of this S-shaped curve to the curves characteristic of autocatalytic action.

Does the Conditioned Stimulus Tend To Lose Its Unconditioned Reaction as a Result of the Conditioning Process? The conditioning process is occasionally referred to by psychologists as a "substitution of stimuli." This expression tends to imply that the conditioned stimulus loses its unconditioned reaction in the process of acquiring the new conditioned reaction. Indeed, Razran (1930) has based a theory of the conditioning process in part on an explicit assumption of this principle. An experiment reported by Pavlov (1927, pp. 29 ff.) as having been performed by Dr. Eroféeva, illustrates and, apparently, furnishes the chief support for the view. The conditioned stimulus was a strong electric shock, and the unconditioned stimulus was the introduction of food into the dog's mouth. The shock naturally produced a vigorous defense motor reaction. It is said, however, that as the shock gradually acquired the conditioned capacity to evoke the salivary reaction the animals progressively lost the tendency to react defensively to the shock. Pavlov reports that even a minute examination of the pulse and respiration of these animals failed to show any trace of disturbance to these stimuli (1927, p. 30). He is of the opinion that "such a remarkable phenomenon is a result of diverting the nervous impulse from one physiological path to another."

Strong evidence of a contradictory nature exists, however. It is well known that the unconditioned reaction of the eyelid to a flash of light is a faint tremor. Hilgard (1931, p. 38) states that this tremor did not disappear with his human subjects when they acquired the major conditioned reaction of winking due to an association of the light with a loud noise. This tendency is clearly illustrated by the records reproduced in Figure 6 from the conditioned lid reaction of the dog by Hilgard and Marquis.

Lastly, there may be mentioned the conditioned–knee-jerk investigation of Wendt (1930), which was designed to yield an answer to this question. Here the conditioned stimulus was a blow on the left tendon, and the unconditioned reaction was a knee-jerk resulting from a blow on the right one. The results obtained do not furnish substantial support for Pavlov's view. It is true that one of Wendt's subjects late in the conditioning process showed a marked reduction in the amplitude of the unconditioned knee-jerk to the conditioned stimulus. This, however, was not correlated with the course of development of the conditioned response.

An examination of the results of Hudgins' investigation (Figures 13 and 14) possibly furnishes a clue to the solution of this apparent conflict of evidence. It will be recalled that in Hudgins' study the unconditioned reaction of the pupil to a bell is a dilation, whereas the unconditioned reaction to the flash is a constriction. It is evident that these two reactions are definitely in conflict, since the pupil cannot dilate at the same time it is constricting. Clearly, in the course of the conditioning process the constricting tendency must gradually override the opposing tendency. It is significant, however, that even after this has been accomplished the initial reaction to the bell stimulus is regularly a slight dilation which is at once followed by the dominant but more deliberate conditioned constriction. While the antagonistic nature of the defense reaction to a shock and the alimentary reaction to food is not so obvious as the two pupillary reactions involved in Hudgins' experiment, it seems highly probable that the mechanism may prove to be essentially the same. This would tend to account for the results of Dr. Eroféeva as being a special case rather than a universal tendency. As yet we lack sufficient critical evidence on this question from experiments based on pairs of non-antagonistic reactions. Until such data are available, final decisions must remain in abeyance.

Relative Strength of the Conditioned and Unconditioned Reactions. It is a matter of some theoretical importance to know whether the conditioned reaction may equal or exceed the strength of the unconditioned reaction from which it takes its rise. In order to secure a little light on this question we have assembled in Table 2 the results of the relevant

TABLE 2
THE RELATIVE MEAN AMPLITUDE OF THE CONDITIONED AND THE UNCONDITIONED
REACTIONS AS REPORTED IN A NUMBER OF INVESTIGATIONS
All are based on human subjects

Investigator	No. of subjects	Reaction conditioned	Unit of measurement	Strength preceding conditioning	Strength following conditioning	Strength of unconditioned reaction	Ratios of C.R. to U.C.R.
Switzer (1930)	9	wink	mm.	0 (+)	10.1	22.9	44%
Scott (1930)	8	finger retraction	1/50 inch	0	6.1	18.3	33%
Scott (1930)	7	respiratory amplitude	ratio preceding to following stimulation	.06	.41	.94	44% (—)
Scott (1930)	7	respiratory variability	ratio preceding to following stimulation	1.61	2.54	6.29	40% (—)
Hilgard (1931)*	5	wink	mm.	0 (+)	12.30	18.02	68%
Wendt (1930)*	1	knee-jerk	mm.	0	5.8	4.5	129%
Garvey (1933)	32	respiratory variability	oscillometer units	3.9	8.5	15.5	55%
Switzer (1933)	10	galvanic skin reaction	oscillometer units	minimal	24.9	38.3	65%

*Supplemented by a private communication.

investigations at present available. An examination of this table reveals the fact that in very few of these studies has the strength of the conditioned reaction closely approached that of the unconditioned reaction, though it indicates the probability that under certain circumstances the strength or amplitude of the former may even exceed that of the latter. The circumstances which favor such an outcome are not yet clear, though present indications are that they will prove to be rather complex.

It must be remembered, however, that since the strength of the conditioned reflex is a matter of gradual development it will not show its maximum vigor except at the limit of practice. A glance at Figure 25 shows very clearly that in that particular investigation, at least, the process of conditioning had by no means reached its maximum, since there is at the end of the training thus represented no marked evidence of the onset of the inevitable period of negative acceleration. Indeed, it is doubtful whether any of the investigations summarized in Table 2 carried the process to the limit of practice. The values there listed must, therefore, be regarded as a more or less extensive understatement of the possible limits of the strength to which conditioned reflexes may attain.

Relative Latencies of Conditioned and Unconditioned Reactions. In the early work of the reflexologists in Russia and the behaviorists in America there was a marked tendency to regard conditioned reflexes as reflex acts with merely the difference that they were evoked by stimuli originally unable to do so (Pavlov, 1927, p. 103). As careful and precise investigation has more fully revealed the facts, it has gradually become apparent that conditioned reflexes, while usually resembling rather closely the original reflexes from which they have taken their rise, actually differ more or less from these in various ways. One of the most clearly marked differences which has emerged is that of the relative latencies of the two types of reaction: the latency of the ordinary conditioned reaction is definitely longer than that of the unconditioned reaction. This is shown very clearly by the uniform agreement in this respect of the series of investigations summarized in Table 3. As a general thing, these investigations indicate that the latency of the ordinary conditioned reflex is approximately that of the voluntary performance of the act in question.

It should be observed, however, that the more careful scrutiny of conditioned responses which has been made possible by refinements in methods of recording motor reactions has brought to light indications that there may be more than one form of conditioned reflex, even where the same response mechanism is involved. In such cases the differential identification is made largely on the basis of the latency characteristic of each. Thus Wendt (1930) finds with the knee-jerk not only a conditioned reflex with a latency around 166σ, but also a second conditioned reflex of longer latency ranging around 280σ.[7] His evidence is especially con-

---

[7] It is significant that he also reports (1930) two fairly distinct types of voluntary reactions with latencies of approximately 171σ and 230σ respectively, previous to the conditioning process.

TABLE 3

THE RELATIVE LATENCY OF THE CONDITIONED AND UNCONDITIONED REACTIONS

All of these studies have employed human subjects.

Investigator	No. of subjects	Unconditioned stimulus		Conditioned stimulus		Conditioned reaction		Latency of voluntary reaction	Remarks
		Nature of stimulus	Latency of unconditioned reaction	Nature of stimulus	Latency of unconditioned reaction	Reaction	Latency		
Cason (1922b)	6	shock	126 σ ±	click	---	wink	172 σ	239 σ	About 50σ too large, measurements rough (Cason, 1923)
Hamel (1919)	4	shock	100 σ ±	touch on arm	---	finger re-traction	151-200σ	151-200 σ	Unconditioned value very rough
Schlosberg (1928)	3	blow on tendon	40 σ (?)	bell	---	knee-jerk	403 σ	443 σ	Very few measures
Hilgard (1931)*	1	loud sound	40 σ ±	light	110 σ	wink	110 σ	---	Type alpha (p. 431)
	1	loud sound	40 σ ±	light	110 σ	wink	164 σ	167 σ	Type beta (p. 431)
Wendt (1930)*	3	blow on right tendon	30-50 σ	blow on left, k-j right leg	166 σ	knee-jerk right leg	166 σ	171 σ	Type alpha (p. 431)
	1	blow on right tendon	30-50 σ	blow on left, k-j right leg	166 σ	knee-jerk right leg	280 σ	230 σ†	Type beta (p. 431)
Hudgins (1933)	2	light di-minished	200-500σ	bell	?	pupil di-lation	1560 σ	---	Unconditioned latencies taken from literature
	2	light in-creased	200-500σ	bell	?	pupil con-striction	2290 σ	---	

*These subjects were selected in conference with the author from a much larger number, on basis of general dependability of data.

†An estimate. A voluntary response appears to have a latency roughly proportional to the conditioned-reflex latency but not subject to precise measurement because preceded by the alpha-type response.

vincing since he occasionally finds these two reactions appearing one superposed on the other in a single record. Theoretically there should be a different conditioned reflex at each possible level of neural integration.

Some light as to the possible origin of the short-latency conditioned reflex may be afforded by Wendt's observation (Table 3) that a blow on the left tendon occasionally evokes a cross reflex kick of the right leg with a latency of about 166σ. Wendt believes that the conditioning process merely sensitized this reflex already in existence, making it more readily evokable. Hilgard has made a similar observation. One of his subjects, instead of acquiring the ordinary conditioned reaction of the lid to light, based on the reflex to sound with its characteristic long latency, tended rather to develop a greatly increased amplitude of his original short-latency unconditioned lid reaction to light (Figure 6). These observations suggest the likelihood that the conditioning process may result in conditioned reactions of at least two different types which, for the present, we may conveniently refer to as alpha and beta. Alpha may be used to designate conditioned reactions which are merely sensitizations or augmentations of the original unconditioned reaction of the conditioned stimulus; these will have relatively short reflex latencies. Beta will be used to designate the type which results from the acquisition by the conditioned stimulus of the power of evoking reactions at least functionally similar to that evoked by the unconditioned stimulus; this type will have a latency substantially that of ordinary voluntary reactions.

Qualitative Resemblance of the Conditioned to the Unconditioned Reaction. As frequently pointed out in a preceding section of this chapter, the conditioned reaction as a rule resembles very closely the unconditioned reaction. Indeed, in some situations such as those of salivary secretion, it is at present nearly or quite impossible to distinguish the two except for their relative strength and latency. The same tends more or less to be true in the case of various defense reactions such as those involving disturbances in the rhythm of breathing, pulse, the galvanic skin reaction, and certain physiological defense reactions related to immunity. On the other hand, closer and more minute examination has revealed in many cases appreciable differences and, in some cases, very large ones. For example, Shipley (1932) observed that in some subjects the conditioned plantar reaction showed a movement of the toes in the direction opposite that characteristic of the true plantar reflex. Hilgard (1931) and Wendt (1930) observed slight but fairly characteristic differences in the shape of the record made by the conditioned lid and knee-jerk respectively when carefully compared with records of the true reflex. It is rare, however, for the change in the reaction materially to affect the function originally performed by the reflex. This fact must not be lost sight of.

One of the most striking qualitative differences between the conditioned and the unconditioned reactions has been observed by Upton (1929) and by Wever (1930) in conditioning to pure tones of high pitch the breathing response to shocks in the guinea pig and the cat respectively. The tone in both these experiments was given for at least five seconds, at the end of which time the shock was delivered.   Upton observed that, instead of the animal's giving at the beginning of the tone the sharp inspiration characteristic of the shock, there was a remarkable smoothing-out of the normally somewhat uneven respiration.   Protracted training, however, ultimately resulted in the conditioning, apparently, of the *termination* of the tone to the true reflex inspiration.   But this reaction was always preceded by the very smooth and even breathing already mentioned (Figure 26).   Wever's work with cats seems never to have gotten beyond the

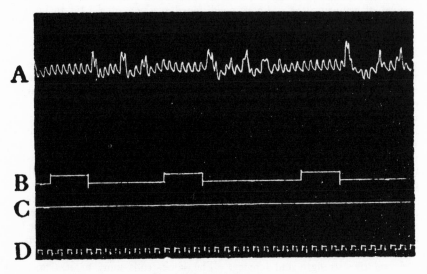

FIGURE 26

RECORD SHOWING A CONDITIONED REACTION IN THE GUINEA PIG TO A TONE

A, respiration; *B*, tone presented during the high portions of this line; *C*, record of electrical stimulation (none given in this record) ; *D*, time intervals in seconds. The reactions to the tone are (1) a smoothing-out of the otherwise irregular breathing during the continuation of the tone, which is followed by (2) an inspiration of relatively wide amplitude at the tonal termination.
(From Upton, 1929, p. 419.)

stage of preliminary inhibition of breathing disturbances, which with his animals took the somewhat different form of a rapid "flutter."

Wever calls attention to the resemblance of his flutter reaction to a similar response observed in animals when the central end of the vagus nerve is stimulated artificially (Howell, 1927, p. 703).   It is conceivable that this action of the vagus nerve may really have been involved in the unconditioned reaction, but as a minor component which was overridden and masked by the more vigorous tendency to deep, sharp inspirations, and that this component for some unknown reason chanced to be more susceptible of conditioning than the more conspicuous inspiration.   Such differential ease of conditioning for the several components of an unconditioned reaction has frequently been reported. Thus Marquis and Sears observed the abdominal reflex to be composed of two fairly distinct components (p. 395). They succeeded in conditioning one of these but not the other. Similar differences as regards component reactions and their conditioning were also observed by Shipley.

Differences between Conditioned and Unconditioned Reflexes in Their Conduction Paths in the Spinal Cord. Some light on the differences between conditioned and unconditioned reflexes sketched above is furnished by the neurological investigation performed by Lang and Olmsted (1923). These writers conditioned to the sound of a buzzer the reflex lifting of the left hind leg in dogs. The unconditioned stimulus was a painful induction shock. They then performed a hemisection of the spinal cord at the level of the first lumbar vertebra on the side opposite the trained leg. This resulted in a complete abolition of the foot-lifting component of the conditioned reflex, though the respiratory component remained. Training on the reflex was then resumed with the result that the animal reacquired the conditioned tendency, though this required protracted training and the latent period of the reestablished reflex was much longer than that of the original conditioned reaction. This reestablished conditioned reflex was abolished by a second hemisection of the cord on the side opposite the trained leg, but several segments nearer the brain than the first.

It was found, however, when a conditioned reflex to sound was set up in which the unconditioned stimulus was the pressure produced by the pulling of a cord attached to the leg, that the conditioned reflex did *not* disappear even after both low and high hemisection of the cord. Lang and Olmsted account for this superficial discrepancy between the two experiments on the ground that owing to the difference in the path of the fibers for pain and pressure the hemisection of the cord, as performed, severed the former but not the latter. They conclude that the whole neural mechanism must be complete; that is, the pathways for both sets of stimuli (the conditioned and the unconditioned) must be intact for the conditioned reflex to take place.

Anticipatory Characteristics of the Conditioned Reaction. It will be recalled (p. 388) that in Anrep's experiment the salivary reaction took place in advance of the giving of food. It may also be recalled (pp. 390 ff.) that in the investigation of Hilgard and Marquis, after conditioning had taken place, the winking reaction of the dog was definitely anticipatory in nature. The puff of air against the right eyeball may be regarded essentially as an injurious stimulus. The conditioned lid closure as shown in record *B,* Figure 6 anticipates the blast of air in such a way that the lid is closed at least 135 thousandths of a second before the impact of the air takes place, thus completely protecting the eyeball. The frequency with which examples of anticipatory reaction are encountered in the conditioned-reflex literature indicates that it is a fundamental physiological tendency.

The biological significance of this primitive adaptive mechanism thus effectively demonstrated can hardly be overestimated (Hull, 1929). In the violent struggle for existence pictured by organic evolution it is not difficult to understand that those animals which responded by flight and other defense reactions in *advance* of injury would be far more likely to escape and hence would have immensely greater chance of survival and ultimate reproduction than would animals which did not possess such a tendency. There thus stands revealed an automatic neural mechanism possessing a function quite as obvious as those of the hand or the eye, and probably of far greater significance to the organism. Moreover, there is reason to believe that the mechanism is also basic in the functioning of the higher mental processes, e.g., in a great variety of anticipatory and short-circuiting reactions (Hull, 1930*b*).

The Retention of Conditioned Reflexes. No systematic study of the retention of conditioned reflexes appears to have been made. There are, however, scattered through the literature occasional references to the subject. Pavlov, for example, has emphasized the relative permanency of conditioned reflexes which have been thoroughly established. Watson remarks that his human subjects usually retained their conditioned reflexes at least 24 hours, though occasionally a single reinforcement was required to resuscitate them. Mateer (1918, p. 202) found that 70 per cent of unselected children retained conditioned food-taking reactions for a period of 24 hours. Jones (1931) reports that infants retained a conditioned galvanic reaction for as much as seven weeks. Switzer (1933) reports with an adult subject an exceedingly vigorous conditioned galvanic reaction after 16 days. While no investigation comparing the relative retention of conditioned reflexes with other forms of learning has been made, the incidental observations so far reported seem to indicate no very obvious differences. There is great need for a reliable study of the curve of forgetting of conditioned reactions.

Summation. It has long been recognized that, if two stimuli are each independently able to evoke the same reflex act, both stimuli when applied simultaneously will usually evoke a stronger reaction than that produced by either stimulus alone. This tendency is known as *summation*. Sometimes this physiological summation amounts to less than the arithmetical total of the two stimuli acting separately, but occasionally it amounts to more. Recently Sherrington (1931) has indicated the characteristic conditions under which one of the two above outcomes is likely to take place. Examples of true reflex summation of an act extensively studied from the point of view of conditioning are given as the last two entries at the bottom of Table 4. There it may be seen that five of Hilgard's subjects showed a mean reflex lid movement of .1 millimeter to a light stimulus, and of 1.4 millimeters to a sound stimulus, which make up an arithmetical total of 1.5 millimeters. When both stimuli are delivered in such a way as to evoke simultaneous reactions, the physiological summation amounts to 5.3 millimeters, a value decidedly in excess of the arithmetical total of the two acting separately.

It is our task here to inquire whether conditioned reflexes operate according to the principles known to hold for true reflexes. In general, the

TABLE 4

SUMMARY OF VARIOUS STUDIES INVOLVING THE SUMMATION OF CONDITIONED REFLEXES, AND, FOR PURPOSES OF COMPARISON, THAT OF UNCONDITIONED REFLEXES AND OF CONDITIONED WITH UNCONDITIONED REFLEXES

Author	Organism	No. of subjects	Nature of reaction	Unit of measurement	Native or acquired	Stimulus	Strength alone	Arithmetical total	Physiological summation
Pavlov (1927)	dog	1	salivation	drops	conditioned conditioned	tone rotating object	21 23	44	32
Evans (1930)	dog	1	salivation	drops	conditioned conditioned	odor of camphor electrical stimulation	60 30	90	90
Garvey (1932b)	man	8	breathing finger retraction	oscillometer units % positive reaction	conditioned conditioned	buzzer vibrator buzzer vibrator	1.63 2.38 12.5 25.0	4.01 37.5	15.94 81.3
Wendt (1930)	man	1	knee-jerk	mm.	conditioned unconditioned	blow on left tendon blow on right tendon	2.7 2.3	5.0	10.0
Hilgard (1933a)	man	1	lid closure	mm.	conditioned unconditioned	light sound	6.6 8.6	15.2	20.0
Hilgard (1933a)	man	5	lid closure	mm.	unconditioned unconditioned	light sound	1.9 25.0	26.9	31.6
	man	5	lid closure	mm.	unconditioned unconditioned	light sound	.1 1.4	1.5	5.3

answer is definitely in the affirmative. Perhaps Garvey's (1933) investigation with human subjects will serve as well as any to illustrate this point. The breathing disturbances from receiving an electric shock were conditioned separately to a buzzer and to a vibration applied to the skin. The buzzer alone yielded 1.63 units of respiratory disturbance, and the vibrator yielded 2.38 units, the arithmetical total of the two being 4.01 (Table 4). When both stimuli were applied simultaneously, however, there resulted a physiological summation amounting to 15.94 oscillometer units, a value greatly in excess of a simple arithmetical total of the independent effects. Entirely similar results were observed with the same subjects when their conditioned finger retractions were examined.

There remains the further question of whether conditioned reactions summate with unconditioned reactions (true reflexes). Table 4 shows two investigations bearing on this question—one by Wendt and one by Hilgard. Both investigations show definite positive outcomes in excess of the simple arithmetical summation.

The evidence is accordingly quite clear that conditioned reflexes manifest the phenomenon of physiological summation and frequently to a degree in excess of an arithmetical summation.

External Inhibition. One of the most conspicuous characteristics of conditioned reflexes is their extreme susceptibility to what is known as external inhibition. Conditioned reflexes even when well established and of long standing are very likely to become greatly weakened or to disappear entirely at the intrusion of any "extra" stimulus, that is, one to which the animal has not been accustomed in the experimental situation. Thus Pavlov reports (1927, p. 45) the frequent inability of his students to demonstrate to him a newly established conditioned reflex, because his presence constituted an extra stimulus which produced an external inhibition of the conditioned reaction. Evans (1930, p. 350) gives a quantitative example of the same tendency. A phonograph record was played for a few seconds at about the time a conditioned salivary stimulus was applied to a dog. This resulted in a drop of the conditioned reaction from 100 per cent to 10 per cent. This phenomenon has constituted a serious difficulty in the conduct of conditioned-reflex experiments, at least with dogs. Among other things, it practically forced the Russians to construct special stimulus-proof laboratories in order to avoid the intrusion of extra stimuli.

It is important to observe that external inhibition operates on negative as well as positive excitatory tendencies; it will accordingly be considered again in connection with inhibitions of the extinctive variety (pp. 440 ff.).

Extinctive Inhibition and Spontaneous Recovery. Probably the most significant work of Pavlov and his school has been the experimental delineation of the phenomena which he calls *internal inhibition.* One of the most conspicuous and important forms of internal inhibition appears as the result of the process known as *experimental extinction.* This consists merely of the presentation of the conditioned stimulus on successive occasions with the omission of the application of the unconditioned stimulus. The process may be illustrated by two cases of experimental extinction re-

TABLE 5
Two Typical Experimental-Extinction Series from Pavlov's Laboratory
(From Pavlov, 1927, pp. 49 and 55.)

Successive unreinforced stimulations	Alimentary salivation conditioned to a metronome		Acid salivation conditioned to tactile (weakly), to metronome (medium), and to buzzer (strongly)	
	Stimulus	No. of drops	Stimulus	No. of drops
1	metronome	10	metronome	13
2	"	7	"	7
3	"	8	"	5
4	"	5	"	6
5	"	7*	"	3
6	"	4	"	2.5
7	"	3	"	0
8			"	0
9			tactile	0
10			metronome	0
11			buzzer	2.5

*Professor Pavlov entered the laboratory at this stimulation, causing disinhibition.

ported in some detail by Pavlov, and summarized in Table 5. In the first case a metronome was associated with the giving of food, and in the second three different stimuli were independently associated with the giving of acid. The reactions of the dogs in both cases show a rapid and fairly

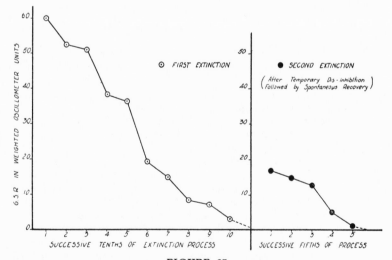

FIGURE 27
Equally Weighted Composite Vincent Graphs of the Curve of Experimental Extinction from Ten Subjects

The curve at the left represents the extinction at once after establishment; that at the right, the extinction after a spontaneous recovery from the first extinction. (From Switzer, 1933.)

progressive decrement in the strength of response until it entirely disappears.

This process readily lends itself to quantitative investigation. Some of the more important studies, in addition to those of the Russians, have been reported by Kleitman and Crisler (1927), Switzer (1930, 1933), and Hudgins (1933). These investigations reveal two fairly distinct types of curves. Perhaps the most common is that reported by Switzer and reproduced as Figure 27. This is an equally weighted composite Vincent graph based on a rather protracted experimental-extinction series from ten subjects. The conditioned stimulus was a faint light, and the activity measured was the galvanic skin reaction originally caused by an electric shock. This type of curve usually shows a fairly steep fall at the beginning, which gradually approaches the horizontal as complete extinction is approximated.

The second type of experimental-extinction curve was first reported by Switzer in 1930. Since that time, similar observations have been made by Scott (1930), by Hudgins (1933), and by Hilgard and Marquis in an as yet unpublished study.[8] This second type of experimental-extinction curve is well illustrated by the pair of composite graphs plotted from Hudgins' data and reproduced as Figure 28. It may be seen that this curve rises sharply at the outset for one or two stimulations, after which it proceeds to fall rather steeply and then more gradually as it approaches zero, exactly like the more usual curve of extinction. As yet the experimental conditions which bring about these two types of curve have not been determined.

Curves of experimental extinction must not be confused with curves of forgetting, as has sometimes been done (Kleitman and Crisler, 1927). The two are clearly distinguished by the fact that if the organism in which experimental extinction has been produced is left alone for a time and then tested it will usually be found that the reaction has again become active. This important characteristic is known as *spontaneous recovery*. Apparently, in some cases, particularly with very thoroughly established conditioned reflexes, this spontaneous recovery may be complete (Pavlov, 1927, p. 58). With only moderately well-established reactions, however, the recovery is likely to be incomplete and the extinction process on successive occasions usually becomes more and more rapid (Pavlov, 1927, p. 61). A concrete illustration of both the incompleteness of recovery and the more prompt extinction on the second occasion is shown on the right-hand portion of Switzer's composite graph (Figure 28).

Pavlov (1927, p. 57) has called attention to the extremely significant fact that, if the presentation of the conditioned stimulus is continued after it has ceased to yield any detectable response, the extinction process still goes on as a "silent extinction" below or beyond zero. Since salivation cannot directly yield a negative value, Pavlov was forced to resort to indirect means in proving the reality of this sub-zero extinction. One

---

[8]By permission of the investigators.

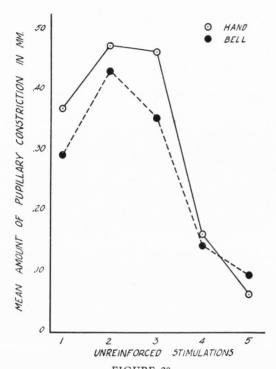

FIGURE 28

COMPOSITE GRAPHS SHOWING THE PROGRESS OF EXPERIMENTAL EXTINCTION OF THE
CONDITIONED CONSTRICTION OF THE HUMAN IRIS

Each graph represents independent extinctions from eight subjects.
(Plotted from data published by Hudgins, 1933.)

typical bit of evidence adduced is that, where the conditioned stimulus
is presented repeatedly after it has ceased to evoke a reaction, the time
required for spontaneous recovery is lengthened (1927, p. 58). Garvey
(1933), however, has reported some direct experimental results which appear to support Pavlov's thesis. Human subjects were stimulated by a
buzzer and a cutaneous vibrator for 30 successive times. The variability
of the respiration was measured (p. 402) for the five breaths preceding
and following the stimulus, and the reaction score was the former subtracted from the latter. The mean differences for six subjects in groups
of five stimulations were as follows:

$$+2.7, \qquad +.9, \qquad +1.7, \qquad +1.0, \qquad 0.0, \qquad -2.6$$

Here the adaptation process seems to have declined progressively with
continued stimulation, passed through the zero on the fifth group of
stimuli, and into a negative phase on the sixth. These results, while

suggestive, are in need of confirmation from experiments based on other processes capable of yielding direct negative values.

Hudgins has made a novel observation in this connection. Three of his subjects (pp. 399 ff.) were given an experimental-extinction series of 21 stimulations. The conditioned stimulations were verbalizations as given by the experimenter and the same words when spoken by the subjects. In no case was there any sign whatever of a diminished reaction throughout the extinction series. Indeed, there was some indication of an increased vigor of reaction. It is possible that we have in these results a distinctly significant phenomenon, whether the resistance to experimental extinction was the result of the nature of the stimuli, or whether due to the fact that the conditioning had been more protracted than usual. These observations are greatly in need of verification. See Steckle and Renshaw (1934).

Finally, it must be emphasized that experimental extinction, while troublesome to the experimentalist working in this field, must not be regarded as a failure or defect in the learning process but rather as in the highest degree an adaptive learning reaction. The primary or positive conditioning mechanism, as we have had ample occasion to observe in the preceding pages, appears to be an almost totally indiscriminate process; any stimulus which impinges on the organism shortly before the impact of a strong unconditioned stimulus tends to acquire the capacity to evoke a functional equivalent of the unconditioned reaction. Naturally, many such stimulus-combinations must take place in the life-history of every organism by purely fortuitous associations of conditioned with unconditioned stimuli. Such tendencies to the evocation of conditioned reactions must, for the most part, be maladaptive. The mechanism of experimental extinction thus furnishes an absolutely necessary corrective to a wholly indiscriminate primary tendency to excitatory conditioning. The basic conditioning process may thus be regarded as a primary physiological adaptive mechanism of absolutely vital importance, and the tendency to experimental extinction may be considered as a secondary or corrective mechanism to eliminate those fortuitously acquired proclivities to action which are useless.

Disinhibition. We have seen above (p. 436) that the intrusion of an extra stimulus into a conditioned-reflex situation will usually weaken or completely abolish the conditioned reaction. We must now point out that such an extra stimulus applied to the organism after the setting-up of an extinctive inhibition also disrupts the inhibition. There is this difference, however, between the two situations: The complete external inhibition of the conditioned reflex leaves no reaction whatever, whereas the complete external inhibition of an extinctive inhibition tendency leaves the positive or excitatory tendency, upon which the extinctive inhibition was based, at substantially its original strength.

The phenomenon of disinhibition is illustrated in an excellent manner by one of Pavlov's tables (1927, p. 65), which is reproduced as Table 6. In this experiment the dog had two fistulas, one from the submaxillary and one from the parotid gland. Both gave entirely concordant results.

TABLE 6

A TABLE SUMMARIZING DR. ZAVADSKY'S EXPERIMENT ILLUSTRATING BOTH SIMUL-
TANEOUS AND PERSEVERATIVE DISINHIBITION

(From Pavlov, 1927, p. 65.)

Time	Stimulus applied during one minute	Amount of saliva in drops during one minute	
		From submaxillary gland	From parotid gland
1:53 P.M.	Meat powder presented at a distance	11	7
1:58 "	" " " " " "	4	2
2:3 "	" " " " " "	0	0
2:8 "	Same + tactile stimulation of skin	3	1
2:13 "	Same + knocks under the table	2	1
2:18 "	Meat powder at a distance	0	0
2:20 "	Prof. Pavlov enters the room containing the dog, talks, and stays for two minutes.		
2:23 "	Meat powder at a distance	5	2
2:28 "	Same	0	0

NOTE. Previous to this experiment it had been repeatedly shown that neither the tactile nor the auditory stimulus, nor the entry of Professor Pavlov into the experimental room, produced any secretory effect at all.

The first three stimulations were not reinforced and produced an extremely rapid experimental extinction. At the fourth trial, however, the presentation of the meat powder was accompanied by an "extra" stimulus in the form of a tactile stimulation of the skin. Three drops of saliva are secreted, which indicates that the inhibition is partly abolished. Five minutes later the meat powder is again presented, this time accompanied by knocks under the table. Disinhibition is again manifested by a secretion of two drops. After five minutes the meat powder is presented alone; the zero reaction indicates that the extinctive inhibition has returned.

The reactions just considered are cases of simultaneous disinhibition. Disinhibition, however, shows the additional characteristic of a tendency to *perseveration,* or *after-effect.* The entrance of Professor Pavlov into the experimental room for two minutes (Table 6) served as an obvious external inhibition. One minute after he had left, the meat powder was presented at a distance and it evoked the conditioned reaction of five drops; this illustrates the perseveration effect. Five minutes after this, however, the same stimulus produces no reaction, which shows that the perseveration was distinctly limited.

Rapid oscillation of the reaction as just described naturally raises a certain degree of skepticism concerning its interpretation, particularly since Pavlov and his pupils do not publish detailed results, but only present samples such as that shown in Table 6. Obviously, it should be possible to choose samples which would illustrate almost any conceivable hypothesis. Such tables serve as illustrations rather than proof. For this reason an extremely careful and systematic investigation of this question recently performed by Switzer (1933) has special relevance. In this connection it is important to observe that a complete proof of the principle of disinhibition involves no less than seven distinct steps, as follows:

1. The conditioned stimulus must be tested at the outset to establish its substantial neutrality so far as the reaction being investigated is concerned.

2. The conditioned reflex must be established.

3. The conditioned reflex so established must undergo extinctive inhibition.

4. An extra stimulus must be introduced.

5. The conditioned stimulus when applied soon after must show a definite recovery of its capacity to evoke the conditioned reaction.

6. After a quiet period of some minutes the application of the conditioned stimulus should again have lost its excitatory power.

7. After a period of some hours the application of the conditioned stimulus must, through the power of spontaneous recovery, have regained its excitatory capacity in order to show that the excitatory tendency really existed at point 6, but failed to evoke its reaction because of the reappearance of the inhibition originally set up by the extinction.

Switzer's experiment conformed to these requirements in a rather elaborate manner. The conditioned stimulus was a faint light; the unconditioned stimulus was a shock on the finger; the response recorded was the galvanic skin reaction; and the extra or disinhibiting stimulus was a buzzer. Ten subjects were carried through this routine, and all of them showed clear indications of the genuineness of the principle of disinhibition. The results of the investigation as a whole are shown by Switzer's diagram reproduced as Figure 29. Between columns 2 and 3, the conditioned galvanic reaction had been extinguished to zero, but after the giving of the extra stimulus (buzzer) the reaction rose to 16.59 oscillometer units, only to sink to 1.93 (column 4) within three or four minutes. Some hours later, however, spontaneous recovery brought it up to 7.30 (column 5). When this in its turn had suffered extinctive inhibition, the extra or disinhibiting stimulus (buzzer) was applied once more and the reaction rose to a height of 7.57 (column 6), which was higher than it was prior to the second extinctive inhibition. Three minutes later, however, the inhibition had returned, as shown by the insignificant reaction of 1.27 (column 7).

Conditioned Inhibition. To superficial observation, extinctive inhibition appears to be merely the loss of an excitatory tendency, much the same as happens in ordinary forgetting through the lapse of time. This is by no means the case. Instead, internal inhibition is a definitely active tendency. Because of its essentially hidden nature this does not become manifest except by special experimental means. Quite possibly this is the reason it has so long passed unnoticed in the psychology of the higher learning processes.

One of the most convincing evidences that extinctive inhibition, for example, is a living though negative force is furnished by the fact that it may be conditioned like any positive excitatory tendency. Consider the following example taken from Pavlov: A rotating object, the flash of a

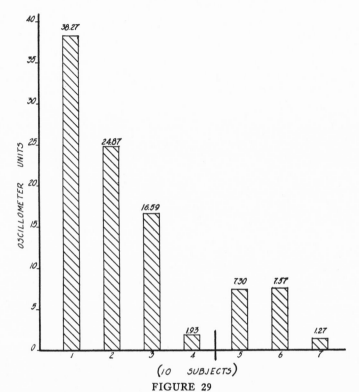

FIGURE 29

COMPOSITE COLUMN DIAGRAM SHOWING MEAN GSR OF EXPERIMENTAL GROUP AT VARIOUS STAGES IN EXPERIMENTAL PROCEDURE

1, mean of last three unconditioned responses to shock preceded by light
2, mean of first three conditioned responses to light
3, mean of first three responses to light after disinhibition by buzzer following experimental extinction (27 tests)
4, mean of first three responses to light following average delay of 198 seconds
5, mean of first three conditioned responses to light after spontaneous recovery periods varying from 3.5 hours to 16 days
6, mean of first three conditioned responses to light after disinhibition following second experimental extinction (23 tests)
7, mean of first three responses to light following average delay of 184 seconds
(From Switzer, 1933, p. 92.)

lamp, and the tone from a tuning fork were each conditioned independently to the alimentary salivary reaction, the first normally yielding 16 drops of saliva in one minute, and the second, 17. Next the rotating object was given a good many times in conjunction with a tactile stimulus, but without reinforcement. In such a combination the tactile stimulus is known as the *conditioned inhibitor*. This combination naturally suffered extinctive inhibition, though the rotating object (which meanwhile was oc-

casionally reinforced) retained its strength. After the above preparation, the tactile stimulus was given in conjunction with the flash of the
lamp. Its dynamic negativism is shown by the fact that under these
conditions the flash of the lamp yielded a secretion of only 2 drops in one
minute. It has also been shown that the negative power of the conditioned
inhibitor applied in combination with another stimulus, as above, will persist in such a way as to inhibit a reaction occurring some minutes later.
Even when the conditioned inhibitor is given by itself it produces an
appreciable inhibitory after-effect.

Perhaps a still more convincing evidence of the dynamic negativism of
internal inhibition is found in the fact (Pavlov, 1927, p. 107) that the
conditioning of internal inhibition may be carried even to the second order.
The experiment to demonstrate this may be set up as follows: Two
alimentary conditioned reactions may be established independently, one,
say, to a rotating object and the other to a flash of light. Then the rotating object may be subjected to extinctive inhibition. Next the sound of a
metronome, which has previously proved itself entirely neutral and so
incapable of producing external inhibition, is given in conjunction with
the extinguished rotating object a number of times. Now, if at this
juncture the second conditioned stimulus (the flash of light) is presented
alone it may produce 7 drops of saliva in 30 seconds. But if it is presented
in conjunction with the previously neutral metronome the yield may be
only 2 drops, thus showing that the metronome has acquired inhibitory
characteristics.

The Inhibition of Delay. In connection with the development of delayed conditioned reflexes and trace conditioned reflexes (pp. 421 ff.) the
extremely important phenomenon of inhibition of delay has been observed.
If, for example, a tactile stimulus is delivered continuously for four minutes and at the end of three minutes acid is placed in the dog's mouth,
there will in time develop a delayed conditioned reflex, the characteristic
phenomenon consisting of the fact that the reaction does not normally begin
for some time after the onset of the stimulus. Thus in one experiment
reported by Pavlov (1927, p. 93) the salivary secretions during successive
half minutes after the beginning of the tactile stimulus were:

$$0, \qquad 0, \qquad 0, \qquad 5, \qquad 11, \qquad 13.$$

It is our concern here to point out that the failure of the reaction to take
place during the first three periods suggests the presence of internal inhibition. The evidence for this, as usual in this field, must be indirect.
One method of proof is to test it for disinhibition by accompanying the
tactile stimulus by an external inhibiting stimulus in the shape of a metronome sound. When that was done the following secretions were obtained
at half-minute intervals:

$$4, \qquad 7, \qquad 7, \qquad 3, \qquad 5, \qquad 9.$$

That this disinhibition was temporary, as is usually the case, is shown by
the fact that 15 minutes later the tactile stimulus alone gave the reaction:

$$0, \qquad 0, \qquad 0, \qquad 3, \qquad 12, \qquad 14.$$

Sleep. Pavlov (1927) and his associates frequently observed that in the setting-up of delayed and trace conditioned reflexes the animals had a strong tendency to fall asleep. In some cases the dog would begin sleeping almost on the instant of the delivery of the conditioned stimulus and would sleep throughout the period of delay, but would awake at the point when the reaction took place. Pavlov also believes that inhibitions spread in such a way as occasionally to involve the reactions of all parts of the body. This, in conjunction with the above observations, led him to a characteristic theory of sleep. He states in substance that sleep results from a profound degree of irradiation of internal inhibition. This is in harmony with the observations of numerous investigators that true reflexes such as the knee-jerk either disappear entirely or are greatly weakened during sleep (Bass, 1931).

Hypnosis. As a kind of corollary to his theory of sleep, Pavlov (1927) has put forward an hypothesis concerning the nature of hypnosis. This is in substance that hypnosis is fragmentary sleep resulting from a partial irradiation of inhibition from some central source. Bass (1931), however, has produced evidence which indicates that Pavlov's conjecture in this case is distinctly less promising than has been his hypothesis concerning sleep. Bass showed experimentally that the knee-jerk and voluntary reaction to signals, both of which either disappear or are greatly weakened during sleep, show a behavior during hypnosis hardly, if at all, distinguishable from that of the waking condition. It accordingly seems in this instance that Pavlov's hypothesis is incorrect.

Generalization, Irradiation, and Differential Inhibition. When conditioned reflexes are in the process of being established to a stimulus such as a particular tone, or to a touch on a particular spot, there is a marked tendency for all other tones and for touches on all other places on the skin of the organism to evoke the reaction. This appears to be especially characteristic of trace reflexes, where the generalization is so profound as to spread even from one sense field to another. An example of the cutaneous irradiation of a conditioned reflex in a dog studied by Anrep (1923) is as follows: He set up an alimentary conditioned salivary reflex to a spot on the left thigh of the dog, which yielded on the average 53 drops of saliva in 30 seconds. He then tested out systematically five other places at progressive steps distant from the point originally conditioned, and obtained mean secretions of 45, 39, 23, 21, and 19 drops respectively. Anrep also reports a similar spread of conditioned inhibition.

Pavlov believes that irradiation is not only characterized by a spatial gradient as just described, but that the spread has fairly marked temporal characteristics as well. A great deal of space is devoted to the elaboration of this principle in his major work (1927). Loucks (1933) has made a careful examination of a great part of the Russian experimental evidence regarding these alleged gradients and is of the opinion that it is far from conclusive.

Recently, however, an American experiment on human subjects in which the galvanic skin reaction was employed seems to have demonstrated in an unambiguous manner the alleged phenomenon of an irradiation gradient on the skin, both for excitation and for inhibition. The subject lay completely nude on a cot, as shown in Figure 30. Four practically

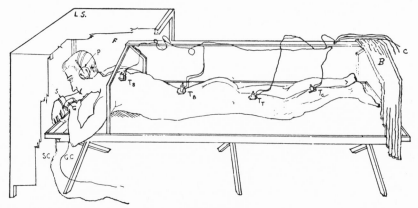

FIGURE 30

DIAGRAMMATIC REPRESENTATION OF THE SUBJECT'S IMMEDIATE ENVIRONMENT, THE BLANKET (B) WHICH COVERED THE FRAMEWORK (F) AND A PORTION OF THE BOX-LIKE LIGHT SCREEN ($L.S.$) BEING REMOVED TO REVEAL THE INTERIOR

P, one of the two ear phones used to produce a sound screen; S, the strap binding the silver electrodes used to deliver shocks to the subject's right wrist; $S.C.$, conductor for shock current; G, the strap binding the silver electrodes used to take off the electric current from the left hand; $G. C.$, conductor of the skin E.M.F.; T_S, T_B, T_T, and T_C, vibratory tactual stimulators; C, conductors supplying the vibratory-tactual stimulators.

(From Bass and Hull, 1934.)

silent vibratory tactual stimulators were placed at intervals along the left side of the body, as may be seen. In the excitatory-irradiation experiment, one stimulus, e.g., that on the shoulder, would be conditioned to a shock delivered to the wrist. After this conditioned reaction had been set up it was found that not only the shoulder stimulus would evoke the galvanic skin reaction characteristic of the shock but all the other stimulators would do so as well and with an intensity diminishing with the remoteness from the point specifically conditioned. In the inhibitory-irradiation experiment the substance of the technique was to condition all four points to the shock and then submit one, e.g., that on the shoulder, to a partial experimental extinction, and measure the magnitude of the responses evoked by stimulating each of the four points impartially. It was found that the point specifically extinguished showed the weakest reaction and the other points progressively weakened reactions, according to their proximity to the inhibited point, exactly in accordance with the claims of the reflexologists. Bass and Hull's graph representing the inhibitory gradient is reproduced as Figure 31.

It is important to observe that the tendency to generalization is of

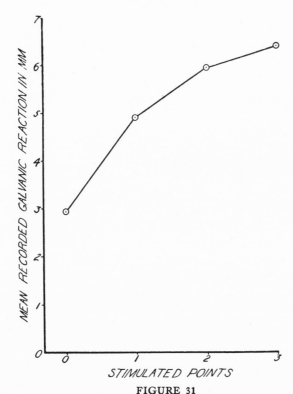

FIGURE 31

COMPOSITE GRAPH SHOWING GRADIENT OF IRRADIATION OR GENERALIZATION OF THE
EXTINCTIVE INHIBITION OF A TACTILE GALVANIC SKIN REACTION IN MAN
Zero is the point inhibited (see Figure 30). Each point represents the mean from
256 measurements, 32 from each of eight male subjects.
(From Bass and Hull, 1934.)

primary importance in biological economy, since without it organisms would
need to undergo separate conditioning in order to react to every slightest
variation in the conditioned stimuli which, strictly speaking, are never
exactly alike on any two occasions. On the other hand, many situations
really demand a restriction on the range of the reaction. Here once more
the mechanism of extinctive inhibition enters as a corrective agency; those
situations which are not followed by reinforcement gradually develop an
inhibition while the related stimuli which are reinforced continue at full
strength. The inhibition thus produced is known as *differential inhibition*.

Some Applications of the Conditioned Reflex. One of the most extensive
applications of the conditioned reflex has been in the determination of the
sensory capacity of the lower organisms. A second method of determining
sensory capacity of animals has been that of choice reaction. In this con-

nection a controversy took place between Anrep (1920) and Johnson (1913) as to whether dogs could discriminate pure tones, the former using the conditioned-reflex technique and the latter the choice reaction. The outcome of the controversy in the main was a rather strong indication that the conditioned reflex is a distinctly more precise instrument for the determination of sensory thresholds with animals than is the choice reaction.

Until recently the interpretation of the conditioned-reflex thresholds determined on lower organisms has been hampered because their relation to the thresholds determined by ordinary psychophysical judgments was not known. This uncertainty has been cleared up by a careful experimental study by Newhall and Sears (1933). The absolute threshold for light was determined on seven subjects, both by the conditioned-reflex method and by the ordinary method of verbal report. The reaction employed was the finger retraction to an induction shock. The two methods were found to yield substantially equivalent results.

A second wide application of the conditioned reflex, because it offers a precise method of determining the sensory capacity of the lower organisms, has taken place in the investigation of the effects produced by experimental destruction of various portions of the nervous system. An extensive literature is being developed in this field (Pavlov, 1927, p. 320) but it lies outside the scope of the present account.

A third application of the conditioned reflex concerns the so-called higher mental processes. In this connection there have been two points of view: One hypothesis prominent in the earlier behavioristic literature (Watson, 1924) conceives reflexes as the basic units from which all adaptive behavior is built. They are supposed to be organized into chain sequences by the principle of conditioning. Recent work by Coghill (1929) on the young of lower organisms and extensive work of others on human infants seems to make this hypothesis less and less likely of ultimate verification.

A second hypothesis concerning the relationship of the conditioned reflex to the higher adaptive processes conceives the former as a comparatively simple type of learning which, through its simplicity, enables the basic learning mechanisms to be laid bare with relative ease. A brilliant example of such an outcome is seen in the discovery of the complex phenomena of internal inhibition. According to this hypothesis, internal inhibition with its various and complex characteristics should be found present, though hidden as usual, in ordinary habits (Hull, 1930a, 1931).

A concrete illustration may serve to make this point clear. In order to test the hypothesis, the writer (1934) ran albino rats in a 42-foot straight alley in which the speed of running of each successive 5-foot section could be accurately determined. It was found that if a slight sound was made the animals slowed their pace markedly, which agrees perfectly with the principle of external inhibition (Pavlov, 1910). It was also found that when the food reward was taken away these animals ran progressively more slowly, thus manifesting a weakening of the excitatory tendency, which is exactly what would be expected on the principle of experimental extinction. A period of 24 hours, however, regularly produced an almost complete recovery of speed of running, which is precisely what one would deduce from the principle of spontaneous recovery. Moreover, there was evidence that each destruction of the running-tendency took place more promptly than the preceding one, which again conforms to expectation on the hypothesis that the same principles are operative in ordinary habit structures as in conditioned reactions. By the same hypothesis, if a disturbing sound should be given just before the animals are released from the starting-box when in a state of experimental extinction, they should temporarily recover much of their previous speed, though within a few minutes they should revert to their former state of inhibition. Some preliminary attempts have been made by the author to test this expectation, but they have yielded only ambiguous and inconclusive results.

A special hypothesis concerning internal inhibition has been put forward by Lepley (1932). The substance of this lies in an identification of the trace conditioned reaction with the remote excitatory tendencies shown to exist in rote learning by Ebbinghaus (1913) and more recently by Hall (1928). If this identification is true in any important sense, two alleged characteristics of trace conditioned reflexes should be found operative in rote series: (*a*) the reactions should tend, under a number of distinct circumstances, to appear at greater or less distances in advance of the point of reinforcement (Switzer, 1934), and (*b*) the internal inhibition which is supposed somehow to occupy the period of delay should tend to weaken all reactions which occur within this interval (Pavlov, 1927, pp. 173 ff.). From these principles, in conjunction with conditions characteristic of rote series, it is possible to deduce and, in this sense, genuinely integrate and explain a considerable number of rote-learning phenomena which have hitherto appeared to be quite unrelated (Hull, 1935*a*). Out of a score of such deductions which have been made to date, there is fairly good evidence in support of seventeen, there is as yet no available evidence regarding two, and one deduction appears to be definitely opposed by the evidence.

In conclusion it may be pointed out that it is in connection with the application of principles discoverable in conditioned-reaction experiments to the interpretation of more complex behavioral processes that conditioned-reaction investigations such as have been discussed in the foregoing pages are likely to have their greatest significance. Two concrete segments of such a development have been alluded to in the immediately preceding paragraphs. Similar studies have been made in the field of simple trial-and-error learning (Hull, 1930*a*), the maze learning of rats (Hull, 1932, 1934*a*), the locomotor behavior of young children in the face of obstacles, extensively studied by Lewin and his pupils (Hull, 1935*b*), and a form of insight involving the assembly for concrete problem solution of habit segments never previously used in that particular combination (Hull, 1935*c*). There is reason to believe that parallel developments will presently take place in the fields of learning the school subjects and educational psychology generally, of social psychology, of moral behavior and delinquency, of psychoanalysis and the whole field of psychogenic disorders, of the theory of empirical knowledge, of the more complex forms of systematic symbolic behavior including various forms of insight, thought, and reasoning—in short, wherever in human or animal behavior habits play a significant rôle.

To a very large extent, what has passed for theory among the classical psychologists has really been metaphysics in the sense that the principles have not been of such a nature as to yield concrete deductions which might be submitted to critical experimental test.   Even today, despite universal agreement that untestable hypotheses have no place in truly scientific theory, dogmas essentially metaphysical in this sense continue to be put forward in the name of science and to be widely accepted; thus do the misfortunes of its metaphysical origin continue to afflict the science of behavior.   In contrast to this, the attempts at theoretical systematization of mammalian behavior which are evolving from principles discovered in conditioned-reflex experimentation take as their aim the development of a structure of scientific theory analogous to that of quantum mechanics in modern physics—an aggregate of unambiguous principles from which may be deduced numbers of novel phenomena which, in turn, will be ruthlessly subjected to experimental trial at the earliest opportunity.   Whether such a development will prove possible in the field of mammalian behavior on the basis of conditioned-reaction and related principles, or indeed of any principles whatever, time alone can tell.   Meanwhile the criterion of success of this program is of such a nature that it applies equally to any and all systems, however diverse, which seriously aspire to a scientific status, and they should all alike be judged on this rigorous basis by students of behavior.

BIBLIOGRAPHY

ANREP, G. V. 1919-20. Pitch discrimination in the dog. *J. Physiol.*, **53**, 367-385.
————. 1923. Irradiation of conditioned reflexes. *Proc. Roy. Soc. London*, **94B**, 404-426.
ARISTOTLE. De anima. Book II, Chap. 12; Book III, Chaps. 2-4.
BACHRACH, M., & MORIN, G. 1932. Un nouveau réflexe acquis (conditionnel) de la vie végétative. *C. r. Acad. des sci.*, **194**, 746.
BASS, M. J. 1931. Differentiation of the hypnotic trance from normal sleep. *J. Exper. Psychol.*, **14**, 382-399.
BASS, M. J., & HULL, C. L. 1934. The irradiation of a tactile conditioned reflex in man. *J. Comp. Psychol.*, **17**, 47-66.
BECHTEREV, V. 1913. La psychologie objektive. (Trans. by N. Kostyleff.) Paris: Alcan. Pp. iii+473.
————. 1926. Allgemeine Grundlagen der Reflexologie des Menschen. (Trans. from the 3rd Russian ed. by M. Pappenheim.) Leipzig & Vienna: Deuticke. Pp. xviii+436.
BIDDER, F., & SCHMIDT, C. 1852. Die Verdauungssäfte und der Stoffwechsel. (Eine physiologischchemische Untersuchung.) Mitau & Leipzig: Reyher. Pp. 413.
BOGEN, H. 1907. Experimentelle Untersuchungen über psychische und assoziative Magensaftsekretion beim Menschen. *Pflüg. Arch. f. d. ges. Physiol.*, **117**, 150-160.

BRUNACCI, B. 1910. Sulle funzione secretoria della parotid nell'uoma. *Arch. di fisiol.,* **8**, 421-457.

BYKOW, K. M., & ALEXEJEW-BERKMANN, I. A. 1930. Die Ausbildung bedingter Reflexe auf Harnausscheidung. *Pflüg. Arch. f. d. ges. Physiol.,* **224**, 710-721.

CASON, H. 1922a. The conditioned pupillary reaction. *J. Exper. Psychol.,* **5**, 108-146.

———. 1922b. The conditioned eyelid reaction. *J. Exper. Psychol.,* **5**, 153-196.

———. 1923. A note on the conditioned eyelid reaction. *J. Exper. Psychol.,* **6**, 82-83.

COGHILL, G. E. 1929. Anatomy and the problem of behavior. New York: Macmillan; Cambridge, England: Univ. Press. Pp. xii+113.

COLLINS, K. H., & TATUM, A. L. 1925. A conditioned salivary reflex established by chronic morphine poisoning. *Amer. J. Physiol.,* **74**, 14-15.

CORNIL, L., & GOLDENFOUN, Z. 1930. Réflexes conditionnels ou réflexes associatifs? *Encéph.,* **25**, 391-394.

CYTOVITCH, I. S., & FOLKMAN, N. F. 1917. Pléthysmographie, comme méthode d'enregistrement des réflexes conditionnels chez l'homme. *C. r. Soc. de biol.,* **80**, 762-764.

DODGE, R. 1926. A pendulum-photochronograph. *J. Exper. Psychol.,* **9**, 155-161.

EBBINGHAUS, H. 1913. Memory: a contribution to experimental psychology. (Trans. by H. A. Ruger and C. E. Bussenius.) (*Columbia Univ., Teach. Coll., Educ. Reprints,* No. 3.) New York: Teach. Coll., Columbia Univ. Pp. xiii+123.

EVANS, C. L. 1930. Recent advances in physiology. (4th ed.) Philadelphia: Blakiston's. Pp. xii+446.

FREEMAN, G. L. 1930. The galvanic phenomenon and conditioned response. *J. Gen. Psychol.,* **3**, 529-539.

GARVEY, C. R. 1932a. The difficulty of conditioning the Achilles reflex. *Psychol. Bull.,* **29**, 555.

———. 1932b. Conditioned respiratory changes. *Psychol. Bull.,* **29**, 676-677.

———. 1933. A study of conditioned respiratory changes. *J. Exper. Psychol.,* **16**, 471-503.

GLEY, E., & MENDELSOHN, M. 1915. Quelques expériences sur les réflexe salivaire conditionnel chez l'homme. *C. r. Soc. de biol.,* **78**, 646-649.

GOLLA, F. L. 1921. The objective study of neurosis. *Lancet,* **2**, 215-221.

GROSSMAN, W. 1929. Diurese als bedingter Reflex beim Hunde. *Klin. Woch.,* **8**, 1500.

GUTHRIE, E. R. 1930. Conditioning as a principle of learning. *Psychol. Rev.,* **37**, 412-428.

HALL, M. E. 1928. Remote associative tendencies in serial learning. *J. Exper. Psychol.,* **11**, 65-76.

HAMEL, J. A. 1919. A study and analysis of the conditioned reflex. *Psychol. Monog.,* **27**, No. 118. Pp. 65.

HILGARD, E. R. 1931. Conditioned eyelid reactions to a light stimulus based on the reflex wink to sound. *Psychol. Monog.,* **41**, No. 184. Pp. 50.

———. 1933a. Reinforcement and inhibition of eyelid reflexes. *J. Gen. Psychol.,* **8**, 85-113.

———. 1933b. Modification of reflexes and conditioned reactions. *J. Gen. Psychol.,* **9**, 210-215.

HOWELL, W. H. 1927. A text-book of physiology. (10th ed.) Philadelphia: Saunders. Pp. 1081.

HUDGINS, C. V. 1933. Conditioning and the voluntary control of the pupillary light reflex. *J. Gen. Psychol.*, **8**, 3-51.

HULL, C. L. 1920. Quantitative aspects of the evolution of concepts. *Psychol. Monog.*, **28**, No. 123. Pp. 85.

————. 1929a. An instrument for summating the oscillations of a line. *J. Exper. Psychol.*, **12**, 359-361.

————. 1929b. A functional interpretation of the conditioned reflex. *Psychol. Rev.*, **36**, 498-511.

————. 1930a. Simple trial-and-error learning: a study in psychological theory. *Psychol. Rev.*, **37**, 241-256.

————. 1930b. Knowledge and purpose as habit mechanisms. *Psychol. Rev.*, **37**, 511-525.

————. 1931. Goal attraction and directing ideas conceived as habit phenomena. *Psychol. Rev.*, **38**, 487-506.

————. 1932. The goal gradient hypothesis and maze learning. *Psychol. Rev.*, **39**, 25-43.

————. 1934a. The concept of the habit-family hierarchy and maze learning. *Psychol. Rev.*, **41**, 33-54, 134-152.

————. 1934b. The rat's speed-of-locomotion gradient in the approach to food. *J. Comp. Psychol.*, 1934, **17**, 393-422.

————. 1935a. The trace conditioned reflex and serial learning. (To appear.)

————. 1935b. Some implications of the goal gradient and the habit-family hypothesis for the behavior of young children. (To appear.)

————. 1935c. The mechanism of the assembly of behavior segments in novel combinations suitable for problem solution. (To appear.)

JOHNSON, H. M. 1913. Audition and habit formation in the dog. *Behav. Monog.*, **2**, No. 8. Pp. iv+78.

JONES, H. E. 1928. Conditioned psychogalvanic responses in infants. *Psychol. Bull.*, **25**, 183-184.

————. 1930. The retention of conditioned emotional reactions in infancy. *J. Genet. Psychol.*, **37**, 485-498.

KLEITMAN, N., & CRISLER, G. 1927. A quantitative study of the salivary conditioned reflex. *Amer. J. Physiol.*, **79**, 571-614.

KONORSKI, J., & MILLER, S. 1930a. Méthode d'examen de l'analysateur moteur par les réactions salivo-motrices. *C. r. Soc. de biol.*, **104**, 907-910.

————. 1930b. L'influence des excitateurs absolus et conditionnels sur les réflexes conditionnels de l'analysateur. *C. r. Soc. de. biol.*, **104**, 911-913.

KRASNOGORSKI, N. 1909. Über die Bedingungsreflexe im Kindesalter. *Jahrb. f. Kinderhk.*, **69**, 1-24.

————. 1913. Über die Grundmechanismen der Arbeit in der Grosshirnrinde bei Kindern. *Jahrb. f. Kinderhk.*, **78**, 373-398.

————. 1926. Die letzten Fortschritte in der Methodik der Erforschung der bedingten Reflexe in Kindern. *Jahrb. f. Kinderhk.*, **114**, 256-269.

LANG, J. M., & OLMSTED, J. M. D. 1923. Conditioned reflexes and pathways in the spinal cord. *Amer. J. Physiol.*, **65**, 603-611.

LASHLEY, K. S. 1916a. Reflex secretion of the human parotid gland. *J. Exper. Psychol.*, **1**, 461-493.

————. 1916b. The human salivary reflex and its use in psychology. *Psychol. Rev.*, **23**, 446-464.

LEPLEY, W. M. 1932. A theory of serial learning and forgetting based upon conditioned reflex principles. *Psychol. Rev.*, **39**, 279-288.

LIDDELL, H. S., & ANDERSON, O. D. 1928 Certain characteristics of formation of conditioned reflexes in sheep. *Proc. Soc. Exper. Biol. & Med.*, **26**, 81-82.

————. 1931. A comparative study of the conditioned motor reflex in the rabbit, sheep, goat, and pig. *Amer. J. Physiol.*, **97**, 539.

LOCKE, J. 1690. An essay concerning human understanding. London: Basset. Pp. 362.

LOUCKS, R. B. 1933. An appraisal of Pavlov's systematization of behavior from the experimental standpoint. *J. Comp. Psychol.*, **15**, 1-45.

MARQUIS, D. P. 1931. Can conditioned responses be established in the newborn infant? *J. Genet. Psychol.*, **39**, 479-492.

MARX, H. 1926. Untersuchungen über den Wasserhaushalt: II. Mitteilung die psychische Beeinflussung des Wasserhaushaltes. *Klin. Woch.*, **5**, 92-94.

————. 1931*a*. Diuresis by conditioned reflex. *Amer. J. Physiol.*, **96**, 356-362.

————. 1931*b*. Diurese durch bedingten Reflex. *Klin. Woch.*, **10**, 64-67.

MATEER, F. 1918. Child behavior. Boston: Badger. Pp. v+239.

METALNIKOV, S., & CHORINE, V. 1926. Rôle des réflexes conditionnels dans l'immunité. *Ann. de Instit. Pasteur*, **40**, 893-900.

————. 1928*a*. Étude sur le rôle des réflexes conditionnels dans l'immunité. *Zsch. f. Immunitätsforsch.*, **57**, 326-336.

————. 1928*b*. Rôle des réflexes conditionnels dans la formation des anticorps. *C. r. Soc. de biol.*, **99**, 142-145.

MILLER, S., & KONORSKI, J. 1928*a*. Sur une forme particulière des réflexes conditionnels. *C. r. Soc. de biol.*, **99**, 1155-1157.

————. 1928*b*. Le phénomène de la généralisation motrice. *C. r. Soc. de biol.*, **99**, 1158.

NEWHALL, S. M., & SEARS, R. R. 1933. Conditioned finger retraction to visual stimuli near the absolute threshold. *Comp. Psychol. Monog.*, **9**, No. 43. Pp. 25.

NICOLAU, I., & ANTINESCU-DIMITRIV, O. 1929*a*. Rôle des réflexes conditionnels dans la formation des anticorps. *C. r. Soc. de biol.*, **102**, 133-134.

————. 1929*b*. Réflexe conditionnel et formule leucocytaire. *C. r. Soc. de biol.*, **102**, 135-136.

————. 1929*c*. L'influence des réflexes conditionnels sur l'exsudat péritonéal. *C. r. Soc. de biol.*, **102**, 144-145.

OSTROVSKAYA, ————. 1930. Le réflexe conditionnel et les réactions de l'immunité. *Ann. de Instit. Pasteur*, **44**, 340-345.

PAVLOV, I. P. 1910. The work of the digestive glands: lectures. (Trans. by W. H. Thompson.) (2nd ed.) London: Griffin. Pp. 266.

————. 1927. Conditioned reflexes: an investigation of the physiological activity of the cerebral cortex. (Trans. and ed. by G. V. Anrep.) London: Oxford Univ. Press. Pp. xv+430.

————. 1928. Lectures on conditioned reflexes: twenty-five years of objective study of the higher nervous activity (behavior) of animals. (Trans. by W. H. Gantt.) New York: Int. Publishers. Pp. 414.

PERRIN, F. A. C. 1932. Psychology: its methods and principles. (Rev. ed.) New York: Holt. Pp. xii+336.

PLATO. Phaedo. Sec. 73-76.

PODKOPAEFF, N. A., & SAATCHIAN, R. L. 1929. Conditioned reflexes for immunity; conditioned reflexes in rabbits for cellular reaction of peritoneal fluid. *Bull. Battle Creek Sanit. & Hosp. Clin.*, **24**, 375-378.

RAMON, G. 1929. Essais sur l'immunité antitoxique. Sur le rôle des antigens specifiques et non specifiques et des réflexes conditionnels dans la production des antitoxines. *C. r. Soc. de biol.*, **100**, 487-490.

RAY, W. S. 1932. A preliminary study of fetal conditioning. *Child Develop.*, **3**, 175-177.

RAZRAN, H. S. 1930. Theory of conditioning and related phenomena. *Psychol. Rev.*, **37**, 25-43.

RICHTER, C. P., & WADA, T. 1924. Method of measuring salivary secretions in human beings. *J. Lab. & Clin. Med.*, **9**, 271-273.

SCHLOSBERG, H. A. 1928. A study of the conditioned patellar reflex. *J. Exper. Psychol.*, **11**, 468-494.

SCOTT, H. D. 1930. Hypnosis and the conditioned reflex. *J. Gen. Psychol.*, **4**, 113-130.

SEARS, R. R. 1932. An experimental study of hypnotic anesthesia. *J. Exper. Psychol.*, **15**, 1-22.

SHERRINGTON, C. S. 1931. Quantitative management of contraction in lowest level co-ordination. *Brain*, **54**, Pt. 1, 1-28.

SHEVALEV, E. A. 1926. [The associated patellar reflex.] In *Sbornik Posviaschchonny Vladimiru Mikhailoviche Bekhterevu k 40-Lyetiv Professorskoy Deyatel'nosti.* Leningrad: Gos. Psikhonevr. Akad. i Gos. Refleks. Instit. po Izucheniyu Mozga. Pp. 105-123.

SHIPLEY, W. C. 1929. A comparative study of the rate of experimental extinction in conditioned reflexes. M.A. thesis, Univ. Wis.

⸺. 1932. Conditioning the human plantar reflex. *J. Exper. Psychol.*, **15**, 422-426.

⸺. 1933. An apparent transfer of conditioning. *J. Gen. Psychol.*, **8**, 382-391.

SMITH, G. H., & SALINGER, R. 1933. Hyper-sensitiveness and the conditioned reflex. *Yale J. Biol. & Med.*, **5**, 387-402.

STECKLE, L. C., & RENSHAW, S. 1934. An investigation of the conditioned iridic reflex. *J. Gen. Psychol.*, **11** (in press).

SWITZER, S. A. 1930. Backward conditioning of the lid reflex. *J. Exper. Psychol.*, **13**, 76-97.

⸺. 1933. Disinhibition of the conditioned galvanic skin response. *J. Gen. Psychol.*, **9**, 77-100.

⸺. 1934. Anticipatory and inhibitory characteristics of delayed conditioned reactions. *J. Exper. Psychol.* (in press).

TAYLOR, H. C. 1933. A conditioned change in vocal pitch. *J. Gen. Psychol.*, **8**, 465-467.

THURSTONE, L. L. 1919. The learning curve equation. *Psychol. Monog.*, **26**, No. 114. Pp. 51.

TWITMYER, E. B. 1902. A study of the knee jerk. Ph.D. thesis, Univ. Pa. (Privately printed—Philadelphia: Winston.)

UPTON, M. 1929. The auditory sensitivity of guinea pigs. *Amer. J. Psychol.*, **41**, 412-421.

WARREN, H. C. 1921. A history of the association psychology. New York: Scribner's. Pp. ix+328.

WATSON, J. B. 1916. The place of the conditioned reflex in psychology. *Psychol. Rev.*, **23**, 89-117.

⸺. 1924. Psychology from the standpoint of the behaviorist. (2nd ed.) Philadelphia: Lippincott. Pp. ix+429.

WENDT, G. R. 1930. An analytical study of the conditioned knee-jerk. *Arch. Psychol.*, **18**, No. 123. Pp. 97.

WEVER, E. G. 1930. The upper limit of hearing in the cat. *J. Comp. Psychol.*, **10**, 221-233.

WINSOR, A. L. 1929. Inhibition and learning. *Psychol. Rev.*, **36**, 389-401.

WOLFLE, D. 1931. An experimental approach to the study of language. In *Readings in experimental psychology,* ed. by W. L. Valentine. New York: Harpers. Pp. 537-551.

WOLFLE, H. M. 1930. Time factors in conditioning finger-withdrawal. *J. Gen. Psychol.,* 4, 372-379.

―――. 1932. Conditioning as a function of the interval between the conditioned and the original stimulus. *J. Gen. Psychol.,* 7, 80-103.

YERKES, R. M., & MORGULIS, S. 1909. The method of Pavlov in animal psychology. *Psychol. Bull.,* 6, 257-273.

ZEBROWSKI, E. 1905. Zur Frage der sekretorischen Funktion der Parotis beim Menschen. *Pflüg. Arch. f. d. ges. Physiol.,* 110, 105-173.

CHAPTER 10

LEARNING: III. NERVOUS MECHANISMS IN LEARNING

K. S. LASHLEY

University of Chicago

The adult animal shows few reactions which have not been modified by experience. These modifications appear in a variety of forms whose relations to one another are not yet clear. Hysteresis, fatigue, adaptation or acclimatization, increase in excitability, progression of physiological states, associative memory or conditioned reflexes, after-imagery, immediate memory, and recognition have been variously distinguished as constituting different types of alteration. So little is known of the determining factors in any of these phenomena that they can be differentiated only in terms of the stimulus-response relationships involved. Hysteresis, fatigue, adaptation, and increase in excitability imply only a change in the intensity of stimulation necessary to elicit the response. In progression of physiological states (the successive reactions of *Stentor* reported by Jennings, the succession of movements in spinal irradiation described by Sherrington) the external stimulus is constant while the reaction varies. This type of alteration does not indicate any change in the innate pattern of internal connections between receptor and effector, but only a temporary change in the relative conductivity of different systems.

A different mechanism seems to be implied by the remaining types of modification. In associative memory a reaction is called out by a stimulus which, before training, was incapable of eliciting it. The reaction to one stimulus is transferred to another which differs from the first, not merely in intensity but in location on the receptor surfaces. This change in the relations of pattern between stimulus and response suggests a corresponding change in the pattern of the conducting system. It has led to the conception of the formation of new paths between receptors and effectors which is the basis of most theories of learning.

By many writers this is regarded as the type of all true learning and the effort is made to describe every sort of association in terms of combinations of simple associative reactions. Habits become chains of conditioned reflexes, images are motor reactions, logical memory the product of implicit trial and error. By others, reproductive memory is distinguished from habit or motor memory on the ground that the former does not involve activity of the effector systems, but is a purely intraneural process resulting in a reproduction of the sensory impressions orginally aroused by peripheral stimulation. Immediate memory differs from other forms in its temporary character and ease of inhibition. Logical memory and recognition are distinguished by Bergson and others, chiefly on the ground that they are not subject to the law of exercise, and made the basis for animistic speculation. Poppelreuter (1915) considers all learning to be of the type of logical memory. Hering, Semon, Rignano, and others have held that memory is a basic property of protoplasm; neurologists have been inclined to regard it as the product of some particular organization of nerve cells.

With this variety of description and interpretation we are justified in raising the question whether the concept of learning or of memory embraces a unitary process which can be studied as a single problem, or whether it may not instead cover a great variety of phenomena having no common organic basis. The question cannot be answered until the physiological mechanisms of a variety of habits and memories have been worked out.

Evidence as to the nature of learning and the organic changes involved is to be sought in a number of fields of investigation. The nervous system is of unquestioned importance for the adaptive responses of the adult organism, and a study of its development as well as of its mature structure is significant for an understanding of its functioning. The investigation of the factors which determine the differentiation and growth of the nervous system in the embryo bears directly on the problems of the origin of the functional connections for both instinctive and acquired behavior. Study of the limitations placed upon learning by injuries to the nervous systems of higher animals gives evidence on the same points.

Another means of attacking the problem of learning is by analysis of the sensory and motor components of habits and the general nature of the disturbances of memory resulting from destruction within the integrating system. This material sets certain problems of integration which any theory of the nature of the learning process must take into account. Finally, a study of the conditions under which learning occurs, of the agents which accelerate or retard the process and of the uniformity of their action provides the material upon which general theories of the nature of learning have been directly based. We shall take up these various approaches to the problem in order, then review the chief current theories of the mechanism of learning to determine in how far they are consistent with the facts revealed by experimental studies.

The Origin of Behavior Patterns during Growth

Most species of animals at birth show complex and well-integrated responses, for the learning of which there seems to have been little, if any, opportunity. The neural patterns leading to these responses are a product of heredity and growth, in the same sense that other bodily structures are. The many recent attacks upon the conception of instinct have neither altered this fact nor advanced our understanding of it. The mechanisms contributing to the development of instinctive patterns are of interest, not only because a knowledge of them may contribute means for control of the fundamental patterns of behavior but also because the forces which contribute to development are probably not greatly different from those which enter into later functional activity and an analysis of them may throw some light upon the more difficult problems of integration.

Factors Influencing Growth. The fertilized ovum already shows certain structural differentiations—fertilization pore, centrosomes, nuclear structures, internal fibers—to which the succeeding stages of development may be referred. Before segmentation the axial direction is, in most cases, determined, and the first segmentation plane follows this polarization. The division into two cells at once introduces new complexities in the relation of parts. The contact of the two cells limits respiration through the contiguous membranes and introduces a secondary lateral polarity which is certainly influential in determining the position of the next segmentation plane. And so, throughout the history of segmentation, each new structure produced serves to complicate the physicochemical relations of the parts and lays the foundation for the next step in differentiation.

In part, the potential plasticity of the cells is retained so that when the influences of adjacent structures are altered they undergo a de-differentiation and develop into structures other than those which they would have formed had they retained their normal position within the organism. Thus in some frog larvae the ectoderm on any part of the body may be induced to differentiate into a lens under the influence of a developing eye-cup. But definite limits to the developmental potentialities of most tissues are set at an early stage of growth. Thus when differentiation of a limb bud is once begun, the growing tissue will form a limb though it is transplanted to an entirely different part of the body. Growth thus presents a continuous compromise between this tendency to self-differentiation and a subjection of the tissues to influences and limitations of development arising from their relationships to other developing parts of the body. After the first few cell divisions, potentiality for development is probably never wholly unlimited except in the germinal tissue. On the other hand, the differentiated tissue, though limited to the formation of certain structures, is still subject to important influences from other parts. The developing limb bud from the right side will produce a right leg even when transplanted to the left side, but if its growing point is injured it may produce two legs, a right and a left, the polarity of each determined by the near presence of the other.

The forces contributing to the development of the nervous system are essentially the same as those entering into the development of other systems. Neural tissue, once differentiated in the neural tube, grows into nerve cells, in large measure independent of its environment, and normal production of gross structures, such as optic vesicles, cerebellum, or midbrain, continues even when the rudiments of these structures have early been transplanted to unusual positions. But although self-differentiation of such gross structures appears and the general characters of nervous tissue are irreversibly determined early in development, at the time of constriction of the neural tube, the fate of the individual neuroblasts (the undeveloped nerve cells) is determined much later and primarily by their relations to other structures. This is illustrated by the experiments of Hooker and of Detwiler (1923) upon the effects of reversing segments of the spinal cord of salamanders. In the normal cord the first coordinating axons developed from the neuroblasts grow toward the head. If a portion of the neural tube before the development of axons is cut out and replaced so that its normal anterior end is now posterior, the first axons formed are still directed toward the head. They thus grow in the opposite direction, with respect to the position of the neuroblasts from which they are derived, to that which they would normally have taken. The course of the fibers is determined, not by the character of the cells from which they are derived, nor by the immediate surroundings of those cells, but by their relation to the polarization of the whole body.

Child (1921) points out the importance of the rapid growth of the posterior segments of the embryo at this time in establishing a gradient and determining the anterior direction of growth of the neurons, and the later suppression of these primitive nervous connections and the establishment of others when the activity of growth in the posterior region declines.

In determining the direction of development of the nerve fibers, mechanical, chemical, and probably electrical stimuli play a part. Harrison has shown that neuroblasts growing in tissue cultures are responsive to mechanical and chemical stimuli. Recent theories of the factors in growth have inclined more to stress the electrical or electrochemical. Kappers (1917), in the doctrine of neurobiotaxis, has developed a general theory to account for the gross structural relationships and the finer connections of nerve fibers. He assumes that excitatory processes give rise to differences in electrical potential, resulting in currents to which the neuroblasts are susceptible. Under the influence of these electric currents the axons are directed and grow toward the cathode, the dendrites toward the anode. When the neurons begin to conduct, the passage of the nerve impulse gives rise to differences in potential which serve as further stimuli to cell growth and determine the intercellular connections which are established. Kappers' theory of selective interconnection of cells assumes that when a cell is stimulated its conductivity is increased. If, then, another cell in its vicinity is excited, the resultant potential will discharge along the previously excited neuron, the dendrites of which will be attracted toward the new source of excitation. The axon will at the same time grow out along the path of electric discharge, until contact is made between it and the attracted dendrites. In this formulation Kappers has probably overemphasized the rôle of intraneural conduction at the expense of more general organic forces. Carmichael (1927) has shown that the mechanisms of the first reflex responses of salamanders develop normally although the embryos are continually immobilized by a general anaesthetic. The doctrine that the reflex paths are established as a result of sensory stimulation begs the question in any case, for, in assuming that electrical currents from the point of stimulation determine the direction of growth, it presupposes the existence of those paths of high conductivity between sensory and motor zones whose origin it seeks to explain.

The broader principles of polarity, of physical, chemical, and electrical interaction among the parts of the developing embryo sketched by Child seem a more fundamental approach to the problem of morphogenesis, although they do not supply an explicit theory of the selective connection of neurons which is supposed to underlie the reflex response.

This theory of specific intercellular connections as a basis of response, so widely accepted in psychological and physiological writings, calls for closer scrutiny. Must we assume that continuous and relatively isolated paths from specific sense-organs to effectors are laid down in growth, or are the anatomical details of growth of relatively little importance for the later functional relationships? The enormous variability in details of cellular structure gives little support to the strict anatomical interpretation of the problem. The evidence for functional plasticity accords with it even less. Detwiler (1925) has shown that when the limb buds of salamanders are transplanted to positions behind their normal ones they are, at least in part, innervated by the outgrowth of fibers from neuroblasts which would normally supply the intercostal muscles. Nevertheless, when the connections are established, the movements of the limb exhibit normal coordination. Still more striking is the case in which injury to the growing tip results in the production of two oppositely symmetrical limbs from the same bud. In this case the coordination in movements of the limbs is determined by their symmetry and not by their anatomical position. Of course it may be assumed for such cases that each developing axon seeks out the muscle which its central connections fit it to innervate, but there is evidence from experiments on nerve-suturing that axons which originally supply one set of muscles will readily grow to and innervate another, so this assumption of selectivity of growth has little support.

In a later section we shall present other evidence against the importance of the individual neuron for behavior. The evidence from growth is not conclusive on this point, yet it requires rather far-fetched assumptions concerning the selective attraction of neurons for developing axons to save the theory of specific cell-to-cell connection in the face of such experiments as those of Detwiler (1925) and Weiss (1926). The latter has recognized the difficulty and abandoned the theory of specific paths in favor of one based upon the differentiation of muscle fibers to respond to critical frequencies of excitation derived from any source.

After birth, in mammals there is a protracted development of new patterns and potentialities for behavior. These have been roughly classed as maturation of instincts, the appearance of delayed instincts, learning, and the growth of intelligence. There is little cell division in the nervous tissue after birth, but transformation of neuroblasts into neurons continues for a long time. The basis for further development of behavior is to be sought in this and in further growth and proliferation of nerve fibers, myelinization of fibers, increase in cell size, or chemical changes which increase functional efficiency. We have little basis for judging which of these is the most important in determining patterns of behavior.

Maturation. Breed, Bird (1926), and others have given evidence that without opportunity for practice there is improvement in the functions appearing at birth. Whether this is due to the development of further specific integrations or to a more general improvement in coordination is unsettled. Bird's observations suggest that the latter is probably the important factor. Tilney and Casamajor report a close correspondence between the development of myelin sheaths in the tracts of the medulla and the appearance of new patterns of reaction in kittens.

Delayed Instincts. The most conspicuous group of delayed instincts are the activities which appear at the time of sexual maturity. There can be no doubt that many of these are complex patterns of behavior which appear fully integrated during the sexual cycle, without previous practice. Mating, nest-building, recognition and care of the young, are all activities of this sort. The sex behavior of the male rat has been most thoroughly studied. Steinach and, more recently, Stone (1922) have shown that the internal secretion of the testis is usually essential for the first appearance of the behavior. In some way the particular neural pattern is activated by the hormone so that the mating response is given to stimuli which are otherwise inadequate. We can imagine several possible ways in which this might be brought about. The effect of the hormone might be a mere increase in vigor resulting in a general increase in nervous excitability. There might be an action upon the vegetative nervous system to increase the tone of the pelvic organs (for which there is some experimental evidence), and this, in accord with Kempf's theory of segmental strivings, might reflexly facilitate the spinal integrations; these possibilities are opposed by evidence of the specific effects of the male and female hormones. Finally, the hormone may act selectively upon certain organized systems within the brain or cord, either to stimulate growth or to increase their excitability. The possibility of stimulation of growth seems ruled out by the rapidity with which the reactions are restored in castrates by implantation of testicular tissue and also by the fact that, in other animals at least, the reactions may sometimes appear before sexual maturity.

The most probable explanation of the delayed sexual reactions thus seems to lie in the special sensitivity of a definite neural system, previously organized by growth, to a specific chemical circulating in the blood. Of course there are many complicating factors. The male tern reacts at once to an egg in his nest, the female only after she herself has laid an egg; the feminized male rat will respond to young, the female only after she herself has borne a litter. The effectiveness of the hormones is modified by many factors. Habits soon come to play a rôle and obscure the congenital integrations.

The experimental studies indicate the importance of three factors for the initiation of delayed instincts: the growth of fiber connections, the maturation of these fibers as indicated by the formation of the myelin sheaths, and the chemical activation of neural systems. There are probably still other factors involved, as yet unrevealed by actual experiments.

The Growth of Intelligence. The increase in potentialities for complex behavior which parallels physiological development may, like the maturation of instinct, be ascribed to any of a number of changes in the central nervous system. The studies of Hammarberg and of Bolton show that there is a measurably smaller number of mature ganglion cells in the cerebral cortex of the imbecile than in that of the normal individual of the same age. Data which we shall present in a later section indicate that the complexity of the habits which can be formed and functional efficiency in performance is conditioned by the mere mass of cerebral tissue. These facts suggest that the development of intelligence with age may be a function of the increase in number of mature ganglion cells resulting from the differentiation of neuroblasts. There is a little evidence that the development of nerve cells is stimulated by functional activity so that it is possible that education as well as innately determined growth processes contributes to the growth of intelligence. The independent development of neuroblasts, on the other hand, is difficult to harmonize with the constancy of the intelligence quotient, since the latter would require a great regularity in the number of neuroblasts reaching maturity each year. The alternative, that the grade of intelligence is determined by the number of neurons formed at birth or shortly after, and that growth of intelligence is the result of a gradual maturing of these cells, is not ruled out by any available evidence.

Even before the development of the neuroblasts the organism presents a complicated pattern in which, although there are no known specific coordinating structures, a great deal of integrated activity of the parts is carried out, slowly to be sure, but with great precision. The coordinating processes are chemical diffusion, the creation and conduction of electric currents, and a high degree of selective sensitivity to these factors on the part of the developing cells. With maturity these forces do not cease to exist and it would be strange if the susceptibility of the nerve cells to their action were to terminate with the completion of their growth. The myelin sheaths may serve to remove the axons from a large part of such influences, but the unmedullated portions of the cells within the gray matter still remain exposed and subject to the general chemical and electrical influences as well as to specific excitations from other neurons. We have as yet no means of estimating the part played by such extraneuronic influences in determining coordination. There is little direct evidence of their action, yet the difficulties which the reflex theories encounter in application to the more complex forms of behavior may force us to seek the sources of integration in such factors rather than in specific connections of neurons.

Development of Learning Capacity in the Evolutionary Series

Few animals lack tissue specifically differentiated for the conduction of impulses to movement. If we are to study the capacities for modification without such structures, we must turn to plants or to the rhizopods among animals. The various modifications of behavior reported for plants may be grouped roughly in three classes: acclimatization, adaptation to stimuli, and the acquisition and maintenance of various rhythms of activity. The first of these shows few analogies with learning in animals, since it seems to involve an alteration of the tissues through the local action of environmental agents upon them. Adaptation to stimulation has been described most adequately for *Mimosa*. When these plants are stimulated by mechanical or other nocuous stimuli, they respond by folding their leaves. With repeated mechanical stimulation it becomes more difficult to elicit this response, and plants may finally be brought to a state in which they will fail to react to continuous strong stimulation. Left unstimulated for a time, they recover the capacity to respond.

Alterations in rhythmic activities have been reported for the time of discharge of spores in several marine algae and for the growth processes in relation to illumination in higher plants. Their relation to other phenomena of adaptation is not clear.

Acclimatization in ameba has been described by several writers, but it is not clear that anything beyond a general change in excitability is involved. Mast and Pusch have recorded changes in behavior of *Amoeba proteus* which they interpret as analogous to learning in higher forms. The amebae were repeatedly stimulated by a beam of light directed across their paths, and the number of contacts with the beam before a complete reversal of direction occurred was recorded. This was repeated 27 times with each of five animals. On the average there was a gradual reduction in the number of false starts before the reversal of direction, which suggests a learning curve. The animals were kept on vaseline-sealed slides in darkness except when tested under the microscope. No controls were reported to rule out the influence of the continued adaptation to darkness or the effects of possible progressive chemical change in the medium. Only two of the five individual records show progressive improvement and there is no indication of loss of the effect after interruptions of training as long as 50 hours. The data are thus inadequate to establish an identity of the results with associative memory.

The problem of modifiability of behavior in other protozoa is complicated by the presence of a primitive nervous system in the form of a neuro-motor apparatus, which is present in the flagellates, infusoria, and probably in other higher forms. The function of this apparatus for conduction and coordination of movements has been demonstrated, but little is known as to the nature of its activities beyond what may be inferred from the observed coordinations of ciliary beat such as the progression of waves of movement, reversal of direction of such waves in restricted areas, and the like.

Adaptation to mechanical stimulation may readily be observed in sessile forms such as *Vorticella* and *Stentor*. Summation of the effects of continued stimulation leading through a series of avoiding reactions to a final release from the substratum was described by Jennings for *Stentor*. Attempts to demonstrate effects of practice by Day and Bentley, Metalnikow, Buytendijk, and others have given questionable or negative results.

The available evidence shows for organisms lacking a true nervous system the possibility of decreased excitability following continued stimulation, the summation of stimulation resulting in increased excitability under certain conditions, and something like an irradiation of the effects of stimulation, resulting in a succession of responses, but there is no demonstration of an acquired change in the pattern of response or of any phenomena analogous to the associative learning of higher forms.

Among metazoa the evolution of the nervous system has involved three radical steps: the transition from syncytial to synaptic organization, the transfer from the ventral position of the nervous system in invertebrates to the dorsal position in vertebrates, and cephalization or the concentration and development of nervous tissue in the head region. We shall inquire what influence each of these steps has had upon the capacity for modification of behavior.

In the coelenterates and echinoderms, coordination of movement is probably brought about by a diffuse irradiation of impulses from the areas of stimulation through a continuous network of nerve fibers. Even in the simplest of these forms there is some concentration of nervous tissue in the oral region and at the bases of the tentacles, and the spread of excitation seems most rapid through these regions of denser tissue, so that very specific reactions may be given to localized stimulation. In the more highly differentiated forms, anemones and many of the echinoderms, there are well-marked conduction paths forming a nerve ring about the mouth region, with radiating nerve trunks to the organs of the radial segments. In the sea-cucumbers (*Holothuria*) a synaptic type of organization probably makes its first appearance. Behavior of forms with a simple nerve net has not been correlated in detail with nervous function. The behavior is quite complex and implies an elaborate interplay of diverse impulses from different excited regions, modified in various ways by the general level of physiological activity.

In the simpler coelenterates (*Hydra*) adaptation to stimulation and summation of the effects of stimulation have been demonstrated. Successive patterns of behavior may be called out by continued stimulation, as in *Stentor*, but there is no evidence that such progressions can be modified by practice. In the anemones Jennings found changes in behavior depending upon the state of hunger, upon acclimatization to stimuli, and upon the previous reactions of the animals. Of the latter the most striking is the maintenance of postures imposed by the irregularities of the surfaces upon which the animals live. The posture is maintained by a local contraction of one side of the polyp, which is not relaxed during the usual minor changes in form. If the polyp is forced to a maximal contraction by strong stimulation, the bend does not reappear when the polyp again extends. Apparently the enforced position results in an area of maximal tonus within the nerve net, which persists until it is suppressed by a general maximal excitation. Jennings suggests that this may represent in rudimentary form the mechanism by which habits are retained in higher animals.

It is not certain where the synaptic type of nervous system first appears in the evolutionary series. Crozier, on grounds of behavior, ascribes it to echinoderms, and it is in these forms that the first evidence for reorganization of reflex connections as a result of practice appears. Experiments with starfish have been reported by Jennings (1907) and by Ven. Usually two of the rays of the starfish, those adjacent to the madreporic plate, are more active than the others, take the lead when the starfish crawls, and play the chief part in the righting reaction. Jennings restrained the movements of these rays, forcing the use of others for righting the animals when placed on the dorsal surface. Training in the use of rays previously not used in the righting reaction for from 70 to 180 trials was followed in some cases by a more frequent use of those rays than of any other, and effects of the training persisted for at least five days after the termination of the training period. Ven restrained the two more active arms of the starfish by wire wickets, forcing them to escape by crawling with the less active arms in advance. He found a gradual reduction in the time required for escape.

The results of these experiments may be interpreted as indicating a shift in the lead or dominance from one region of the nerve net to another. There is little evidence that more precise changes in the pattern of coordinations can be established. When two rays were forced by training to take the lead in activity in Jennings' experiments, they might be so twisted as to oppose each other and make the righting reaction very difficult. Training failed to alter the tendencies to such opposed movements.

The value of the anatomical correlations here is somewhat lessened by the fact that the actual structures responsible for the synaptic type of conduction (transmission of the nerve impulse in one direction only) is not known. The coelenterates and echinoderms give evidence in their behavior of a predominance of diffuse conduction in either direction, which does not permit of precise coordination of limited structures such as is involved in associative reactions. If they showed precise conditioned reflexes we should probably conclude, not that this type of learning is possible in a nerve net, but that the structures characteristic of the intercellular connections of higher forms are not the essential ones for synaptic function.

In animals in which a definite synaptic nervous structure is easier to demonstrate, the association of reactions with stimuli which were not sufficient to elicit them before training is readily obtained. Yerkes (1912) established in a manure worm a habit of turning to the right in a simple maze. Indications of learning appeared after 20 trials, although absolute consistency of performance was not established within 1000 trials. Removal of the first five segments of the body, including the cerebral ganglion, resulted in only temporary and slight disturbance of the habit. Regeneration of the cerebral ganglion, on the contrary, was followed by a loss of the habit. In addition to the usual conditions of maze learning, the experiment offered an opportunity for the formation of a simple sensory association. The entrance of the cul-de-sac was paved with sandpaper, beyond which the punishment grill was located. The animal might thus learn to associate the mechanical stimulus of the sandpaper with the avoiding reaction to the electric current. Inspection of the tables shows, however, that the ratio of contacts with the sandpaper to contacts with the grill remained practically constant, within its probable error, throughout the thousand trials of training so that there is no indication that this association was formed.

Broad generalizations are not justified by this one experiment but it suggests that the learning is a function of the entire ganglionic chain rather than of a limited part, and that the activities of the regenerated anterior ganglia were sufficient to disrupt completely the acquired activity of the posterior segments.

The arthropods and the higher mollusks approach the lower vertebrates in the complexity of their reactions and the readiness with which habits may be acquired. A wealth of experiments shows this and we need cite only a few. Turner's studies (1913) show conditioned reflexes to sound and light in moths and roaches. The rate of learning does not seem significantly slower than that of lower vertebrates. The extensive experiments on form and color discrimination of bees by von Frisch show the ready formation of habits involving rather fine discriminations. Goldsmith reports the establishment of a discrimination habit in the octopus. The shelled mollusks seem to form associations less readily (Thompson).

Evolution of associative memory may be assumed to involve an increase in the rate at which association may be formed, increase in the complexity of associations, that is, in the number of elements or related processes which may be subsumed under a single habit, and perhaps qualitative changes such as are implied in the distinction between habit and reproductive memory. So far as the available studies may be taken as final, there is little difference between the higher invertebrates and the lower vertebrates in any of these respects.

The Rate of Learning. Goldfish require a greater amount of practice to learn a simple maze than do roaches to learn a more complicated one. The discrimination habits described for insects equal in complexity any reactions which have been reported for the cold-blooded vertebrates. It is thus clear that the shift from the ventral to the dorsal position of the main nerve trunks has not, in itself, entailed any fundamental change in the capacity for learning.

Nervous evolution in the vertebrates has involved increase in the relative size of the brain and body, the development of the cerebral cortex, and the differentiation of the so-called association areas as the chief alterations which might be expected to change the capacity for learning. Speed of conduction and probably of all other physiological processes is increased, but the importance of these factors alone for learning may be largely discounted by comparison between birds and mammals and between various orders of mammals.

Comparable quantitative studies of the rate of formation of simple associations or the limits of training in the different classes of the vertebrates are rare so that there are few data upon which to base comparisons of function with structure.

There is little evidence that the rate of formation of simple mechanical habits changes in the mammalian series. Pavlov (1927) reports that the conditioned salivary reflex may be formed in about 60 combined stimulations in the dog. Gley and Mendelsohn did not establish it in man in 40 trials, and Lashley failed after a much larger number of combined stimulations. Conditioned motor reactions seem to be formed about as readily in the dog as in man when the discriminations called for are relatively simple.

Pechstein (1917) trained rats and human subjects in mazes having identical patterns. In one set of experiments the subjects were required to learn the maze by sections ("part method"), in another to learn it as a whole. The results were the following:

	Trials		Errors	
	Whole	Part	Whole	Part
Rats	27	30	217	199
Humans	12	23	126	237

Considering the far greater novelty of the entire training situation for the rats than for the human subjects, the results do not indicate any significantly greater learning ability in the latter.

Such data are not conclusive, but do suggest that the rate of formation of simple habits has increased little, if at all, through the evolution of the cerebral cortex. Other facts bear out this opinion. Simple habits are acquired by the feebleminded about as readily as by normals. Extensive cerebral lesions markedly retard the formation of complex habits, yet produce little effect upon the rate at which simpler ones are formed. In opposition to these facts it may be urged that they concern only acquisition through trial and error in which chance plays a large part, and that direct association, as in immediate and incidental memory, is much more rapid in man than in lower forms. It is difficult to get objective evidence on this point, but there are many indications that even the rat, in the learning of mazes and problem boxes, forms a large number of immediate associations which are comparable only with incidental memories in man. Thus, a nearly decerebrate rat will often re-enter a cul-de-sac more than 100 times before passing on to the next. The normal animal rarely re-enters a cul-de-sac, even on the first trial in the maze, without intervening exploration of other parts. With no differences in bodily orientation to account for the diverse behavior, we seem forced to conclude that the entry into a cul-de-sac leaves traces in the normal rat which for a time inhibit re-entry.

Limits of Training. So far as one may judge from existing evidence, the higher invertebrates compare very favorably with the lower vertebrates, even with the lower mammals, not only in the rate of formation of simple habits but in the complexity of the habits which may be acquired. There are no comparable studies including widely different types of behavior, but certainly the recognition of the nest locality from visual cues reported for honey bees exceeds in complexity any habit which has been observed in fishes or in the smaller rodents.

Within the vertebrate series the limits of training seem to parallel very closely the degree of development of the brain and particularly of the cerebral cortex. The habits reported for rodents, carnivora, lower and higher apes, both under experimental conditions and in the field, form a definitely graded series with respect to the number of elements and the complexity of the relationships involved. It also seems clear that the limits are set by the character of the central organization rather than by the sensory or motor capacities of the animals. Thus it is practically impossible to establish a habit of visual pattern discrimination in the rat with the conventional Yerkes discrimination box. We have many times trained animals with a vertical and a horizontal line as stimuli for 500 to 800 trials without clear evidence of discriminations. The same animals will distinguish lines immediately, if the lines are objects to which they must jump. The rhesus monkeys have a motor and sensory equipment not sensibly inferior to that of the chimpanzee. The habits in which they have been trained are, however, far simpler.

The comparative study of learning in different animals gives little evidence that evolution has brought any change in the rate of formation of the simpler habits. On the other hand, there is a fairly consistent rise in the limits of training and in the formation of complex habits with ascent in the phylogenetic scale. This raises the questions of the meaning of complexity in learning and its relation to the problem of insight or intelligence. Does increase in the number of similar elements set a limit to learning; that is, may complexity of habit be stated as a function of the number of single associations required, or is a qualitative change in the nature of the relationships among the elements the important factor in determining the limits of training? The data at hand are not easy to interpret. In studies of human learning, results have been obtained ranging from those of Henmon, showing practice proportional to the length of the series, to those of Foucault, showing practice proportional to the square of the length. The majority of experimenters have found that the difficulty is disproportionately increased with length even for meaningful material. This would indicate that mere multiplication of elements might set a limit to learning. In tests with rats we have found that increasing the number of culs-de-sac in the maze does not proportionately increase the practice required for learning if the animals are normal, but does in animals with extensive cerebral lesions.

Even in the case of maze learning by defective animals or the memorizing of digits by normal men it is not clear that the difficulty of learning large complexes is due to the number of associations to be formed rather than to the inability to see significant relations within the complex. This problem is still unsolved, and our ignorance of it permits the claim, on the one hand, that all habit or memory is merely the linking-together of conditioned reflexes and, on the other, the assertion that learning is always a product of insight.

LEARNING IN RELATION TO NEURAL STRUCTURE

The Quantity of Tissue. Without much quantitative evidence, one is led to the view by a general survey of learning in the mammalian series that the size of the brain, both absolute and relative to body weight, plays an important part in determining the limits of training. Lapicque (1922) and others have computed the ratio of brain and body weights in a number of animals and sought a general formula to express the amount of increase in brain weight for unit increase in body weight. Lapicque concludes that between different species of animals and between the sexes in man this ratio is expressed by the formula $k = \dfrac{E}{P^{0.56}}$, where k is a constant, E is brain weight, and P is body weight. That is, the weight of the brain increases as the square root of the body weight. Within a given species the exponential relation is reduced from 0.56 to 0.20. Other factors than body weight contribute to the relationship. The most important is the surface area of the sense-organs, which determines the number of cells in the corresponding sensory regions of the nervous system. With due allowance for this, Lapicque is inclined to think that the above equations express the requirements of nervous tissue for the average intellectual level of the groups in question and that any marked departure from the ratio determined for a given group indicates an intelligence above or below the average for the group. There are no valid data on behavior to serve as a check on this conclusion.

Studies of the effects of cerebral destruction in animals show a definite relationship between the quantity of functional tissue and the capacity to learn. Lashley (1929) found a correlation of 0.86 ± 0.03 between the extent of brain injury and the number of errors made by rats in learning a maze. Other experiments indicated that retention is also a function of the amount of intact tissue. The observations of Hammarberg and of Bolton indicate the importance of the number of ganglion cells for learning in man, and, although there are no adequate quantitative data, the opinion is frequently expressed that the degree of deterioration in man after lesions to the cerebral hemispheres is related to the extent of destruction.

Relation of Different Structures to Learning. Many writers of the last century ascribed learning wholly to the cerebral hemispheres. The demonstration of habits in invertebrates and fishes disproves this opinion, but still leaves the question whether the developed cerebrum has taken over the learning function from lower centers. Trevesz and Aggozzotti, Rogers, and Beritoff have shown the capacity of the decerebrate pigeon to learn, Beritoff (1926) finding that it forms a simple conditioned reflex as rapidly as a normal animal. No completely decerebrate mammal has been subjected to systematic training for a long enough period to test the limits of its capacity for learning. Figure 1 shows the curve of improvement in an eight–cul-de-sac maze for four rats with an average destruction of 70.5 per cent of the cerebral cortex. The maze was not learned, but marked improvement occurred and the limit was not reached in the period of training. From such cases we may hazard a guess that, if shock could be avoided, the decerebrate mammal might acquire as complex habits as do fish or amphibia and that the learning capacity of lower centers has not been modified by the acquisition of the cerebral cortex.

The contribution of the different parts of the cortex to the formation of the maze habit has been studied by Lashley (1929). Groups of animals with destruction of each of the chief cytoarchitectural areas were trained in the maze. Since the areas differ in size it was necessary to correct for such differences. This was done by computing from the regression coefficient for errors on extent of lesion for the entire group the expected errors for the magnitude of each area. The results were the following:

Errors	Motor	Somaesthetic	Visual	Auditory	Primitive associational
Experimental	468	414	649	148	521
Computed	484	597	570	145	598

The departure of experimental from computed values here is small in proportion to the difference from normal controls which made only 47 errors under the same conditions. No difference in behavior in the maze could be detected between groups with different loci of lesion. The experiment indicates that the differentiated areas of the cortex all contribute in the same way to the formation of the maze habit and in proportion to their areas.

Quantitative data for other animals are not available. Jacobsen has shown that destruction of the frontal or parietal association areas does not retard the formation of simple habits in rhesus monkeys, although the animals may have trouble with complicated problem boxes. For the learning of other problems the data are difficult to evaluate. In the rat the habit of brightness discrimination and certain problem-box habits are formed at normal rate after destruction of the cerebral hemispheres up to at least 50 per cent, and in no case has a greater retardation in the formation of a habit resulted from injury in one place than in another.

In man there seems to be a more definite restriction of learning by destruction of local areas. Improvement in every sort of activity seems possible after lesion in any locus (unless perhaps the total destruction of

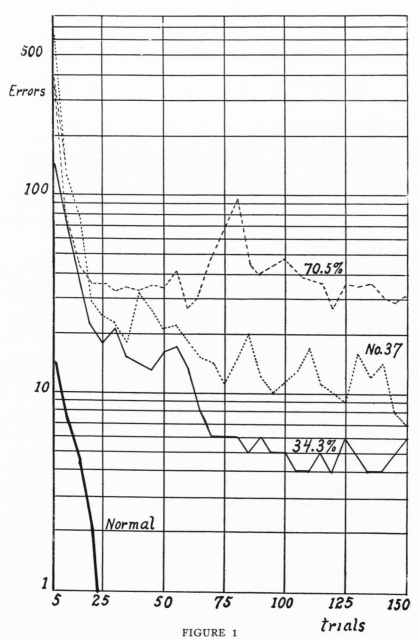

FIGURE 1

LEARNING CURVES FOR ANIMALS WITH EXTENSIVE DESTRUCTION OF THE CEREBRAL
CORTEX COMPARED WITH CURVES FOR NORMAL ANIMALS

━━ Average of normal animals; ── average of four animals with approximately 34 per cent of the cortex destroyed; ____ average of four animals with
about 70 per cent of the cortex destroyed; .... record of one case with more than
80-per-cent destruction. (After Lashley, 1929.)

a projection area is involved) if the patient is not senile and can be properly motivated, but the rate of improvement in certain functions may be retarded. Thus the patient with severe aphasia seems to have much greater difficulty in forming verbal associations than in learning non-verbal material.

This does not prove, however, that the areas, destruction of which produced the aphasia, were particularly well adapted for the formation of verbal association by virtue of any internal structural peculiarity or that other areas may not serve as well for the acquisition of verbal associations. The rate of learning in human adults is largely dependent upon pre-existing associations, as indicated by the importance of mediate associations in the learning of series of unrelated words. If all word associations are abolished by a cerebral lesion, slow learning is to be expected even though the vicariously functioning parts are structurally as well adapted for the learning as was the original speech area. Much of the difference between the results with the animals and man is probably referable to the use of acquired mnemonic aids by the latter.

Localization of the Engram. We have progressed a long way from the notion that individual ideas are stored in single cells of the brain. Ideas are recognized as composites involving the relation of many elements and dependent not upon one but upon many cells. Yet in a way this advance has only transferred the idea from the cell to the synapse, for the current theories of the dependence of habit upon specific neural arcs still localize the essential element of the habit in particular intercellular junctions. Are the engrams so definitely localized? Different experiments seem to give different answers to the question. In the rat the habit of brightness discrimination is abolished by destruction of the occipital lobes. Something essential to the performance of the habit is certainly located there. But it is not definitely localized within the general region, for smaller injuries within the area do not abolish the reaction but only weaken it in proportion to their extent. For the maze habit, on the other hand, there is no evidence for localization. It is weakened after any injury to the hemispheres but survives any small injury and is abolished by any large one, irrespective of location.

For man a great variety of habitual activities is known to be dependent upon particular areas of the cerebrum, but the localization is rather gross. Very small injuries rarely produce symptoms; larger injuries lower the efficiency of many complex related functions.

Clearly no habit can be ascribed to conduction paths restricted to a narrowly limited cerebral area, but beyond this the data are capable of at least two interpretations. It may be that each habit is mediated by a number of equivalent and scattered conduction paths and that efficiency of performance is reduced but not abolished by destruction of some of these. Or it may be that performance is not dependent upon the conduction of impulses over definite paths, but is dependent upon some general property of the propagated disturbances, such as periodicity of discharge, irrespective of the paths followed through the cortex.

Critical experiments upon this point are not available. Lashley (1929) has reported cases where the interruption of projection fibers to certain cortical areas resulted in less disturbance of behavior than the destruction of the cortical areas supplied by the fibers, which would indicate that the conduction path is of less importance than the area to which it conducts, but the experiment may be susceptible to other interpretations. This problem of specific paths will arise again in the discussion of the characteristics of coordination involved in habit. From the anatomical and physiological data we cannot conclude with any confidence that the alterations of nervous structure underlying habits are located in any particular part of the nervous system or of the reflex path.

Significance of Finer Structures. The general belief that the neuron alone of the structural elements of the nervous system participates in the coordination of activity is supported by a large mass of indirect physiological and anatomical evidence, yet is not established beyond question. Ramon y Cajal has suggested that differential response may be determined by the movements of neuroglia cells, their processes serving as insulators when extended between the neurons. There is no evidence to support such an hypothesis, beyond the variable forms of the neuroglia, but the suggestion, coming from an eminent neurologist, illustrates how little we know of the medium in which the neurons lie and of its possible influences upon their excitability.

The surface membranes separating the neurons have been most stressed in theories of the mechanism of integration, since they form the only known break in continuity of fibers where diffuse conduction seems likely to occur. The fundamental importance of the synapse seems a logical conclusion, yet we must bear in mind when evaluating theories of learning that the properties of the synapse are still entirely hypothetical. If we deduce its properties from the facts of learning, we gain nothing by explaining learning in terms of these hypothetical properties.

The recent work on nerve conduction seems to limit the possible theories of integration and of learning. If the propagated disturbance in the nerve fiber may pass equally well in either direction, is subject to the all-or-nothing law, and is capable of modification only at the junction between cells, then the whole theory of learning must be worked out in terms of such processes. It seems well established that volleys of nerve impulses are set up by sensory stimulation, their number and rate of succession being determined by the intensity of the stimulus, and their spatial distribution by the number and position of the end-organs stimulated. Their further distribution is determined by the state of excitability of succeeding neurons in the chain, by the intensity of the impulses (a product of the rate of succession and condition of excitability of the conducting neurons), and by the resistance offered by postulated regions of decrement (a resultant of initial condition and contemporal excitation from other sources).

Actually these facts have little relevance to the problem of learning since they leave it an open question whether the alteration of learning takes place in the excitability of the cell, in its rate of recovery from the refractory phase, or in the conductivity of the intercellular membrane; whether the phase relationships, the intensity of discharges, or the resistance to transmission is altered. Furthermore, we do not know whether the laws of conduction in nerve trunks apply within the gray matter. It may be that they do, but it is also possible that diffuse electrical or chemical processes within the non-medullated regions are equally important with the propagated disturbances in determining integration.

The data on the relation of nervous structure to learning offer little of constructive value. It is probable that simple associations may be formed in any part of the nervous system, so long as there is continuity of tissue between the afferent and efferent tracts associated. The cerebral hemispheres are somehow concerned in the formation of the more complex associations, but the nature of their contribution to learning is still a complete mystery. Special parts may be essential to the retention of a habit once formed, yet learning of that habit is not impeded by their absence. Learning of other habits may be retarded in the absence of parts of the cortex yet with no evidence of any localization of the habit mechanism in those parts when it has been formed. The cerebral hemispheres present no peculiarities of finer structure either in the character of the cells or in their connections which can be pointed out as of especial importance for the learning function, and the simple mass of tissue is the only feature which thus far has been correlated with rate and complexity of learning.

General Characteristics of the Organization of Habits

We must now analyze more in detail the character of learned activities. It is customary to speak of them as reactions to stimuli, without analysis either of the nature of the reaction or of the nature of the stimulus. Thus an animal is said to learn a positive reaction to the door of a problem box; a familiar face is a stimulus to the pronunciation of a name. As brief descriptions of behavior such statements are permissible, but for the formulation of the learning problem they are very misleading. Just what is the stimulus in terms of the sensory fibers excited; what is a positive reaction or the pronunciation of a name in terms of muscular contraction? If we are to understand the mechanism of the habit, we must deal with it in these terms, for the integration is evidently between sense-organs and effectors and not between doors and directions of movement.

The Nature of the Stimulus. The theory of the specificity of conduction paths in habit demands that the reaction learned be given only to the excitation of the same receptor cells as were stimulated during training, or at least a significant number of them, these receptor cells being connected with the effectors by a system throughout which there is a point-for-point correspondence. These conditions are rarely if ever met in any training experiment. On the contrary, it is clear in most cases that the response is, within wide limits, independent of the particular sensory cells stimulated.

Figure 2 illustrates this in an experiment with rats. The animals, incidentally lacking the visual cortex, were trained to jump to a platform

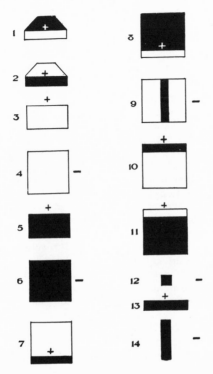

FIGURE 2

EQUIVALENT STIMULI FOR A HABIT OF JUMPING IN THE RAT

Animals were trained to jump to a platform having the appearance of *1*, seen against the background of the room. The following figures were then presented in succession. The + sign indicates the position to which the animals jumped promptly; the —, failure to jump in five minutes.

presenting a black surface and a white edge, seen against the background of the room. The appearance of the platform was then changed as indicated in the succeeding figures, by placing cardboard screens before it, or by substituting a large white screen on which paper figures were pasted. The animals jumped to any horizontal rectangle, whether black or white, but would not jump to a vertical rectangle or a plain figure. It seems clear that the stimulus here cannot be described as the excitation of such and such retinal cells. The elements common to the various situations are the proportions of the object seen against a varying background.

The writer previously reported the transfer of the habit of brightness discrimination from one eye to the other which had not been used during training. In this experiment the same sensory cells were certainly not stimulated in the formation and in the performance of the habit. Where is the common conduction path for the two sensory systems established by training? By one theory corresponding points of the two retinas are supposed to be projected to corresponding positions in the superimposed layers of the stripe of Baillarger. Here one set of retinal fibers might, by drainage, condition the corresponding fibers from the other eye. But the experiment also showed that the transfer took place readily in an animal without a visual cortex. Of course, as long as we know nothing of the actual central nervous processes involved, the common neurons may be postulated in any remaining nervous tissue, but this is only an appeal to ignorance to save a weakened theory. If these were isolated instances, it would be worth while to try to explain them away, but such conditions are the rule, not the exception. We may state as a general principle that the stimulus to any reaction above the level of a spinal reflex involves, not the excitation of certain definite sensory cells, but the excitation of any cells of a system in certain ratios, and that the response may be given to the ratio, even though the particular cells involved have not previously been excited in the same way during the formation of the habitual reaction.

The performance of the habit cannot be ascribed to the functioning of stereotyped paths from sensory to effector cells. This characteristic of the stimulus has been emphasized by Driesch, Bergson, Wertheimer, Koffka, Goldstein, and many others, and, although we need not accept the anti-physiological conclusions which have sometimes been based upon it, we must recognize the problem as a serious one for psychological and neurological theory.

The Nature of the Reaction. In the simplest habits, such as the conditioned reflexes, the activities associated with the conditioned stimulus are those which were originally called out by the primary stimulus. This is essentially true of all habitual responses, but only if the word "act" is used in a broader sense than the contraction of a definite pattern of muscles. The rat learns to run the maze. Is the maze habit a chaining-together of those movements which were used to traverse the maze during learning, or is it something else? A study of rats with severe motor incoordination from cerebellar lesions (Lashley and McCarthy) shows that, once the maze is learned, it may be traversed by a method of progression which involves no patterns of muscular movement that can be recognized as identical with those utilized in learning.

In a study of the effects of destruction of the motor cortex, Lashley has reported the immediate transfer of a complex pattern of movements from one arm to the other, which was paralyzed throughout the course of training, concluding that conduction paths used in this performance could not have been used during training. Herrick (1926) has criticized this conclusion on the ground that, since the impulses controlling habitual movements do not all pass through the motor cortex, the necessary impulses may have reached the motor paths of the paralyzed arm, even when the arm was inactive. But in other cases it was found that the head or leg might be used directly for the solution of the problem. This seems to demand either the assumption that during training specific conduction paths are laid down to every effector, whether it is used or not, or that the habit is not dependent upon specific paths.

As in the case of our conclusions concerning the nature of the adequate stimulus to habit, this type of behavior is the rule rather than the exception in habitual behavior. Similar instances are so common in human behavior that we need not cite specific instances. The facts are those which are held to characterize behavior as purposive rather than mechanical and, although we need not admit the finalistic implications of "purpose," we must recognize that a definite type of neurological problem is involved and that the behavior does not have the commonly admitted properties of the reflex.

Attempts have been made to meet this sort of problem by explanations based upon "symbolism." A stimulus is said to be associated with a verbal or other symbol; another stimulus arouses the same verbal reaction, and the two stimuli are therefore identified. Or the verbal reaction serves as a common stimulus to the various motor responses which may be used alternatively in the performance of the reaction.

If it could be demonstrated that similarity among stimuli is never recognized unless each has previously been associated with the same symbolic response, this explanation would be sufficient, but there is clear evidence that the use of symbols depends upon the recognition of similarity, and not the reverse, so that the identification of the symbol with the object involves exactly the problem which it was proposed to solve.

The appeal to symbolism is a variation of the doctrine of common elements which has been used widely to explain the transfer of training. It is held that the stimuli may be diverse but certain elements of each activate the same afferent paths, exciting identical nerve cells and so eliciting the same reactions. Or transfer of training takes place because certain efferent nerve cells supply two motor paths (the accepted theory of crossed education).

The conditions of visual stimulation which we presented on pages 474 f. seem absolutely to preclude any such common neurons, and it is equally difficult to find them in many cases of motor transfer (for example, the rhythm of two against three, once acquired, may be directly imposed upon any independent pair of muscle groups). The common elements in transfer are not common neurons, but common ratios of excitation in different neuronic systems.

THE NATURE OF CENTRAL INTEGRATION DEDUCED FROM THE DEFECTS
FOLLOWING INJURIES TO THE NERVOUS SYSTEM

Studies of the symptoms of destruction of tissue within the central nervous system point to two seemingly conflicting principles of organization. There is evidence for a high degree of specialization for some functions corresponding to the conceptions of exact cerebral localization, and also evidence for an entire lack of specificity in the contributions of different structures to other functions. The evidence for exact localization arises chiefly from injuries within the anatomically defined sensory and motor projection areas of the cortex; that for diffusion of function, from the injuries to the association areas and from the more careful studies of symptomatology in all lesions.

The evidence for exact localization is not conclusive, even for the projection areas. Small lesions within the motor areas produce only temporary paralyses (Leyton and Sherrington), and the variations in function from time to time suggest that some of the apparent specificity of function of the motor cortex is a matter of temporary physiological organization rather than of permanent anatomical structure.

The doctrine of the "cortical retina" first proposed by Munk has led to the most extreme views of specificity of function of the cortical cells, up to the claim that there is a cell-to-cell correspondence between rods and cones and the ganglion cells of the area striata. Observations upon scotomas following occipital lesions show some correspondence (Holmes and Lister, 1916), but, as Poppelreuter (1917) has pointed out, the variety in form exhibited by scotomas is far less than would be expected from the variety of lesions and may be interpreted as a centripetal or centrifugal irradiation of a disorganizing process within an undifferentiated area, as well as by the assumption of a cortical retina.

Data reported above (page 470) show that in lower animals habits are either not localized, as in the case of the maze, or only very vaguely in a general area, as in brightness discrimination. It appeared also that the capacity to learn and to retain habits formed after cerebral lesion may be a function of the total quantity of functional tissue.

For higher forms, including man, there are no comparable data. There are no controlled studies of the rate of learning in men with cerebral lesions, nor are there any attempts to take into consideration the extent of injury in evaluating symptoms, beyond vague statements that symptoms are slight or absent if the lesions are small. Inspection of the data on motor aphasia reviewed by von Monakow suggests that there is a fairly close relationship between the amount of destruction and the time required for recovery, but the data on rate of improvement are inadequate.

We may approach the problem of specificity of function in man in another way by inquiring into the general nature of the defects following injuries to the cerebrum. There seem to be three diverse types of disorder: simple sensory and motor defects, disturbances of memory, and disorders of the organization of functions. These distinctions are more apparent than real, but they serve to illustrate certain problems of neural function.

The purely sensory and motor disturbances have, as pointed out above, the closest association with structure. Franz (1915) has shown that even these defects are not absolute, but are capable of a considerable degree of recovery and fluctuate in severity from time to time. There is some evidence that the motor defects are due to a weakening of some facilitating function rather than to loss of any definite coordinating mechanism. There may be, for example, a partial restitution of function during emotional excitement. The motor type of aphasia or anarthria is probably of this type. On the sensory side also, the suggestions of Poppelreuter concerning the nature of scotomas, the observations of Gelb and Goldstein (1920) upon pseudofovea and the completion of figures in scotomatous areas are an argument against strict localization and in favor of a dynamic interpretation of the symptoms.

The notions of strict localization and limited defects in aphasia, apraxia, and visual agnosia were in large measure the result of inadequate analysis of the defects. The earlier observers noted the prominent symptoms, such as defects of speech, but had no means of testing other functions involved. They overlooked the milder degrees of dementia accompanying aphasia or ascribed them to involvement of other than the speech areas and made few efforts toward empirical analysis of the disorders of language and thinking.

The classification of aphasia is still a matter of controversy but many of the cases reported suggest two primary types of disturbances. The amnesic types present a picture of difficulty in the recall of verbal material, a difficulty which is more severe but not otherwise different from lapses of memory in normal individuals. In many cases recall is possible under favorable conditions. Speech occurs in excitement, or the proper word can be recalled with effort or by the use of mnemonic aids. Isolated words cannot be recalled, but come readily in certain contexts, or round-about expressions for the same thought are found. In general, there is not a selective loss of some words with retention of others but rather an increase in the threshold for recall of all verbal material. The exceptions will usually be found to be words having a considerable emotional reinforcement—the "emotional language" of Hughlings Jackson.

Such a condition is not to be accounted for on the assumption that specific associations have been interrupted. The lesion affects uniformly a large range of activities and reduces the efficiency of all without abolishing any. The areas concerned in speech seem to behave as does the whole cortex of the rat in the performance of the maze habit; injury reduces its general efficiency without selective effects upon the individual units of behavior.

Other aphasic symptoms imply a disruption of the normal mechanisms of organization rather than an amnesia. In extreme cases the speech is an unintelligible jargon; in milder cases grammatical form is lost, words are mispronounced or distorted, and the rhythm and orderliness of speech is disturbed. Such are the verbal and syntactical types of Head and the agrammatism of Pick.

The problem of the ordering of sequences of behavior, as in grammatical speech, is the most baffling of all neurological problems. It does not help to say that the order is a matter of habit for, although the general arrangements typical of any language are certainly acquired, the specific reactions employing any given word are not. If we learn a new word, such as the name of an object, that word will later be used in its proper relation to other parts of speech, although the context is one in which it has never before been heard. It is not linked to the other words of the sentence by habit, except in so far as it belongs to some general category of parts of speech.

To form any notion of the neurology of grammar we must assume that the entire mechanism involved in the verbalization of a proposition or idea is thrown into a state of partial excitation before actual speech, internal or overt, occurs; that in the preliminary activation the relations implicit in the idea are organized; and that this organization is impressed upon the verbal mechanism as from without. The problem is not that of the activation of successive links in a chain of associated reactions, but the determination of the order in a conglomerate of processes in which there are not previously formed associative bonds.

Jackson formulated this notion in his recognition of the importance of the proposition and Head has emphasized it in distinguishing the syntactical and semantic types of aphasia. The same sort of problem appears at every level of neural organization. Some of the difficulties in reading after occipital lesion have been ascribed to loss of spatial organization within the visual field. The patients see the letters or words but these no longer have a recognizable spatial position with respect to one another. Defects of insight and the intelligent manipulation of ideas evidently involve the same sort of confusion in organization, and it seems possible to distinguish a continuous series of such disorders, ranging from serious intellectual defects to slight disorganization within sensory fields. In how far the defects are called general or specific seems largely a matter of interpretation. Head (1926) considers that intellectual defect occurs in aphasia only in so far as the lack of language is a handicap. Bouman and Grünbaum (1925), on the other hand, consider the aphasias as primarily a defect of intellect. "The patient is not able to hold in mind the concrete elements of a problem and at the same time manipulate them in thought." This difficulty is evident in all behavior of the aphasic, and the difficulty of speech is only one expression of it.

Whatever the final conclusion as to the general cerebral localization of speech, it is clear that this localization does not extend to the logically differentiated elements of speech. These do not correspond to the physiological elements. The problem of cerebral function is characterized by the interplay of many organized systems in which equilibrium or dominance of excitation and the relations among the parts, rhythms and timing of activities, patterns of excitation, rather than of performed association paths, express the significant facts.

Another group of phenomena important for an understanding of cerebral mechanisms is indicated by the relative fragility of functions. In the visual field, for example, the discrimination of colors is more frequently disturbed than any other function and by slighter injuries. When recovery occurs from an initial severe hemianopsia, the visual functions reappear in a rather definite order. Poppelreuter lists sensitivity to light, recognition of differences in illumination in different parts of the visual field, recognition of the direction of single lines without identification of figures, recognition of simple geometrical patterns, vision for complex forms with confusion of meaning, and normal vision as stages in the recovery of pattern vision.

Attempts to localize these different functions in different areas have not been supported by anatomical findings, and the stages of recovery or the relative ease of abolition of the functions can be interpreted only as an indication that the same area may function at different levels of complexity. The problem here is like that presented by cerebral function in maze learning, where a limit to the complexity of the habits which may be formed is set by the extent of the injury. With increase in mass and physiological development the complexity of the situations which can be integrated increases. We have as yet no clue to the nature of these "levels" of integration, except the evident importance of the quantity of tissue.

The symptoms of lesions in man emphasize the dynamic rather than the static in neural organization. There is a simplification of behavior, a reduction in the number of elements which can be dealt with or integrated in a single reaction. This simplification may be so general as to involve almost every aspect of behavior, constituting a general dementia; it may be limited to some one field of activity such as the verbal formulation of propositions or the synthesis of visual impressions; but in every case it affects the majority of reactions of the given type. It is not the specific reaction but the mode of synthesizing activity which is affected by cerebral lesion.

Along with this there may go an apparent weakening of the reaction mechanism. Reactions are not absolutely abolished but only rendered difficult, so that some extraneous facilitation is required before they can be elicited. Here also, not specific reactions but groups of reactions are affected and the grouping is determined by such relations as object-name. It seems as though the unit of cerebral organization can be expressed only in terms of relationships among activities, rather than in terms of individual reactions.

Peripheral versus Central Processes in Habit. The last decade has witnessed a bitter controversy concerning the nature of reproductive memory. Until the development of objective psychology the doctrine that memory involves the re-arousal of central nervous processes reproducing more or less completely the original sensory experience was generally accepted. No clear neurological theory concerning their production was formulated beyond the general notion that they were produced by the action of centers which were thrown into activity by associative processes.

Watson (1914) attacked the theory of imagery on the ground that memory-images are not objectively demonstrable, that introspective studies purporting to deal with them become involved in a futile mentalism which has no explanatory value for behavior, and that the phenomena of memory and thought may be dealt with more adequately on the assumption that recall is the reinstatement of those bodily movements which were first elicited by the stimuli recalled. Thus all memory was reduced to terms of motor habit, and thought to chains of motor reactions in which muscular contractions serve as stimuli to further activity. Dunlap's theory of homeodetic arcs and Washburn's of "tentative movements" have much in common with Watson's doctrine of "implicit movement," but the former admits a central short-circuiting and the latter ascribes the image to the blocking of the motor response.

Recent attempts to establish the importance of implicit movements or movement systems in thinking have given negative results (Washburn), while the evidence for centrally maintained coordinating processes has accumulated. Lashley and Ball (1929) found that the performance of the maze habit was not disturbed by the destruction of the somaesthetic paths in the cervical cord and concluded that the maze habit cannot be interpreted as a chain of somaesthetic-motor reactions. Attempts to demonstrate implicit movements in the verbal mechanisms during thinking have shown movements, it is true, but they are irregular, by no means always present, and do not correspond in rhythm or pattern to those of overt speech (Thorsen, 1925). They can be interpreted only as chance irradiation to the verbal mechanisms from centrally maintained processes. The writer has obtained similar results in a study of eye movements during thinking of geometrical forms and relations.

The argument that the interference with thinking by maintained postures of the articulatory organs, as in the difficulty of thinking "bubble" with the mouth widely opened, as an evidence for peripheral interference is not valid, for a similar interference can be demonstrated between different motor organs where the blocking can be only central. For example, it is difficult to tap a rhythm of three with one hand against two with the other, although these processes can be dissociated by practice. Similarly, Pintner showed that verbal thinking could be dissociated from the interference of articulatory activity. Reports of the effects of operative removal of the larynx or other articulatory mechanisms do not indicate any resulting disturbance of thinking.

On the other hand, something like objective evidence in support of imagery is accumulating. Visual after-images have never been denied by the opponents of the memory-image, but have been discussed as genuine phenomena and ascribed to residual excitations within the peripheral mechanisms. Recent studies of eidetic imagery reveal objectively a very close parallelism between the eidetic image and the visual after-image. Naïve subjects, who could not possibly be familiar with the laws of color mixture, report phenomena of color contrast, changes in the apparent size of the image when projected to different distances, and the like, which can be explained only on the assumption that there is aroused in them by association some process which corresponds very closely to the excitation originally aroused by peripheral stimulation (Klüver, 1926).

Since the motor theory of imagery assumes that recall is a reinstatement of the reaction originally given to the stimulus recalled, the image should contain no elements which were not reacted to or noted in the original situation. Woodworth has held that this is true of the image, but some of the descriptions of the content of images given by eidetic subjects include a wealth of detail which almost certainly was not noted by specific reactions during the period of exposure of the stimulus.

Although perhaps not conclusive, this evidence seems to favor the older doctrine of imagery and to throw us back upon the concept of activity maintained within the central nervous system for an understanding of serial habits and the mechanisms of thinking.

THE PHENOMENA OF LEARNING

The foregoing discussion serves to define some of the characteristics of the learned reaction and the properties of the mechanism by which the performance is brought about. Not all experiences come to be associated and, since we cannot observe directly the nervous changes, we must fall back upon analysis of the external conditions which favor association and try to infer from them the nature of the central nervous processes which occur during practice.

Psychological studies have given a series of "laws of learning" which define conditions under which learning occurs and which have served as the points of departure for theories as to the nature of the process. The laws of contiguity, exercise, effect, and completeness of response are the ones most stressed in recent literature. In addition, primacy, recency, vividness, intensity, and the older laws of association, such as similarity, have been cited by various writers as significant for the theory of learning. Since apparent exceptions to each of these laws are numerous, we must examine them briefly before admitting that they form an adequate basis for the theory of learning.

The *law of contiguity* seems the most clearly established of these generalizations. In order that association occur, the associated experiences must fall within a certain time interval. For conditioned reflexes in lower animals this interval is a matter of seconds or minutes; for man, perhaps through mediate associations, it may be much prolonged. Exceptions may be the seeming facts of association by similarity, as when a visual pattern suggests an auditory rhythm. Since not all experiences which occur simultaneously are associated, the law clearly defines only one of the conditions necessary for learning.

The *law of exercise* has been more emphasized than any other in recent theories. Repetition of experiences in contiguity leads to their firmer association. Repetition of a function results in its improvement in speed or accuracy, according to the law of diminishing returns. These statements express common facts. But their universality and fundamental importance for learning theory is questionable. Most of the learning of human adults does not involve repetition and frequent instances of animals' learning in a single trial are available. Moreover, the functions which are improved by repetition are invariably complex, involving the formation of numerous associations, many of which may be seen to be formed in a single trial. The learning curve may be explained as well on the assumption that single associations are formed in one trial and do not improve with practice as by the theory that they improve gradually. Thorndike (1913) has so dealt with the learning curve in discussion of changes in the rate of improvement, although he has elsewhere adhered to the doctrine of gradual improvement in the strength of bonds. Cason

(1924) has pointed out that improvement in the function usually involves not an improvement in the specific acts but a change in the character of the acts; that this is the establishment of new associations, not the improvement of old. Thus for the greater number of habits it is questionable whether improvement involves a strengthening of associations.

The facts which seem best to support the law of exercise are those revealed by the savings method and nonsense material. Repetition of the series seems to strengthen the associations, since, with increased practice, less and less is lost by equal periods of disuse. This would be a more impressive argument if nonsense syllables were truly nonsensical, but actually their acquisition is helped by various mnemonic aids, and it is quite possible that overlearning multiplies the number of such associative bonds rather than strengthens those first formed.

The improvement during conditioned-reflex experiments, involving apparently the association of a single stimulus and response, might be interpreted as evidence for improvement in conduction over a single path, but a considerable part of the improvement, which is measured by a greater regularity in the appearance of the reflex, is obviously due to a blocking of specific inhibitions, and it is not clearly demonstrated that any strengthening of bonds occurs even here.

Data on "fatigue" or experimental extinction of the conditioned reflex and the phenomenon of "going stale" from overpractice show that repetition may weaken rather than strengthen associations. Pavlov (1927) has contended that this is due to the development of inhibition, on the ground that it cannot be a fatigue of the conditioned-reflex path. The term inhibition is meaningless in this connection, since we are not dealing with the suppression of one activity by another, which is all that inhibition means today, but with the suppression of an activity by simple repetition. The phenomenon seems related to that of adaptation in lower organisms, to which there is still less reason to apply the notion of inhibition. Experimental extinction stands today unexplained and in opposition to the law of exercise.

It is not our purpose to minimize the importance of exercise for learning, but only to point out that the facts of improvement with practice are susceptible of various interpretations and do not justify the usual inferences drawn from them concerning the nature of the nervous processes involved. Associative connections are strengthened by practice but it does not follow that these connections are nerve tracts in which resistance is lowered by repeated passage of impulses. On the contrary, the changes in the character of the responses with practice indicate the continuous formation of new associative bonds, and there seems to be no instance of learning on record to which this explanation of the law of exercise could not apply.

The *law of effect* has been variously expressed. Beginning as the notion that pleasant or unpleasant results of an act determine its repetition, it has evolved through successive stages to the theory of the fixation of habit through the influence of the "consummatory reaction."

The pleasure-pain theory has been criticized on the grounds that it is mentalistic, that it begs the question by assuming that the consequences for every case of learning have been pleasant, that it fails to account for the acquisition of likes and dislikes, that it fails to account for selective association in such cases as maze learning, and that it is not true for reproductive memory, in which unpleasant experiences are recalled as readily as pleasant.

In many of the studies of learning in animals it is customary to use incentives such as hunger, punishment, and the like, and in most cases the acts learned are those which result in removal of the incentive. The predominance of this type of situation in experimental studies has led to a great emphasis upon the importance of the "drive" and the "consummatory reaction." It has been assumed that the hunger or other organic need serves to increase the general tension of the organism and that the cessation of the tension, following the consummatory reaction, with its satisfaction of the need, somehow fixes the habit.

Two major theories of the mechanism of the drive have been implied in recent writings. The one takes its departure from the hunger mechanism and assumes that a continued state of visceral tension supplies a mass of sensory impulses which, by irradiation or specific facilitation, increase the excitability or responsiveness of the nervous mechanisms involved in exploratory behavior. This notion of organic hunger is probably correct, but it does not provide a comprehensible mechanism for the fixation of habits. The action of glands of internal secretion has been suggested as a second factor in the drive on the assumption that the heightened activity during emotional disturbance is referable to the increased adrenalin output and that other endocrine organs may work in the same way. We have carried out a number of experiments with adrenalectomized and castrated animals and other tests in which attempts were made to swamp the normal variations in secretions of the pituitary, adrenal, and sex glands by subcutaneous injection of extracts. All gave negative results on learning.

A good bit of evidence, such as the studies of relation of strength of incentive to rate of learning, shows that the drives play an important part in the formation of habits, but it is not clear whether this is by heightening the general activity of the animal and so increasing his chances of exposure to the proper conditions for learning, by increasing excitability so that the effects of the associated stimuli are more intense, or by some specific action whereby the associations are fixed. Certainly what is known of the mechanisms of the drive provides no comprehensible mechanism for fixation. Moreover, in the greater part of human learning, particularly in incidental memory and recognition, there is no evidence for any factors comparable to the drive.

The assumption has been based upon the successive formation of conditioned reflexes that the drive may be transferred from one reaction to another and that the primitive drives may thus play a part even where they are not apparent. The latter conclusion is, however, purely speculative and is really an attempt to explain the more common phenomena of learning in terms of the less.

The law of effect, in its various forms, confuses learning with performance. The animal learns to go where food is obtained in the maze and when hungry goes there. Under other conditions he may show an equal familiarity with other paths in the maze. The evidence suggests that the drive is one of the associated elements in the maze habit rather than the agent responsible for the association.

A view of the learning problem which is allied to the emphasis on the law of effect is that stressing the unity in the act of learning. Peterson (1916) has pointed out that maze learning and similar activities cannot be understood in terms of independent *acts,* but must be looked upon as a unitary function in which all behavior is fused into a harmonious whole. The perfected habit is more complete, in that it involves fewer conflicts of impulses than the initial random activity, and the learning is the selection of these more complete responses. Poppelreuter (1915) denies that simple association ever occurs. Learning results from the "coexistence of experiences in one total experience whose physical correlate then constitutes the engram." These statements foreshadow the doctrine of "closure" of the configurationists. Koffka (1928) has developed this notion in some detail. In solving a problem the organism is working toward a definite end or goal which is unknown but nevertheless effective in producing activity. Until this goal is reached, the activity is incomplete or "unclosed." With the attainment of the goal the series of activities is completed or closed; that is, it assumes a configuration or equal distribution of tensions which is normal for the organism, as the spherical form is normal for a bubble. With closure, retention is somehow assured. Koffka's statement of the law of closure parallels closely the law of effect. The unclosed situation corresponds to the drive to activity, the closure to the consummatory reaction. At present the closed system is not defined except in terms of analogy with physical systems in equilibrium. Underlying the theory of closure is the notion that the nervous system is so constituted as to limit and prescribe the relations into which excitatory processes must fall, as the shape of a surface determines the distribution of a static charge upon it. Description of insight is description of these necessary configurations, although in terms of stimulus relations or sensations. We cannot find that any clear positive statement of the neural processes has been given. Wertheimer speaks of direct relations between centers of excitation, independent of the specific intercellular connections, but does not elaborate the suggestion. The recent emphasis upon the concept of configuration has been valuable in bringing out the ubiquity of the problem of reaction to relations in psychology and the inadequacy of the simple mechanical hypotheses to meet the problems, but it has provided no adequate substitute for these explanations. As applied to learning, there is no present criterion of closure of a system of activity except the fact of learning so that, if the hypothesis does not beg the question, it at least is inapplicable in advance to any particular learning problem.

The *laws of primacy and recency* have not usually been considered as fundamental conditions for learning. The theory of backward association of Hachet-Souplet assumed that, when a series of acts leading to food is learned, the last act of the series is first associated with the food, and in the following practice the preceding acts are associated in order. Studies of the order of elimination of errors in the maze have not supported this view of backward association. It seems probable that primacy and recency are effective only when they increase the intensity or stimulating value of the situations.

The *laws of intensity and vividness* seem to apply more widely than any of the other generalizations concerning conditions favoring learning, with the exception of the law of contiguity, but this is perhaps only because we know so little about them. Within limits, the rate of formation of the conditioned reflex varies with the intensity of the associated stimulus. The rate of learning of a discrimination problem varies with the intensity or stimulating value of the stimuli, but here at once we meet with difficulties, for, although factors in brightness discrimination can be stated in terms of the energy of the stimulus, it is evidently not the energy of the stimuli which makes one pattern more easily learned than another. The effectiveness of a situation as a stimulus can rarely be stated in terms of objective intensity and only such vague notions as the value for attention can be used to define the subjective intensity or vividness. Yet it seems clear that the effectiveness of situations as stimuli is of prime importance for their association. A few exceptions complicate the problem, as the formation of associations with subthreshold stimuli. There are not data upon which to base a neurological theory of stimulating value. On the whole, the problem seems more closely allied to that of logical memory than to the mere intensity of excitation.

The importance of the *logical relations* of the material to be learned is shown by a large number of studies. The use and value of mnemonic aids is sufficient evidence of this. There is, however, little evidence as to how the ordering of the material to be memorized favors learning. The most commonly expressed theory implies that logical learning requires fewer new associations than rote learning of an equivalent amount of material. Meumann has expressed this in the statement that "learning is not a mere matter of the number of elements but of the number of independent memorial units." It seems doubtful whether this interpretation can be substantiated. The following verbatim statement from a subject with an unusually good memory for numbers shows the multiplicity of relations which are recognized and retained in the memorizing of a simple number. The subject was asked to remember the number 8264 and replied, "That's easy because my telephone number is 8238. The first two numbers are the same: multiply by 2 and divide by 2—that is, the last numbers—gives 6 and 4: then 8264 goes down in steps of two, except that the 2 is transposed to the second place." These are, of course, familiar relations for the subject but they are in an unfamiliar order. Where to multiply or divide is dependent on the new number, and the order of these procedures must be remembered. The assumption that few associative bonds are required is wholly gratuitous. Where large groups of numbers are remembered as familiar units, there is doubtless a reduction in the number of new associative connections, but such are no more instances of logical memory than is the learning of nonsense words instead of their constituent letters. The logical ordering and memorization of material seems always to involve the construction of some sort of relational framework and the association of the elements to be remembered with parts of the logical frame: a process which would seem to involve more rather than fewer associative bonds.

In the discussion of the symptoms of cerebral lesion in man we have seen that the functional units must be regarded as modes of organization rather than single reactions, methods of relating rather than specific associations. There is a resemblance between this and the phenomena of logical memory, as though the material to be memorized were fitted into some one of the modes of organization, and as though retention were better if the material fits into some general schema of facilitation such as we have suggested to be functional in determining grammatical form.

It is difficult to distinguish logical from rote memory. It is not impossible that even the supposedly most mechanical learning, such as the rat's acquisition of the maze habit, involves something akin to logical memory. There is certainly evidence of a generalization of directions in the maze as an important factor in the formation of the habit. There seems to be as much justification for Poppelreuter's conclusion that all learning is of the type of logical memory as for the opposed view that all learning is the formation of fewer or more conditioned reflexes.

THEORIES OF THE MECHANISM OF LEARNING

Attempts to formulate a physiological account of the learning process have been concerned either with descriptions of the supposed structural changes underlying new modes of behavior or with speculations concerning the processes by which such structural changes are brought about. Occasionally the two aspects of the problem have been included in one theory. The speculations concerning the nature of the memory trace or engram may be divided roughly into five groups.

1. *Growth of New Processes Connecting the Neurons.*[1] Earlier views of the dendrites as ameboid processes, capable of extension and contraction in the establishment of temporary anatomical connections, led to the supposition that learning might consist of alterations in the contractility of the cells (Ramon y Cajal, Hellwig). Sherrington's demonstration that reflex latent time does not involve a preparatory setting of the path, with more recent studies of finer cellular structures, has led to the abandonment of these theories. More recently, Kappers (1917) has

---

[1] A good review of the anatomical theories is given by Matthaei (1921).

suggested that learning involves the establishment of new relatively permanent connections through the growth of axons and dendrites under the influence of bio-electric currents. His general theory of neurobiotaxis was sketched on page 459.

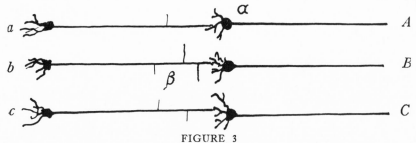

FIGURE 3
DIAGRAM TO ILLUSTRATE KAPPERS' THEORY OF ASSOCIATION
For explanation see text.

Its application to the problem of learning is illustrated in Figure 3. $a - A$ and $c - C$ represent two conducting systems, and β a cell of a sensory tract, not associated with either but in close proximity. If a is excited, cell a is thrown into a condition of heightened "electrolytic dissociation" so that the surrounding field is ionized. If now β is stimulated, growth of its axon and collaterals is induced. The growth occurs most strongly in the ionized field of a, rather than toward any of the cells of $c - C$. The approach of a collateral from β stimulates development of dendrites from a until contact is finally made.

Certain inadequacies of the theory are apparent. It accounts for selective association between two paths, but does not account for the direction of association. The rate of ameboid movement and cell growth seems too slow to account for the speed with which associations may be formed.

2. *Increase in Conducting Substance as a Result of Exercise.* Verworn argued, from the growth of exercised muscles and the atrophy of the cells of the visual cortex in blinded animals, that the nerve cells increase in size under the influence of stimulation, and that with increase in size there is a corresponding increase in the intensity of the nerve impulses. Others have stressed the growth of parts of the cell, the axon (Exner), the neurofibrillae (Ziegler). Alterations in the conducting substance without implied change in the morphology of the cells have been discussed by many writers. Robertson, from similarities between the experimental curves of Ebbinghaus and certain curves of rate of chemical action, has deduced that learning consists of the deposition within the cell of a product of an "autocatalytic monomolecular reaction," the diffusion of which through the cell membranes constitutes forgetting. Matthews and Crile have pointed out the similarity between hysteresis of linseed oil and the phenomena of memory, and have suggested that

since linolinic acid occurs in the central nervous system it may be responsible for learning.

3. *Chemical Changes in the Regions of Contact between Cells.* The most widely cited theory of the engram is derived from Sherrington's theory of the synapse as a semipermeable membrane whose resistance to the passage of nerve impulses is primarily responsible for the patterns of integration. From this it was but a step to the conception of a change in the permeability of this membrane as the basis of memory. Other theories concerning this mechanism have been suggested. Goldscheider postulates specific molecular changes at the intercellular junctions, by which a specific chemical sensitization between cells is produced.

Cason (1925) has enumerated many ways in which the cellular relations might be modified by the learning process. Reorienting the molecules of the synaptic membrane by electronic bombardment so as to alter its permeability, physical growth in accord with Kappers' theory, changes in the colloidal dispersion within the neuron, according to McDonald's theories of conduction, and changes in surface tension are the chief possibilities suggested. No evidence is given that all or any of these changes are actually involved in learning.

Johnson (1927) has formulated a detailed hypothesis concerning the structure of the synaptic junction, of which only a brief and inadequate sketch can be included here. He assumes that ionized molecules are absorbed on the cell membranes, constituting a surface film in which the charged ions are oriented with respect to the membrane. The ordinary metabolic processes of the cells, involving a constant transfer of ions through the membranes, produce a continuous oscillatory change in the orientation of the molecules of the surface film. The rate of this oscillation is constant for any given set of conditions. In order that conduction from cell to cell should occur, the periods of oscillation of their films must be synchronous. The periods of oscillation are altered during the learning process by a "forcing" of their frequencies resulting from the simultaneous stimulation of the membrane by the sensory impulses which later come to be associated. The hypothesis is chiefly of interest because of the modification of the theory of drainage which is introduced.

4. *Persistence of Excitatory Processes.* Ebbecke (1919) has pointed out the resemblance between visual after-images, memory-images, and a wide range of other phenomena and, on the assumption that the simpler of these are due to an after-discharge, has attempted to account for all memory in terms of residual excitation in the cells.

5. *Diffuse Functional Correlations.* Loeb (1902) followed Goltz to a large extent in rejecting cerebral localization of function and proposed a theory of learning in accord with this view. The theory was rather vaguely expressed but involved the assumptions that integration in the nervous system is determined by the periodicity of discharge of nerve impulses rather than by specific connections of cells and that learning consists of a tuning of motor systems so that they become resonant to

particular sensory frequencies. A similar conception of the mechanism of integration is proposed by Weiss (1926), although he has not applied it to the problem of learning. This alteration in periodicity of activity may be ascribed either to individual cells making up distinct paths or to large masses of cells. Its locus has not been discussed by the writers.

This list of theories includes almost every conceivable change which could occur in a system made up of nerve cells. There is little to choose between the different ones. They are not developed in detailed relation to the various phenomena of learning and retention and so are not readily capable of experimental test. No one more than another serves to unify and make more intelligible the diverse phenomena of learning. None provides any basis for prediction of the results in any new learning experiment.

Almost all of the theories take for granted the law of exercise, the formation of associations by the forced passage of nerve impulses over the paths later associated, and the functioning of these paths in the performance of the learned activities. As we have seen in the foregoing sections, these are not established facts and indeed seem to be contradicted by a considerable amount of evidence. If it is true that a learned response may be carried out by the activation of conduction paths, either afferent or efferent, which were not employed during the process of learning, or if practice does not lower resistance to conduction in established paths, but only leads to the formation of different paths, the theories lose all their relevance.

The theories reviewed above have been concerned chiefly with attempts to describe the engram. Another group has attempted to account specifically for the initial passage of impulses from one tract to another, assuming that the law of exercise will explain the fixation. They start with the fact of simultaneous or successive excitation of two tracts which are in anatomical but not in functional connection. Drainage and irradiation of nerve impulses are the two mechanisms most frequently cited.

Drainage. The theory of drainage was first definitely propounded by McDougall to account for the phenomena of inhibition. It involved the postulation of a particular kind of energy, "neurin," stored in or flowing through nerve cells. When a neuron is stimulated, it not only conducts the energy received from the stimulating cell but also drains off the energy of other cells with which it has organic connections. The theory has been applied to the learning process by Meyer and by Adams. In brief, they assume that when two reflex paths are excited simultaneously the dominant final common path drains off energy from the other. The connections opened by the force of this drainage are later permeable to impulses coming from the previously drained path alone.

The theory of drainage is opposed by all of the more recent data upon the nature of the propagated disturbance in nerves. The phenomena which it was devised to explain can be more adequately treated in terms of interference of nerve impulses. Johnson (1927) has attempted to rehabilitate the theory in order to explain the induction of retinal fatigue in one eye by stimulation of the other. To the writer this seems only a special case of central elaboration in vision, presenting the same problems as binocular color mixture, filling-in of the blind-spot, completion of forms in the hemianopic field, and the like. These phenomena cannot be dealt with in terms of drainage so that its postulation for the special case of fatigue and for learning seems unjustified.

Irradiation. The theory of irradiation as proposed by Goldscheider assumes that regions intermediate between two excited centers receive nervous impulses from both and are, therefore, subject to stronger excitation than non-intermediate zones. As a result of this intense excitation, the region undergoes changes of stable character which result in a more ready excitation of either center by the other. The more recent formulation of Pyle seems essentially the same as this.

Watson (1914) has approached the problem in a somewhat different way. He assumes that the excitability of the final common path of the associated reaction is increased during stimulation. When the associated stimulus is applied, it excites sensory fibers, and weak impulses irradiating from these may stimulate the hyperexcitable final common path. This excitation results in a lowering of threshold for impulses coming later over the same sensory path.

The theory of Kappers (see page 489) also appeals to irradiation but assumes that the spreading electric current resulting from the nervous discharge stimulates the growth of processes from the cells.

Direct evidence for the theories of irradiation is lacking. The writer attempted a test of them by training animals under the influence of strychnine and caffeine. These drugs are supposed to have a similar physiological action, promoting irradiation in spinal nervous centers. Strychnine was found to facilitate learning, caffeine to retard it markedly, which proves only the inadequacy of our knowledge of pharmacology.

Learning by Trial and Error. Most of the recent attempts to develop a theory of learning have started from the problem of random activity and the selection of successful acts. The statement of the problem is usually some variant of the following: a stimulus (hunger, maze, or what not) initiates a series of activities which may be called *a-b-c-d-e-f-g-h*, and which follow each other in a natural order. Acts *b, d, f,* and *h* contribute to success in the problem. With practice, the others are dropped out, leaving the series *b-d-f-h* as a direct solution. No question of the association of *b* with *d* and so on is raised; it is taken for granted when *c* is omitted.

This we believe to be a wholly misleading statement of the problem of learning in the maze or problem box. The acts do not form an internally conditioned series from which the dropping of some will leave the remainder in association. On the contrary, it is a chance sequence determined by the environmental stimuli which the animal encounters, an odor here, a contact there, calling out specific unrelated activities. The linking of the successful acts is not explained by the dropping of the unsuccessful.

The acts making up the final series are not those which originally intervened between the unsuccessful movements. Entering the true path from a section of the cul-de-sac in the maze is the same act as entering the section from the preceding part of the true path only when ·the act is defined in terms of its end result; the movements involved are never the same.

The first evidence of learning is a focalization of activity to which the elimination of errors seems purely subsidiary. In the maze the animal pushes forward in the direction of the food compartment; in the problem box his responses to the latch become prolonged. The effectiveness of certain stimuli is heightened, responsiveness to other stimuli drops out in consequence. The problem of learning by trial and error is thus not one of the mechanism of dropping of useless movements, but of the fixation of the effective behavior. The behavior shows a responsiveness to relationships and a unity which is difficult to express in terms of simple associations and for which none of the suggested principles of selection is a satisfactory explanation.

The Problem

The conclusions from this review of the problem of learning must be largely negative. In spite of the vast experimental literature which has grown up since the studies of Ebbinghaus and the advancement which has been made in the study of nervous structure, it is doubtful that we know anything more about the mechanism of learning than did Descartes when he described the opening of the pores in the nerves by the passage of animal spirits. His statement sounds remarkably like the reduction of synaptic resistance by the passage of the nerve impulse.

The evidence from many lines of investigation opposes interpretation of learning as the formation of definite "conditioned-reflex arcs" through the cerebral hemispheres or through any other part of the central nervous system. It is doubtful whether the conception of limited conduction paths through the gray matter can be applied even in the case of spinal reflexes. The adequate stimulus to habitual reactions and even to instinctive acts is a ratio of intensities distributed in time or space and capable of calling out the response when applied to any sensory cells, within a wide range. Analysis of the central nervous mechanisms reveals likewise an independence of individual nerve cells and a determination of response by masses of tissue and relative excitation of different parts. The same sort of independence of structural elements appears in a study of the motor responses. The phenomena can be described only in vague dynamic terms, and attempts to particularize either in terms of individual reactions or of anatomical units fail to express the most striking characteristics of the problem of organization. The unit of functional organization seems to be not the reflex arc of Sherrington or the mechanism of reciprocal innervation of T. G. Brown, but the mechanism, whatever be its nature, by which response to a ratio of intensities is brought about.

If our analysis of the problems of behavior and of neural·mechanism is correct, it follows that the current theories of neural organization have started from false premises and offer no hope of a solution of the problems. Such a sweeping conclusion is still premature, but its possibility emphasizes the need for a more critical experimental analysis of the evidence upon which current theories are based.

A review of the literature on learning reveals many suggestive relationships between the various forms of modification of behavior. We have pointed out the similarity between the problems of morphogenesis and of integration in the developed nervous system; the relations of fatigue, acclimatization, experimental extinction of the conditioned reflex, and "going stale"; the problem of the organization of behavior in relation to differentiated structure and to undifferentiated mass of neural tissue; the interrelation of speed of learning, limits of training, and cerebral development; questions of the nature of the adequate stimulus and the seeming differences between learned reactions and the mere contraction of muscle groups; various instances where specific laws of learning seem not to apply. In none of these examples are the data adequate to give a clear insight into the relations involved, and until these relations are revealed there is no starting-point for a general theory of learning.

In the present stage of psychological science, the sole value of hypotheses is to define alternative possibilities which can be tested by experiment. The slight value of current formulation of learning theory is attested by the small number of studies which attempt a critical evaluation either of the laws of learning or of the postulated nervous processes underlying them. The fact is that most of the laws and theories are couched in such form as neither to be susceptible of experimental verification nor to suggest any experimental procedures which will lead to a more profitable formulation. Descriptive studies of learning must be extended over a far wider range and in much greater detail than at present and must reveal the similarities and differences between the many types and levels of modification of behavior before any attempt to formulate a general theory of learning will be of value.

BIBLIOGRAPHY

BERITOFF, J. 1926. Ueber die individuell erworbene Tätigkeit des Zentralnervensystems bei Tauben. *Pflüg. Arch. f. d. ges. Physiol.*, **213**, 370-406.

BIRD, C. 1926. The effect of maturation upon the pecking instinct of chicks. *Ped. Sem.*, **33**, 212-234.

BOUMAN, L., & GRÜNBAUM, A. A. 1925. Experimentelle-pychologische Untersuchungen zur Aphasie und Paraphasie. *Zsch. f. d. ges. Neur. u. Psychiat.* **96**, 481-538.

CARMICHAEL, L. 1927. A further study of the development of behavior in vertebrates experimentally removed from the influence of external stimulation. *Psychol. Rev.*, **34**, 34-47.

CASON, H. 1924. Criticisms of the laws of exercise and effect. *Psychol. Rev.*, **31**, 397-417.

————. 1925. The physical basis of the conditioned response. *Amer. J. Psychol.*, **36**, 371-393.

CHILD, C. M. 1921. The origin and development of the nervous system. Chicago: Univ. Chicago Press. Pp. xiii+296.

DETWILER, S. R. 1923. Experiments on the reversal of the spinal cord in Amblystoma embryos at the level of the anterior limb. *J. Exper. Zoöl.*, **38**, 293-321.

————. 1925. Coordinated movements in supernumerary transplanted limbs. *J. Comp. Neur.*, **38**, 461-490.

EBBECKE, U. 1919. Die kortikalen Erregungen. Leipzig: Barth. Pp. x+305.

FRANZ, S. I. 1915. Variation in the distribution of the motor centers. *Psychol. Monog.*, 1915, **19**, No. 81, 80-162.

GELB, A., & GOLDSTEIN, K. 1920. Psychologische Analysen hirnpathologischer Fälle. Leipzig: Barth. Pp. v+561.

GOLDSTEIN, K. 1924. Das Wesen der amnetischen Aphasie. *Schweiz. Arch. f. Neur. u. Psychiat.*, **15**, 163-175.

HEAD, H. 1926. Aphasia and kindred disorders of speech. (2 vols.) London: Cambridge Univ. Press; New York: Macmillan. Pp. xvi+550; xxxiv +430.

HERRICK, C. J. 1926. Brains of rats and men. Chicago: Univ. Chicago Press. Pp. xiii+382.

HOLMES, G., & LISTER, W. T. 1916. Disturbances of vision from cerebral lesions with special reference to the macula. *Brain*, **39**, 34-73.

JENNINGS, H. S. 1905. Modifiability in behavior: I. Behavior of sea anemones. *J. Exper. Zoöl.*, **2**, 447-485.

————. 1907. Behavior of the starfish *Asterias forreri* de Loriol. *Univ. Calif. Publ. Zoöl.*, **4**, 53-185.

JOHNSON, H. M. 1927. A simpler principle of explanation of imaginative and ideational behavior and of learning. *J. Comp. Psychol.*, **7**, 187-235.

KAPPERS, C. U. A. 1917. Further contributions on neurobiotaxis: IX. An attempt to compare the phenomena of neurobiotaxis with other phenomena of taxis and tropism. *J. Comp. Neur.*, **27**, 261-298.

KLÜVER, H. 1926. An experimental study of the eidetic type. *Genet. Psychol. Monog.*, **1**, 71-230.

KOFFKA, K. 1928. The growth of the mind: an introduction to child psychology. (2nd ed.) (Trans. by R. M. Ogden.) New York: Harcourt, Brace; London: Kegan Paul. Pp. xix+427.

LAPICQUE, L. 1922. Le poids du cerveau et l'intelligence. *J. de psychol.*, **19**, 5-23.

LASHLEY, K. S. 1929. Brain mechanisms and intelligence. Chicago: Univ. Chicago Press. Pp. xi+186.

LASHLEY, K. S., & BALL, J. 1929. Spinal conduction and kinaesthetic sensitivity in maze habit. *J. Comp. Psychol.*, **9**, 70-106.

LOEB, J. 1902. Comparative physiology of the brain and comparative psychology. New York: Putnam. Pp. x+309.

MATTHAEI, R. 1921. Von den Theorien über eine allgemein-physiologische Grundläge des Gedächtnisses. *Zsch. f. allg. Physiol.*, **19**, 1-46.

MONAKOW, C. v. 1914. Die Lokalization im Grosshirn. Wiesbaden: Bergmann. Pp. xi+1033.

PAVLOV, I. P. 1927. Conditioned reflexes: an investigation of the physiological activity of the cerebral cortex. (Trans. and ed. by G. V. Anrep.) London: Oxford Univ. Press. Pp. xv+430.

PECHSTEIN, L. A. 1917. Whole vs. part methods in motor learning. *Psychol. Monog.*, **33**, No. 99. Pp. 80.

PETERSON, J. 1916. Completeness of response as an explanation principle in learning. *Psychol. Rev.*, **23**, 153-162.

PIÉRON, H. 1927. Thought and the brain. New York: Harcourt, Brace. Pp. xvi+262.

POPPELREUTER, W. 1915. Ueber den Versuch einer Revision der psychophysiologischen Lehre von der elementaren Assoziation und Reproduction. *Monatssch. f. Psychol., Psychiat. u. Neur.*, **37**, 278-323.

————. 1917. Die psychischen Schädigungen durch Kopfschuss. Leipzig: Voss. Pp. viii+473.

STONE, C. P. 1922. The congenital sexual behavior of the young male albino rat. *J. Comp. Psychol.*, **2**, 95-153.

THORNDIKE, E. L. 1913. Educational psychology: Vol. 1. The original nature of man. New York: Teach. Coll., Columbia Univ. Pp. xii+327.

THORSEN, A. M. 1925. The relation of tongue movements to internal speech. *J. Exper. Psychol.*, **8**, 1-32.

TRAVIS, L. E., & HUNTER, T. A. 1928. The relation between 'intelligence' and reflex conduction rate. *J. Exper. Psychol.*, **11**, 342-354.

TURNER, C. H. 1913. Behavior of the common roach (*Periplaneta orientalis* L.) on an open maze. *Biol. Bull.*, **25**, 348-365.

WATSON, J. B. 1914. Behavior: an introduction to comparative psychology. New York: Holt. Pp. xii+439.

WEISS, P. 1926. The relation between central and peripheral coordination. *J. Comp. Neur.*, **40**, 241-252.

YERKES, R. M. 1912. The intelligence of earthworms. *J. Anim. Behav.*, **2**, 332-352.

CHAPTER 11

LEARNING: IV. EXPERIMENTAL STUDIES OF LEARNING

WALTER S. HUNTER

Clark University

THE GENERAL CHARACTER OF STUDIES OF THE LEARNING PROCESS

Learning is one of the most characteristic aspects of human and infra-human behavior. It is difficult in certain limiting conditions to distinguish between those changes in behavior which constitute genuine cases of learning and other changes in behavior which may be due to modifications of receptor function or to actual changes in the effectors, such as increased muscular strength. In general, however, we may say that learning is taking place wherever behavior shows a *progressive change,* or *trend,* with a repetition of the same stimulating situation and where the change cannot be accounted for on the basis of fatigue or of receptor and effector changes. Those trends in behavior which thus earn the title of learning are presumably due to changes in the nervous system and are possible because of the plasticity and retentivity of this system.

Studies of learning cover both the fact of acquisition and that of retention. Acquisition is itself cumulative and is to be understood only upon the assumption of the retention of the effects of previous stimulus-response activities. The evidences for retention and the methods of testing it, I have elsewhere (1928, pp. 276-279) described as follows: "When we say that the co-ordination [of a stimulus-response activity] is retained, we mean one or all of three very concrete things: (1) The response can be aroused, or reinstated, by a presentation of the stimulus. Thus a subject who has learned to run a maze or to repeat the French equivalents of a list of English words may still be able to respond correctly to the respective stimuli after an interval of one week during which there has been no practice. (2) Although the subject may no longer be able to make the response to the stimulus as he has been trained to do, he may still be able to designate which stimuli he has been trained with and which stimuli he has not been trained with. In other words, he behaves differently to the maze or to the words on which he has been trained than he does to mazes or words on which he has not been trained. (3) Although the subject may no longer be able to make the response which he has been trained to make to the stimulus, and although he may react no differently to this stimulus, e.g., the list of English words, than to other comparable stimuli, e.g., other lists of English words, nevertheless his organism may still retain traces of the results of previous training. We can establish this fact by having the subject relearn the original stimulus-response co-ordination. If we compare the amount of time required for the original learning with the time required for the relearning, we shall find, if there is any retention, that the relearning requires less time than did the original learning.

"The three conditions of behavior which constitute the evidence for the retention of stimulus-response co-ordinations also suggest the methods by which retention can be experimentally studied. The first method is that of recall or *reinstatement*. This method is used in all studies which involve recitation [the arousal of a response in the absence of its usual stimuli] or other form of recall of the specific co-ordination under investigation. A specific form of this method is that of *paired associates*, devised by Calkins [1896] and perfected by Müller and Pilzecker [1900]. In this form of the method the material to be used as stimuli is presented in pairs (of words, pictures, etc.). The subject is instructed to speak the words, *e.g.*, and the entire series of paired stimuli are presented serially a specified number of times. Then the first members of the pairs are presented to the subject in a changed order. He is now instructed to recall, *i.e.*, to reinstate, the response formerly aroused by the second member of the pair. Retention is measured by the length of time that it takes him to reinstate the required response and by the proportion of right and wrong responses. Thus the series *a-b, c-d, e-f, g-h* is presented to the subject one pair at a time, each pair for one second. After the fifth reading, let us say, the subject is then shown *c, g, a* and *e*, and instructed to reinstate the responses (*d, h, b, f*) which had formerly been given to the absent stimulus of the pair.

"The second method of studying retention is usually called the method of recognition. This method requires the subject to discriminate between old and new stimuli, *i.e.*, between stimuli with which the subject has been trained and stimuli with which he has not been trained. We shall therefore call this second method the *age of stimulus method*. A typical procedure in the use of this method is as follows: (1) Colors, grays, odors, tones, pictures, advertisements, words, whatever it be, the stimuli for the experiment are chosen. (2) This selected material is now presented to the subject either serially or in pairs. During the presentation the subject is instructed to respond with the verbal response which he has learned to call the name of the stimulus, or he is permitted to make no overt response. (3) The stimuli may be presented any number of times up to the point where the subject can reinstate all of the responses which he has learned for the series. And (4) at the end of any presentation the stimuli may be presented to the subject in the same arrangement in which they were originally or in a different one, but in either case new stimuli will be mixed in with the old. The subject is now instructed to make one type of response to the old stimuli and another to the new. This discriminative test need not be given immediately after training. It may be deferred for any length of time chosen by the experimenter.

"The third method of studying retention is *the saving method* of Ebbinghaus [1913]. In this method we record the number of trials, the amount of time, and the number of errors in the learning process for any given stimulus-response co-ordination. Later, after the lapse of a certain length of time, the subject again learns the co-ordination up to the same level of skill required in the original learning. The difference between the records for the original learning and the same measurements for the relearning is an indication of the amount of retention. If a subject requires as much time for the second learning as for the original learning, there is no evidence that he has retained any of the initial practice effects."

The vast range of experimentation and discussion in the field of the learning process precludes the possibility of our covering the entire field in the present chapter. Learning is intimately involved in the development of all behavior patterns. This is clearly indicated in the field of reflexes by Pavlov's (1927) work on the conditioned reflexes and in the field of instinct by the work of Shepard and Breed (1913), Moseley (1925), Bird (1926), and Carmichael (1927) on the possible rôle of maturation in the development of behavior. We shall discuss one aspect of the maturation problem when we consider the relation of age to learning capacity; but the aspect raised by the studies just mentioned will not concern us because the maturation of the specific stimulus-response mechanisms involved in experiments upon learning has apparently been completed before the subject reaches the experiment. Learning is also intimately related to the problem of work, i.e., to the problem of the exercise of forms of response, and to that of thinking behavior where the acquisition and use of symbolic processes is of characteristic importance. The limitations of space will prevent our developing these topics. Furthermore, we can only mention the importance of a study of the learning process for the adequate understanding of those topics which the psychologist has labeled attention and testimony. Thus studies on the span of attention, the immediate memory span, and testimony are all alike in that they require the subject to reinstate certain learned responses after a single presentation of the stimulus. They differ only in the temporal duration of the stimulus. If the stimulus is presented for 1/50 of a second, the experiment is classified as one on attention; whereas with longer exposure times, the behavior is classified as testimony or memory.

Since the problem of acquisition and retention concerns stimulus-response coordinations in an individual subject, the complete experimental record of the problem involves a study of the effect upon acquisition and retention of: (1) variations in the stimulating conditions, such as temporal duration, frequency, whole vs. partial presentation, and amount; and (2) variations in the condition of the subject, such as fatigue, age, sex, cultural status, ability, incentive, neural condition, and character, amount, and recency of past training. In the present chapter we shall discuss certain of the more important problems here suggested, stressing constantly the analysis of experimental findings. The references at the close of the chapter will afford the reader not only an opportunity to examine the original experimental material referred to in this chapter but to extend his reading to other experiments which it was not possible to analyze. Let us turn first, then, to a study of the curve of acquisition.

THE LEARNING CURVE

The learning curve is a graphic representation of the change in behavior which is brought about by successive periods of practice all of which are represented on the curve. In contrast to this is the sample performance curve illustrated in Figure 3. In this graph improvement is not the result of the practice represented by the scores on the curve but is a result of the practice which occurs outside of the experimental period. No particular difficulty arises in the construction of either type of curve for an individual subject. In such a case values along the abscissa represent successive practice (or test) periods equal in magnitude one to the other, and the values along the ordinate represent some quantitative aspect of behavior such as the number of errors, the number of correct responses, or the time consumed per unit on the abscissa. Curves for individual subjects usually fluctuate considerably from practice period to practice period, not because learning is an intrinsically fluctuating process but because the experimenter does not sufficiently control the experimental conditions under which the learning takes place. It is furthermore to be noted that any particular learning curve can represent but one aspect of the trend in behavior and that it may not faithfully and accurately represent even this aspect. Thus progress may be rapid in the error aspect of the behavior and relatively slow in the time aspect; and when progress is slow, as shown in a plateau, the lack of apparent improvement may be due only to the crudeness of the measures employed.

We have spoken so far only of learning curves for individual subjects. The construction of curves which shall represent the learning process in groups of subjects is not so simple. The learning process extends from the beginning of practice until some arbitrarily established degree of skill is attained, e.g., three perfect trials in succession in the maze. Subjects will differ in the number of trials required for mastery of the problem. If, therefore, all subjects are given the same number of trials, let us say 30, and, if the curve is constructed by averaging the records of all subjects for each successive trial, the resulting graph will represent how the average performance changes from the first to the 30th trial. (See Figure 13.) It will not represent the progress made in learning the problem set, for some of the subjects will have mastered the problem in much less than 30 trials, or practice periods, and hence will be greatly overtrained. The conventional method of constructing a curve which will portray the learning process in a group of subjects is illustrated below in Table 1. Vincent (1912, pp. 16-17) has suggested the best method of constructing a curve which throughout its extent will be representative of the whole group of subjects and which will portray the change of behavior from the beginning of practice until the problem is mastered.

TABLE 1
ERROR RECORDS FOR FIVE RATS IN LEARNING A SIMPLE MAZE
The table shows two conventional methods of obtaining averages.

Trial	Rat 1	2	3	4	5	Av. error	Av. error
			Errors				
1	40	20	30	25	10	25	25
2	25	30	24	10	12	20.2	20.2
3	8	20	18	7	6	11.8	11.8
4	2	15	10	4	3	6.8	6.8
5	1	10	5	1	5	4.4	4.4
6	0	3	0	1	2	1.2	2.
7	0	2	3	0	3	1.6	3.6
8	0	1	0	1	2	.8	1.3
9	0	1	0	0	1	.4	1.
10	0	0	0	0	1	.2	1.
11	0	0	0	0	2	.4	2.
12	0	1	0	0	1	.4	1.
13	0	0	0	0	0	0	0
14	0	0	0	0	0	0	0
15	0	0	0	0	0	0	0

The construction of a Vincent learning curve can be illustrated from the data of Table 1, which contains the error records for five rats in a simple maze. If three perfect records in succession are taken as the criterion of mastery, learning was completed as follows: rat No. 1, 5 trials; rat No. 2, 12 trials; rat No. 3, 7 trials; rat No. 4, 8 trials; and rat No. 5, 12 trials. If we average the material by trials as is done in either of the last two columns of the table, we either include some records beyond the completion of learning or we omit some of the subjects. The Vincent curve, which is not open to these criticisms, is constructed by dividing the learning periods into an equal number of parts on the basis of the number of trials required for mastery. These parts are then averaged as a basis for the graph. Suppose we divide the learning of each subject into ten equal parts. Rat No. 1, who learned in 5 trials, learned in ten parts each of which is one-half a trial. The ten parts of No. 2's learning are each 1.2 trials long. When the number of errors in each tenth are calculated and averaged for the group, the values of Table 2 result.[1]

An excellent illustration of the practical value of the Vincent type curve is to be found in the studies by Kjerstad (1919), Robinson and Darrow (1924), and Robinson and Heron (1922), where the curves of learning for materials of different lengths are compared. Figure 1 from Robinson and Darrow plots, in the conventional fashion, the average amount learned against the learning time. It would appear from these curves that learning progresses more rapidly in the initial stages as the length of the material to be learned decreases. Such a conclusion, however, would be unjustified because the learning process is more condensed in the shorter

---

[1]Kjerstad (1919, p. 26) describes a graphic method of arriving at the values for the Vincent curve.

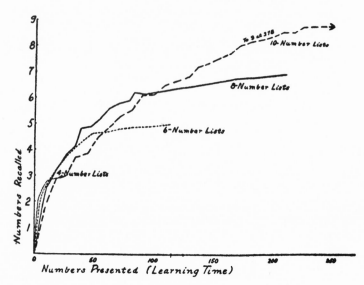

FIGURE 1

CURVES FOR DIFFERENT AMOUNTS OF MATERIAL, SHOWING THE RELATION BETWEEN
AMOUNT RECALLED AND LEARNING TIME
(From E. S. Robinson and C. W. Darrow's "Effect of Length of Lists upon
Memory for Numbers," *Amer. J. Psychol.*, 1924.)

curves than in the longer ones. In order to compare progress in the various problems, curves must be constructed which will be of equal length. When the results are averaged by the Vincent method, the authors secure the data of Table 3, which shows that the progress of learning is essentially the same for all lengths of material, the shortest list of numbers and of syllables offering the only discrepancy. Robinson and Darrow thus confirm the prior findings of Kjerstad that the form of the learning curve is independent of the amount of material learned.

Learning curves have one of two general forms depending upon the values that are plotted on the ordinate. If correct responses are recorded on the ordinate, the resulting curve will be some variant of the type shown in Figures 1 and 3 because the number of correct responses increases with the increase in practice. When, however, time or error records are plotted on the ordinate, the curve is of the general character of Figure 7. Aside from this ascending or descending characteristic of the curve of learning, attention should be directed to changes in the form of the curve which result from changing rates of the acquisition or elimination of responses. We shall reserve for following sections the discussion of long periods of little or no change in the curve, *the plateaus,* and the discussion of sudden improvements in the subject's performance which have been accredited to *insight.* At present we shall confine ourselves to comments upon those changes in the curve which occur at the beginning and end of learning.

TABLE 2
RECORDS FOR A VINCENT CURVE BASED ON THE DATA OF TABLE 1

Rat	1	2	3	4	5	
Tenths			Errors in successive tenths			Av.
1	20	26	21	20	12.4	19.8
2	20	32	18.6	11	12	18.7
3	12.5	21	16.2	6.8	5.4	12.3
4	12.5	14	12.6	5	5.2	9.8
5	4.	5	8.6	3.2	3.	4.7
6	4.	2.2	9.	.8	3.4	3.8
7	1.	1.2	3.5	.8	2.	1.3
8	1.	.6	.5	.4	1.2	.7
9	.5	0.0	.9	.2	2.	.6
10	.5	1.	2.1	.8	1.4	1.1

TABLE 3
THE RELATIONSHIP BETWEEN AMOUNT OF MATERIAL TO BE LEARNED AND THE
PROGRESS OF LEARNING AS REVEALED BY THE PERCENTAGES OF MATERIAL
LEARNED IN SUCCESSIVE SIXTHS OF THE LEARNING PROCESS
(After Robinson and Darrow)

Percentage of total learning time	Percentage of materials mastered (three-place numbers) for lists of different lengths			
	4 nos.	6 nos.	8 nos.	10 nos.
16.7	19.4	31.8	29.3	30.4
33.3	36.1	44.5	45.9	45.3
50.	49.8	54.0	55.3	54.6
66.7	63.1	62.7	64.0	64.7
83.3	82.3	71.0	75.8	70.4
100.	100.	100.	100.	100.

	Percentage mastered for nonsense syllable lists of different lengths				
	6 syl.	9 syl.	12 syl.	15 syl.	18 syl.
16.7	23.3	33.9	34.6	30.9	33.1
33.3	45.	51.2	52.3	52.2	53.2
50.	60.5	62.	66.3	62.0	66.3
66.7	72.3	73.6	74.9	74.2	76.3
83.3	83.4	80.8	80.5	80.3	82.8
100.	100.	100.	100.	100.	100.

The initial period of learning as portrayed by time and error curves is usually one of rapid change as indicated in Figures 1 and 7. Such a change indicates either that the factors, e.g., emotional disturbances, making for high time and error scores quickly disappear as the subject becomes adjusted to the experimental situation or that certain easily established components of the final habit have been acquired. Figure 9 shows an error curve which remains on the same level for several trials and then drops. In the absence of an experimental analysis of the situation from which the curve is taken, we must content ourselves with the hypothesis that an adjustment must be made to certain factors which are difficult to master before learning can proceed.   This difficulty of the initial aspects of the problem would be adequate to account for the curve. Curves drawn for correct responses may also show initial periods either of rapid change, Figure 1, or of slow change, Figure 2.   Peterson's (1917a) study of ball-

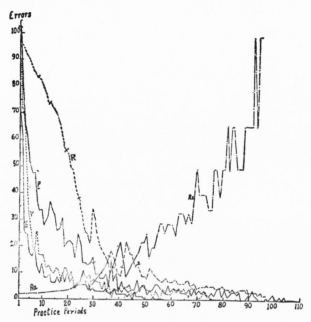

FIGURE 2

CURVES FOR THE ELIMINATION OF ERRORS AND FOR ACHIEVEMENT (*Ra*) IN BALL-TOSSING

(From J. Peterson's "Experiments in Ball-Tossing: the Significance of Learning Curves," *J. Exper. Psychol.,* 1917.)

tossing gives us this latter curve. *Ra* represents the average number of successive catches per practice period.   The curve is concave to the ordinate, as are also curves constructed by Swift (1903) and Batson (1916) for the same habit, thus indicating that the early adjustments necessary to score successive catches are acquired with difficulty.   After the preliminary stages of learning, progress becomes more rapid until the final level of performance is reached.   Stroud (1931), in a brief study of the learning of poetry, where progress was indicated in terms of large units (lines recited), secured learning curves approximating the above *Ra* type but showing a definite final negative acceleration.   (For a further discussion, by Hull, of such S-shaped curves, see pages 425-426 of this book.)

If practice is continued long enough, all curves of learning reach a final level of attainment.   Probably all curves reach this level through a period

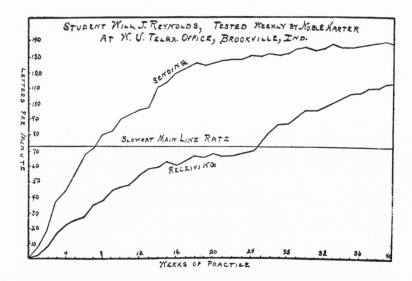

FIGURE 3

SAMPLE PERFORMANCE CURVES FOR SENDING AND RECEIVING TELEGRAPHIC MESSAGES
(From W. L. Bryan and N. Harter's "Studies in the Physiology and Psychology
of the Telegraphic Language," *Psychol. Rev.,* 1899.)

of negative acceleration.   Peterson's curve shows a final level which is attained suddenly.   This, however, is an artifact due to the limitation of
each practice period to 200 catches and to the consequent fact that not
more than 200 successive catches could be made per practice period.   If
the subject had been instructed to increase his number of successive catches
as much as possible, the resulting curve would undoubtedly have leveled
off gradually rather than sharply.   The final negative acceleration of learning curves may be due to the difficulty in mastering the final aspects of the
habit either because the most difficult components tend to be learned last[2]
or because the integration of the total series of responses is itself an accomplishment difficult to attain.   Thus the individual stimulus-response
components may be mastered, but their appearance in the proper sequence
and in the minimum time may yet constitute a problem for mastery.

Whenever a problem is set for the subject in such a form that small
differences in the accuracy of responses may be measured and whenever
speed is a factor in the behavior, the physiological limit of the organism
sets the limit beyond which the subject's performance cannot go.   The
physiological limit is rarely if ever reached.   The subject's performance
rather ends on a level determined by the incentive under which he works
as well as by the difficulty of making additional improvement.   Whether

[2]On this point see G. M. Peterson (1928).

the activity engaged in be golf, typesetting, or addition, the subject tends to remain on a final level of attainment which is socially and economically acceptable. Even though practice is long continued, no improvement may result unless new incentives, such as higher wages or personal competition, are added to the working conditions.

PLATEAUS

A plateau in the learning curve is a period during which the subject makes little or no progress toward mastery of the problem. Bryan and Harter (1897) were the first to emphasize the problem presented by the occurrence of plateaus and to seek for their explanation. Figure 3 presents two curves, one for sending and the other for receiving telegraphic messages. These curves are sample performance curves, which indicate the degree of skill attained by the subject after the indicated weeks of practice. Once each week the subject was tested and the number of words (selected from standard sentences) sent or received during several two-minute intervals were averaged and translated into letters per minute to give the values entered on the ordinate. Figure 4, a receiving curve, was constructed in the same way for a subject who had studied telegraphy about six weeks before beginning the experiment. This curve shows the pro-

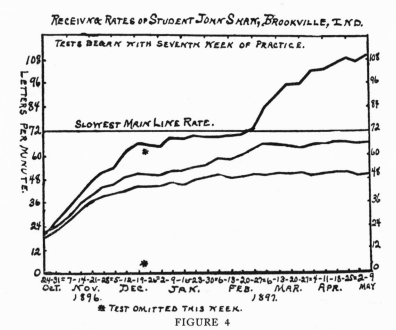

FIGURE 4

SAMPLE PERFORMANCE CURVES FOR RECEIVING TELEGRAPHIC MESSAGES
(From W. L. Bryan and N. Harter's "Studies in the Physiology and Psychology of the Telegraphic Language," *Psychol. Rev.*, 1899.)

gress made in the ability to receive letters not making words, words not making sentences, and words which did make sentences.

Bryan and Harter explain the plateau of the receiving curve in terms of the acquisition of a hierarchy of verbal habits. "The curves of figure [4] show also, however, that for many months the chief gain is in the letter and word habits, that the rate of receiving sentences is, in this period, mainly determined by the rate of receiving letters and words, and that rapid gain in the higher language habits does not begin until letter and word habits are well fixed" (p. 356). The sending curve shows no plateau "because, as in the early part of the receiving curve, the various habits are acquired simultaneously."

Swift (1903, 1906, 1907), in his studies of ball-tossing, typewriting, and learning Russian, and Book (1908), in his study of typewriting, found plateaus of greater or lesser length. Swift believes that the plateaus are partly due to failure in the subject's effort and enthusiasm, partly to the experimenter's inability to measure the progress that is taking place, and partly to the necessity for the subject to perfect certain responses before he can proceed to a higher level of efficiency. One of Book's figures is reproduced as our Figure 5. The curves represent the number of strokes per minute on successive days of practice in copying material by the sight method of typewriting. Book partially agrees with Swift that the plateaus are due to a relaxation of effort on the part of the subject rather than to the influ-

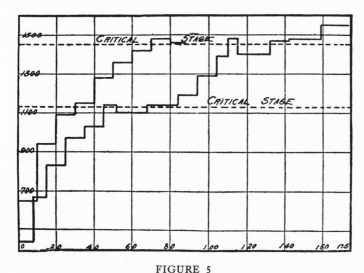

FIGURE 5
CURVE FOR LEARNING TYPEWRITING
(From W. F. Book's *The Psychology of Skill*, 1925, by permission of the publishers, The Gregg Publishing Co., New York.)

ence of a hierarchy of habits, but he adds to the former factor that of excessive effort wrongly applied.

Batson (1916), who has made the most extended study of plateaus since the work by Bryan and Harter, trained his subjects in tossing and catching two balls. In order to perform such a task accurately, it is necessary to throw the ball in the proper direction, to throw it with the proper force, and to time the opening and closing of the hand accurately enough to catch the ball. Batson devised tests in which the subject must react primarily to directional, distance (force), and time factors. The directional test involved rolling a steel ball along a smooth board in an attempt to strike a small wooden block. The force, or distance, test required the subject to roll a rubber ball so that it would stop as near to a given mark as possible. The timing test required the subject to release a small lead shot so that it would roll down a groove and reach the end at the proper time to fall into the pocket of a disc which rotated at a constant speed past the end of the groove. Since these three analytical learning tests were not given simultaneously with the ball-tossing test which they were designed to analyze, it is impossible to correlate progress in ball-tossing with improvement in the reactions to direction, distance, and time as it is possible in Figure 4 to compare the progress in receiving letters and words with the progress in receiving connected discourse. In any case it is highly questionable whether time, distance, and direction are involved in Batson's analytical tests in the way that they are in ball-tossing. One could hardly look, in that case, to these tests to clarify the curve for ball-tossing. Batson concludes that plateaus do not occur in simple types of learning (and yet his Figure 16a, presenting the scores in the direction test, shows a well-marked plateau), and that they may or may not occur in complex learning.

The whole problem of plateaus is greatly in need of experimental clarification. Since the plateau is a period of little or no progress in learning, any factor which retards learning may theoretically produce plateaus. Lack of effort, misdirected effort, lack of incentive, emotional upset, fatigue, habit interference, and the presence of unusually difficult components of the problem to be learned are some of these factors. Trow and Sears (1927) have recently presented evidence indicating the possible rôle of habit interference in the production of plateaus; and Hunter (1929, p. 522) has secured maze curves for rats which show marked plateaus due to the great difficulty in eliminating certain errors. Before we can be certain that hierarchies of habits are concerned in the production of plateaus, we must have additional experiments like those of Bryan and Harter where the external and internal conditions of work are carefully controlled. Plateaus may be a genuine and necessary aspect of certain processes of learning and in other instances they may merely indicate the experimenter's failure to keep working conditions constant for his subject.

THE NATURE OF INSIGHT

In the topic of insight we not only extend our consideration of the learning curve to include the problem of a sudden improvement in efficiency, but we also face the theory that there is present in some learning a factor, designated as insight, which is not of the same order as the factors involved in the conditioning of reflexes or in so-called trial-and-error learning. Our general conclusion will be that there is no adequate evidence for the assumption of a peculiar insight factor or for the assumption that there is more than one kind of learning. Let us begin with a consideration of Köhler's work on apes.

Köhler (1925), in his extension of Hobhouse's (1901) type of animal experimentation, defends the thesis that insight plays a rôle in the learning process. Although Köhler gives no analysis of the nature of insight, he contrasts his own experiments with those of Thorndike (1911) and hence may be said to treat insight as a form of intelligence. Intelligent solutions of problems, from Köhler's point of view, are to be contrasted with accidental solutions as follows: "The genuine achievement takes place as a single continuous occurrence, a unity, as it were, in space as well as in time; in our example, as one continuous run without a second's stop, right up to the objective. A successful chance solution consists of an agglomeration of separate movements, which start, finish, start again, remain independent of one another in direction and speed, and only in a geometrical summation start at the starting point, and finish at the objective" (1925, pp. 16-17). Successful chance solutions would be illustrated by the behavior of a subject in his first trial in a maze where almost every possible error is made and where the exit is merely blundered upon. Another illustration of the same phenomenon is found in the behavior of Thorndike's cats (1911), who were confined in a box from which they could escape only after having turned a latch. At first the cats attacked every portion of the cage and effected their escape only after having turned the latch in the process of this random scrambling. In contrast with these chance solutions, Köhler emphasizes that genuine achievement, i.e., intelligent behavior (or behavior with insight), involves but little if any useless activity, that it occurs as a single continuous and integrated response. In order that such behavior may be manifested Köhler says that all aspects which are essential to the solution of the problem must be simultaneously present to the subject so that he can obtain a view of the entire situation in all of its relevant aspects. This is equivalent to saying that all of the stimuli whose action is necessary for the correct response must be simultaneously present. Such a condition is fulfilled only with visual stimuli, and the result is that insight would thus be limited to visually determined behavior. This in itself leads one to question the hypothesis, for it is highly doubtful that so important a factor as insight is alleged to be would be limited in this manner. However, the question is one of fact to be determined only by experiment.

In order that the reader may have a concrete example from Köhler of intelligent, or insight, behavior, I quote the following: "A species of reversal of the 'tool-using' experiments consists in placing a movable object across the path of the objective so that the problem can be solved only by its *removal*: . . .The box [which was the obstacle] was placed in the barred room in immediate contact with the bars and standing on the smaller end so that it could easily be knocked over. Outside the bars, and immediately opposite the center of the box, the bananas lay on the ground; they could be reached at once with a stick, if the box were pushed aside or even knocked over . . . She [Tschego] crouched beside the box, facing the bars. For some time nothing happened. Then, however, some of the smaller apes approached from outside the cage . . . Each time, though, Tschego repulsed them with threatening gestures . . . The young-sters finally gathered closely around the fruit, but the danger inspired Tschego; she gripped the box, which was like a toy in her arms, jerked it backwards, stepped up to the bars, and took the fruit . . . The 'obstacle' test was *not* solved . . . by a series of imperceptible pushes involuntarily given to the [box] in the act of stretching towards the prize. Quite the contrary: *during the lapse of two hours, Tschego did not move the [box] one millimeter from its original position,* and when the solution arrived, the [box] was not *shouldered* to one side, but *suddenly gripped* with both hands, and thrust back. It was a *genuine* solution" (1925, pp. 61-65).

With these illustrations before us, we may proceed with our analysis. There are two ways of defining insight: one method is to make insight a purely descriptive term referring to a certain type of behavior; the other is to make it an explanatory term referring to something (usually psychic) which influences and controls behavior. Köhler has usually adopted the first course although much of his discussion involves the second. Other investigators, notably Koffka (1924) and Yerkes (1916, 1927), who dis-cuss insight also use first one and then the other meaning of the term. Thus Koffka writes: "It has been shown that improvement in efficiency goes hand in hand with an increased insight into the nature of the task. We use this word, insight, without theoretical presuppositions, in the common sense in which everyone takes it. If one knows that he is to remove a ring in a certain puzzle, and that in order to do so he must first move this piece and then that, turn the puzzle over and do something else, his procedure will be said to possess a greater degree of insight than the procedure of another person who simply goes ahead without any plan at all" (1924, p. 179). And again, "The sudden grasping of the solution which results is a process that runs its course in accordance with the nature of the situation, so that the complete solution of the problem takes place with reference to the configuration of the field of perception; and this is what Köhler maintains to be the criterion of insight" (1924, p. 214). Yerkes' use of the term in an explanatory way is indicated by the following quotation: "Insight is used throughout this report to designate varieties of experience which in us are accompani-ments of sudden, effective, individually wrought adaptations to more or less distinctly new and problematic situations" (1927, p. 155). It is impossible to do more than philosophize when dealing with such definitions of insight. The only practical and scientific problem is this: Are there types of behavior or characteristics of behavior so different from those present in the formation and use of habit in general that we are justified in speaking of insightful behavior?

Insight is described by Köhler as a form of response which appears suddenly and runs its course smoothly from the beginning until the attainment of the goal, under conditions where all of the essential aspects of the problem can be viewed at one time by the subject. We have already rejected this last characteristic because it seeks to confine the alleged phenomenon to visually controlled behavior. The "smooth, continuous" aspect of behavior is characteristic of all well-established habits, including the maze habit, and so cannot serve to mark off one habit from another. (Köhler did not know the past history of his apes, and so could not know to what extent the "solutions" were merely reinstated habits.) This leaves us with the possibility that behavior which appears suddenly is insight. We shall discuss this after noting the characteristics proposed by Yerkes. Yerkes writes as follows: "In acts which by us are performed with insight or understanding of relations of means to ends, we are familiar with certain characteristics which are important if not also differential. The following is a partial list of features of such behavior. . . .(1) Survey, inspection, or persistent examination of problematic situation. (2) Hesitation, pause, attitude of concentrated attention. (3) Trial of more or less adequate mode of response. (4) In case initial mode of response proves inadequate, trial of some other mode of response, the transition from one method to the other being sharp and often sudden. (5) Persistent or frequently recurrent attention to the objective or goal and motivation thereby. (6) Appearance of critical point at which the organism suddenly, directly, and definitely performs required adaptive act. (7) Ready repetition of adaptive response after once performed. (8) Notable ability to discover and attend to the essential aspect or relation in the problematic situation and to neglect, relatively, variations in non-essentials" (1927, p. 156).

Yerkes' list of characteristics is proposed as a basis for the identification of a specific form of behavior called insight. And yet nos. 1, 2, 3, 4, 5, and possibly 8 are features of all learning processes whether they involve rats or men and whether the material to be learned is a maze, a brightness discrimination, or a list of nonsense syllables. Furthermore, all of the eight features occur where learning is completed in one trial. Indeed the eight features are all revealed in the behavior of the unicellular organism *Stentor* as described by Jennings (1906, Chap. 10). A child who refuses bitter medicine after one trial, or a chick who after one trial refuses to peck at certain food would qualify for insight behavior, and yet the well-established principle of conditioned reflexes makes the assumption of insight unnecessary for the explanation of the behavior. As in Köhler's statement so here the one feature that calls for extended discussion is that of the sudden drop in the learning curve.

Figures 6-9 present certain learning curves relevant to the problem of insight. Figure 6, presented by Thorndike (1911, p. 41), represents

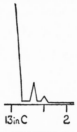

FIGURE 6

A CURVE SHOWING THE DECREASE IN TIME REQUIRED BY A CAT TO ESCAPE FROM A PROBLEM BOX

(From E. L. Thorndike's "Animal Intelligence," *Psychol. Rev., Monog. Suppl.,* 1898.)

the change in time during 13 trials in which a cat was trained to escape from a latch box. Figure 7 is a curve from Watson (1907) showing the time records of 19 rats in a maze. Figure 8 is a curve representing the work of an ape in a multiple-choice problem studied by Yerkes (1916, p. 27). Figure 9 reproduces curves from Clements' (1928) study of the effect of different lengths of delay upon the learning by rats of the

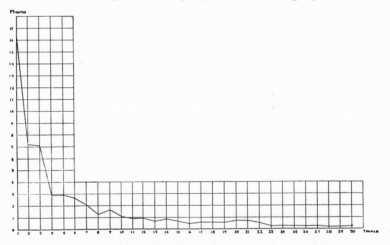

FIGURE 7

A CURVE SHOWING THE AVERAGE TIME REQUIRED BY NINETEEN RATS IN LEARNING A MAZE

(From J. B. Watson's "Kinaesthetic and Organic Sensations: Their Rôle in the Reactions of the White Rat in the Maze," *Psychol. Rev., Monog. Suppl.,* 1907.)

shorter of two paths each leading to a food box. All of these curves show sudden drops. Are we, therefore, to conclude that insight was present in all instances? How sudden must a drop be before insight behavior is involved? Or how much of a drop must be present? If a complete elimination of error within one or two trials shows insight, does a partial elimination show partial insight? There seems to be no proper objection to the affirmative answer to this last question, and yet such an answer makes any inference from drops in the learning curve to the presence of insight seem futile, for all learning curves are composed of a series of drops. The most pertinent and practical question to raise concerning such changes in the curve of learning is not "Does such a curve reveal the presence of insight?" but "What factors cause such drops in the learning curve?" This latter question is quite within the range of experimental solution. For example, the sudden drop in the maze curve, Figure 7, is largely due to the adaptation of the subject to the experimental situation and to the establishment of behavior oriented toward the exit of the maze. Undoubtedly other factors exist which are equally susceptible to a concrete determination. No experiments have been conducted to determine why the sudden changes occur in the curves of Figures 6, 8, and 9. However, Figure 6 indicates learning in one trial, and the experimental results on conditioned reflexes indicate that the phenomenon may well be due to the conditioning of the non-effective stimulus by some other stimulus which has a pronounced "right of way." Figure 8 suggests very strongly either (1) that certain factors blocked the appearance of learning so that our crude methods did not reveal what was taking place until suddenly the correct response appeared, or (2) that, as probably in Köhler's work, the sudden appearance of the correct response was essentially a reinstatement of previously learned behavior. The two curves in the middle of Figure 9 were clearly derived from responses which took place under conditions which for a time failed to produce a measured degree of learning, but just what these detrimental conditions were has not been determined. (It

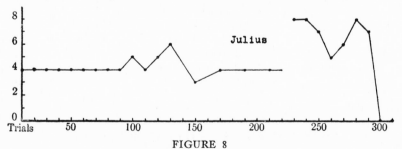

FIGURE 8

A CURVE SHOWING THE PROGRESS MADE BY AN APE TOWARD THE MASTERY OF A
MULTIPLE-CHOICE PROBLEM

(From R. M. Yerkes' "The Mental Life of Monkeys and Apes," *Behav.
Monog.*, 1916.)

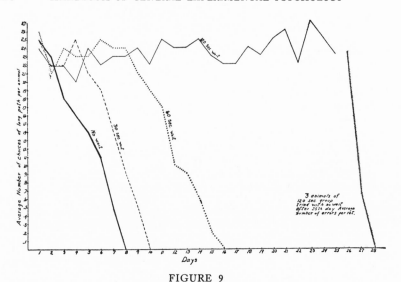

FIGURE 9
LEARNING CURVES FOR RATS
The figure is described in the text.
(From F. E. Clements' "The Effect of Time on Distance Discrimination in the
Albino Rat," *J. Comp. Psychol.*, 1928.)

should be noted that curves 1 and 4 of this figure were not secured under
conditions comparable with those which produced curves 2 and 3.)
We are thus forced to the conclusion that no causal factor of insight has
been demonstrated and that to resort to such an hypothesis is to desert
the straight-forward experimental attack upon the determining conditions
of behavior from which alone an adequate solution can be derived. All
learning is essentially of a kind—the modification of behavior as a result
of repeated stimulation under specified conditions. Some learning periods
may be shorter than others, or may result in a higher degree of efficiency
than others, or may involve verbal guidance, but there is no adequate
reason for believing in two kinds of learning.

We turn now to a consideration of two important ways in which
the stimuli involved in learning may be presented to the subject: one
involves the whole versus the part method of presenting the stimuli which
are to be responded to, and the other concerns the frequency with which
the stimuli are given.

WHOLE VERSUS PART METHODS OF LEARNING

If a subject is to learn a sequence of responses such as reciting a poem
or running a maze, will it be more economical to repeat the entire
sequence of responses at each trial or should the problem be broken
up into parts and the parts learned separately? What will be the

relative merits of the two methods when they are evaluated in terms of retention? These problems have been extensively investigated and discussed since Steffens' work in 1900. In general, the results have indicated that the whole method is more economical than the part method both in learning and in retention. Exceptions, however, have been found by those who favor this conclusion, and Reed (1924), Winch (1924), and Pechstein (1917) have presented definite experimental evidence in favor of the part method. Let us, therefore, examine briefly some of the experiments bearing upon the problem.

Steffens' work was carried out with poetry and nonsense syllables. The subjects, when allowed to study the material without definite instructions, followed a part method in which they studied a few lines, then added a few more lines, and repeated the first ones. Difficult passages were frequently and slowly read. When this normal method was compared with the whole method, the former required an average of 9 per cent more time for learning than the latter. With nonsense syllables, the normal method was superior for the first 10 days' work; but during the last 24 days this was reversed. An experiment was conducted where the subject learned three eight-line stanzas daily. One half of a stanza was mastered, then the second half, and finally the whole was read and mastered. On the average this method was inferior to the whole method by 63.6 sec. and by 1.6 trials. The work continued for 16 days. On only one of these days was the part method superior. When the stimulus material was presented on a rotating drum so that the exposure time during learning was the same for both methods, the whole method had an advantage of three trials.

Larguier des Bancels (1901) confirmed Steffens' work and added the fact that the whole method of learning is more favorable for the retention of poetry than is the part method. This finding for retention was confirmed by Pentschew (1903), who found, however, that with children the part method was slightly superior both in learning and relearning when nonsense syllables were used. Pentschew also found that where the whole method was superior in number of repetitions required the part method often had the advantage from the standpoint of time consumed. Pyle and Snyder (1911) extended the problem to longer selections of poetry and report as follows: ". . . .without any exception, the method of the whole is more economical than is the part-method, and . . . .the saving is much greater in the case of the long units, which required more than one sitting. The greatest saving in the short units was about 11 per cent. in the 20-line and the 50-line units. In the larger units the saving was about 20 per cent. in one 60-line test and 22 per cent. in the other, 17 per cent. in the 120-line test and 20 per cent. in the 240-line test" (1911, p. 138). Lakenan's work (1913), carried out with prose material, verified Pyle and Snyder's findings on the length of material and gave evidence that subjects who at first learned or retained better by the part method, after additional practice, gave better results by the whole method. Ephrussi (1904), using recall with adult subjects, found the whole method superior to the part method except for nonsense syllables and vocabularies; but the later experiments of Neumann (1907) and of Brown (1924*b*) give the superiority to the whole method when vocabulary material is used. Crafts (1929), in a study of card sorting, found the whole method of learning superior to the various part methods. Where a substitution test was used (1930), however, no reliable differences between the methods were found.

We come now to the consideration of the work which is less favorable to the whole method. Winch, working with 38 school children, organized two groups of subjects of equal age and of equal ability as judged by their performances in preliminary learning tests. One group learned poems by the part method, and the other, by the whole method. In the former case the subject was instructed to learn a line at a time until one stanza was mastered. After the first stanza was learned, the second was begun. The first two stanzas were than repeated until they could be recalled correctly, and a new unit was then learned. Sample results are shown in Table 4, and Winch's comments upon the work are as follows: "There is a differential advantage of 26 per cent. in the four final tests in favor of the part method: this differential advantage falls to $5\frac{1}{2}$ per cent. in the case of *Dora* [one of the poems] and rises to 52 per cent. for the *Seagull*" (1924, p. 70). In this and other experiments by Winch, the part method tends to be superior when the material to be learned is short, or markedly disjointed and rhymed.

Reed (1924), also working with poetry and using 113 college students, states that the whole method was superior for only 26 students. Thirty-one students did best with the pure part method in which stanzas were learned separately and then as a whole. Fifty-six students did best with

TABLE 4

WHOLE VS. PART METHODS IN LEARNING POETRY

(From Winch)

N	Age	Total marks in preliminary tests	Total marks in exper.	Marks for *Dora*	Marks for *Seagull*
			Results by the Part Method		
19	11 yrs. 8 mos.	273	279	173	125
			Results by the Whole Method		
19	11 yrs. 7 mos.	273	222	164	82

a progressive part method in which stanza 1 was learned, then stanza 2, then 1 and 2, then 3, then the first three together, etc.

Pechstein (1917) compared maze learning by the whole method with that by several varieties of the part method, using as subjects both white rats and college students. The maze was constructed of four well-defined parts which could be learned independently one of the other. The part methods of training adopted were as follows: (1) Pure part. (2) Progressive part. (3) Direct repetitive, where part 1 was first learned, then the subject ran through this part and on into part 2.

TABLE 5
WHOLE VS. PART LEARNING FOR RATS AND HUMAN SUBJECTS
(From Pechstein)

Method	No. of rats	Av. trials	Av. time sec.	Av. total errors
Progressive part	9	11	662	65
Reversed repetitive	8	17	882	76
Direct repetitive	11	21	1442	142
Whole— returns prevented	9	30	1666	111
Pure part	9	30	1907	199
Whole— returns allowed	12	27	4174	217

Method	No. of human subjects	Av. trials	Av. time sec.	Av. total errors
Progressive part	6	10	352	57
Direct repetitive	6	11	618	96
Whole— returns allowed	6	12	641	126
Whole— returns prevented	6	17	541	81
Reversed repetitive	6	22	1014	226
Pure part	6	23	1220	237

When this was mastered, part 3 was added to parts 1 and 2, after which part 4 was added in the same manner. (4) Reversed repetitive. In some of the experiments by the whole method the subject was allowed to retrace as much as he would. In other experiments the amount of return permitted was no greater in the whole method than in the part method. Table 5 summarizes some of the results secured. The number of subjects in each group is too small to make the averages dependable, and the records undoubtedly have a low reliability. As the results stand, however, the progressive part and the direct repetitive part methods are superior to the whole method for both groups of subjects. For the rats the whole method with returns permitted, which is the usual method followed in maze experimentation, is the least efficient. In a later study with nonsense syllables, Pechstein (1918) found the whole method inferior to the various part methods, the progressive part method being the best.

Our brief analysis of the problem of whole versus part learning can lead only to the conclusion that in some way as yet undetermined learning and retention are influenced by the whole versus the partial presentation of the stimulus series at each trial. Which method will prove most advantageous will probably vary with the character of the stimulus material, with the individual subject experimented upon, with the subject's age, with the amount of training which he has had, and with other as yet undetermined factors. We cannot generalize and say without qualification that either method is superior to the other.

THE DISTRIBUTION OF EFFORT

The problem of the distribution of effort concerns the influence upon learning and retention of the introduction of rest periods between each two successive periods of practice. In the study of this problem we may vary the length of the periods of rest while keeping the magnitude of the work periods constant, or the conditions may be reversed. In the first instance the period of work may consist of one trial in the maze and the rest periods may be of one, two, and three days. One group of subjects would work for one trial per day; one, for one trial every two days; and one, for one trial every three days. In the second instance one group of subjects would have one trial per day; another group, two trials per day; and a third group, three trials per day.

Many investigators, beginning with Ebbinghaus, have contributed to the solution of this problem. The experimental findings indicate that, within limits, learning is accomplished with less work when practice is distributed than when it is concentrated. This principle is drawn from experiments upon a great variety of problems: maze habits, problem boxes, verbal material, archery, and arithmetic. Ebbinghaus used nonsense syllables as the learning material. His results, secured with himself as subject, are as follows: Six lists of 12 nonsense syllables each were learned at a given time with an average of 410 repetitions. Twenty-four hours later the relearning of the lists required an average of 41 repetitions. One list therefore required 68.3 repetitions in immediate succession for initial learning and 6.8 repetitions for relearning. When on the other hand a list of 12 syllables was learned to the point of one correct recall on each of three successive days, the total figures for the three days of distributed effort are 17.5 trials, 12.1 trials, and 8.3 trials, or a total of 37.9. Twenty-four hours later, the 12 syllables were relearned, on the average, in 6.2 trials. Thus 37.9 repetitions distributed over three days gave essentially the same retention after 24 hours as did 68.3 repetitions in immediate succession.

Jost (1897) made a more thorough study of the same problem. He also found that concentrated repetitions of the responses to be mastered gave a poorer retention than did the same number of repetitions distributed over a number of days. This was true when retention was tested by the relearning method of Ebbinghaus and also when tested by the method of reinstatement. Jost was also able to show that the explanation of the greater effectiveness of the distributed work did not lie in the lesser fatigue that might accompany the shorter periods of work.

The greater effectiveness of distributed work can also be shown in the curves of learning. Starch (1912) had 42 subjects divided into four groups work on a problem of digit-letter substitution. "The first group

worked ten minutes at a time twice a day for six days. The second group
worked for twenty minutes at a time once a day for six days. The third
group worked forty minutes at a time every other day for six days. And
the fourth group did the entire task at one continuous sitting. In each
case the total time was 120 minutes" (1912, p. 211). Figure 10 shows
the degree of skill in the substitution for successive five-minute intervals
of work. There is very little difference between the 10-minute and the
20-minute groups, but the 40-minute group is decidedly inferior, and the
group that did all of its work at one sitting made the worst record of all.

Two important studies of the effect of distributed effort on the learning of infrahuman animals have been made by Ulrich (1915) and Warden
(1923). Ulrich tested white rats with one, three, and five trials daily
on a problem in which they had to lift a latch in order to enter a box
and secure food. Tests were also made with a maze and with an inclined-
plane box. From the distribution tables which record both the number
of trials and the number of days required to perfect the habits under the
several conditions, the general conclusion can be drawn that the less

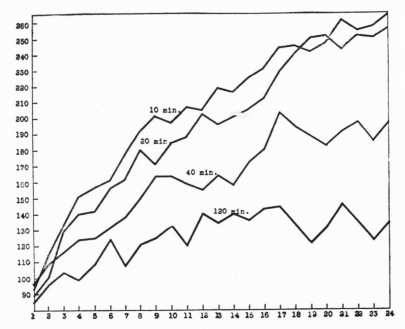

FIGURE 10

THE EFFECT OF DIFFERENT DISTRIBUTIONS OF EFFORT ON THE LEARNING CURVE
The ordinate values represent achievement; the abscissa values, successive
five-minute periods.

(From D. A. Starch's "Periods of Work in Learning," *J. Educ. Psychol.*, 1912.)

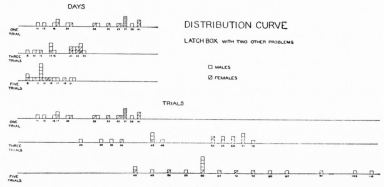

FIGURE 11

THE EFFECT OF THE DISTRIBUTION UPON THE NUMBER OF DAYS AND THE NUMBER
OF TRIALS REQUIRED BY RATS TO MASTER A PROBLEM BOX
(From J. L. Ulrich's "Distribution of Effort in Learning in the White Rat,"
Behav. Monog., 1915.)

frequent the trials the more economical the learning when measured by
total trials, but the less economical when measured by the number of
days required. Figure 11 presents one of Ulrich's distribution curves.

Warden's work was conducted on a maze. Table 6 gives the average
number of trials required by the various groups to reach a degree of
mastery where nine trials out of ten were without error. The table indicates that four groups were trained with one trial per day where the
length of the interpolated interval varied from six hours with one group
to three days with another group. The results suggest that the interpolation of a 12-hour rest period is the most efficient, whether it occurs after
1, 3, or 5 trials. Furthermore, one trial is preferable to a sequence of
three or five trials under all conditions here represented. Warden's experiment indicates clearly the method of determining the optimal combination of length of interval and amount of practice for the acquisition of
any stimulus-response coordination. However, the size of the M.D.'s in

TABLE 6

EFFECT OF LENGTH AND FREQUENCY OF INTERVAL UPON MAZE LEARNING STATED
IN TERMS OF THE MEAN NUMBER OF TRIALS REQUIRED FOR MASTERY
(From Warden)

| Length of interval | Frequency of interpolated interval | | | | | |
| | After 1 trial | | After 3 trials | | After 5 trials | |
	Trials	M. D.	Trials	M. D.	Trials	M. D.
6 hrs.	45.	12.	62.4	11.1	74.1	17.5
12 hrs.	36.8	9.7	54.8	12.1	63.6	11.4
1 day	46.4	13.1	65.4	18.4	86.1	15.2
3 days	71.9	13.5	91.1	24.2	86.1	18.4
5 days			129.7	26.	107.1	20.7

Table 6 and the low reliability of the maze make us cautious in accepting the data of this table at their face value.

Carr (1919) in work with a stylus maze and Cummins (1919) in experiments with a French-English vocabulary have shown that the effect of the distribution of effort varies with the point in the learning process at which the distribution is introduced. Carr finds that rest periods inserted in the first trials are more effective in reducing the total error score than if introduced in the later trials. Cummins' work indicates the desirability of short rest periods during the initial stages of learning and of longer intervals in the final stages. [See Ruch (1929) for a general survey of the problem of distributed effort.]

Various theories have been proposed to account for the increased efficiency in learning and retention that comes with the distribution of effort. Müller and Pilzecker's doctrine of perseveration, which they elaborated in connection with the effect of interpolated work upon the retention of previously learned coordinations, has been applied also as an explanation for the present phenomenon. According to this hypothesis, the neural processes involved in behavior persevere for an appreciable interval of time after the behavior ceases and so are better retained if allowed to set without interference. This is a purely hypothetical explanation and one, moreover, which it is difficult to reconcile with the apparent fact that efficiency varies both with the length of the interpolated rest interval and with the quantity of work done during the work intervals. Lashley (1917, 1918) has suggested that there may be no general and fundamental law at the basis of the increased efficiency, but that specific factors, varying with the specific responses studied, may account for the results. As a concrete example he has been able to show, with rats learning the maze, that concentrated trials make for less diversity in behavior than do distributed trials, i.e., that with concentrated trials the same errors tend to be repeated to a higher degree than with distributed trials. In addition Lashley has the following comment to make: "In other forms of learning there are many agents such as fatigue and loss of interest in long practice periods which may interfere with efficient performance and so prolong the apparent learning time, while with verbal habits the possibility of practice outside of the experimental practice periods has not been altogether eliminated where short practice periods were used" (1918, p. 366).

AGE AND LEARNING

As the human individual passes from infancy through adolescence and maturity to senescence, his apparent ability to cope with environmental difficulties changes. Our present problem concerns the possible influence of the age factor itself upon these changes. If it can be shown by careful experimentation that learning performance does vary with age, the phenomenon may be due either to intrinsic factors of neural growth and decline operative during the organism's life-history or to such extrinsic factors as habits which facilitate or impede learning and socio-economic conditions whose variations during the individual's lifetime may cause significant changes in the motivating processes involved in learning.

Our first problem is one of fact. Let us therefore inspect briefly some of the more important experimental studies of the problem. Hubbert (1915), Liu (1928), and Stone (1929) have studied maze learning with white rats belonging to various age groups. Hubbert used the Watson circular maze with a *camera lucida* attachment (Figure 12), which made possible the accurate recording of the pathways followed by the subject. Table 7 summarizes her findings. Hubbert says: "Young rats learn the

TABLE 7
AVERAGES REQUIRED FOR MASTERY OF MAZE
(Based on Hubbert)

Age	Trials	Time in min.	Distance in meters
25 days			
11 males	32	21.2	277
16 females	29	23.1	267
all	30	22.4	271
Range of score	14-51	6.4-64	139-418
65 days			
16 males	26.8	19.2	228
11 females	36.5	25.7	307
all	30.7	21.8	260
Range of score	14-65	6.4-73.1	91-750
200 days			
15 males	39.4	25.2	296
13 females	44.5	46.5	388
all	41.7	35.1	339
Range of score	14-112	8.2-94.9	125-912
300 days			
13 males	40.4	73.3	344
15 females	41.3	75.2	380
all	40.7	74.3	367
Range of score	14-78	15.9-227.3	117-723

maze more rapidly than the old ones, the rapidity with which the habit may be formed decreasing with increase in age" (1915, p. 54). An inspection of the table of results, however, reveals a large overlapping of the records made by the various age groups, which are also small in number of subjects; and Paterson (1917) has pointed out the statistical inadequacy of the data to support such a conclusion. Hubbert also says that the most rapid improvement comes earlier in the learning process for younger than for older animals. This is not supported by Stone's later and more careful work.

Liu's investigation was conducted with rats of 30, 45, 60, 75, 100, 150, and 250 days of age. Table 8 shows the mean trial, error, and time scores for the different groups in learning one of Carr's mazes. It would appear from the data of this table that ability to master the maze

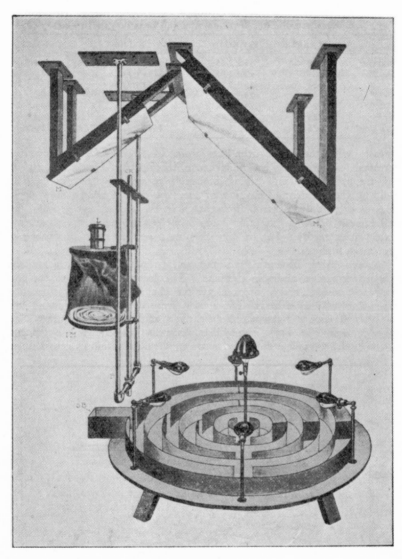

FIGURE 12
THE WATSON CIRCULAR MAZE WITH *Camera Lucida* ATTACHMENT
(From J. B. Watson's "A Circular Maze with *Camera Lucida* Attachment,"
J. Anim. Behav., 1914.)

TABLE 8

A SUMMARY OF LIU'S DATA ON AGE AND LEARNING IN THE RAT

Age	No. of animals	Av. trials	Av. total time	Av. total errors
30 days	40	53±2.35	1182±50.31	170±7.01
45 "	24	48±3.08	1155±71.66	151±8.12
60 "	24	39±2.94	1054±73.96	145±9.79
75 "	43	25±1.34	664±30.13	69±2.46
100 "	25	29±2.28	859±58.	83±5.
150 "	25	31±1.88	976±72.8	85±5.
250 "	25	40±5.37	1542±89.6	137±10.

increases with the age of the rats from 30 to 75 days and decreases
thereafter. The results are much more definite than Hubbert's, and yet
they are not convincing. It is impossible to tell whether they are the
result of the accidental selection of animals, of the unreliability of the
maze, or of a faulty control of incentives in the various age groups. We
shall present below a quotation from Stone bearing upon the significance
of this latter factor. Let us turn then to a consideration of Stone's experimental findings.

He used three different problems: an inclined-plane box, a modified
Carr maze, and a multiple-T maze. The last problem gives the most
dependable results, and it is from this one that we shall draw illustrative
data. Rats of four different life-periods were used: 31 days, about half-
way from infancy to puberty; 56 days, about mid-puberty; 456 days, about
mid-life; and 730 days, somewhere between mid-life and senescence.
Figure 13 shows typical results in terms of the elimination of errors during

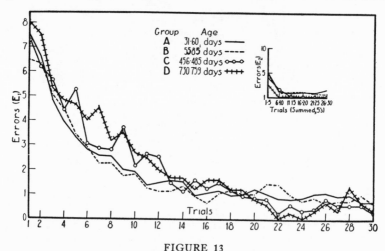

FIGURE 13

THE ELIMINATION OF ERRORS IN A MAZE BY RATS OF FOUR DIFFERENT AGE GROUPS
(From C. P. Stone's "The Age Factor in Animal Learning: I. Rats in the
Problem Box and the Maze," *Genet. Psychol. Monog.*, 1929.)

30 trials. These results were all secured from rats whose diet was carefully controlled through its effect upon the rats' body weights. All age groups worked with as high a degree of hunger incentive as dietary restrictions could give. From the figure it is clear that no difference in the progress of mastery can be correlated with the different ages of the subjects. (Curves on the Vincent-Kjerstad plan would be more desirable from the standpoint of group comparisons. However, as we shall soon see, Stone's data in general fail to show any clear effects of an age factor, and Vincent curves which I have constructed from data supplied by Stone also show no age effects.) The number of trials required for mastery likewise fails to show significant age differences. The following statement by Stone is so important for the study of such differences, and also for other problems involving the maze, that I quote it at some length: "Striking would have been the *apparent age* difference obtained, if in a single experiment we had motivated young animals [strongly and the middle-aged groups less strongly]. In that case, the obtained results would have shown statistically significant inferiority in error scores for the two middle-aged groups and even would have yielded slightly inferior results for the older of the two middle-aged groups. With the prevalent rule of thumb and non-uniform methods of motivating animals by different experimenters working in the field of maze studies, the foregoing hypothetical case is not at all far-fetched. *In fact, it is exactly the result that an experimenter using present-day techniques is most likely to obtain, because, in the absence of adequate growth norms for the diet used, it is much easier to overlook the fact that young animals with constant weight increase while on the maze experiment may actually be subjected to a greater degree of chronic inanition than mature animals which are held at maintenance or allowed to increase or decrease slightly in weight.* . . . Age differences in maze records obtained under any condition in which either group is not exercising its maximum learning ability may be regarded with suspicion of being spurious, whatever their direction, until a scientific method of equating the motivation of different groups has been devised. Likewise, it is equally important that similarities in maze performances of rats not held to the maximum of their ability be regarded with suspicion of being spurious unless evidence of a less equivocal nature may be brought to bear upon the case in question" (1929, pp. 103-105).

With the failure to demonstrate variations in learning ability with age in rats, we are left without a factual basis for the hypothesis that the plasticity of the nervous system varies with age. With the rats we are able to control the amount and character of the habits established prior to the experimental study in a way that is impossible with human subjects. We are thus with animal subjects in a highly advantageous position for discovering any intrinsic change in neural plasticity which might be present. With human subjects, when differences in the learning performance of individuals of different ages are found, it is impossible to separate the influence of previously established habits from the possible influence of a neural plasticity.

Let us consider briefly certain of the findings where human subjects have been used. In the section on *Reminiscence* we shall see some evidence that the recall of imperfectly learned response is partly a function of age. Thorndike and his colleagues (1928) have made the most extensive study of different adult age groups, and numerous investigators have confirmed the popular impression that the ability to form habits improves during childhood. Thorndike presents Figure 14 as a fair generalization

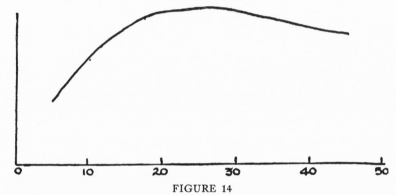

FIGURE 14
"The General Form of the Curve of Ability To Learn in Relation to Age"
in Human Subjects
(From E. L. Thorndike's *Adult Learning,* 1928, by permission of the publishers, Macmillan Co., New York.)

of the relation of age to learning in human subjects. His own data concern adults whom he has tested with a great variety of learning problems such as substitution tests, writing with the wrong hand, learning to typewrite, learning Esperanto, mastery of school subjects, and learning to respond to four signals with four simple acts. In this latter experiment 12 subjects ranging in age from 20-24 years were compared with 12 subjects over 35 years of age (average age, 42), the two groups having about equal ability on the CAVD behavior test. [See Thorndike (1926) for a description of this test.] The subjects were blindfolded and instructed to draw a line 3, 4, 5, or 6 inches long. Six hundred such lines were drawn by the subject while ignorant of the accuracy of his performance. Then for seven days, the subject drew 600 lines per day and was told each time whether the response was right or wrong. After this came a third test in which the subjects drew 600 lines without being told whether the lines were right or wrong. In the first period there was no essential difference between the age groups. In the last part of the seven days' work, however, the old scored only 83 per cent as much as the young, and in the third test only 70 per cent as much as the young. Although the number of subjects is small, the results are in harmony with those derived from Thorndike's other work. The results are chiefly significant because the kind and amount of previous specific training possessed by the various subjects can hardly have influenced the relative performance of the two groups. Differences in motivation and in the adjustments of the two groups to the social aspects of the experimental situation, however, remain as possible explanatory factors.

TABLE 9

SUMMARY OF THE RELATION OF AGE TO ABILITY TO LEARN

(From Thorndike)

U, university group; P, prisoners; H, evening-high-school students; S, students in secretarial schools

Group	Ability	Gain in score			Percentage which O is of Y
		Y 20-24 yrs.	25-34 yrs.	O 35 yrs. & over	
U	Drawing lines				64
	Wrong hand writing	57	51	41	72
	Substitution (words)	28.0	27.9	22.8	81
	Learning code	10.4	8.3	6.3	61
	Esperanto	31.5	26.3	24.7	79
	Learning nos. to fit nonsense syllables	21.9	18.2	14.0	64
	University studies				over 100
P	Substitution (digits)	9.0	9.2	9.4	104
	Elementary school subjects	100	100	88	88
	Addition practice	5.0	4.6	4.8	96
H	Algebra, Civics, English, etc.				87 for 30 or over
S	Typewriting				95 for 30 or over
	Learning stenographic symbols				100 for 30 or over

Table 9 from Thorndike summarizes the results of his experiments. Thorndike comments upon this table as follows: "The facts of table [9] in general are fairly consistent with the hypothesis that the old are considerably inferior to those around 22 in general basic modifiability but compensate for this inferiority somehow (probably by better appreciation and organization and use of what is learned, possibly by greater interest) when learning typewriting or stenography or school studies. . . . The general tendency from all our experiments is for an inferiority of about 15 per cent as a result of 20 years from twenty-two on. Learning representing an approximation to sheer modifiability unaided by past learning [the line-drawing experiment] shows considerable more inferiority than this. Actual learning of such things as adults commonly have to learn shows considerably less" (1928, pp. 104 and 106).

Two different stories of the relationship of age and learning are told by the animal experimentation by Stone and the human tests by Thorndike. Even though practical learning situations give the curve of Figure 14 for human ability, there are too many factors involved other than those of neural development and regression to enable us to infer that these latter factors exist and are responsible for the shape of the curve. Thorndike distinctly recognizes such possibilities as the awkwardness of adults in certain social situations, the difficulty of securing the adult's complete cooperation, and the inhibiting effects of habits and customs. One cannot argue directly from rats to men, but, until experiments upon man have been carried out with an equating of incentive and previous relevant training for the various age groups, we must remain skeptical of the rôle of intrinsic neural changes as a causal factor in those learning problems which the various age groups can all undertake.

The Relation between Speed of Learning and Retention

The experimental investigations of this problem indicate not only that the responses first learned are best retained but also that the individuals who learn most rapidly also tend to make the best records in retention tests.

Woodworth (1914) conducted an experiment using 20 words of an Italian-English vocabulary as the stimulus material. After the subject had read the list once, the experimenter gave the Italian words as stimuli and the subject was to respond with the English equivalent. From 3-5 sec. were allowed for each response, and the subject was prompted and corrected when necessary. This training was continued until each correct response was given once. As soon as an Italian-English combination was learned to the point of one correct recall that pair of words was dropped from the list (to prevent overlearning), and the training was continued with the remaining pairs. When all had been learned, the entire list was again presented once. After an interval of 2-20 hours the Italian words were presented singly and the recall score for the corresponding English words was determined. The results were as follows:

Of the pairs learned in x readings	y per cent were retained
x	y
1	73
2	72
3	63
4	58
5	38
6-11	27

A part of this decrease in retention with increased difficulty of learning might be due to differences in the associative responses called out by the various words. Woodworth, however, reports that when only words not so supplemented are considered the relationship between speed of learning and excellence of retention remains the same.

Important work on the retention of learned material by individuals who learn quickly and by those who do not has been carried out particularly by Norsworthy (1912), Pyle (1913), and Lyon (1916). Norsworthy, using 83 subjects and a German-English vocabulary of 1200 words, found that the quicker the learning, the better the retention. In this experiment the amount of time during which the subjects worked was kept constant, and the speed of learning was shown by the number of correct responses which the subjects learned. A high positive correlation (0.41-0.50) was found between the number of responses learned and the number that could be correctly reinstated. It was also found that the subjects who learned over 700 word responses (the quick learners) had a better relative retention score than did those (slow) learners who mastered only 33 word responses.

Lyon's work was carried out with three methods: In method 1 the subject learned the required responses and, after an interval of delay, attempted to reinstate as many as possible without having had the original material represented. Method 2 immediately followed method 1. The stimulus material—words, digits, nonsense syllables, or prose—was again presented once, and the subject was then asked to reinstate the appropriate responses. Method 3 immediately followed method 2. In this case the stimulus material was again presented to the subject, and a complete relearning was required. The chief defect in Lyon's method seems to lie in his lack of control of the learning periods. In place of rigidly controlling the amount of time and the number of trials required for mastery, he permitted the subjects to study until they were certain that they could reinstate the required responses without error. This method certainly resulted in a variable and undetermined amount of overlearning. Table 10 shows results based upon the records of 24 normal-school seniors who were divided into two groups (upper and lower halves) on the basis of the quickness of initial learning.

An examination of this table shows that the quicker half of the learners was superior in retention to the slower half with all materials when

TABLE 10

RELATION OF SPEED OF LEARNING TO RETENTION

(From Lyon)

Materials Subjects		Method 1 % reinstated	Method 2 % reinstated	Method 3 Av. learning time	Av. relearning time	% saved
Digits						
	quicker half	27	34	5.5	2.0	63
	slower half	22	36	15.0	4.0	71
Nonsense syllables						
	quicker half	26	44	24.1	6.5	71
	slower half	21	36	38.0	12.1	68
Words						
	quicker half	23	44	10.0	5.5	40
	slower half	20	35	14.8	5.7	61
Prose						
	quicker half	59	80	14.3	4.8	68
	slower half	46	67	27.3	9.1	66
Poetry						
	quicker half	59	73	7.0	2.8	61
	slower half	40	57	14.5	5.2	65

method 1 was used. With method 2 the slower learners surpassed the quicker learners in the case of digits only. With method 3 the slower learners retained more in the case of digits, words, and poetry than did the quicker learners. Lyon also calculated coefficients of correlation between learning and relearning. Although clear-cut relationships were not generally demonstrated, the results favor the conclusion that quick learning is accompanied by good retention.

Numerous studies have been made of the relation between the amount learned, as measured by a test of recall immediately after learning, and the amount retained at some later time. These studies have shown a positive correlation between immediate and delayed recall which may be as high as 0.82, found by Winch (1924), or 0.71, found by Gordon (1925). The score for immediate retention, however, can represent speed of learning only where the learning occupies a constant period. This condition is fulfilled in Gordon's study, and the coefficient of 0.71 may be regarded as an indication of the relationship between speed of learning and retention. Brown (1924a), also working with a constant time period for learning, finds positive correlations between speed of learning and retention. Brown believes "that a positive relation is normal and that when conditions are favorable the correlation is very close between amount learned and amount retained." This point of Brown's is further brought out by the fact that the methods of stimulus presentation, e.g., the distribution of stimuli as opposed to their concentration, which favor learning also favor retention.

The Influence of Active and Passive Recall upon Retention

In the ordinary experiment upon the learning of verbal habits, the subject is instructed not to practice on the problem between trials, i.e., not to attempt to reinstate the verbal responses except when the stimuli are presented by the experimenter. Obviously such *active* recall will affect the rate of learning. If erroneous responses are made, they will tend to retard learning; and, if correct responses are made, they will facilitate learning. In any case the experimenter would not have a record of what responses had been made and so would not be able adequately to interpret the results.

The topic of our present discussion raises a slightly different aspect of the problem of repetitions not controlled by the experimenter: Does the *active* reinstatement of responses have a more advantageous effect upon learning than *passive* reinstatement? The terms *active* and *passive* are not aptly chosen to designate the experimental facts, but our descriptions of experimental procedures will show that active reinstatement occurs in the absence of the stimulus material and that passive reinstatement occurs in response to the presentation of that material. Reading and recitation are other terms used to designate the same phenomenon. The investigation of recall with and without the aid of the stimulus was begun in 1907 by Witasek (1908) and continued particularly by Katzaroff (1908),

Kühn (1914), Knors (1910), Gates (1917), and Skaggs (1920). Although the experimental methods used by these investigators have varied greatly, their results justify the general conclusion that under certain conditions the reinstatement of a response, without the aid of its usual stimulus, aids learning more than a reinstatement called forth by the presentation of that stimulus.

Gates's work, the most complete recent investigation of the problem, was carried out upon large numbers of school children and a few adults. The material to be learned was either nonsense syllables or consecutive verbal material patterned after the biographical sketches in *Who's Who*. Table 11 shows the various combinations of active and passive recall

TABLE 11

METHODS USED BY GATES IN THE STUDY OF READING AND RECITATION

Method	Time of reading	Time of recitation	% reading	% recitation
1	9 min.	0	100	0
2	7 min. 12 sec.	1 min. 48 sec.	80	20
3	5 min. 24 sec.	3 min. 36 sec.	60	40
4	3 min. 36 sec.	5 min. 24 sec.	40	60
5	1 min. 48 sec.	7 min. 12 sec.	20	80
	With biographical sketches method 6 was added			
6	54 sec.	8 min. 6 sec.	10	90

(recitation and reading) utilized with school grades 4, 6, and 8. In method 1 the subjects read the material for 9 minutes. In method 2 the reading occupied the first 7 mins. and 12 sec. of the study period, and the final 1 min. and 48 sec. was devoted to recitation. When the subject recited, he did so quietly and to himself. He was instructed to glance at the material to be learned only when he was otherwise unable to reinstate the appropriate responses. The remaining methods of the table are to be similarly understood. At the close of the 9 minutes of work by each method, the subject was asked to write down as much of the material as possible. These records were then scored by a conventional method.

Table 12 is based upon nonsense material and shows the average scores and their P.E.'s for each of the five methods. These results indicate that as the amount of recitation increases, within the limits tested, the average

TABLE 12

AVERAGE SCORE FOR EACH OF THREE GRADES FOR THE VARIOUS METHODS USING NONSENSE MATERIAL

(From Gates)

Method		1	2	3	4	5
Grade 8	Av.	16.92	23.86	25.79	27.28	35.51
	P.E.	0.61	0.69	0.65	0.66	0.86
Grade 6	Av.	13.21	20.18	22.64	25.15	30.52
	P.E.	0.61	0.84	0.60	0.91	1.07
Grade 4	Av.	9.45	12.00	16.10	16.95	20.03
	P.E.	0.57	0.46	0.56	0.75	0.79

TABLE 13

AVERAGE SCORE FOR EACH OF FOUR GRADES FOR THE VARIOUS METHODS USING
BIOGRAPHICAL MATERIAL

(From Gates)

Method		1	2	3	4	5	6
Grade 8	Av.	20.77	22.39	24.84	24.95	25.28	23.75
	P.E.	0.72	0.87	0.70	0.69	0.50	0.82
Grade 6	AV.	15.13	16.55	18.01	17.70	17.77	16.63
	P.E.	0.75	0.59	0.69	0.68	0.82	0.68
Grade 5	Av.	11.79	13.95	15.21	15.96	15.33	15.74
	P.E.	0.40	0.43	0.48	0.56	0.50	0.5ĩ
Grade 4	Av.	14.61	16.91	16.36	18.81	17.62	17.2(
	P.E.	0.77	0.78	0.86	0.77	0.70	0.7ĩ

recall also increases. Table 13 is based upon biographical material. The results indicate that for all four grades the efficiency of recall increases up to a certain point, with the increase in the amount of recitation, and declines after that. Of the six methods employed no. 5 is the most advantageous for grades 6 and 8, and no. 4, for grades 4 and 5. Where an interval of from three to four hours elapsed before the subjects were required to write down the material, similar results were secured; but there was a greater difference between the worst and the best methods than was found for immediate recall.

Gates's results indicate that a larger and larger amount of recitation relative to reading when inserted earlier and earlier in the learning period significantly affects the efficiency of work. Various explanations have been offered for this general phenomenon. It seems probable that recitation as here conducted derives its advantage from the opportunity which it affords the subject for correcting his errors and from the fact that during recitation the subject is practicing the type of response which he will be required to make finally, viz., the recall of the learned material without dependence upon the text. This latter point is particularly well supported by the work of Katzaroff (1908), who used the paired-associates method of recall both for the recitation and for the final test of retention.

In spite of the fact that careful laboratory investigations of this problem reveal that the proper introduction of recitation into the study period is advantageous to learning, the extension of these conclusions to the schoolroom is not justified. It may well be that a detailed and accurate scoring of returns from a carefully controlled laboratory experiment will reveal advantages of certain methods of work and yet all of these advantages may either be lost in the hurly-burly of schoolroom conditions or fail to be reflected in the rough scoring methods applied by teachers. Furthermore, the tables show that recitation aided the mastery of the biographical material less than it did the nonsense material. This fact we get by comparing the difference in score between the poorest and the best methods for each material. Thus for nonsense syllables the poorest method was no. 1 and the best was no. 5, which was 100 per cent or more better than no 1. In grade 8 for biographical material the best method is only about 20 per cent better than the worst.

The Influence of Activity upon the Retention of Previously Established Habits

Let us assume that a subject has been trained for any given number of trials on a problem like repeating nonsense syllables or running a maze. During this training certain changes have been set up in his nervous system in virtue of which his behavior is different at the end of the training from what it was at the start. If training is now discontinued on the problem, as time passes, the subject shows less and less of the effects of his training, no matter what method of testing retention we use. Recall becomes impossible; the subject can no longer distinguish between the material on which he was trained and new material (the age of stimulus method); and even the relearning time shows no saving over that of the original learning. Theoretically such a loss of retention might be brought about merely as a result of the lapse of time, as a result of the metabolic processes in the body whereby the neural changes set up by training would gradually fade away. In order to prove that lapse of time itself brought a loss of retention, it would be necessary to conduct an experiment in which the influence of the activities interpolated between the original learning and the later test of retention could be ruled out as explanatory factors in the loss. The conventional method of conducting an experiment upon the influence of interpolated activities is as follows:

Experimental group	Control group
Training on habit no. 1	Training on habit no. 1
Rest, i.e., no activity	Interpolated work
Retest of habit no. 1	Retest of habit no. 1

It is impossible, however, in a living organism to have a period of "no activity." All that we can do experimentally is to vary the character and amount of the activity which is interpolated between the original learning and the retest period and to study the influence of such changes upon retention. We shall present data later showing how the loss of retention varies with the lapse of time; but, as the lapse of time increases, the quantity of interpolated activity also increases. It is to this latter factor that we must look for the explanation of the loss. When investigators speak of periods of rest or of the mere lapse of time, we are to understand that the ordinary uncontrolled routine of the subject's life filled the period in question, or that some activity like newspaper reading (see experiments below) was present.

Ebbinghaus was the first experimenter to attack the problem of loss of retention as a result of increasing the quantity and duration of the interpolated activities. Müller and Pilzecker were the first to vary experimentally the character of the interpolated work and to study the resulting changes in retention. We shall begin our examination of the experimental evidence bearing upon the loss of retention with a brief survey of the work conceived in the manner of Müller and Pilzecker and then study the problem from the angle suggested by Ebbinghaus' work.

Müller and Pilzecker (1900) used both the paired-associates and the relearning methods. The material to be learned was nonsense syllables presented on a revolving drum. The interpolated work was varied in a number of ways: (1) the subject rested for the entire period; (2) other lists of nonsense syllables were learned; (3) the subject studied pictures in order to describe them later; and (4) the material of nos. 2 and 3 sometimes came immediately after the completion of the original learning and sometimes after intervals of rest. Condition 1 was the standard with which the results of the other conditions were compared. Although very few subjects were used, the results indicate that, when conditions 2, 3, and 4 follow learning, the scores on the retention tests are lower than when condition 1 follows learning. The use of nonsense syllables in the interpolated work was no more disadvantageous than the study of pictures. Retention scores are less if the interpolated work comes immediately after learning than if a rest interval intervenes before the interpolated work is done. (In order to test this phase of the problem, called the temporal position of the interpolation, the interpolated period might be 8 min. long divided into 4 min. work and 4 min. rest, 4 min. rest and 4 min. work, or all 8 min. either rest or work.) These findings of Müller and Pilzecker have very largely set the problems for later investigators, although the general fact of the disadvantageous effect of interpolated activities is the only result upon which most students are agreed.

Robinson (1920) has made careful studies of the effect of various kinds

TABLE 14

THE INFLUENCE OF THE TEMPORAL POSITION OF THE INTERPOLATED WORK UPON RETENTION SCORES

(After Robinson)

Condition	Interpolated period	Amount recalled	Errors of recall
A	20 min. reading	29.1	6.1%
B	5 min. study of 3-place nos. 15 min. reading	18.6	31.9%
C	5 min. reading 5 min. study of 3-place nos. 10 min. reading	19.7	29.0%
D	10 min. reading 5 min. study 5 min. reading	19.2	32.6%
E	15 min. reading 5 min. study	18.4	30.3%

of interpolated work and also of the influence of the temporal position of the work upon the retention scores. In both cases the results disagree with those of Müller and Pilzecker. Table 14 shows Robinson's results on the influence of temporal position. The interpolated periods (conditions) are each 20 min. long. In condition A, the 20 min. were spent in reading a newspaper. Conditions B, C, D, and E are described in the table. After eight exposures of a list of 10 three-place numbers, a period of 20 min. was interpolated after which the subject wrote down as many of the numbers as possible. Table 14 shows how the amount recalled and the errors made varied with the nature of the interpolated period. Condition A is notably better than B, C, D, or E, but there is no essential difference between these four conditions. Although Robinson's work is undoubtedly dependable for the conditions under which he worked, the divergent results of other studies made under different conditions by Skaggs (1925) and Whitely (1924, 1927) must make us cautious in generalizing Robinson's results.

Historically one of the most important problems concerning the influence of interpolated activity upon retention may be formulated as follows: How does retention vary as the similarity between the original learning and the interpolated work varies? Müller and Pilzecker found no difference in the disadvantageous effects of nonsense syllables and picture study upon the recall of nonsense material. This would indicate that the similarity of original and interpolated work is not an important factor in the problem. This result, however, is not confirmed by the later investigations of Robinson, Skaggs, Whitely, Harden, and Johnson (1933). Whitely (1927), for example, examined the variation in the retention of words and phrases when just prior to attempts at learning and recall the subject was given either a résumé of material within the field of the original learning or a résumé from some field quite different from that of the material to be learned. While the difference was small, it indicates that recall was poorest when the résumé was drawn from the same field as the material to be learned. Robinson secured like results indicating the positive rôle of similarity when he used numbers for the original learning material and either numbers, nonsense material, poetry, multiplication, or prose reading for the interpolated work.

Skaggs and Robinson point out certain interesting theoretical aspects of the similarity problem. If the interpolated work is identical with the original learning, this amounts to continued training and no loss of retention will occur, rather there will be an increase in efficiency due to the prolongation of practice. As this identity decreases with the introduction of a less and less similar material, retention of the original material becomes less and less until a minimum is reached. Beyond this point further decreases in similarity, i.e., increases in dissimilarity, have less effect upon retention, and the retention score thus rises. (See Figure 15.) Robinson (1927) has sought to verify this theoretical relationship between original and interpolated work. The experiment was conducted by the memory-span method with consonants for the original and for

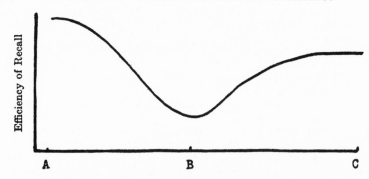

Degree of Similarity between Interpolated Activity and Original
Memorization—Descending Scale

FIGURE 15

THE THEORETICAL RELATIONSHIP BETWEEN EFFICIENCY OF RECALL AND THE SIMI-
LARITY BETWEEN INTERPOLATED ACTIVITY AND ORIGINAL ACTIVITY

(From E. S. Robinson's "The Similarity Factor in Retroaction," *Amer. J.
Psychol.,* 1927.)

the interpolated material. Where 12 consonants were used, the first
six were considered the original learning material and the last six were
considered the interpolated work. The recall score was the number of the
first six consonants correctly reproduced. Dissimilarity was varied from
the condition where all of the last six letters were different from
the first six to that where they were identical with the first six. There
might thus be from one to six letters common to the two sets. The
results show that the score falls regularly from that with six letters
in common to that with none in common, but the curve does not rise
again as the theoretical consideration indicated that it should. Perhaps
the difficulty lies in the concept of *similarity.* Robinson interprets degrees
of similarity in terms of the identity of letters. Harden (1929) used
numbers and letters in a study of the same problem and found that the
recall score again mounts when the interpolated material is numbers and
the original material is letters. The future development of the problem
of similarity of interpolated work depends upon the ability of experimenters to approach the problem quantitatively as Robinson, Harden,
and Johnson have done. At present, experiments clearly indicate that
one interpolated activity may differ markedly from another activity in
its effect upon retention, but the reasons for the difference are as yet
undetermined.

Heine (1914) was unable to find disadvantageous results for interpolated work when retention was tested by the age of stimulus method.
This was probably because the original material was so well learned that
the interpolated activity used had but little effect. Since the age of
stimulus method will reveal traces of retention when the recall method

will not, the former method would fail to show a loss of retention unless that loss were considerable.

We come now to the consideration of experimental data which bear upon our theoretical analysis at the beginning of the present section. Is the loss in retention under conditions of *disuse* due to the fading-away of neural changes or to the disrupting influence of subsequent activities? Let us first note the relationship between amount of material to be learned and loss of retention where the ordinary activities of the subject fill in the period between learning and the retest. Ebbinghaus (1913, p. 84), working by the relearning method, found a saving of 33 per cent after 24 hours for a list of 12 nonsense syllables. For 24 syllables the saving was 48 per cent; and for 36 syllables, 58 per cent. This general relationship between amount of material learned and retention after periods of no practice has been found by other investigators. Thus Robinson and Darrow (1924) found that retention was greater as the amount of material to be learned increased. Their results show 60-per-cent recall for 4 numbers, 66.5-per-cent for 6 numbers, 66.6-per-cent for 8 numbers, and 70.8-per-cent for 10 numbers. Recall was tested after a 15-minute interval devoted to casual newspaper reading. If now the reading is replaced by a study of other lists of numbers, the degree of retention is further decreased, but the longer lists of numbers are less affected than the shorter lists. The general conclusion is indicated that the decrease in the retention of previously learned material which is brought about by interpolated activities varies inversely with the length of the material learned, which is exactly the effect that Ebbinghaus assigned to the influence of the lapse of time.

So far we have considered experiments where, after learning a given response, the subject is either allowed to continue his routine activities or is subjected to training of a controlled character. The former case is called the condition of rest in comparison with which one estimates the influence which the activities of the latter case have upon the retention of the learned response. We may now ask what effect the activities of the alleged rest period have upon retention by comparing the results for the rest period with those for a period of equal length where the subject sleeps, a condition of much decreased activity. Jenkins and Dallenbach (1924) have performed such an experiment for periods of one, two, four, and eight hours. Series of 10 nonsense syllables were employed, and the two subjects used were tested by the method of recall. Great care was exercised to make the tests comparable for the two interpolated conditions of sleep and waking. Figure 16 shows the results. After one hour's sleep seven syllables were recalled, a loss of only about 28 per cent. After one hour of routine working activity, the loss was about 46 per cent. The noteworthy point in the figure is the relatively slight forgetting after sleep where the activities which might interfere with retention have been reduced to a minimum. [Nicolai, in his work (1922) cited in the section on *Reminiscence*, also found retention better after sleep.] The authors also sought to rule out the influence of interpolated activities

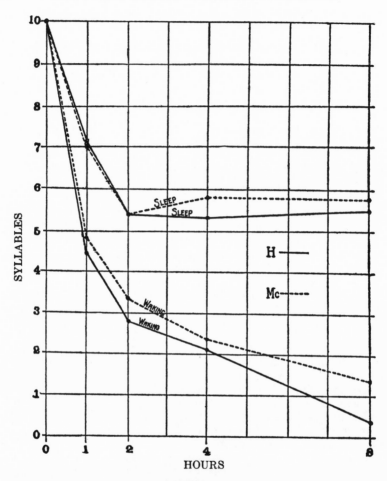

FIGURE 16

THE NUMBER OF SYLLABLES RECALLED AFTER VARIOUS INTERVALS OF TIME DURING
WHICH THE SUBJECT WAS EITHER ASLEEP OR AWAKE

(From J. G. Jenkins and K. M. Dallenbach's "Obliviscence during Sleep and
Waking," *Amer. J. Psychol.*, 1924.)

in another experiment where they utilized a hypnotized subject. The
subject learned the syllables while hypnotized. He was then brought
out of the hypnotic state and allowed to continue his daily duties until
the time for recall when he was again hypnotized for the test. Recall
was perfect after intervals of two, four, and eight hours, and was 80 per
cent perfect after 24 hours. Results in general harmony with this have also
been secured by Mitchell (1932).

The findings of Jenkins and Dallenbach have been partially confirmed by Dahl (1928), using the recognition method. In Dahl's work, retention after periods of 4 to 8 hours' sleep was better than after similar periods of normal waking activities. For 1- and 2-hour intervals, the reverse findings were secured. Van Ormer (1932) has conducted an extensive experiment on the same problem, using nonsense syllables and the relearning method. Again the results indicate that at 4 and 8 hours retention is better after sleep than after waking. There was no difference between the two conditions for the 1-hour interval, but possibly a difference for the 2-hour interval. Hunter (1932) has studied the effect of immobilization by cold upon learning and retention in the cockroach. Animals so inactivized learned more slowly and retained more poorly than animals who had spent the corresponding periods in normal temperatures and at normal activities.

The position taken in the present section is in harmony with that of Jenkins and Dallenbach when they say: "The results of our study as a whole indicate that forgetting is not so much a matter of decay of old impressions and associations as it is a matter of interference, inhibition, or obliteration of the old by the new" (1924, p. 612). McGeoch (1932a) also favors such an interpretation, which is further supported by the experimental facts and theoretical analyses of this same writer presented in later papers (1933a, 1933b).

THE RATE OF FORGETTING

In the preceding section we have discussed certain aspects of our present problem. We saw in Figure 16 that the amount of loss of retention after different intervals of time depended upon the character of the activities which filled the intervals. These curves show a rapid initial loss, and this characteristic is also present in the data of Table 15 based upon the findings of Ebbinghaus and Radossawljewitsch (1906). The explanation of the rapid initial loss is not entirely clear, but the most reasonable explanation seems to lie in the activities of the organism which immediately succeed the learning period. This view is supported by the work of Jenkins and Dallenbach which we have already presented. It is probable that such experiments, involving interpolated intervals of sleep, would show no rapid initial drop if it were possible for the subject to go to sleep immediately after learning.

There is no one curve of forgetting; rather there are many curves the natures of which vary with such factors as the following: the degree of mastery of the initial learning, the character of the material originally learned, the speed of the initial learning, the amount and character of the activity which follows the learning, and the method by which retention is tested. In the present section we shall consider only the second factor, i.e., the relation between loss of retention and the character of the material originally learned.

Such conventional verbal material as prose, poetry, or even unrelated

TABLE 15

The Rate of Forgetting for Different Materials

(From Radossawljewitsch and Ebbinghaus)

Period since learning was completed	Radossawljewitsch Percentage of saving, nonsense material	Percentage of saving, poetry	Ebbinghaus Percentage of saving, nonsense material
5 min.	98	100	—
20 min.	89	96	59
1 hr.	71	78	44
8 hrs.	47	58	36
24 hrs.	68	79	34
2 days	61	67	28
6 days	49	42	25
14 days	41	30	—
21 days	37	48	—
30 days	20	24	21
120 days	3	—	—

words is better retained than the relatively novel verbal material composed of nonsense syllables. Table 15 shows the difference between such materials when retention is tested by the savings method. Experiment has not made precise the reason for this difference between the two types of material, but theoretical analysis indicates pretty clearly that the advantage of the conventional material lies in the range of established associations which are present when the experiment begins. This insures not only a greater number of cues for the recall of the required responses but it also makes a large and uncertain degree of overlearning inevitable. And responses that are overlearned are better retained than those which are not so firmly established. [See, for example, Krueger (1929).]

It has been widely held that verbal habits are less well retained than non-verbal habits. Watson (1919, pp. 307-308), for example, writes: "It is thus seen that the rate of deterioration in habits such as we have considered [typewriting and ball-tossing], while in all cases positive, is very slow indeed. Ordinary observations show that the same is true in regard to swimming, skating, dancing, tennis playing, and skilled mechanical work. We shall see . . . . that this is in marked contrast to the rapid deterioration observed in habits which belong primarily to the language groups. There the deterioration is so rapid that in some cases, for example, in the learning of a series of nonsense syllables, the organization is lost in from fifteen minutes to half an hour so far as concerns the subject's ability to speak or write the words." Ordinary observations, however, are not adequate for the solution of the problem. Indeed it would be possible for any teacher of swimming or dancing to cite numerous cases where certain responses have appeared correctly once (which corresponds to one correct recall of a list of nonsense syllables) and yet are forgotten, i.e., cannot be reinstated, five minutes later. There is a dearth of carefully controlled experimental data bearing upon the problem. Many observations upon infrahuman subjects suggest a very high degree

TABLE 16

RETENTION OF TYPEWRITING SKILL AS SHOWN BY NUMBER OF STROKES ON MACHINE PER 10-MINUTE TEST

(From Book)

Tests	1	2	3	4	5	6	7	8	9	10	Av.	Av. correct strokes	% error
Last reg. prac. Jan. 7-16, 1906	1503	1509	1404	1572	1494	1436	1501	1455	1508	1698	1508	1475	2.21
1st memory test June 1-10, 1906	1365	1421	1421	1433	1529	1443	1523	1504	1313	1472	1443	1391	3.54
2nd memory test, June 1-10, 1907	1390	1344	1345	1537	1681	1694	1634	1845	1761	1850	1611	1560	3.15

of retention over long periods of time. Thus Davis (1907) says that some of his raccoons showed but slight loss of ability to operate fastenings on puzzle boxes after more than a year without practice. With human subjects who have been trained in typewriting, Book (1908) finds a high degree of retention after periods of six months and of one year during which the subject had no practice. Table 16 gives the results for one subject. As Book presents the results in the table, the first six months' interval shows that the average number of correct strokes made in the 10-day test is less than for the last 10-day period of the regular training test. The percentage of error was also greater. One year later the average for a period of equal length is even better than in the corresponding period 1.5 years before, although the error score remains high. At the beginning of each retest period the score is below what it was at the close of the last test. However, the relearning is accomplished within three or four 10-minute intervals. Book accounts for the high records made on the retests as follows: "The increase in score shown by our second memory series was due, so far as we could make out, rather *to the disappearance, with the lapse of time, of numerous psycho-physical difficulties, interfering associations, bad habits of attention, incidentally acquired in the course of learning, interfering habits and tendencies, which, as they faded, left the more firmly established typewriting associations free to act"* (1908, p. 107). Results which in general are similar to those of Book have been found by Swift (1903) and Bourdon (1901) among others. Book's explanation may indicate one of the factors responsible for the high retention and rapid relearning. In addition one must indicate that the following factors may have played an important rôle: (1) The two subjects may have applied themselves in the retention tests with a vigor not present in the last of the training series. (2) The materials typed in the retest series may not have been so difficult as those of the original series. (3) There was a very great amount of overlearning of many of the responses involved. This overlearning would account for a high degree of retention and would make the results non-comparable with the work on nonsense syllables where there is a minimum of overlearning. And (4) Book's subjects had not reached their limits of performance during the training series and indeed were steadily improving. Under these conditions relearning may occur very quickly and the total score on the retest period may be superior to that of the final section of the training series. This problem needs much additional investigation before it can be adequately understood.

McGeoch and Melton (1929) have made a direct experimental comparison of the retention of a non-verbal response and of a verbal response with human subjects. They compared the retention of three maze habits after seven days with the retention of 8-, 12-, and 16-syllable lists after the same period of time. Mazes and lists were learned to the point of one correct repetition. Retention was tested by the savings method. In terms of saving in trials, the nonsense syllables were uniformly better retained than were mazes. This superiority ranged from 33 to 67 per cent. In terms of saving in time, neither problem was uniformly superior. In terms of saving in errors, the mazes excelled in seven out of nine comparisons. In no case, save in trials, where the syllables were very superior, were the differences great. The work just reported is confirmed for a period of 14 days in the study made by Freeman and Abernethy (1930). These investigators trained one group of subjects to substitute number symbols for the contents of a given paragraph and trained a second group to typewrite the paragraph using a blank keyboard. For every response with the typewriter a number symbol was utilized by the first group. The same criterion of mastery, two correct repetitions of the paragraph, was used for both groups. When tested after a 14-day rest, the two groups were essentially equal; but, when again tested 8 weeks later, the typewriter group was definitely superior to the substitution group. The authors later repeated this experiment omitting the interpolated 14-day test and measuring retention after a total rest period of 10 weeks (1932). The retention of the typewriting response was again definitely superior to that of the substitution response. However, McGeoch (1932b) has presented additional evidence on the comparative retention of the maze habit and the nonsense-syllable habit showing that non-verbal responses are no better retained than verbal ones. Theoretically, this is what one should expect, since there is no obvious reason why the responses of the oral muscles should differ in retention from the responses of the hand or leg muscles. Further experimental analysis of the differences between the results secured by Freeman and by McGeoch are necessary for the clarification of the problem.

REMINISCENCE

The loss of retention, as it has been traced by Ebbinghaus and his successors, shows a progress which is initially rapid and which then becomes less and less as time elapses. In 1913 Ballard published the results of an experiment upon partially learned poetry with children as the subjects. The curves of retention secured from this work were radically different from anything heretofore described. The experiment was conducted as follows: A typewritten copy of the poetry to be learned was given each child. The experimenter then read the selection, and for 15 minutes the children were allowed to study the typewritten copies. These were then collected, and the children were told to write as much of the poetry as they could remember. Nothing was said about a second test, but at some predetermined later time another written reproduction was called for. Figures 17 and 18 show typical results. The amount of immediate recall is taken as 100 per cent and subsequent recalls are rated with this as a base. Each point on the curves represents a separate group of subjects; i.e., one group was tested after one day; another group, after two days; etc. These curves do not mean that all children reproduced more after a lapse of time than they did immediately. Table 17 shows the actual percentages of children who reproduced more, less, or the

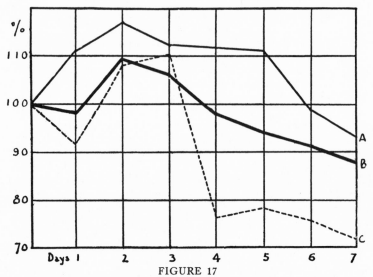

FIGURE 17

MEMORY CURVES FOR CHILDREN OF ABOUT TWELVE YEARS OF AGE
A is for the recall of "The Wreck of the Hesperus"; *B*, of "The Ancient Mariner";
and *C*, of nonsense verses.
(From P. B. Ballard's "Obliviscence and Reminiscence," *Brit. J. Psychol.,
Monog. Suppl.*, 1913.)

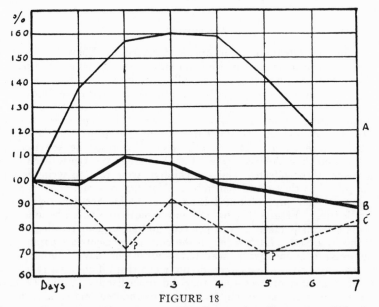

FIGURE 18

MEMORY CURVES FOR CHILDREN OF (*A*) ABOUT SIX YEARS OLD, (*B*) ABOUT
TWELVE, AND (*C*) ABOUT TWENTY-ONE
(From P. B. Ballard's "Obliviscence and Reminiscence," *Brit. J. Psychol.,
Monog. Suppl.*, 1913.)

TABLE 17

THE PERCENTAGE OF CHILDREN SHOWING REMINISCENCE AFTER VARIOUS
INTERVALS OF TIME

(From Ballard)

Interval in days	Number of children	Percentage of children who after the interval remembered:		
		more	same	less
1	644	45.5	14.9	39.6
2	841	55.3	13.9	30.8
3	646	47.5	13.3	39.2
4	1086	40.6	15.1	44.3
5	657	42.2	13.1	44.7
6	660	30.	14.1	55.9
7	658	28.4	13.4	58.2

same amount as they did immediately after study. The maximum reproduction for the six-year-olds is after an interval of three days; for 12-year-olds, after two days; and for 21-year-olds, immediately after study. Reminiscent items, i.e., items not contained in the immediate reproduction, may be present even though the total score on the second test is not so high as that on the first. The second reproduction is, therefore, not solely determined by the first, a conclusion supported by Nicolai's (1922) findings when the effects of the practice secured on the first reproduction were controlled. The influence of fatigue upon the initial test has also been ruled out as an explanatory factor. Luh (1922) has failed to secure the phenomenon with adult subjects tested with nonsense syllables where learning was incomplete and where different methods of measuring retention were employed. Williams (1926) and Huguenin (1914) confirmed Ballard's work in extended studies with children where the material again was incompletely learned. In spite of the fact that Brown (1923) found some signs of reminiscence in adults, the weight of evidence so far would indicate that age is the important accompanying condition of the phenomenon in human subjects. Ballard found that the younger children and the defective children learned least and showed the greatest gain on the second reproduction. Bunch and Magdsick (1933) investigated the retention of partially learned maze responses by young white rats after varying intervals of time, from 0 to 48 hours. Their results show that retention is much less when tested immediately than when tested after 1, 3, 6, 12, 24, and 48 hours, but that it does not vary significantly for these latter intervals. Bunch and Magdsick point out the significance of these findings for the interpretation of the phenomena of retroactive inhibition and of the distribution of effort.

No adequate explanation for reminiscence is at present established. Ballard assumed that the neural processes involved in learning continue to set for an appreciable interval of time after the learning period has ended. "Reminiscence may be said to be due to the inertia of the nervous system, which does not yield to an influence at once. Nor does the inertia stop yielding at once. Evidence of this positive change is afforded by the phenomena of retro-active amnesia, and by the increase of skill in bodily activities that takes place during long periods of intermission of practice. While it is admitted that many of the facts seem to fit into either the theory of inhibition or the theory of neural growth, it seems to the writer that the latter is the only theory that adequately explains the whole of the phenomena with which we have been dealing " (1913, p. 82). Huguenin and Ballard both, however, indicate that some items are lost as well as some recovered in the second test. Ballard's theory would account for the recovery but not for the loss. Brown regards the appearance of individual items in the second recall partly as a matter of chance and partly as a result of the fixating effect of the first recall. An adequate explanatory theory must await future experimentation; but the general findings in the study of conditioned responses very strongly suggest that the principles of inhibition and experimental extinction there revealed are vitally involved in the present phenomenon. [See also Lepley's (1932) penetrating analysis.]

TRANSFER OF TRAINING

No stimulus-response coordination can be acquired uninfluenced by the action system already possessed by the subject. Indeed it seems probable to many investigators that all new coordinations are merely the regroupings of simple responses which the organism has inherited. We have already considered the effect of training upon the retention of *previously* established habits, and we are now to discuss the effect of training upon the *subsequent* formation of habits. This effect may be positive or negative, that is, the formation of a stimulus-response coordination may be either facilitated or hindered by the training which has preceded it. In the former case we speak of habit transfer, and in the latter, of habit interference. The standard method of investigating such phenomena utilizes two groups of subjects of equal ability. One group is trained for a certain period of time on response no. 1, and then both groups are trained on response no. 2. A comparison of the records made by the two groups on response no. 2 will reveal whether or not the preliminary training has appreciably influenced the subsequent learning. Such comparisons are usually made in terms of the total time, trials, errors, or achievement of the groups, although they may also be made in terms of the learning curves. We shall first present typical experiments where non-verbal habits are concerned and then outline one or more experiments dealing with verbal habits.

Let us begin with observations made on cross-education. Investigations by Scripture (1894), Davis (1898, 1900), Thorndike and Woodworth (1901), Starch (1910), Ewert (1926), and Bray (1928) have shown that the training of responses made on one side of the body results in an increased facility of response on the opposite side of the body. Scripture studied strength of grip; Davis, quickness of tapping with the hands and feet; Thorndike and Woodworth, accuracy of tapping with the hands;

Swift, ball-tossing; and Starch, Ewert, and Bray, mirror tests. Ewert used two groups of subjects having approximately equal ability as rated in terms of the Otis behavior test. These two groups were tested in tracing a star in the mirror apparatus under the following conditions:

> Training group (26 subjects, average Otis score 164)
> (a) One trial with the non-preferred hand
> (b) Fifty trials with the preferred hand
> (c) One trial with the non-preferred hand
>
> Control group (26 subjects, average Otis score 154)
> (a) One trial with the non-preferred hand
> (b) Interpolated rest, one hour
> (c) One trial with the non-preferred hand

Table 18 shows that the training group made 82-per-cent and 76-per-cent improvement in time and errors respectively in tracing with the non-preferred hand after an hour's practice with the preferred hand, while the control group made only 46-per-cent and 55-per-cent improvement after an equivalent rest period. The approximate amount of transfer from the training of the preferred hand is thus 36 per cent for time and 21 per cent for errors.

TABLE 18

RESULTS OF CROSS-EDUCATION IN MIRROR DRAWING

(After Ewert)

	Training group		Control group	
(a) 1st trial	237.7 sec.	86.6 errors	256.6 sec.	101 errors
(c) 2nd trial	43.6 sec.	20.7 errors	135.0 sec.	44.8 errors
% of improvement	82	76	46	55
gain due to training	36%	21%		

Hunter and Yarbrough (1917), Pearce (1917), and Hunter (1922) have shown that habits established in the rat may interfere greatly with the acquisition of subsequent habits. In the last-mentioned study, rats were trained in a T-shaped discrimination box to go to the right side when a light was presented and to the left side for darkness. When this habit (habit no. 1) was mastered, the rats were trained to go to the right for darkness and to the left for the light. An average of 286 trials was required to master habit no. 1 and an average of 603 trials to master habit no. 2 which, when not preceded by habit no. 1, was no more difficult than that habit. Figure 19, which gives Vincent learning curves for the two habits, shows that the locus of the interference was in the first one-half of the learning process.

Wylie's work (1919) on white rats utilized avoiding reactions to different visual, auditory, and electrical stimuli. When the rat had learned to avoid one stimulus, another was substituted and the training was continued. In each case subsequent learning profited by the previous training. Hunter (1918), in repeating this work, found that rats trained to make a given response to an auditory stimulus would, without additional training, make

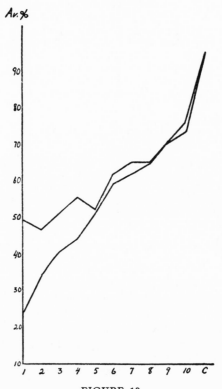

FIGURE 19

VINCENT CURVES TO SHOW THE LOCUS OF INTERFERENCE BETWEEN HABIT NO. 1
(UPPER CURVE) AND HABIT NO. 2 (LOWER CURVE)
(From W. S. Hunter's "Habit Interference in the White Rat and in Human
Subjects," *J. Comp. Psychol.*, 1922.)

the same response to a visual stimulus. Positive transfer was thus indicated
where all of the stimulating conditions were identical save one, the sound
or the light.

Webb (1917) and Wiltbank (1919) have made important studies of
the influence of learning one maze upon the mastery of later maze habits.
In practically all cases transfer has been demonstrated. Even when
the second maze requires a reversal of the turns made in the first, Hunter
(1922) has found transfer when the two learning records are compared in
terms of total time, errors, and trials.

The early work on cross-education and most of the studies on the
transfer of training using verbal material have been interpreted with
reference to the educational theory of formal discipline. Formal discipline assumes that the explanation of positive transfer lies in the general

improvement of behavior capacities and, conversely, that training in such forms of behavior as mathematics, logic, and Latin will improve the subject's general capacity to analyze and remember. The opponents of this doctrine explain transfer in terms of the training of elements which are identical in the forms of response concerned, and they base this interpretation upon experiments which show that training a given response results not in a general spread of improvement but in gains in a limited number of responses. The extensive literature on the subject is summarized by Thorndike (1913) and Coover (1916).

Thorndike and Woodworth (1901) were the first to present experiments showing a very limited spread of improvement as a result of training in discriminative responses. The authors conclude as follows: "Improvement in any single mental function need not improve the ability in functions commonly called by the same name. It may injure it. . . . Improvement in any single mental function rarely brings about equal improvement in any other function, no matter how similar, for the working of every mental function-group is conditioned by the nature of the data in each particular case. . . . The general consideration of the cases of retention or of loss of practice effect seems to make it likely that spread of practice occurs only where identical elements are concerned in the influencing and influenced function" (1901, p. 250). Somewhat greater spread of improvement was found by Fracker (1908), who worked with visual and auditory stimuli, while the important study by Sleight (1911) upon a variety of verbal habits shows almost no spread of improvement outside of the responses practiced.

Judd (1908) has given a very brief description of an experiment which indicates that the verbal instruction which is given to the subject can aid in the mastery of a non-verbal habit, a result supported by one of Bray's (1928) experiments.

"Two groups of pupils in the fifth and sixth grades were required to hit with a small dart a target which was placed under water. The difficulty of hitting the target arises, of course, from the deflection which the light suffers thru diffraction. . . . In this experiment one group of boys was given a full theoretical explanation of refraction. The other group of boys was left to work out experience without theoretical training. These two groups began practise with the target under twelve inches of water. It is a very striking fact that in the first series of trials the boys who knew the theory of refraction and those who did not, gave about the same results. That is, theory seemed to be of no value in the first tests. All the boys had to learn how to use the dart, and theory proved to be no substitute for practise. At this point the conditions were changed. The twelve inches of water were reduced to four. The difference between the two groups of boys now came out very strikingly. The boys without theory were very much confused. The practice gained with twelve inches of water did not help them with four inches. Their errors were large and persistent. On the other hand, the boys who had the theory fitted themselves to four inches very rapidly. Their theory evidently helped them to see the reason why they must not apply the twelve-inch habit to four inches of water" (Judd, 1908, pp. 36-37).

Poffenberger (1915) carried out a series of tests upon control and training groups using the following tests: color naming, form naming, opposites, adjective-noun test, cancellation, and arithmetic. Table 19 summarizes

TABLE 19

EXPERIMENTS UPON TRANSFER WITH VERBAL RESPONSES
(After Poffenberger)

Type of experiment	Control group	Training group	Type of transfer
	Gross gain from 1st to last test	Gross gain from 1st to last test	
Influence of:			
Color naming upon form naming	6.0±1.2	—2.2±3.2	0
Opposites test upon adjective-noun test	15.6±3.2	—2.0±2.2	negative
Cancellation of 3 & 5 upon cancellation of groups containing 3 & 5	11.5±4	23.7±3.2	positive
Cancellation of 3 & 5 upon cancellation of groups containing 4 & 7	15.9±1.8	15.0±1.6	0
Addition upon substraction	15.1±4.8	8.8±0.7	0
Addition upon multiplication	29.7±3.8	11.4±5.3	negative
Addition upon division	19.5±4.3	21.3±6.3	0

the results. The last column indicates the presence or absence and the character of the transfer found when the figures in columns two and three are considered in the light of their probable errors.

We are still far from a satisfactory explanation of the facts of transfer. At present the theory of identical elements seems most adequate, and yet it is all but impossible to bring the theory to a rigorous experimental test. Perhaps work on conditioned reflexes may finally give us the explanatory key to the type of behavior interrelationships described in the present section.

THE RELATION OF INITIAL AND FINAL ABILITIES

This problem of the relation of initial ability to final ability has two important subdivisions: (1) What effect does training have upon the differences in ability revealed by individual subjects during the initial periods of the learning process? And (2) do the subjects used in a learning experiment tend to retain, at the close of training, the same relative ranks which they had at the beginning of training?

Let us comment briefly upon this latter question first. The method of investigation is clear and relatively uncomplicated. Correlations are made between the initial and final performances. In order to promote the reliability of the initial and final records chosen, one may average the first two or three trials for the record of the initial standing of a given subject and average the records of the last two or three trials for the record of final performance. If the correlation secured is significant, we can predict final performance on the basis of initial scores. Where the correlation is positive, individuals who rank high initially will also tend to rank high finally. With negative correlations those subjects who rank high initially will tend to rank low finally. Many investigators have made correlations of the type suggested where the subjects have been trained on a great diversity of responses such as addition, multiplication, cancellation of letters on a page, color naming, typewriting, and running the maze. The correlations in the great majority of cases are positive, although the P.E.'s, and consequently the dependability of the coefficients, vary greatly. [Kincaid (1925) has summarized results of this type from twenty-four different studies.] We may generalize the results as follows: the relationship between initial and final performances will in all probability be positive; but the closeness of the relationship, and therefore the degree to which valid predictions can be made, will vary from high to low and must be determined for each particular experimental setting.

Let us now turn to a consideration of the first question raised in the present section. What is the result of training upon individual differences? Do these differences increase, decrease, or remain the same? The sociological and educational significance of this problem is clear and important. Do social pressure and school training tend to make individuals more nearly alike or do they serve to accentuate the differences between individuals? In a superficial sense and from a qualitative point of view, social conditions may result in a decrease of individual differences: immigrants become Americanized; children all learn the responses of reading, writing, and arithmetic; a code of moral behavior is known, even if not practiced, by the members of a group. Our interest in the problem, however, lies in another direction. Let us grant that 10 individuals have become more alike than they were by virtue of the fact that they are now all typists or calculators whereas formerly only some of them had these accomplishments. The quantitative and experimental problem which concerns us is this: Will the differences in skill which separate the 10 subjects one from the other in their initial efforts at typing or calculating increase, decrease, or remain the same after all subjects have received the same amount of training in typing or calculating?

Many different methods have been used in the attempted solution of this problem. These methods will be found listed with other items in column 1 of Table 20, and the results of the methods plus some of the data upon which they are based will be found in the later columns of the table. The results of this table seem to indicate, so far as the data here concerned are valid for an examination of the question, that individual differences in performance tend to decrease with practice. Where the standard deviation, S.D., is larger finally than it is initially, the amount of variability about the mean has increased. Since, however, the initial and final means are different, the coefficient of variability, S.D./Av., gives

TABLE 20

DATA ON INDIVIDUAL DIFFERENCES AS AFFECTED BY TRAINING

(From Kincaid)

	Thorndike '08 Multiplication	Chapman '14 Addition	Chapman '14 Multiplication	Chapman '14 Color naming	Chapman '14 Opposites	Chapman '14 Cancelling 2's	Chapman '14 Cancelling 3's	Thorndike '16 Cancelling 2's	Thorndike '16 Cancelling 3's	Thorndike '16 Addition	Thorndike '16 Multiplication	Thorndike '10 Addition
Average (beginning)	261	65	43	201	68	91	95	113	128	61	61	159
Average (end)	521	84	75	222	117	110	111	173	162	108	189	231
S.D. beginning (B)	96	19	14	25+	14	12	11	15	15	16	17	41
S.D. end (E)	217	22	21	25−	17	15	16	18	13	23	76	66
Greater S.D.	E	E	E	B	E	E	E	E	B	E	E	E
S.D./Av. (beginning)	.37	.29	.33	.13	.21	.13	.12	.13	.12	.26	.28	.26
S.D./Av. (end)	.42	.26	.28	.11	.15	.14	.14	.10	.08	.21	.40	.29
Greater S.D./Av.	E	B	B	B	B	B	E	B	B	B	E	E
Ratio worst/best (beginning)	.22	.38	.20	.60	.42	.60	.67	.66	.65	.40	.35	.41
Ratio worst/best (end)	.21	.39	.25	.68	.58	.56	.55	.76	.78	.45	.25	.30
Greater ratio	B	E	E	E	E	B	B	E	E	E	B	B
Av. highest 25% beginning	397	93	63	189	87	105	109	133	145	82	81	213
Av. highest 25% end	703	116	97	245	136	110	129	175	171	126	231	287
Av. lowest 25% beginning	158	42	26	131	48	85	78	95	109	42	38	109
Av. lowest 25% end	316	63	52	189	105	92	70	166	152	84	133	162
Gross gain highest 25%	306	23	34	56	49	5	20	42	26	44	150	74
Gross gain lowest 25%	158	21	26	58	57	7	12	71	43	42	95	53
Greater gross gain	L	L	L	L	L	L	H	L	L	H	H	H
% gain highest 25%	.77	.25	.54	.30	.56	.05	.18	.32	.18	.54	1.85	.35
% gain lowest 25%	1.00	.50	1.00	.44	1.19	.08	.15	.75	.39	1.00	2.50	.49
Greater % gain	L	L	L	L	L	L	H	L	L	L	L	L
Correlation between initial performance and gross gain	.17	.34	.41	−.14	−.19	.05	.30	−.62	−.09	.27	.20	.05
P.E. of correlation	.12	.14	.13	.15	.14	.15	.14	.10	.15	.14	.14	.15
Correlation between initial per. and % gain	−.26.	−.43	−.38	−.36	−.55	−.24	.15	−.89	−.58	−.56	−.18	−.22

TABLE 20 (*continued*)

	Maze Whitely '11	Multiplication Whitely '11	Cancelling A's Whitely '11	Typewriting Thorndike '16	Form sorting, F.M. Woodrow '17	Form sorting, Normal Woodrow '17	Cancelling S's McCall '16	Cancelling 3's McCall '16	Addition McCall '16	Copying addresses McCall '16	Kincaid Braille writing	Kincaid Dart throwing
Average (beginning)	580	363	205	205	121	122	43	90	31	11	102	193
Average (end)	.781	698	379	336	175	176	72	137	57	26	543	250
S.D. beginning (B)	172	198	56	84	17	16	22	27	14	4	29	73
S.D. end (E)	193	258	115	60	32	22	15	24	29	6	92	77
Greater S.D.	E	E	E	B	E	E	B	B	E	E	E	E
S.D./Av. (beginning)	.30	.55	.27	.41	.14	.13+	.51	.30	.45	.36	.29	.38
S.D./Av. (end)	.25	.37	.30	.18	.18	.13-	.21	.18	.51	.23	.17	.31
Greater S.D./Av.	B	B	E	E	E	B	B	B	E	E	E	E
Ratio worst/best (beginning)	.49	.18	.40	.23	.54	.64	.35	.24	.14	.05	.32	.16
Ratio worst/best (end)	.71	.38	.42	.58	.48	.62	.26	.14	.03	.33	.50	.32
Greater ratio	L	E	E	B	B	B	B	B	B	L	E	E
Av. highest 25% beginning	734	594	278	327	142	149	59	123	51	16	140	283
Av. highest 25% end	929	1043	558	427	195	192	84	148	94	31	607	301
Av. lowest 25% beginning	458	205	144	129	97	102	17	61	16	6	70	96
Av. lowest 25% end	695	579	294	278	156	153	59	130	31	22	505	188
Gross gain highest 25%	195	449	280	100	53	43	25	25	43	15	467	18
Gross gain lowest 25%	237	374	150	149	59	51	42	69	15	16	435	92
Greater gross gain	L	H	H	L	L	L	L	L	H	L	H	L
% gain highest 25%	.27	.76	1.01	.31	.37	.29	.42	.20	.84	.94	3.34	.06
% gain lowest 25%	.52	1.82	1.04	1.16	.61	.50	2.47	1.13	.94	2.67	6.21	.96
Greater % gain	L	L	L	L	L	L	L	L	L	L	L	L
Correlation between initial performance and gross gain	-.23	.18	.48	-.42	-.13	-.11	-.69	-.57	.57	-.10	.10	-.46
P.E. of correlation	.14	.14	.11	.13	.15	.15	.04	.05	.05	.05	.12	.09
Correlation between initial per. and % gain	-.42	-.33	-.27	-.79	-.36	-.40	-.55	-.81	.27	-.63	-.89	-.60

a more comparable measure of the spread of performance. "Ratio worst/ best" is secured by dividing the worst initial performance by the best initial performance. This is then compared with a similar ratio from the final performances. "Gross gain" is secured by subtracting the initial score from the final score. Where the gross gain by the poorest 25 per cent of the subjects was less than that made by the best 25 per cent of the subjects, the letter L is used in the table. The same designation is used for the results secured by comparing "percentage gain."

Although Kincaid's tabulation and analysis point definitely to the conclusion that the differences in individual performance decrease with practice, we are not justified in accepting such a conclusion as final. As Chapman (1925) and Stoddard (1928) in particular have noted, certain factors which are vital and indispensable for a solution of the problem have been neglected by experimenters. (1) The subjects used have not only usually been too few in number but they have not been selected with reference to learning ability nor can we be reasonably sure that adequate incentives have been present, particularly in the final stages of training where improvement is most difficult. Behavior tests of the Binet or U. S. Army type give a rough measure of ability to profit by training. The suggestion is obvious, therefore, that experiments should be planned in such a way that different learning abilities should not complicate the results. (2) Account must be taken of the arbitrary character of the scale used for scoring. If one subject, A, receives an initial score of 10 and another subject, B, receives 20, B is not twice as good as A because zero on the arbitrary scale does not represent a zero of ability in the performance in question. The absolute or true zero may be 50 points below the arbitrary zero, and hence the true scores for A and B may be 60 and 70, respectively, rather than 10 and 20. In the absence of a determination of the true zero, no method of determining individual differences in terms of score ratios can properly be employed. Thurstone (1928) has devised a method of determining the absolute zero which may be correct and applicable to the present problem. The method rests upon an absolute scaling of performance scores and upon the linear relationship which is claimed to exist between the standard deviation and the mean performance for various age groups. The use of gross gains from initial to final scores does not encounter this difficulty with the absolute zero, because this zero is common to both initial and final scores and is cancelled when one is subtracted from the other. (3) We come, therefore, to a consideration of the third important factor which has been neglected in the studies of individual differences. This factor is that of the inequality of units of achievement. The supposition has been that scores in addition, multiplication, or cancellation are composites of equal units. As Chapman (1925, p. 230) wrote concerning the use of gross scores, "The only assumption that this method makes is that the units at different points of the scale are equal." And yet this assumption can readily be shown to be untenable. Ordinarily the units of achievement in the early part of training are easier than those in the middle portion of the learning process, and the final units are the most difficult. The result, when graphically expressed, is a curve which changes rapidly at first and which then gradually levels off on the final plateau of achievement. As the limits of achievement are reached, and particularly as the performance approximates a physiological limit, the additional increments of accomplishment become more and more difficult to attain, and fewer and fewer subjects can master them. It therefore follows that the differences in individual performance may actually increase although the gross scores may indicate a decrease. Subject A may be 10 units better than subject B initially and only one point superior finally. And yet this one unit may mark an enormous difference between the two. At the close of 10 trials on a maze one rat may be able to run without error while another rat may make but one error. In certain mazes this difference in performance is not small but great because the one error that remains is the most difficult one to eliminate, indeed many subjects fail to eliminate it at all. We may choose still other illustrations of the same thing. To reduce one's golf score from 100 to 98 is not nearly so difficult as to reduce one's score 2 points below par. Five-tenths of a second clipped off the world's record for the 100-yard dash is a much more considerable achievement than to reduce the time from 20 sec. to 19.5 sec. for the same distance. In these cases in which improvement involves an approximation to the physiological limits of the organism, the work by Hill (1927) on the physiology of achievement in athletics suggests the importance of finding some way to relate the difficulty of units to the capacities of the working organisms.

Before we can solve this question of the influence of training upon individual differences a practical method must be found for weighting the units of score in terms of their difficulty. If in addition we can secure probable determinations of the true zero, our work will be facilitated. The rôle of the prophet in science is not a secure one, and yet we hesitate but little in predicting that future investigations made in the light of the above requirements will show that individual differences in degree of skill increase rather than diminish with training.[3]

BACKWARD ASSOCIATION

For the adequate understanding of this topic one must give particular consideration to three problems which have loomed large in experimental work: (1) reverse associations, as the problem was formulated by Ebbinghaus; (2) the temporal order of stimuli involved in the establishment of conditioned responses; and (3) the order of the elimination of culs-de-sac in a maze. These problems will be considered briefly in the above order.

If stimuli, for example, nonsense syllables, are presented in the order a, b, c, d, e, f, and if the subject is instructed to learn them in that order, after a certain number of trials he will be able to perform the task. In

---

[3]Ewert (1934) has conducted such an investigation.

this case the order of recall will be forward. Tests will also show that the subject has some capacity for recalling the syllables in the reverse order. Ebbinghaus (1913) raised the question of whether or not, during the learning of such a series, associations were formed not merely forward from *a* to *b* to *c* but also backward from *f* to *e* to *d,* etc. He tested for this possibility by learning a series of nonsense syllables forward and then relearning them in a backward order. A certain amount of saving would be expected due to familiarity with the individual syllables; but, when this was allowed for, there still remained a significant saving in the time required for relearning over that required for the original learning. Thus the original series could be learned in 1249 sec., while the reversed series was learned in 1094 sec., a saving of 155 sec., of which about 6 sec. could be accredited to familiarity. There is thus reason for concluding that reverse associations are formed during forward learning. Ebbinghaus does so conclude, with the addition that fewer (or weaker) reverse associations are formed than forward ones. This latter part of his conclusion is not justified, as will appear later in our discussion. His method is not adapted to the determination of where the association begins in a series, nor in what order (forward or backward) from this point the associations are established. The smallness of the saving may be as much due to habit interference as to the weakness of the reverse associations which Ebbinghaus assumes to be the explanation of the smallness of the saving. Cason (1926) and Garrett and Hartman (1926) have in general confirmed Ebbinghaus' findings. Wohlgemuth (1913), using the method of recall and presenting nonsense syllables, colors, and diagrams, found that backward recall was as frequent as forward recall, although to secure these results with nonsense syllables certain motor distractions were employed during learning.

In order to determine the direction in which associations are established in a series of nonsense syllables an examination should be made of the order in which the syllables are learned. If the items are mastered in the order *f* to *a,* the suggested conclusion would be that associations are established in a backward order even though the *reinstatement* or *recall* of the series would be predominantly forward. Unfortunately, the conditions under which the learning of nonsense syllables is conducted are so complex that no such simple result has been secured. In general, it has been found that the first and last syllables are learned first and the middle syllables last. The absence of a marked reward at the end of each repetition, the emphasis given the beginning of each repetition, and the instruction stimulus are all factors that have affected the order of mastery in a list of nonsense syllables and that have rendered such experiments unsuited to the determination of associative spread.

All stimuli are necessarily presented in a forward-going sequence in time. However, any one stimulus may be chosen as a point of reference, S_{ref}. Those stimuli which have preceded it lie in a backward direction from the reference point, and those which follow lie in a forward direction. If the S_{ref} is the initiator of such an unconditioned response as the withdrawal from shock or the eating of food, associations with this stimulus-response coordination will be set up in forward and backward directions, i.e., both antecedently and subsequently to the S_{ref}, unless some other factors are present to counteract or mask this action.   It is obvious that, if S_{ref} is the last stimulus presented, the experimental data can show no subsequent associations, and, if S_{ref} is the first stimulus, no antecedent ones can be found.   Therefore, in order to secure data on both directions of association, it is necessary to introduce S_{ref} somewhere in the middle of the series.

Experiments approximating in varying degrees these requirements have been made by Pavlov (1928), Carr and Freeman (1919), Yarbrough (1921), Switzer (1930), Wolfle (1932), Warner (1932), Thorndike (1933), and others.   Pavlov found that unconditioned stimuli presented before or simultaneously with an unconditioned stimulus would, in time, arouse the unconditioned response.   If presented subsequently, conditioning was possible, but slight.   Carr and Freeman found it possible to train rats to turn back in a maze when a buzzer was sounded if they had been trained with the buzzer stimulus presented simultaneously or 1 sec. before a shock stimulus.   If the buzzer was given 1 sec. after the shock, the rats did not learn to turn when the buzzer alone was given. Yarbrough, using a similar method, found that rats could be trained to turn at the sound of a buzzer when this stimulus preceded a shock by as much a 6 sec.   If the buzzer came immediately after the shock, the association was formed; but this was not the result when the buzzer was 1 sec. later than the shock.   Thus backward (antecedent) associations were more readily established than forward (subsequent) ones.   Wolfle, using a finger-withdrawal response in human subjects, has studied the conditioning of an auditory stimulus to a shock stimulus with different time intervals.   Where the auditory stimulus followed the shock, almost no conditioning occurred.   In Warner's work with rats the two stimuli employed were shock and a buzzer.   The response to the shock was jumping or climbing a low partition.   It was found that the auditory stimulus could be conditioned to arouse this response if that stimulus preceded the shock by 20 sec. but by less than 30 sec.   Switzer was able to secure a conditioned eyelid response in human subjects when, during training, the conditioned stimulus (a buzzer) followed the unconditioned stimulus by as much as 2 sec.

The problem of backward association has been studied in the field of non-verbal behavior by means of the maze.   Interest in the problem arose from the theory that the pleasurable effects of the food-reward served to stamp in the correct responses.   The opposition to such a view on behavioristic grounds was so strong that the obvious similarity between learning the maze and acquiring conditioned responses to food went almost unnoticed.   In a maze there is temporal and spatial sequence of stimuli from the entrance to the exit where food is usually found.   After the subject has mastered the maze, all stimuli from the culs-de-sac are either non-effective or set up avoiding reactions.   The question now arises:

Are the culs-de-sac eliminated in a counterclockwise direction from the exit? Are associative connections established in a backward direction from the feeding response toward the responses in the first unit of the maze? To be sure, the stimuli in the maze and the ensuing responses must be encountered and executed in the forward order of *a, b, c, d, e, food*; but the question at issue is whether or not the *associative connections* are established in the backward direction of *food, e, d, c, b, a*.

The order of elimination of cul-de-sac responses in the rat maze is dependent upon the general plan of the maze and probably also upon the degree of motivation. In the human maze the order of elimination is also probably affected by the character of the terminal reward response, which is usually not a prominent unconditioned response, and by the propensity of the subject to verbalize. Rats soon learn a general orientation which leads from the entrance to the exit and consequently tend to enter all culs-de-sac that point in that direction, passing by those which point away from the exit. Furthermore, Hunter (1929) and Spence (1932) have pointed out that the final response, or turn, made before entering the food box tends to be anticipated and made before the proper time. And Perkins (1927) and Lumley (1932) have shown that the rat will make, at one point in the maze, responses which are appropriate only later. [See also Mitchell's (1934) extensive observations on place-errors in memorizing.] In order to study the relative order of elimination of culs-de-sac with the possibility of revealing the influence of the one factor of the direction of spread of associative connections, it is necessary to use a maze in which the blinds shall differ one from the other only in temporal distance from the food box. The possibility of retracing in the maze must be reduced to a minimum in order to equalize the opportunities for making the various cul-de-sac responses.

Although many analyses of the temporal order of cul-de-sac elimination have been made [for example by Carr (1917), Warden and Cummings (1929), Peterson (1920), and Spence (1932)], no experiment [with the possible exception of one by de Montpellier (1933)] is on record in which an adequate control has been made of the factors above listed. However, even under the unfavorable experimental conditions which have prevailed there is evidence of a general tendency for cul-de-sac responses to be eliminated in a backward direction during learning. De Montpellier has further shown that as the maze habit disintegrates, when feeding is delayed for two hours after the completion of a trial, errors first reappear in that portion of the maze nearest the exit. Since animals trained in the maze without reward make little or no progress in learning (Blodgett, 1929; Tolman and Honzik, 1930), we may plausibly infer that the backward elimination of culs-de-sac is largely influenced by the physiological effects of the feeding response. Such an order of elimination is what one would expect if the mechanism of the conditioned response is involved in maze learning. In harmony with such a view, Hull (1932) has formulated a goal-gradient hypothesis to explain the backward elimination of errors in the maze in terms of the decreasing effectiveness of the reward responses in determining associations as the distance of the culs-de-sac from the maze exit increases. This theory, so brilliantly formulated, when combined with such work as Wolfle's is extremely illuminating as an explanation of learning and recall. [See Hunter (1933) for an extended discussion of the problem.]

There is much confusion in the literature on "backward association" due to the failure to distinguish between the temporal direction in which associations are established and the following three factors: (1) the temporal order of the *stimuli,* (2) the direction of *recall,* and (3) the direction of the neural impulse across the synapse. There is, of course, no relationship between the two factors last mentioned. The fact that the neural impulse goes from receptor to effector and not vice versa has no possible bearing upon whether or not associations spread forward or backward. Furthermore, in one of the conditioned-response experiments above cited, for example, the buzzer stimulus arouses the turning response in the maze, and the direction of recall is forward; but the association between buzzer and shock has been established in a backward direction. If the training has been with the buzzer after the shock, the relation of the stimuli is a backward one, since the shock is the $S_{ref.}$; and the results show that the association has spread in a forward direction, although the spread is but slight. If we are to emphasize basic mechanisms of learning rather than superficial stimulus relationships, we shall conclude that a backward order and not a forward order of associations is fundamental in learning. In so far as nervous processes are concerned, there is no need for the terms *backward* and *forward* either in the present context or in that of the law of effect. Sensory nervous impulses so affect the central nervous system that subsequent sensory impulses impinge upon a modified central nervous system and are followed by modified behavior.

THE CONDITIONS ESSENTIAL FOR LEARNING

The conditions essential for learning will vary with the nature of the problem to be learned and with the nature and condition of the organism in which the learning takes place. The factors affecting maze learning in rats where food is the incentive will not be the same as the factors affecting the learning of nonsense syllables where instruction stimuli are given the subject and where the incentive is difficult to define. The suggestion is therefore apparent that all situations are not equally suitable for the analysis of the fundamental conditions which must be met if learning is to take place at all; although once these conditions have been identified, one may expect to find evidence for their presence in all learning.[4]

---

[4]It should also be said that an investigator no more disproves the fundamental nature of one of the established conditions of learning by designing an experiment in which the effect of that condition is modified by extraneous factors than one disproves the rôle or magnitude of gravitation by the introduction of masking factors.

In the previous section we have seen that if learning is to take place the stimuli concerned must fall within a certain temporal span. Within such limits associations are established in both forward and backward directions, although the latter is the more extended of the two. Under the conditions where these phenomena occur most clearly, the point of reference is the stimulus for an unconditioned response, in Thorndike's terminology a "satisfier" or an "annoyer." In the present section we shall extend our discussion briefly in order to consider some of the factors whose theoretical importance in this connection is so great that they have been designated laws of learning. The factors which are generally so emphasized are *frequency, recency,* and *effect.* Thorndike, on the basis of recent experiments, postulates a new factor of *belongingness.* Watson (1914) contended that frequency and recency were the only essential factors operative in habit formation. To these Carr (1914) added *intensity,* a variation of effect. Thorndike (1911) limited himself to frequency and effect, and formulated their laws as follows: "The Law of Effect is that: *Of several responses made to the same situation, those which are accompanied or closely followed by satisfaction to the animal will, other things being equal, be more firmly connected with the situation, so that, when it recurs, they will be more likely to recur; those which are accompanied or closely followed by discomfort to the animal will, other things being equal, have their connections with that situation weakened, so that, when it recurs, they will be less likely to occur. The greater the satisfaction or discomfort, the greater the strengthening or weakening of the bond.*

"*The Law of Exercise is that: Any response to a situation will, other things being equal, be more strongly connected with the situation in proportion to the number of times it has been connected with that situation and to the average vigor and duration of the connection.*"

Let us comment briefly upon the influence upon learning of the following factors: recency, frequency, belongingness, and effect. The problem of the rôle played by *recency* in the learning problem confronts us in two forms: first, the temporal relationship between two stimuli which are to be associated; and, secondly, the correlation between elapsed time and retention. The first form of the problem is best answered at the present time by the statement that one stimulus (conditioned) must be sufficiently recent to fall within the range of the stimulus gradients if it is to be connected with another stimulus (unconditioned) by means of learning. The second form of the problem is likewise answered positively. In so far as loss of retention is a function of time, lapse of time (degree of recency) will affect the reinstatement of a stimulus-response coordination and thereby affect learning. However, whether or not in any specific case recency can be a determining factor in the arousal of one of several possible responses will depend upon the magnitudes of the several recencies. This follows since no difference can be expected to affect learning if the difference is subliminal. Thus in any single run through a maze there may be at one moment, or at one point in the maze, the possibility of reinstating two responses which differ in the times which have elapsed since they were last made. Such a temporal difference is known to affect reinstatement, if the difference has a sufficient magnitude.

On the basis of extensive experiments Thorndike (1927, 1932) has challenged the rôle of *frequency* in determining learning. In certain of these experiments the subjects were presented, for example, with a series of tasks such as estimating the lengths of lines, and drawing lines of specified lengths or angles of specified sizes. A comparison was made between the records of the first part of each experiment and the records of the last part, in order to determine whether the response made most frequently initially was also made still more frequently at the close. In no case did the most frequently made response profit significantly from its greater frequency. These experiments deal with what Thorndike terms the frequency of a "situation" where no one response is invariably made to the same stimulating condition. In other experiments each stimulus (a word) called forth a single definite response (a number). Here, in Thorndike's terminology, the investigation concerned the effect of frequency upon the strength of a "connection." The results show that the relative frequency of the exercise of a "connection" has no effect, unless *belongingness* was also present.

Such results are in accordance with the well-known phenomenon of incidental memory which also shows that mere frequency of occurrence is insufficient for learning. We cannot follow Thorndike in the apparently outright rejection of the factor of frequency or of frequency minus belongingness, although its rôle in learning has often been grossly overemphasized and misinterpreted. Frequency, like recency, is a temporal factor and involves the duration of stimulation as opposed to recency which involves the lapse of time since stimulation. Time itself will not fixate a process any more than it will eliminate one. *A certain duration of time, or a certain amount of frequency, however, is necessary in order to permit the effective factors to play their rôles.* In much of the discussion of frequency there has been the assumption that the sheer presence, or repeated presence, of the neural impulses set up by stimulation and response is the adequate factor for learning. Such a view seems to rest upon some form of the theory that brain paths are deepened by repeated exercise. Thorndike in his experiments has again shown the inadequacy of such a view.

In order to understand and evaluate the factor of *belongingness* it will be best to turn to those experiments of Thorndike which have given rise to the concept (1932). Two types of experiments were performed. In the first the subject was told to listen to the reading of certain material which consisted of sentences containing some phrases and personal names. When the subject was tested later for recall, it was found that words or phrases would often recall others which followed them *in the same sentence;* that the last word of a sentence rarely recalled the first of the *next;* and that first names recalled last names. Thus first names *belong* to last names, and the parts of a sentence *belong* to each other more than they do to parts of another sentence. In the second type of experiment the subject was told to attend to the reading of *pairs* (a word and a number). When tested later the subject was found to have learned the pairs, but to show poor ability to recall a member of one pair when given a member of another pair.

It is unnecessary to postulate a factor of belongingness to account for results of the above character. In the first experiment the results would be expected upon the basis of positive and negative transfer from previous training plus the effect of self-administered instruction stimuli. Certain linguistic habits which the subject has acquired not only modify the type of learning, but probably also result in the subject's giving himself the instruction to learn by sentences. [This interpretation is in harmony with a statement made by Thorndike himself (1932, pp. 70-71).] In the second experiment the subject is definitely instructed to listen to such pairs as *bread 29, wall 16,* etc. The result is that when the subject is asked what comes after 29 the response wall is but rarely given. These results show clearly the influence of instruction stimuli upon learning, and in this respect they are in harmony with the findings in *Aussage* experiments where if colors and figures are given, and if the subject is instructed to observe the former, it will be found that he has a negligible ability to report the latter.

All organizations of behavior, all stimulus-response coordinations, may be described as possessing a general characteristic of belongingness. Such a term has as much descriptive value as the word *Gestalt,* which some writers prefer; but neither term refers clearly to a specific factor in the learning process. One may say that learning consists in the establishment of *Gestalten* or coordinations whose parts possess belongingness and that recall tends to lie within such wholes. The situation, however, is as well described in more conventional terms utilizing such concepts as stimulus-response, instruction stimulus, and habit.

In the previous section on *Backward Association* we have already presented the essential data indicating the influence of the factor of *effect* upon the learning process. The term *effect* suggests the consequences of a response, its satisfyingness or annoyingness, its aspect of reward or punishment. In many experimental situations such connotations, if objectively interpreted, seem justified. If, however, we are concerned with the problem of learning in its most general and fundamental aspect, the term is less satisfactory since learning may occur, as in the case of the conditioned pupillary response, without any factor that can be readily recognized as satisfying, annoying, rewarding, or punishing (and without, we might add, any factor that might be termed a goal). In its most elemental and general form the term *effect* would seem to refer to the influence upon learning of the arousal of an unconditioned response or of a well-established conditioned response. Whenever such responses are included in a series of stimulus-response activities asociations tend to spread in clockwise and anticlockwise directions. The latter direction of spread is the phenomenon usually called *effect*.

Thorndike (1932) has shown definitely that the factor of effect may operate in a measurable degree even when present as the mere result of telling the subject that his response is right or wrong. Thorndike has in addition offered an analysis of the factor of effect in terms of the kinds of stimulus-response mechanisms which serve as the point of reference. These mechanisms are of two types, satisfiers and annoyers or rewards and punishments (Thorndike's terminology). It is pointed out that rewards lead to the repetition of the rewarded responses whereas punishments lead to the making of some other response than that punished. In addition Thorndike's careful analysis of his results obtained from human and infrahuman subjects leads him to the following conclusion: "Rewards in general tend to maintain and strengthen any connection which leads to them. Punishments often but not always tend to shift from it to something else. . . . They weaken the connection which produced them, when they do weaken it, by strengthening some other connection" (1932, p. 277). In general, the stimulus-response connection which is punished is not weakened. This problem of the variations in learning which result from different kinds of unconditioned responses (punishments and rewards) might well be further clarified if attacked by the conditioned-response method.[5]

Our conclusion is that there are two conditions which must be present if learning is to occur, conditions which are therefore the fundamental factors in habit formation: *unconditioned* (or well-established conditioned) *responses* and *time*. The factor of time must be involved in such a form that a certain amount of stimulation (frequency) may occur and that those factors which modify neural action may have a chance to operate. Furthermore, the span of time (recency) which separates the two stimuli or responses which are to be connected must not be too great for the backward or forward spread of association. Since learning depends upon the retention of practice effects, and since retention is a function of time, relative recency may also influence learning through its relation to retention. The effectiveness of the unconditioned response in learning appears to depend fundamentally upon the gradients which accompany it. *Learning in its basic character thus depends upon the fulfillment of certain temporal conditions in stimulus relationships and upon the presence of unconditioned or well-established conditioned responses with their gradients.*

BIBLIOGRAPHY

BALLARD, P. B. 1913. Obliviscence and reminiscence. *Brit. J. Psychol., Monog. Suppl.,* **1**, No. 2. Pp. 82.

BATSON, W. H. 1916. Acquisition of skill. *Psychol. Monog.,* **31**, No. 91. Pp. 92.

BIRD, C. 1926. The effect of maturation upon the pecking instinct of chicks. *Ped. Sem.,* **33**, 212-234.

---

[5] It is very interesting that Thorndike, who places so much emphasis upon the factor of effect, does not accept the view that learning is of an essentially conditioned-response character and that Watson, who makes so much of the conditioned-response theory, rejects the factor of effect. Our own discussion emphasizes the essential identity of the theories of effect and of conditioned responses.

BLODGETT, H. C. 1929. The effect of the introduction of reward upon the maze performance of rats. *Univ. Calif. Publ. Psychol.,* **4**, 113-134.

BOOK, W. F. 1925. The psychology of skill. (Reprinted from *Univ. Mont. Stud.,* 1908, vol. 1.) New York: Gregg. Pp. 257.

BOURDON, B. 1901. Recherches sur l'habitude. *Année psychol.,* **8**, 327-340.

BRAY, C. W. 1928. Transfer of learning. *J. Exper. Psychol.,* **11**, 443-467.

BROWN, W. 1923. To what extent is memory measured by a single recall? *J. Exper. Psychol.,* **6**, 377-382.

————. 1924a. Effects of interval on recall. *J. Exper. Psychol.,* **7**, 469-474.

————. 1924b. Whole and part methods of learning. *J. Educ. Psychol.,* **15**, 229-233.

BRYAN, W. L., & HARTER, N. 1897. Studies in the physiology and psychology of the telegraphic language. *Psychol. Rev.,* **4**, 27-53.

————. 1899. Studies on the telegraphic language: the acquisition of a hierarchy of habits. *Psychol. Rev.,* **6**, 346-375.

BUNCH, M. E., & MAGDSICK, W. K. 1933. The retention in rats of an incompletely learned maze solution for short intervals of time. *J. Comp. Psychol.,* **16**, 385-409.

CALKINS, M. W. 1896. Association. *Psychol. Monog.,* **1**, No. 2. Pp. 56.

CARMICHAEL, L. 1927. A further study of the development of behavior in vertebrates experimentally removed from the influence of external stimulation. *Psychol. Rev.,* **34**, 34-47.

CARR, H. A. 1914. Principles of selection in animal learning. *Psychol. Rev.,* **21**, 157-165.

————. 1917. The distribution and elimination of errors in the maze. *J. Anim. Behav.,* **7**, 145-160.

————. 1919. Distribution of effort. *Psychol. Bull.,* **16**, 26-28.

CARR, H. A., & FREEMAN, A. S. 1919. Time relationships in the formation of associations. *Psychol. Rev.,* **26**, 465-473.

CASON, H. 1926. Specific serial learning; a study of backward association. *J. Exper. Psychol.,* **9**, 195-227.

CHAPMAN, J. C. 1925. Statistical considerations in interpreting the effects of training on individual differences. *Psychol. Rev.,* **32**, 224-234.

CLEMENTS, F. E. 1928. The effect of time on distance discrimination in the albino rat. *J. Comp. Psychol.,* **8**, 317-324.

COOVER, J. E. 1916. Formal discipline from the standpoint of experimental psychology. *Psychol. Monog.,* **20**, No. 87. Pp. 307.

CRAFTS, L. W. 1929. Whole and part methods with non-serial reactions. *Amer. J. Psychol.,* **41**, 543-563.

————. 1930. Whole and part methods with unrelated reactions. *Amer. J. Psychol.,* **42**, 591-601.

CUMMINS, R. A. 1919. Improvement and the distribution of practice. *Teach. Coll. Contrib. Educ.,* No. 97. Pp. 72.

DAHL, A. 1928. Ueber den Einfluss des Schlafens auf das Wiedererkennen. *Psychol. Forsch.,* **11**, 290-301.

DAVIS, H. B. 1907. The raccoon: a study in animal intelligence. *Amer. J. Psychol.,* **18**, 447-490.

DAVIS, W. W. 1898 & 1900. Researches in cross-education. *Stud. Yale Psychol. Lab.,* **6**, 6-50; **8**, 64-108.

EBBINGHAUS, H. 1913. Memory: a contribution to experimental psychology. (Trans. by H. A. Ruger and C. E. Bussenius.) (*Columbia Univ., Teach. Coll., Educ. Reprints, No. 3.*) New York: Teach. Coll., Columbia Univ. Pp. xiii+123.

EPHRUSSI, P. 1904. Experimentelle Beiträge zur Lehre vom Gedächtnis. *Zsch. f. Psychol.*, **37**, 56-103, 161-224.

EWERT, P. H. 1926. Bilateral transfer in mirror-drawing. *Ped. Sem.*, **33**, 235-249.

―――. 1934. The effect of practice on individual differences when studied with measurements weighted for difficulty. *J. Gen. Psychol.*, **10**, 249-285.

FRACKER, G. C. 1908. On the transference of training in memory. *Psychol. Monog.*, **9**, No. 38, 56-102.

FREEMAN, F. N., & ABERNETHY, E. M. 1930. Comparative retention of typewriting and of substitution with analogous material. *J. Educ. Psychol.*, **21**, 639-647.

―――. 1932. New evidence of the superior retention of typewriting to that of substitution. *J. Educ. Psychol.*, **23**, 331-334.

GARRETT, H. E., & HARTMAN, G. W. 1926. An experiment on backward association in learning. *Amer. J. Psychol.*, **37**, 241-246.

GATES, A. I. 1917. Recitation as a factor in memorizing. *Arch. Psychol.*, **6**, No. 40. Pp. 104.

GORDON, K. 1925. Class results with spaced and unspaced memorizing. *J. Exper. Psychol.*, **8**, 337-343.

HARDEN, L. M. 1929. A quantitative study of the similarity factor in retroactive inhibition. *J. Gen. Psychol.*, **2**, 197-221.

HEINE, R. 1914. Ueber Wiedererkennen und rückwirkende Hemmung. *Zsch. f. Psychol.*, **68**, 161-236.

HILL, A. V. 1927. Muscular movement in man: the factors governing speed and recovery from fatigue. New York: Harcourt, Brace. Pp. 104.

HOBHOUSE, L. T. 1901. Mind in evolution. New York: Macmillan. Pp. 415.

HUBBERT, H. B. 1915. The effect of age on habit formation in the albino rat. *Behav. Monog.*, **2**, No. 11. Pp. 55.

HUGUENIN, C. 1914. Reviviscence paradoxale. *Arch. de psychol.*, **14**, 379-383.

HULL, C. L. 1932. The goal gradient hypothesis and maze learning. *Psychol. Rev.*, **39**, 25-43.

HUNTER, W. S. 1918. Some notes on the auditory sensitivity of the white rat. *Psychobiol.*, **1**, 339-351.

―――. 1922. Habit interference in the white rat and in human subjects. *J. Comp. Psychol.*, **2**, 29-59.

―――. 1928. Human behavior. (Rev. ed. of *General psychology.*) Chicago: Univ. Chicago Press. Pp. x+355.

―――. 1929. The sensory control of the maze habit in the white rat. *J. Genet. Psychol.*, **36**, 505-537.

―――. 1932. The effect of inactivity produced by cold upon learning and retention in the cockroach *Blatella germanica*. *J. Genet. Psychol.*, **41**, 253-266.

―――. 1933. Basic phenomena in learning. *J. Gen. Psychol.*, **8**, 299-317.

HUNTER, W. S., & YARBROUGH, J. U. 1917. The interference of auditory habits in the white rat. *J. Anim. Behav.*, **7**, 49-65.

JENKINS, J. G., & DALLENBACH, K. M. 1924. Obliviscence during sleep and waking. *Amer. J. Psychol.*, **35**, 605-612.

JENNINGS, H. S. 1906. Behavior of lower organisms. New York: Columbia Univ. Press. Pp. viii+366.

JOHNSON, L. M. 1933. Similarity of meaning as a factor in retroactive inhibition. *J. Gen. Psychol.*, **9**, 377-389.

JOST, A. 1897. Die Assoziationsfestigkeit in ihrer Abhängigkeit von der Verteilung der Wiederholungen. *Zsch. f. Psychol.*, **14**, 436-472.

JUDD, C. H. 1908. The relation of special training to general intelligence. *Educ. Rev.*, **32**, 34-53.

KATZAROFF, D. 1908. Le rôle de la récitation comme facteur de la mémorisation. *Arch. de psychol.*, **7**, 224-259.

KINCAID, M. 1925. A study of individual differences in learning. *Psychol. Rev.*, **32**, 34-53.

KJERSTAD, C. L. 1919. The form of the learning curves for memory. *Psychol. Monog.*, **26**, No. 116. Pp. 89.

KNORS, C. 1910. Experimentelle Untersuchungen über den Lernprozen. *Arch. f. d. ges. Psychol.*, **17**, 297-362.

KOFFKA, K. 1924. The growth of the mind: an introduction to child psychology. (Trans. by R. M. Ogden.) New York: Harcourt, Brace; London: Kegan Paul. Pp. 382.

KÖHLER, W. 1925. The mentality of apes. (Trans. by E. Winter.) New York: Harcourt, Brace. Pp. viii+342.

————. 1929. Gestalt psychology. New York: Liveright. Pp. x+403. London: Bell. Pp. 312.

KRUEGER, W. C. F. 1929. The effect of overlearning on retention. *J. Exper. Psychol.*, **12**, 71-78.

KÜHN, A. 1914. Ueber Einprägung durch Lesen und durch Rezitieren. *Zsch. f. Psychol.*, **68**, 396-481.

LAKENAN, M. E. 1913. The whole and part methods of memorizing poetry and prose. *J. Educ. Psychol.*, **4**, 189-198.

LARGUIER DES BANCELS, J. 1901. Sur les méthodes de mémorisation. *Année psychol.*, **8**, 185-213.

LASHLEY, K. S. 1917. A causal factor in the relation of the distribution of practice to the rate of learning. *J. Anim. Behav.*, **7**, 139-142.

————. 1918. A simple maze: with data on the relation of the distribution of practice to the rate of learning. *Psychobiol.*, **1**, 353-367.

LEPLEY, W. M. 1932. A theory of serial learning and forgetting based upon conditioned reflex principles. *Psychol. Rev.*, **39**, 279-288.

LIU, S. Y. 1928. The relation of age to the learning ability of the white rat. *J. Comp. Psychol.*, **8**, 75-86.

LUH, C. W. 1922. The conditions of retention. *Psychol. Monog.*, **31**, No. 142. Pp. 87.

LUMLEY, F. H. 1932. Anticipation as a factor in serial and maze learning. *J. Exper. Psychol.*, **15**, 331-342.

LYON, D. O. 1916. The relation of quickness of learning to retentiveness. *Arch. Psychol.*, **5**, No. 34. Pp. 60.

McGEOCH, J. A. 1932a. Forgetting and the law of disuse. *Psychol. Rev.*, **39**, 352-370.

————. 1932b. The comparative retention values of a maze habit, of nonsense syllables, and of rational learning. *J. Exper. Psychol.*, **15**, 662-680.

————. 1933a. Studies in retroactive inhibition: I. The temporal course of the inhibitory effect of interpolated learning. *J. Gen. Psychol.*, **9**, 24-43.

————. 1933b. Studies in retroactive inhibition: II. Relationships between temporal point of interpolation, length of interval, and amount of retroactive inhibition. *J. Gen. Psychol.*, **9**, 44-57.

McGEOCH, J. A., & MELTON, A. W. 1929. The comparative retention values of maze habits and of nonsense syllables. *J. Exper. Psychol.*, **12**, 392-414.

MEUMANN, E. 1913. The psychology of learning: an experimental investigation of the economy and technique of memory. (Trans. by J. W. Baird.) New York: Appleton. Pp. 387.

MITCHELL, M. B. 1932. Retroactive inhibition and hypnosis. *J. Gen. Psychol.,* **7**, 343-359.

―――. 1934. Anticipatory place-skipping tendencies in the memorization of numbers. *Amer. J. Psychol.,* **46**, 80-91.

MONTPELLIER, G. DE. 1933. An experiment on the order of elimination of blind alleys in maze learning. *J. Genet. Psychol.,* **43**, 123-139.

MOSELEY, D. 1925. The accuracy of the pecking response in chicks. *J. Comp. Psychol.,* **5**, 75-97.

MÜLLER, G. E., & PILZECKER, A. 1900. Experimentelle Beiträge zur Lehre vom Gedachtnis. *Zsch. f. Psychol.,* Ergbd. **1**. Pp. 300.

NEUMANN, G. 1907. Experimentelle Beiträge zur Lehre von der Ökonomie und Technik des Lernens. *Zsch. f. exper. Päd.,* **4**, 63-101.

NICOLAI, F. 1922. Experimentelle Untersuchungen über das Haften von Gesichtseindrücken und dessen zeitlichen Verlauf. *Arch. f. d. ges. Psychol.,* **42**, 132-149.

NORSWORTHY, N. 1912. Acquisition as related to retention. *J. Educ. Psychol.,* **3**, 214-218.

PATERSON, D. G. 1917. The Johns Hopkins circular maze studies. *Psychol. Bull.,* **14**, 294-297.

PAVLOV, I. P. 1927. Conditioned reflexes: an investigation of the physiological activity of the cerebral cortex. (Trans. and ed. by G. V. Anrep.) London: Oxford Univ. Press. Pp. xvi+430.

―――. 1928. Lectures on conditioned reflexes. Twenty-five years of objective study of the higher nervous activity (behavior) of animals. (Trans. by W. H. Gantt.) New York: Int. Publishers. Pp. 414.

PEARCE, B. D. 1917. A note on the interference of visual habits in the white rat. *J. Anim. Behav.,* **7**, 169-177.

PECHSTEIN, L. A. 1917. Whole *vs.* part methods in motor learning. *Psychol. Monog.,* **23**, No. 99. Pp. 80.

―――. 1918. Whole *vs.* part methods in learning nonsense syllables. *J. Educ. Psychol.,* **9**, 381-387.

PENTSCHEW, C. 1903. Untersuchungen zur Ökonomie und Technik des Lernens. *Arch. f. d. ges. Psychol.,* **1**, 417-526.

PERKINS, N. L. 1927. Human reactions in a maze of fixed orientation. *Comp. Psychol. Monog.,* **4**, No. 21. Pp. 91.

PETERSON, G. M. 1928. Negative acceleration with material of varying difficulty. *J. Exper. Psychol.,* **11**, 40-44.

PETERSON, J. 1917*a*. Experiments in ball-tossing: the significance of learning curves. *J. Exper. Psychol.,* **2**, 178-224.

―――. 1917*b*. Frequency and recency factors in maze learning by white rats. *J. Anim. Behav.,* **7**, 338-364.

―――. 1920. The backward elimination of errors in mental maze learning. *J. Exper. Psychol.,* **3**, 257-280.

―――. 1922. Learning when frequency and recency factors are negative. *J. Exper. Psychol.,* **5**, 270-300.

POFFENBERGER, A. T. 1915. The influence of improvement in one mental process upon other related processes. *J. Educ. Psychol.,* **6**, 459-474.

PYLE, W. H. 1913. Standards of mental efficiency. *J. Educ. Psychol.,* **4**, 61-70.

―――. 1921. The psychology of learning. Baltimore, Md.: Warwick & York. Pp. 308.

PYLE, W. H., & SNYDER, J. C. 1911. The most economical unit for committing to memory. *J. Educ. Psychol.,* **2**, 133-142.

RADOSSAWLJEWITSCH, P. 1906. Das Behalten und Vergessen bei Kindern und Erwachsenen. (*Päd. Monog.*) Leipzig: Nemnich. Pp. 197.

REED, H. B. 1924. Part and whole methods of learning. *J. Educ. Psychol.,* 15, 107-115, 248-249.

ROBINSON, E. S. 1920. Some factors determining the degree of retroactive inhibition. *Psychol. Monog.,* 28, No. 128. Pp. 57.

――――. 1927. The similarity factor in retroaction. *Amer. J. Psychol.,* 39, 297-312.

――――. 1932. Association theory today. New York: Century. Pp. viii +142.

ROBINSON, E. S., & DARROW, C. W. 1924. Effect of length of lists upon memory for numbers. *Amer. J. Psychol.,* 35, 235-243.

ROBINSON, E. S., & HERON, W. T. 1922. Result of variations in length of memorized material. *J. Exper. Psychol.,* 5, 428-448.

RUCH, T. C. 1929. Factors influencing the relative economy of massed and distributed practice in learning. *Psychol. Rev.,* 35, 19-45.

SCRIPTURE, E. W., SMITH, T. L., & BROWN, E. M. 1894. On the education of muscular control and power. *Stud. Yale Psychol. Lab.,* 2, 114-119.

SHEPARD, J. F., & BREED, F. S. 1913. Maturation and use in the development of an instinct. *J. Anim. Behav.,* 3, 274-285.

SKAGGS, E. B. 1920. The relative value of grouped and interspersed recitations. *J. Exper. Psychol.,* 3, 424-446.

――――. 1925. Further studies in retroactive inhibition. *Psychol. Monog.,* 34, No. 161. Pp. 59.

SLEIGHT, W. G. 1911. Memory and formal training. *Brit. J. Psychol.,* 4, 386-457.

SPENCE, K. W. 1932. The order of eliminating blinds in maze learning by the rat. *J. Comp. Psychol.,* 14, 9-27.

STARCH, D. A. 1910. A demonstration of the trial and error method of learning. *Psychol. Bull.,* 7, 20-23.

――――. 1912. Periods of work in learning. *J. Educ. Psychol.,* 3, 209-213.

STEFFENS, L. 1900. Experimentelle Beiträge zur Lehre vom ökonomischen Lernen. *Zsch. f. Psychol.,* 22, 321-382.

STODDARD, G. D. 1928. The problem of individual differences in learning. *Psychol. Rev.,* 35, 479-485.

STONE, C. P. 1929. The age factor in animal learning: I. Rats in the problem box and the maze. *Genet. Psychol. Monog.,* 5, 1-130.

STROUD, E. B. 1931. Learning curves for poetry. *Amer. J. Psychol.,* 43, 684-686.

SWIFT, E. J. 1903. Studies in the psychology and physiology of learning. *Amer. J. Psychol.,* 14, 201-251.

――――. 1906. Beginning a language: a contribution to the psychology of learning. In *Amherst studies in philosophy and psychology, Garman Memorial Volume.* Boston: Houghton Mifflin. Pp. 297-314.

SWIFT, E. J., & SCHUYLER, W. 1907. The learning process. *Psychol. Bull.,* 4, 307-310.

SWITZER, S. A. 1930. Backward conditioning of the lid reflex. *J. Exper. Psychol.,* 13, 76-97.

THORNDIKE, E. L. 1911. Animal intelligence. New York: Macmillan. Pp. viii+297.

――――. 1913. Educational psychology: Vol. 2. The learning process. New York: Teach. Coll., Columbia Univ. Pp. xi+452.

――――. 1914. Educational psychology: Vol. 3. Mental work and fatigue and individual differences and their causes. New York: Teach. Coll., Columbia Univ. Pp. xii+442.

————. 1927a. The law of effect. *Amer. J. Psychol.*, **39**, 212-222.

————. 1927b. A fundamental theorem in modifiability. *Proc. Nat. Acad. Sci.*, **13**, 15-18.

THORNDIKE, E. L., *et al.* 1926. The measurement of intelligence. New York: Bur. Publ., Teach. Coll., Columbia Univ. Pp. xxvi+616.

————. 1928. Adult learning. New York: Macmillan. Pp. x+335.

————. 1932. The fundamentals of learning. New York: Bur. Publ., Teach. Coll., Columbia Univ. Pp. 638.

————. 1933. An experimental study of rewards. New York: Bur. Publ., Teach. Coll., Columbia Univ. Pp. 72.

THORNDIKE, E. L., & WOODWORTH, R. S. 1901. The influence of improvement in one mental function upon the efficiency of other functions. *Psychol. Rev.*, **8**, 247-261, 384-395, 553-564.

THURSTONE, L. L. 1928. The absolute zero in intelligence measurement. *Psychol. Rev.*, **35**, 175-197.

TOLMAN, E. C., & HONZIK, C. H. 1930. Introduction and removal of reward, and maze performance in rats. *Univ. Calif. Publ. Psychol.*, **4**, 257-275.

TROW, W. C., & SEARS, R. 1927. A learning plateau due to conflicting methods of practice. *J. Educ. Psychol.*, **18**, 43-47.

ULRICH, J. L. 1915. Distribution of effort in learning in the white rat. *Behav. Monog.*, **2**, No. 10. Pp. 51.

VAN ORMER, E. B. 1932. Retention after intervals of sleep and waking. *Arch. Psychol.*, **21**, No. 137. Pp. 49.

VINCENT, S. B. 1912. The function of the vibrissae in the behavior of the white rat. *Behav. Monog.*, **1**, No. 5. Pp. 81.

WARDEN, C. J. 1923. Distribution of practice in animal learning. *Comp. Psychol. Monog.*, **1**, No. 3. Pp. 64.

WARDEN, C. J., & CUMMINGS, S. B. 1929. Primacy and recency factors in animal motor learning. *J. Genet. Psychol.*, **36**, 240-256.

WARNER, L. H. 1932. The association span of the white rat. *J. Genet. Psychol.*, **41**, 57-90.

WATSON, J. B. 1907. Kinaesthetic and organic sensations: their rôle in the reactions of the white rat in the maze. *Psychol. Rev., Monog. Suppl.*, **8**, No. 33. Pp. vi+100.

————. 1919. Psychology from the standpoint of a behaviorist. Philadelphia: Lippincott. Pp. ix+429.

WEBB, L. W. 1917. Transfer of training and retroaction. *Psychol. Monog.*, **24**, No. 104. Pp. 90.

WHIPPLE, G. M. 1914. Manual of mental and physical tests. Part I: Simpler processes. (2nd ed., rev.) Baltimore, Md.: Warwick & York. Pp. xvi+365.

————. 1915. Manual of mental and physical tests. Part II: Complex processes. (2nd ed., rev.) Baltimore, Md.: Warwick & York. Pp. v+336.

WHITELY, P. 1924. The dependence of learning and recall upon prior mental and physical conditions. *J. Exper. Psychol.*, **7**, 420-428.

————. 1927. The dependence of learning upon prior intellectual activities. *J. Exper. Psychol.*, **10**, 489-508.

WILLIAMS, O. 1926. A study of the phenomenon of reminiscence. *J. Exper. Psychol.*, **9**, 368-387.

WILTBANK, R. T. 1919. Transfer of training in white rats upon various series of mazes. *Behav. Monog.*, **4**, No. 17. Pp. 65.

WINCH, W. H. 1924. Should poems be learnt by school-children as 'wholes' or in 'parts'? *Brit. J. Psychol.*, **15**, 64-79.

WITASEK, S. 1907. Ueber Lesen und Rezitieren in ihrer Beziehungen zum Gedächtnis. *Zsch. f. Psychol.*, **44**, 246-278.

WOHLGEMUTH, A. 1913. On memory and the direction of associations. *Brit. J. Psychol.*, **5**, 447-465.

WOLFLE, H. M. 1932. Conditioning as a function of the interval between the conditioned and the original stimulus. *J. Gen. Psychol.*, **7**, 80-103.

WOODWORTH, R. S. 1914. A contribution to the question of "quick learning, quick forgetting." *Psychol. Bull.*, **11**, 58-59.

WYLIE, H. H. 1919. An experimental study of transfer of response in the white rat. *Behav. Monog.*, **3**, No. 16. Pp. iii+66.

YARBROUGH, J. U. 1921. The influence of the time interval upon the rate of learning of the white rat. *Psychol. Monog.*, **30**, No. 135. Pp. 52.

YERKES, R. M. 1916. The mental life of monkeys and apes. *Behav. Monog.*, **3**, No. 12. Pp. iv+145.

————. 1927. The mind of a gorilla. *Genet. Psychol. Monog.*, **2**, 1-193, 375-551.

CHAPTER 12

WORK OF THE INTEGRATED ORGANISM

EDWARD S. ROBINSON

Yale University

INTRODUCTION

It will be the purpose of the present chapter to treat the fundamental processes involved in the productive operations of the intact organism. We shall hold our discussion close to the enterprises of experimental investigation, but we shall not be able, in the space at our disposal, to mention all of the important studies that have been made in this field. The reader should therefore regard our citations from the literature as merely illustrative. A bibliography of bibliographies at the end of the chapter will aid the student who wishes to take the present treatment as a starting-point for wider reading in this field.

One can make a rough division among the conditions of efficiency: (1) there are such conditions as the continuity of work, or the muscle groups involved in the work, which throw light upon the mechanisms of the work itself; (2) there are such conditions as diet, ventilation, the use of drugs, the effects of which are usually studied for purposes that go beyond the better understanding of the work itself. This chapter will be concerned with conditions of the first kind. Conditions of the second kind have recently been given excellent discussion by Poffenberger in his *Applied Psychology* (1927).

THE CONCEPTION OF WORK

In mechanics, work is done when force moves mass against resistance. Or it may be said that work consists of the transformation of energy from one form into another. Such energy-transformation is an essential feature of all the productive operations of the integrated organsim, but there are other features of such operations that are equally essential and in many cases scientifically more accessible. The solution of an arithmetical problem, the writing of a play, or the memorization of nonsense syllables ordinarily involves energy-transformation by hypothesis rather than by recorded fact. "Even if at some future time a mechanical interpretation of mental life might conceivably become a working hypothesis, at the present time such an hypothesis would be utterly barren and misleading" (Dodge, 1913). Such a statement does not mean that there is nothing mechanical about mental life, but it does mean that mental life requires much more than the principles of mechanics for its complete envisagement. A strictly mechanical conception of work is as inadequate for the physiologist as it is for the psychologist. In so far as the former considers the adjustive operations of organic systems he is able to restrict his think-

571

ing to mechanical principles only by the arbitrary adoption of a kind of philosophical blindness.

While it is generally acknowledged that the activities of the intact organism are more than mechanical, scientific men have frequently taken care of this fact by an oversimplified distinction. They have said that we have bodily work, which can be considered in strictly mechanical terms, and we have mental work, which is on another level. There have been various ways of characterizing this second type of work. Thorndike (1914, p. 3) says:

> There are four important possible criteria for marking off the mental part of the work done by an animal. The first is the production of conscious states. The second is the presence of conscious states, whether produced by the work or not. The third is the absence of explanation by present physiology. The fourth is action by the animal's connection system.

Thorndike recognizes that the third meaning of mental work is reasonable. It implies that there is a fundamental continuity from giving forth CO_2 to giving forth poetry and that ignorance alone renders us unable to bring both of these productions under a single broad conception. Still he feels that clarity will be better served if we confine our use of the term "mental work" to work done by the animal's connection-system. There will then be no danger of confusion with work of the digestive, excretory, action, or other systems. Thorndike realizes that his distinction is not perfectly clean-cut, that some of the work of the connection-system is in practice never called mental. But he seems to feel that, on the average, the distinction will serve a useful intellectual purpose.

Whatever may have been the utility of dividing all of the organism's work into mental and non-mental, into mental and mechanical, or into mental and physiological, there seems to be little advantage in continuing to emphasize such bifurcations. Psychologists and physiologists are almost unanimously aware that the principles of mechanics have limited applicability to the organism's activities. But this does not mean that we should place within a single group all non-mechanical aspects of behavior. Neither is it important to separate all work involving mechanical, chemical, and physiological changes from that which is most distinctly psychological. This latter division appealed most strongly to psychologists who felt that they had to defend the uniqueness of their position among the sciences. Happily this type of motivation seems to be losing ground among men who are actually engaged in experimental investigation.

What is required for the better conduct of investigation is a critical and empirical attitude toward the factors involved in the efficiency of specific productive activities. In the case of a given experimental performance, the question is not so much whether there is conceivably an increase or decrease in oxygen consumption; the important question is whether such a factor can be detected and measured. If, among the results of investigation, there are muscular sensations of pain, the first step is to accept these data. One has the right to form hypotheses about the chemical and neural processes involved—indeed, it would be an unimaginative student who did not do so—but it is important that we remain clear as to what is fact and what is hypothesis.

Emphasis upon speculative classification of the organism's activities may well be replaced by attempts to record for a wide range of performances such facts as amount of oxygen consumed, carbon dioxide produced, changes in breathing, in pulse, and in body temperature, changes in production as measured in kilogrammeters or in seconds per task performed, changes in production as measured in psychological units of accuracy (e.g., the correctness with which a word is spelled or a multiplication done), and introspectable changes in sensory, imaginal, and affective occurrences during the work.

It would be awkward to avoid all use of such terms as "mental work" and "muscular work," but it should be recognized that their application is for purposes of ready description and that it implies little or nothing about underlying processes.

ENERGY-TRANSFORMATIONS

The most direct measurements of total energy-transformation or metabolism during integrated activity are in terms of carbon-dioxide production and oxygen consumption. Pulse rate and rate and character of respiration are other indicators of energy-transformation, and in some investigations alterations in body temperature have been recorded.

The most successful studies of metabolism during work have dealt with activities involving the relatively continuous operation of large groups of muscles. Walking, running, mountain-climbing, bicycle-riding, and swimming are among the activities that have shown pronounced and readily determinable increases in oxygen consumption. The following table (Table 1) from Benedict and Cathcart (1913) presents a comparison of the oxygen consumption during various forms of work all of which involved the continuous operation of larger muscle groups.

We have an example of the use of such a table in the comparison made by the authors of the work of their own subject, M.A.M., who performed on the bicycle ergometer, with that done during mountain-climbing. They say (p. 162):

> It is thus clear by every method of comparison that the subject M.A.M. performed an extraordinary amount of work and that his metabolism was elevated to an abnormally high degree. When it is considered that this high elevation persisted not simply for experimental periods of a few seconds or even 15 minutes, but for an hour or more, and that these long experiments were carried out by the subject without food in his stomach, it will be seen that this subject not only had great strength but very great endurance, and that the amount of work performed was considerably greater than that done in the most active mountain climbing.

In the case of the operation of the larger muscle groups it is frequently possible to state output in physical terms. In their study of horizontal

Table 1

COMPARISON OF THE OXYGEN CONSUMPTION DURING VARIOUS FORMS OF MUSCULAR WORK, AS DETERMINED BY THE ZUNTZ METHOD

Name of subject	Kind of work	Oxygen-consump-tion per minute	Name of subject	Kind of work	Oxygen-consump-tion per minute
		c.c.			c.c.
Waldenburg	Treadmill	1,539	Kolmer	Swimming	2,318
Kolmer	Do	2,280	Durig	Mountain-climbing	2,245
Caspari	Do	2,037	Kolmer	Do	2,662
Muller	Do	2,194	Ranier	Do	2,584
Loewy	Do	1,863	Reichel	Do	2,674
Zuntz	Do	1,542	N.B.*	Bicycle-riding	2,130
L. Zuntz	Bicycle-riding	2,307	M.A.M.*	Do	3,000†
Reach	Turning crank	1,197	M.A.M.*	Do	2,850‡

*For comparison Benedict and Cathcart give three values obtained on the bicycle ergometer.
†For 15 minutes.
‡For 1 hour 10 minutes.

walking, Benedict and Murschhauser (1927) present an interesting table giving an analytic, mechanical comparison of walking at different speeds and running.

TABLE 2

MECHANICS OF LOCOMOTION IN WALKING AND RUNNING

Speed	Average (b) raising of body per minute	(a) minute distance per Average	(c) Average number of steps per minute	(d) Length of step (b÷c)	Raising of body per step (a÷c)
Walking:	meters	meters		cm.	cm.
Low	2.88	69.3	108.2	64.0	2.66
Medium	6.69	109.0	130.9	83.3	5.11
High	7.90	144.5	152.4	94.8	5.18
Running	13.76	147.6	181.9	81.1	7.56

Another interesting type of physical description of heavy muscular work is illustrated by the following table (Table 3) in which Benedict and Cathcart have presented the output during various specimens of such work in terms of kilogrammeters and also in terms of calories.

TABLE 3

EFFECTIVE MUSCULAR WORK IN VARIOUS FORMS OF ACTIVITY, AS REPORTED BY BLIX*

Kind of work	Length of work	Effective muscular work per minute	
		kgm.	cals.
Mountain-climbing, moderate work	Many hours	500	1.16
Mountain-climbing, severe work	1 to 2 hours	750-1,000	1.74-2.33
Steep mountain-climbing, 100 meters	3¾ minutes	2,000	4.65
Climbing a treadmill	30 seconds	2,400-3,600	5.58-8.37
Running up stairs, 10-kgm. load	15 seconds	3,700	8.61
Running up stairs, without load	30 seconds	4,300	10.00
Running up stairs, without load	4 seconds	5,700-6,000	13.26-13.95

*Recomputed in kilogrammeters by Magnus-Levy, and by us in calories per minute.

Decided changes in pulse and respiration are other important findings in connection with the operation of large muscle groups. Indeed, such changes are so closely correlated with more direct measures of energy-transformation that they have themselves sometimes been taken to be reliable indicators of the mechanical character of the organism's perform-ance (Dodge, 1913).

One of the most recent investigations of the background processes of muscular work is that carried on at Columbia by H. J. P. Schubert. Through the kindness of Dr. Schubert we are able to quote an informal abstract (1932):

The metabolic exchange, the breathing and the heart responses were measured during a work period of twenty-two minutes divided into six sections, and during the time necessary for recovery from the work performed. Six weeks were spent in preliminary adjustment to the situation and in practice at the work until all measurements had attained, for both working and resting conditions, a level from which they did not deviate to any great extent.

During work, the metabolism rises rapidly from the resting value to reach a peak by the fourth minute, then to fall off slightly to a low point at the eighth minute, only to rise slightly but steadily thereafter. The first reversal might be considered as a "swing to equilibrium"; and the final rise as evidence of inability to hold this equilibrium due to the spreading of deleterious metabolites. The respiratory rate was not greatly affected by the work. It was largely the increasing respiratory volume, depth of breathing, which accounts for the increase in ventilation. The heart rate rises from about sixty-three beats per minute during resting to a fairly constant rate of one hundred beats per minute after about two minutes of work.

The longer the subject has been engaged at work, the longer the recovery period necessary for the measures here taken—metabolism, heart rate, and breathing response—to return to resting values. The increase in the oxygen debt with increase in the time spent at work, is small. The critical feature is the speed with which the metabolic exchange returns to the resting value. . .

While such physical studies of work as we have just mentioned attain their most conspicuous results in connection with heavy muscular work, this by no means precludes the utilization of their technique in other connections. In respect to work like arithmetical calculation it is not wise to say that physical and chemical facts are here unimportant, even though it may be well to admit that they are difficult to detect.

Several attempts have been made to determine the physical properties of what is generally called "difficult mental work." Recently there appeared a briefly reported but significant study by Benedict and Benedict (1930).[1] Six subjects, five men and one woman (Subject VI), did silent mental multiplication of 2-place by 2-place numbers for three to four successive 15-minute periods. The results appear in Table 4.

To quote the authors (p. 443):

> Our conclusion in general is that with intense, sustained mental effort, such as in multiplication, there is a noticeable increase in heart rate, a rather considerable change in the character of the respiratory movements, an increase in the volume of air passing through the lungs, a small increase in the carbon-dioxide production, a smaller increase in the oxygen consumption, and consequently a slight increase in the apparent respiratory quotient. The increase in oxygen consumption, which may be taken as the best index of energy transformations, is such as to suggest that the increase in heat production as a result of intense mental effort of this type can hardly be of the order of more than 3 or 4 percent. In view of the sense of extreme, almost overpowering fatigue in both mind and body following sustained mental effort, it is surprising that mental effort has such an insignificant effect upon the general metabolism or level of vital activity. [See also the recent study from Columbia by Harmon (1933).]

---

[1]For earlier studies along similar lines see Benedict and Carpenter (1909) and Becker and Olsen (1914).

TABLE 4
EFFECT OF MENTAL EFFORT ON THE HEART AND RESPIRATORY ACTIVITY
(Average values per minute)

Subject	Heart rate		Respiration rate		Ventilation of the lungs	
	Rest	Work	Rest	Work	Rest	Work
					liters	liters
I	62	64	15	16	5.2	5.7
II	55	61	15	18	5.5	6.3
III	60	62	14	16	5.0	5.6
IV	54	57	15	15	7.2	7.7
V	73	77	17	15	5.8	6.7
VI	55	67	10	11	3.9	5.0
Average	60	65	14	15	5.4	6.2

EFFECT OF MENTAL EFFORT ON CARBON-DIOXIDE PRODUCTION
(Cc. per minute)

Subject	I	II	III	IV	V	VI
Rest	178	173	174	202	149	139
Work:						
Period 1	183	197	184	210	168	159
Period 2	183	179	185	205	160	156
Period 3	180	177	183	209	159	157
Period 4	178	179	...	...	...	160

EFFECT OF MENTAL EFFORT ON OXYGEN CONSUMPTION
(Average cc. per minute)

Subject	Rest	Work
I	208	210
II	212	219
III	232	241
IV	242	247
V	174	187
VI	181	191
Average	208	216

In one of his earlier papers Benedict suggested that such metabolic changes as do take place during "mental" work are due largely to accompanying muscular activity (Benedict and Carpenter, 1909). From what we know of the actual tissue masses involved in muscular movement, upon the one hand, and in central nerve processes, on the other, this seems quite likely. But the conclusion is not to be drawn therefrom that truly mental activity is virtually without metabolic cost. There is at present too much evidence for the motor theories of conscious activity to permit the easy identification of mind and brain. Rounds and Poffenberger

(1931) have presented a method of studying the physiological changes associated with articulation.

FACTORS IN ADDITION TO ENERGY-TRANSFORMATIONS

In the case of heavy muscular work that best index of energy-transformation, oxygen consumption, is strikingly affected. This tends toward the attachment of a high degree of physiological importance to oxygen consumption and toward the natural conclusion that changes in pulse and respiration are principally important as less direct indices of the same fundamental metabolic fact. Under these circumstances we are likely to overlook slight alterations in the movements of production and such changes as are accessible only to introspection. But when we move on to such work as mental multiplication, where oxygen consumption is less prominent experimentally than are changes in pulse and respiration and where the introspective facts become relatively obtrusive, we are forced to admit that the work of the intact organism has a high degree of complexity. With that picture of mental work before us which is supplied in the above summary by Benedict and Benedict, we may well turn back for a moment to a consideration of heavy muscular work and ask whether we ought not to seek in such work evidences for circulatory and respiratory facts which are *more* than mere reflections of oxygen consumption. There is reason to believe further that the introspective facts observable during heavy muscular work could profitably receive more systematic attention. In recent studies of arm ergography by Yochelson (1930) fairly full introspective observations have accompanied the more conventional physical and physiological measurements. Aside from the well-known ebb and flow of muscular pain, interesting findings have been obtained regarding temporary states of aboulia which are free from perceptibly relevant sensory or imaginal content. It appears also that the character of the work itself is profoundly altered by the shift of attention from the working muscles to more remote objects.

This brings us back to our earlier methodological point. There is a real temptation to study heavy muscular work with regard only for facts of energy-transformation closely allied to it. There is an equal temptation to study mental work with regard only to introspective facts or to statistical changes in the results of such work, whereas an adequate scientific attitude requires an attempt to secure for all kinds of work all of the facts from oxygen consumption to an empty consciousness of incapacity. Benedict and Benedict are moving in the right direction when they examine oxygen consumption during mental multiplication, and Yochelson is equally right in giving more than customary care to sound introspection in the case of heavy muscular work. We are not suggesting that every investigation in the field of work should be arranged to lay bare all of the physical, chemical, physiological, and psychological factors involved, but merely that there is no type of work done by the intact organism which precludes the possibility of studying any of a wide range of factors. It is this possibility that is likely to be minimized by such easy distinctions as that between bodily work and mental work.

The Work Decrement

Most of the theoretical discussion and experimental investigation of the nature of psychophysiological work has centered about the work decrement. It will, therefore, aid the present exposition if we turn our attention to this phenomenon.

By "work decrement" is meant that loss in efficiency which is typically produced by prolonged and highly continuous performance of a set task. The popular and pseudo-scientific term "fatigue" includes the fact of decrement, but it ordinarily includes assumptions as to the causes of this fact which, for the sake of clear thinking, ought to be kept separate from the fact itself. Thorndike (1914) has sought to avoid the difficulties due to loose usage of the term by defining it in such a manner as to limit it to the work decrement. Dodge (1917) has sought to help the situation by distinguishing between fatigue and *relative fatigue,* according to the causal factors underlying decrement. But it is probably safer to follow the advice of Watson (1919) and Muscio (1921) and to avoid the term "fatigue" except where precision is unnecessary.

Psychologists and physiologists have determined the decrements for a large variety of activities, and before going into the possible and probable

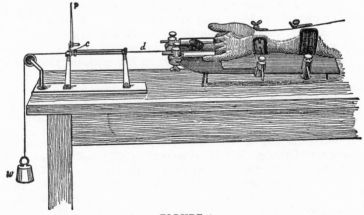

FIGURE 1

Mosso's Ergograph

c is the carriage moving to and fro on runners by means of the cord *d,* which passes from the carriage to a holder attached to the last two phalanges of the middle finger (the adjoining fingers are held in place by clamps); *p,* the writing-point of the carriage, *c,* which makes the record of its movements on the kymographion; *w,* the weight to be lifted.

(From W. H. Howell's *A Textbook of Physiology,* 11th ed., 1930, by permission of the publishers, W. B. Saunders Co., Philadelphia.)

causes of such losses in efficiency we shall present the essential empirical facts as they appear in typical work curves. We shall present such curves for lifting (ergographic work), speed of movement, amplitude of movement, control of movement, speed of mental process, accuracy of mental process, and affective tone.

We begin with ergographic work. The products of such work can be expressed in simple terms of kilogrammeters. The process out of which this product comes is not, of course, so simple. It is quite impossible to confine work to the operation of a single muscle and it is quite impossible to confine it to the operation, in constant relations to each other, of the members of a definite group of muscles. These latter facts have caused many investigators to turn away from the ergographic method. It should be noted, however, that the critics of this method have not been able to set up any other activity of the intact organism which would be devoid of the variability inherent in the weight-lifting or spring-pulling activity of ergography. And it is fair to ask whether the goal implied in such criticism is the only possible goal in the study of work. The ergographic method suffers when it is thought of as an attempt to study in the living individual the type of phenomena observable in the recurrent or continuous stimulation of the nerve-muscle preparation. But if the method is considered as an approach to the activity of the intact and living organism, its lack of simplicity may be thought of as a merit rather than as a deficiency. There also remains the essential fact that, even though the pattern of muscular activity in ergographic work is persistently variable, there is far better hope of understanding such variability here than there is in stair-climbing, tapping, mental arithmetic, or grading compositions. In the writer's opinion this is not an argument against the study of those other activities, but it is an important answer to the criticism that the complexity of ergographic work renders it insusceptible to scientific study.

After the early enthusiastic investigations by such men as Mosso (1904), Maggiora (1890), Lombard (1887), and others, the skeptical attitude toward ergography became pronounced, although studies utilizing this method have appeared from time to time. Lately there has been a renewed interest in the method on the part of psychologists as is shown by the contributions of Crawley (1926), Weinland (1927), and Manzer (1927) of Columbia, and by that of Yochelson (1930) of Yale. These later studies have employed contraction of the single finger, of the hand muscles involved in grasping, of the flexor muscles of the arm, of the flexor muscles of the leg, and of the large muscles of the trunk as they are used in the rowing-machine.

The ergograms in Figure 2 are from Yochelson. Each one represents the performance of a subject who lifted, by a flexion of the arm, a weight of 8 kilograms once every two seconds. In every case there is a complete decrement, so far as objective performance is concerned, within a relatively brief period. It is well known that zero performance in such cases does not mean complete exhaustion of the power to act. A lighter weight could be lifted after this one ceases to move and with sufficient incentive

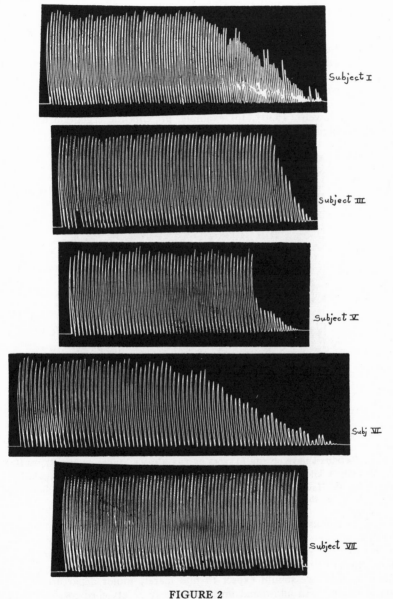

FIGURE 2
ERGOGRAPHIC CURVES FROM EACH OF FIVE SUBJECTS
(From S. Yochelson's "Effects of Rest-Pauses on Work Decrement," Ph.D. thesis,
Yale Univ., 1930.)

even this weight could be at least partially raised. Nevertheless, these curves represent a complete decrement for the experimental conditions represented.

Each of the ergograms of Figure 2 represents a performance typical of a particular subject. Although Mosso in his pioneer studies had recognized that the exact course of the decrement in ergographic work is a function of the individual, later writers have often forgotten this fact and have claimed or implied that there is a curve typical of ergographic work in general. Howell (1930), for example, presents the ergogram of Figure 3 from Maggiora and calls it a "normal fatigue curve."

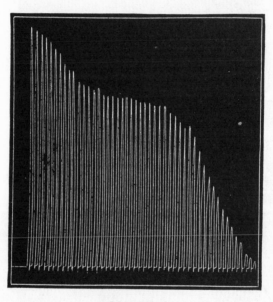

FIGURE 3

NORMAL FATIGUE CURVE OF THE FLEXORS OF THE MIDDLE FINGER OF THE RIGHT HAND
Weight, 3 kilograms, contraction at intervals of 2 seconds.—Maggiori.
(From W. H. Howell's *A Textbook of Physiology*, 11th ed., 1930, by permission of the publishers, W. B. Saunders Co., Philadelphia.)

The variations present in the ergograms of Figure 2 are important, because they suggest that the causes of decrement in a muscular performance of this sort are not to be sought simply in energy-depletion or in the accumulation of "fatigue products." If such chemical factors were the only causal agencies we should expect to find merely minor departures from a typical curve. An additional importance may be attached to these curves because they were obtained from subjects who had had considerable practice under these experimental conditions and because each curve does represent a type for a particular subject. Yochelson's study of these subjects extended over many days and, after a degree of irregularity in the early days of the experiment, each subject settled down to his own type of curve which he produced with very few exceptions.   Experiments utilizing different muscle groups of these same subjects also indicate that the ergograph curve remains fairly constant for the individual.   One might almost say that the curve is a personality trait.   The insistent character of these individual differences indicates more than the presence of factors other than energy-depletion and fatigue-products; it indicates that those other factors may remain fairly constant for the reactive system of a given individual. Many investigators have admitted with deep regret their inability to eliminate psychological factors which complicate the problem of the decrement for muscular work.   They have assumed that such factors, if present, are bound to be so nebulous as to place them beyond the reach of scientific study.   Yochelson's results do not minimize the possible complexity of the decrement for muscular work, but they give a hint that the factors underlying it are definite, even though they are also complex.

Interesting light on ergographic work is also furnished by the two ergograms of Figure 4, both of which were obtained in the early stages of Yochelson's experiment, before his subjects had had a great deal of practice. In one case we have a temporary partial decrement, recovery from which took place with no rest other than that furnished by the decrement itself. In the other we have a nearly complete decrement of the same temporary character.   Both suggest that we are here dealing with the maintenance of a complicated system of activity, the balance of which is susceptible to disturbance, rather than with a simple expenditure of energy.

Both Manzer and Yochelson studied series of work periods in which each complete decrement was followed by a rest interval of varying length.   In Manzer's experiment there was a tendency for the work

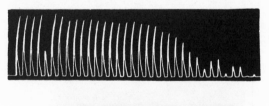

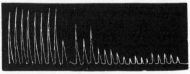

FIGURE 4

ERGOGRAPHIC CURVES FROM EACH OF TWO SUBJECTS
(From S. Yochelson's "Effects of Rest-Pauses on Work Decrement," Ph.D. thesis,
Yale Univ., 1930.)

accomplished in successive periods to diminish.   Yochelson, however, found that after a first and marked diminution the subject early made an adjustment which allowed him to continue almost indefinitely at a

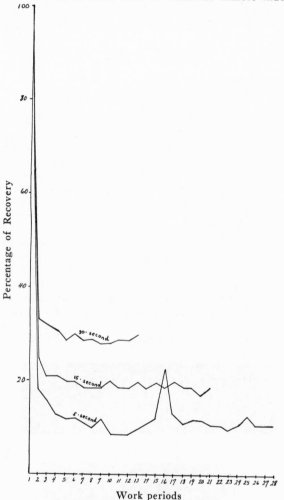

Work periods

FIGURE 5

AVERAGE RECOVERIES FOR ALL SUBJECTS FOR FIVE-, FIFTEEN-, AND THIRTY-SECOND REST SERIES

These curves show the recovery values of 5-, 15-, and 30-second rest series. All points on these curves are averages of six recoveries—two performances by each of three subjects. Note that their general levels were arrived at after four or five work periods.

(From S. Yochelson's "Effects of Rest-Pauses on Work Decrement," Ph.D. thesis. Yale Univ., 1930.)

fairly constant production level. The level maintained depended, of course, upon the length of the rest interval, but only a few such intervals were required in order to define the particular state of equilibrium which could be maintained. The graphs of Figure 5 show this result. Here again we have evidence that in ergographic work we are dealing with a complex, but definite, adjusted system of activity. The subjects were quite unaware of the nature of this state of equilibrium, but their separate records all have this same characteristic.

The fact that Yochelson got this state of equilibrium while Manzer did not is of minor importance so far as our present interest goes. These investigators used different subjects and there were considerable differences in the details of apparatus. There is nothing, however, to suggest that Yochelson's result was a mere accident. The important point is simply that the state of equilibrium found so consistently by Yochelson *can* occur in ergographic work.

Before leaving Figure 5, it should be said that the sudden spurt shown at the fifteenth period for the 5-second curve was due to the performance of a single subject. That such an irregularity could occur emphasizes again the fact that ergographic work depends upon the maintenance of an

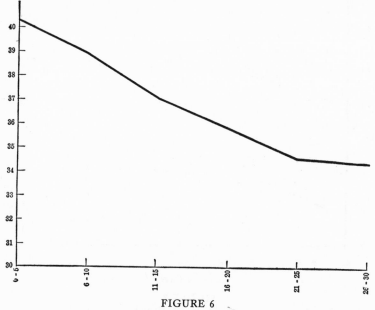

FIGURE 6

Work Curve for Tapping

The vertical axis represents the average number of taps in 5 seconds. The horizontal axis represents the successive 5-second periods of tapping.

[Drawn from data from F. L. Wells (1908) and taken from E. S. Robinson's *Practical Psychology*, 1926, by permission of the publishers, The Macmillan Co., New York.]

adjusted system. Such a spurt, like the temporary decrements of Figure 4, suggests sporadic disturbance of a system.

From these few facts about the ergographic curve and decrement we may conclude that the method here represented does, as has been maintained, represent a poor experiment so far as a strictly mechanical interpretation of its results is concerned. But we may also conclude that the phenomena that are manifested by work of this type are from a broader physiological and psychological point of view extraordinarily interesting and important.

We may now turn from work of the ergographic type, which is done at a constant and moderate speed against relatively heavy physical resistance, to work done at high speed against only such resistance as is offered to the free movements of the limbs. In Figure 6 a work curve is presented for 30 seconds of continuous tapping. This curve is a fair representative of those obtained for speed of movement, even where the total work period is very much longer. Such curves rarely show a complete decrement nor do they give grounds for predicting the later development of such a collapse. During the early portions of the work there is a

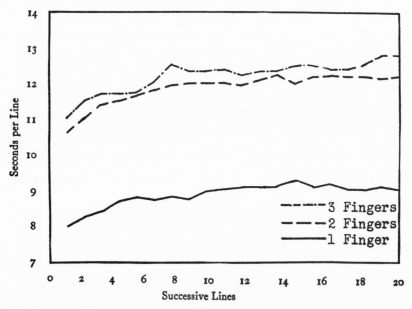

FIGURE 7

WORK CURVES, REPRESENTING THE SPEED AT WHICH THE FIRST TRIALS OF ONE-, TWO-, AND THREE-FINGER TYPING WERE MADE

Horizontal axis represents successive lines written. Vertical axis represents speed in terms of seconds per line. Curves are averages for 21 subjects.

(From E. S. Robinson and A. G. Bills's "Two Factors in the Work Decrement," *J. Exper. Psychol.*, 1926.)

decrement in speed which brings the worker to a level at which he can perform almost indefinitely without exhaustion. There is an inflection in the curve of Figure 6 which suggests that such a level is soon to be reached. The same phenomenon is illustrated in the three curves of Figure 7. The work in this case also is tapping, but the two upper curves represent alternate tapping with two or three fingers, a more definitely coordinated and integrated type of activity than the tapping of the wrist and hand or the tapping of the single finger. Nevertheless, the curves are much alike. (Allowance must, of course, be made for the fact that the method of measuring efficiency in this group of curves is such as to represent a decrement by a rise in the curves.) There is a relatively steep preliminary decrement after which the level of performance remains fairly constant. While the preliminary decrement doubtless is influenced by the presence of blocks, sensory pains, etc., which are warning signals of coming exhaustion, the prompt development of the decrement may be thought of as mainly a protection against the completer decrement of actual exhaustion. One must be careful, however, in speaking thus teleologically not to assume a conscious or unconscious purpose that is not present. Introspective reports from such experiments seldom show any awareness on the subject's part that he is "loafing" for protection, and the experimentalist will hardly be content to postulate an unconscious, purposive striving. Our attitude should simply be that of a willingness to point out that a useful protective function is served by the prompt minor decrement. Much is still to be learned regarding precise mechanisms underlying such protective reductions in efficiency.

There is some interest in comparing the decrement secured in ergographic work with that in speed of unresisted movements. The most striking difference is that one almost always gets a complete decrement in the former case and almost never in the latter. Within the single period of continuous ergographic work under the usual laboratory conditions, the subject does not spontaneously and unconsciously decline to a level of efficiency which can be indefinitely maintained. There is no lack of opportunity for such a phenomenon to occur. It is well known that ergographic work can be continued over long periods of time if the weight is light enough, and there is reason to believe that a reduction in the amount of lift given in each reaction might have a similar influence in staving off complete decrement. As a matter of fact there are two ergograms in Figure 2, those of Subject V and Subject VI, that show what approaches the level characteristic of the curves for speed of movement. Perhaps these levels, which are irregular at best, are not low enough to protect against the final complete decrement. It seems even more likely, however, that their ineffectiveness is due to their late development after a considerable amount of high-level work has been done. But why is this true? Why is there not a partial decrement in the earliest stages of the work? The answer probably lies in the fact that in ergographic work the subject is given a definite standard and rate of performance any departure from which he can easily detect. He therefore resists any tendency which might be present to let his level of efficiency drop until the occurrence of the drop can no longer protect him against the final and complete decrement. In such activities as tapping, the subject has a much less definite basis for judging his own performance. His efficiency can therefore slip off by the required amount without meeting any great subjective resistance.

Although the experimental literature gives us a reasonably adequate picture of the work curve for the speed of small movements, we are still curiously lacking in precise knowledge of the course of efficiency in running, swimming, rowing, and similar performances of the larger muscle groups. Determinations of oxygen consumption, carbon-dioxide production, respiration, heart rate, blood pressure, urine content, etc., have been made in connection with athletic activities, but we are largely ignorant of precisely how the decrement would develop in the case of a runner who started off with a conscious effort to attain maximum speed and to maintain that speed until his gait involuntarily slowed itself. A. V. Hill (1927) and a number of earlier writers have presented what are, after a fashion, work curves for human running. The times required to cover varying amounts of ground have been taken from the athletic records.

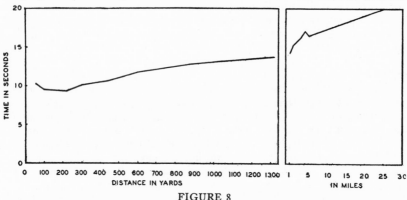

FIGURE 8

Record Time Taken To Run Ten Yards in Various Distance Runs

The horizontal axis represents distances run and the vertical axis represents the record time taken to run 10 yards at these various distances.

(Drawn from American Athletic Union records.)

In Figure 8 we have constructed such a curve from the official records of the American Amateur Athletic Union. The rise in speed from the 100-yard dash to the 220 is due to the time lost in overcoming inertia at the start rather than to warming-up in the usual sense. It is interesting that by the time the mile run is reached the rate of running is very little faster than that at which two miles can be run. To quote Hill (p. 227), who has considered records up to 25 miles: "At ½ mile the average velocity is only about three-quarters of what it is in 220 yards, though it is 25

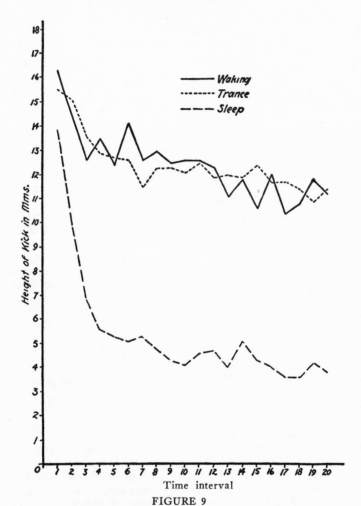

FIGURE 9

<small>THE COURSE OF THE PATELLAR REFLEX OVER A PERIOD OF ABOUT FIFTEEN MINUTES IN STATES OF WAKING, TRANCE, AND SLEEP</small>

(From M. J. Bass's "Differentiation of the Hypnotic Trance from Normal Sleep," *J. Exper. Psychol.*, 1931)

miles before it comes down to a half." There is much in this curve to suggest the results in regard to speed of movement that have been obtained in laboratory investigations of more circumscribed activity. There is a similar sharp initial decrement that puts performance at a level which can be essentially maintained over long distances. Of course, that level is actually subject to decrement, but this decrement is gradual.

The similarity of the curve for running to that for the laboratory experiments is all the more remarkable when we consider that it does not actually represent the continuous performance of the same individual or group. The type of physique and state of training is different for the individuals who have made the records for the short distances and for those who have done best in races of a mile or longer. The conscious "sets" also vary for the different distances. But it would be highly desirable to obtain values for successive distances traversed by the same runner. Hill (pp. 232 f.) has described apparatus for timing electrically the successive sections of the same race and has presented results for a dash of 60 yards. The application of this method to longer races promises important scientific results.

Work curves similar to those for speed of unresisted movement have been obtained for the amplitude of periodically stimulated reflexes. In an experiment designed to compare the knee-jerk during the normal waking state, during normal sleep, and during hypnotic trance, Bass (1931) secured work curves for one hundred successive reactions occurring at intervals of 9.68 seconds. The pooled results for several performances of seven subjects appear in Figure 9. While it is interesting that the work curves for waking and trance conditions are coincident within the limits of statistical reliability and that the curve for the sleep condition shows a much greater initial drop, our main concern is with the general form of these curves. All show the early rapid drop characteristic of curves for speed of movement. Curves of similar type have also been secured by Dodge (1923) for the amplitude of post-rotation nystagmus. The existence of decelerated work decrements for responses at the reflex level indicates that the early diminution in speed or amplitude of response is not conscious malingering.

We may next consider work decrement as it appears in control of movement. As early as 1906 McDougall pointed out that loss of control is an outstanding result of continuous work, and in more recent years Ash (1914) and other writers have emphasized the importance of this phenomenon. One of the best illustrations of decrement in control of movement is given by Dodge (1917) and we shall quote his text (pp. 106-109):

Let me assume your familiarity with the technique of photographically recording the eye-movements from corneal reflection. For the present records (Figure [10]) the eyes moved horizontally through an arc of sixty degrees, fixating successively two knitting needles which were situated thirty degrees on either side of the primary position of the line of regard. Each dot or dash on the records represents one phase of the alternating current, and a time interval of about eight thousandths of a second.

The succession of eye movements in the records that are here reproduced was as rapid as practicable with subjectively adequate successive fixation of the two fixation marks. Some of the more characteristic fatigue phenomena which they show are: (1) The speed of movement becomes less toward the end of the series; (2) the fixations become less accurate; (3) and finally the line of movement itself become more irregular. Figure [10] shows the climax of these processes in a break. The gradual decrease in angle velocity cor-

FIGURE 10

RECORD OF EYE-MOVEMENTS SHOWING THE FATIGUE PHENOMENA

Read from top down. Note the break at end of record on the right.
(From R. Dodge's "The Laws of Relative Fatigue," *Psychol. Rev.*, 1917.)

responds to the work decrement of extirpated muscle. But in this case, in view of Sherrington's demonstration of the reciprocal inhibition of antagonistic eye-muscles, fit doubtless involves something more. The greatest angle velocity of eye-movement could only occur when the relaxation of the antagonistic was perfectly coördinated with the contraction of the antagonistic muscle. The pseudo-work decrement in this case then is not purely muscular but is in part a matter of defective coördination. The increasing errors of coördination have a similar origin. That is, the total elaboration of the contraction impulse and the corresponding relaxation of the antagonistic become less exact in successive repetitions of the act of fixation. But the coördination is not limited to the internal and external recti as one would expect them to be in horizontal movements of the eyes. All the records of 60″ eye-movements, which I have ever seen, show a vertical factor. In all my records this vertical factor results in an elevation of the line of regard. But it varies from movement to movement. That these vertical components are not accidents of purely muscular origin is shown by binocular records. Since the disturbances are homologous for both eyes, their origin must lie in the central nervous system. While occasional gross disturbances occur early in the series of movements, they become more and more conspicuous as the series progresses. The vertical components represent the intercurrent action of related and competing, but this is a case of non-inhibiting systems. When they become extreme they tend to interrupt for a moment the main rhythm of horizontal movements. In some cases these various disturbances produce a moment of confusion and a break in the process, which in ordinary mental fatigue experiments would be interpreted as complete fatigue or exhaustion.

We may take as another instance of decrement in control of movement the increase in size of writing which occurs when simple letter-groups are written over and over again with a set for maximum speed. Figure 11 presents work curves for the continuous writing of such groups as *ab, abc,* and *abcdef* (Robinson and Bills, 1926). In general form these curves suggest those for speed of movement. A fairly sharp initial decrement is followed by a more gradual loss of control. And again we may assume that it is the sharpness of the initial decrement that retards the appearance of anything approaching collapse of the activity. It should be said that the enlargement of the writing as the work progressed was non-voluntary. The subjects simply began each day's work with writing of something like normal size and increased this size spontaneously as the work proceeded. It is true that, with practice, even the initial writing became larger, but throughout some eighteen days of experimentation the enlargement appeared as the day's work progressed.

There are some interesting differences between the nature of the decrement in the eye-movements examined by Dodge and that in the writing movements which we have presented. In the case of the eye-movements there is nothing exactly corresponding to the definite increase of size in writing. Even in normal life the individual does not always restrict his writing to the more finely adjusted movements of a relatively restricted muscle group. On the outskirts of such a group are larger muscles of the arm which have habitually been allowed to creep into the activity of

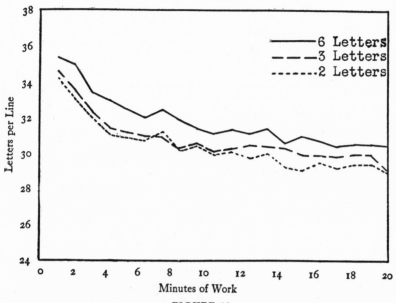

FIGURE 11

WORK CURVES SHOWING INCREASING SIZE OF WRITING DURING PERIOD OF WORK
Horizontal axis represents successive minutes of work. Vertical axis represents
number of letters per line. Curves are averages for 24 subjects.
(From E. S. Robinson and A. G. Bills's "Two Factors in the Work Decrement,"
J. Exper. Psychol., 1926.)

writing as the more finely adjusted group has become partially disorganized. And the introduction of these larger muscles has tended toward the production of grosser movements. We have here something
which looks curiously like a reversal of the developmental sequence from
fundamental to accessory. As a matter of fact, the writing of young
children is strongly suggestive of the later stages of continuous writing
in adults. In the case of the eye-movements described by Dodge there is
no such relation between small, finely adjusted muscle groups and larger
neighboring muscles. What we see, therefore, in such a record as that
of Figure 10 is the development of a decrement in control marked by
erratic movements and by constantly increasing blocking rather than a
decrement of the orderly type suggested by the curves of Figure 11.

Thus far we have dealt with activities involving muscular movements,
the force and character of which could be physically recorded. We may
now turn to activities which have their outcome in some intellectual product such as the solution of an arithmetical problem, the correct identification of a language symbol, etc. In his well-known desire to force
homogeneity of factual content upon psychology, Watson (1919) distinguished work of this latter type as vocal. By stressing the muscles

used in uttering the intellectual response, Watson seemed to feel that he was identifying mental work with muscular work—the only difference being in the muscle groups involved in the two cases. The difficulty with this suggestion is that in the usual studies of such work as arithmetical calculation little attention is given to the precise muscles involved. The question is mainly this: Is the answer correct or not, and how much time was required to arrive at it? If the investigator does record muscular activity involved in such work, he regards it as secondary—as a facilitating or inhibiting factor, perhaps, but not as the work's essential product. In criticizing Watson's naïve effort to rid himself of the philosophical embarrassment of a type of work which cannot be treated in terms of muscle movement, we need not have recourse to the traditional views of mental work, such as that which would make this work largely the production of the brain alone. As a matter of physiological fact we know that work like arithmetical calculation does involve the organism as a whole. But the essential feature of such work is something not found, for example, in ergography. There is in ergography no such thing as an intellectually correct or incorrect answer, or, if there is, it is a matter of minor importance.

Figure 12 presents the work curve for speed of addition as obtained by Chapman and Nolan (1916). Although the total period of work is only 30 seconds, there is apparent an early rapid loss of efficiency followed by the maintenance of a fairly stable level. The authors speak of the high initial level from which the early drop occurs as "initial spurt." This has

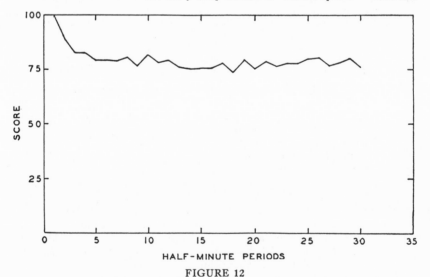

FIGURE 12

WORK CURVE FOR SPEED OF ADDITION

(Drawn from data from J. C. Chapman and W. J. Nolan's "Spurt in a Simple Mental Function," *Amer. J. Psychol.*, 1916.)

long been a customary usage, but it is somewhat unfortunate in that it emphasizes the initial level of efficiency rather than the drop from that level.   Chapman and Nolan felt that work curves often lack this early drop simply because the divisions of time as represented on the base line are too gross.

Our own interest in the above curve rests principally on the fact that it again illustrates the tendency of the worker to fall off to a level of efficiency which can be maintained for a considerable period.

In Figure 13 we have a work curve for speed of mental multiplication constructed from results given by Arai in her noteworthy monograph (1912).   The base line is certainly too grossly divided to reveal any such early decrement as that in the Chapman-Nolan curve.   It is clear, nevertheless, that in this experiment also the subject tended toward a level that

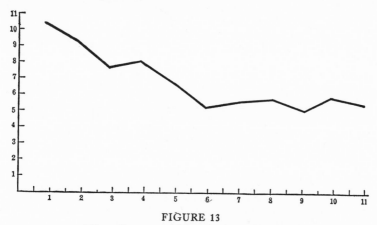

FIGURE 13

WORK CURVE FOR MENTAL MULTIPLICATION

The vertical axis represents the number of 4-place by 4-place examples worked per hour of working time.   The horizontal axis represents the successive hours of work from 11 A.M. until 11 P.M.

[Drawn from data from T. Arai (1912) and taken from E. S. Robinson's *Practical Psychology*, 1926, by permission of the Publishers, The Macmillan Co., New York.]

could be maintained.   True, six hours, or more than half the duration of the experimental sitting, were required to reach this level, but the final attainment of such a level is clear.   We should not conclude from the above curve that efficiency in 4-place by 4-place mental multiplication would follow the same course for every subject.   There are individuals who would not be capable of doing such work at all.   In all likelihood there are many others who could not continue this work for a day at a time.   Even among individuals who could do such multiplying with something like Arai's initial efficiency, the early drop which we have found so characteristic of work curves of all kinds might appear very much earlier or even later than the decrement in Arai's curve.   An experiment reported by Painter (1916) fails to give us a drop to a maintainable level. Instead, we see a growing irregularity and finally a collapse to a point where mental multiplication simply failed to take place.

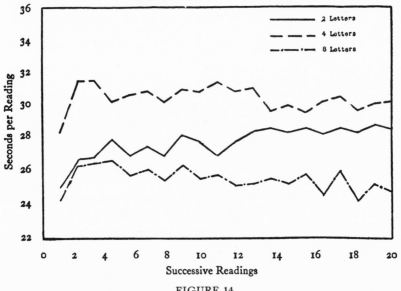

FIGURE 14

WORK CURVES

Horizontal axis represents successive readings of card containing 100 letters. Vertical axis represents seconds per reading. Curves are averages for 18 subjects. (Modified from E. S. Robinson and A. G. Bill's "Two Factors in the Work Decrement," *J. Exper. Psychol.*, 1926.)

In Figure 14 we present work curves for a type of intellectual activity quite unlike the various forms of arithmetical operations that have customarily been used by students of mental work. Upon a cardboard, 12 inches square, there were pasted 10 rows of ¼-inch gummed letters, 10 letters to a row. Such a card might contain 2 different letters, 4 different letters, 8 different letters, and so on to 24. The letters were distributed in random order after the manner of the colored patches in the color-naming test. The subject read through one of these cards as rapidly as possible and then repeated the performance until 20 readings had been made. Although decided blockings occurred, actual errors were negligible, so that speed is the essential variable. The curves of Figure 14 represent the average performance of 18 practiced subjects.

Each of these curves for speed of letter-naming shows an early decrement followed by a prolonged period during which efficiency either falls very slowly (2-letter condition) or actually shows a gradual rise (4-letter and 8-letter conditions). Whether the rise, when it occurs, is due to the fact that the general influence of practice is still present or to the fact that there is a temporary warming-up effect within the work period is not so important as the additional exemplification of the tendency of the worker to diminish his efficiency to a level that he can maintain. This early decrement does not represent any conscious malingering. If it did, we should expect to find practiced subjects beginning the work at a level which experience had taught them they could maintain. In the case of the present experiment the early decrement was marked even in the fourth cycle of experimentation and the initial level of efficiency had not diminished but had actually increased.

The tendency toward early decrement that leaves the individual upon a maintainable level is probably only one of the reasons why complete decrements are so rare for the speed of intellectual work. It has frequently been noticed that work curves when secured for the individual performance rather than from a pooling of many performances are characterized by more or less periodic fluctuations in efficiency [as for instance in Flügel (1928).] Such fluctuations may, themselves, provide short periods of relative rest which act to postpone any more serious decrement. A recent and thorough study of this question has been reported by Bills (1931a, 1931b). Five tasks were employed: continuous addition and subtraction, voluntary perspective reversal, color naming, opposites, and substitution. Time was recorded by a kymographic technique in such a manner as to show the speed of each successive response. The findings are summarized as follows (1931a, pp. 209-210):

> 1. In all five forms of mental work there occur, with almost regularity, blocks or pauses during which no response occurs. These blocks occupy the time of from two to six responses. They have an average frequency of about three per minute, although individuals differ in rhythm.
> 2. Practice reduces the frequency and size of the blocks.
> 3. Fatigue increases their frequency and size, producing much greater irregularity in the flow of responses, after an hour.
> 4. The responses between the blocks tend to bunch toward a center, such that a regular wave-like effect of alternate crest and trough, or condensation and rarefaction results. Fatigue exaggerates the bunching.
> 5. Individuals who respond rapidly tend to have fewer and shorter blocks than slow individuals.
> 6. Errors occur consistently opposite blocks, suggesting that the same cause is responsible for both; i.e. a refractory phase in mental functioning.

While these results regarding periodic blocks or decrements do not, themselves, prove that such blocks act protectively against more serious decrements, it seems altogether reasonable that they do act in that way.

There is little doubt that highly continuous intellectual work is capable of producing a decrement in the accuracy of such work. An examination of the literature, however, fails to reveal any number of satisfactory demonstrations of this decrement. In the earlier studies there was an almost complete absence of any attempt to control the influence of practice, and for this reason we often find accuracy actually increasing during a period of continuous work. Another factor which has tended to diminish the decrement apparent in accuracy has been the widespread existence of decrement in speed. Subjects have ordinarily been instructed to work both rapidly and accurately. Under such conditions it is conceivable that the subject might allow his accuracy to become reduced in order to keep up his speed or he might reduce his speed in order to maintain accuracy. That the second of these alternatives should most often be chosen is fairly easy to understand. Arithmetical activity has customarily been employed, and, in regard to this, subjective norms of accuracy are far more definite than are those of speed. The subject who makes an error in addition or multiplication is quite likely to notice this error and to feel required to correct it before proceeding. Thus, what appears in the objective record is a loss in speed rather than in accuracy.

There is an obvious need for studies of the accuracy decrement in intellectual work that is maintained at high speed. Such investigations could make use of any of the many devices for continuous exposure. The subject who received a new problem to solve, a new letter to name, or a new syllable to memorize at sufficiently frequent intervals would not have the opportunity to correct as he went along. We do not make the prediction that under these circumstances accuracy would decrease after the customary manner of speed. Indeed, such a prediction would be foolish in light of our introspective knowledge of intellectual work. It is well known to investigators who have given any attention to work activities that many of the delays that crop up are not due to the conscious correction of erroneous reactions or partial reactions. To the subject such delays are frequently (perhaps more frequently than not) marked simply by the failure of any response to take place.

Another obvious need is for the investigation of decrements in intellectual accuracy of functions lacking the definite subjective norms of arithmetical calculation. Possibly rapid and continuous work in giving reasonably difficult analogies or other relations would reveal a substantial decrement in accuracy.

In summarizing the results of his own experimental investigations of intellectual work as well as those of many other students, Thorndike (1914, p. 69) makes the following statement:

> The most important fact about the curve of efficiency of a function under two hours or less continuous maximal exercise is that it is, when freed from daily eccentricities, so near a straight line and so near a horizontal line. The work grows much less satisfying or much more unbearable, but not much less effective. The commonest instinctive response to the intolerability of mental work is to stop it altogether. When, as under the conditions of the experiments, this response is not allowed, habit leads us to continue work at our standard of speed and accuracy. Such falling off from this standard as does occur is, in the writer's opinion, due to an unconscious reduction of the intolerability, by intermitting the work or some part of it.

There is some reason to believe that this is an oversimplification of the facts. Prior to 1914, when Thorndike's statement appeared, there were few studies of the work curve that adequately eliminated the practice effect, and, of course, so long as such an effect is present, decrement is to that extent masked or counterbalanced. At least in regard to speed of mental processes it is easy to show that a pronounced decrement can be produced as a result of continuous work. In the present writer's opinion, Thorndike's statement of the influence of feelings of intolerability is also too simple. In the ergograph experiment discomfort and actual sensory pain often occur in greatest intensity early in the work and then recede before any marked decrement in output appears. Of course, Thorndike is talking about work of a more intellectual character, such as arithmetical calculation, but even here there are other possibilities for the causation of decrement than the instinctive avoidance of discomfort. Later we shall see evidence that something closely akin to the physiological phenomenon of refractory phase may be an underlying factor in decrements in intellectual efficiency.

But with all of his oversimplification of the probable causes of decrement, Thorndike's view has been productive. Farther along in the discussion from which we have quoted he proposed that a curve of satisfyingness is as legitimate and important as a curve of production. In 1917 a paper appeared reporting an experimental study of such a curve. A group of 29 adults graded printed compositions for approximately 2 hours on each of two days.

> The speed of the work was scored by the time required for each 10 compositions; the quality of the work was scored by the average deviation (regardless of signs) of their grades from the average judgment of twenty or more competent graders; the satisfyingness or tolerability or zest or interest of the work was scored from 0 to 10 at the end of each approximate twenty minutes, 0 meaning the greatest discomfort or distaste or aversion the subject had ever experienced for mental work in his life; 5, his average enjoyment of mental work during the year or so past; and 10, the greatest interest, zeal or satisfaction he had ever experienced in mental work or play.

In a second experiment five individuals did the same work for four hours continuously instead of for two hours.

Dividing each individual's work during the 2-hour period into three approximately equal successive parts, the average errors per composition are reported as standing in the proportions:

100	103.8	101.6

The average times stand in the proportions:

100	97.3	100.6

The average degrees of satisfyingness in successive sixths were:

4.4	4.0	3.6	3.4	2.8	2.6

In the second, or 4-hour, experiment similar results are given for successive sixths in errors and time and for successive twelfths in satisfyingness.

Errors:

| 100 | 99 | 98½ | 98 | 92 | 92 |

Time:

| 100 | 95 | 93 | 95 | 94 | 97 |

Satisfyingness:

| 6.0 | 5.7 | 5.2 | 5.0 | 4.6 | 4.3 | 3.6 | 3.3 | 2.8 | 2.4 | 2.5 | 2.2 |

Results which agree with the above in showing a steeper and prompter decrement in feelings of comfort than in actual production are indicated by Figure 15 as given by Poffenberger (1912). Although subjects who have undergone a night of enforced insomnia show little diminution in

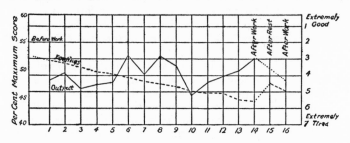

FIGURE 15

RELATION BETWEEN FEELINGS AND OUTPUT

(From A. T. Poffenberger's *Applied Psychology*, 1927, by permission of the publishers, D. Appleton & Co., New York.)

mental efficiency as measured by laboratory tests, there is a marked decrement present in feeling-tone as is shown when they make ratings of their own tiredness (Robinson and Robinson, 1922).

There thus seems to be a good deal in Thorndike's (1917, p. 266) conclusion that:

> These facts support the general doctrine that the effect of lack of rest is far greater upon whatever is the physiological basis of interest, willingness, or tolerability, than upon the physiological basis of quantity and quality of product produced. Or, in other words, the mechanisms determining the mind's achievement are left able to do their customary work, but in such a condition that their customary action is less satisfying, so that (except for extrinsic motives) the individual would relax, intermit, or abandon the action in question.

We should not assume, however, that loss of satisfyingness is the *only* cause of decrement in production simply because it appears so promptly and so markedly. And we should keep in mind the possibility that loss of satisfyingness may, itself, be partially due to loss in productive efficiency. The subject who is naming colors or solving arithmetical problems suffers from other factors than eye strain, cramped posture, and general boredom. He suffers also because the color names and the answers simply fail to come forth with customary alacrity. In such a case we have a loss of satisfyingness which is caused by a loss in productive efficiency rather than the reverse.

Before we turn our attention away from the curves of satisfyingness, there is a factual point that should not be neglected. In none of the results cited is there clear evidence of that early decrement followed by a relatively level state which has characterized so many of the work curves hitherto examined. Thorndike's curves of satisfyingness approximate linearity. There is a slight suggestion of negative inflection toward the end of the 4-hour experiment, but there is no more than a suggestion. The 2-hour experiment yields an approximately linear function for satisfyingness. This is true not only for the composite of all subjects, but also for the separate curves when the subjects are divided into three groups differing in initial satisfyingness. (See Thorndike's paper, Figure 2.) In Poffenberger's experiment (see our Figure 15), the curve of "feeling" represents a continuous 5-hour work period and here again there is a remarkable approximation to linearity. A prediction upon the basis of such results might be to the effect that satisfyingness typically falls off at a constant rate until the work becomes completely unbearable whereupon there is a collapse in productive capacity. There is reason, however, for questioning any such extrapolation. It is well established that in the performance of muscular tasks like ergographic work or distance running, there are periods during which satisfyingness no longer decreases. Great discomfort may follow such periods of "second wind," but the point is that there certainly are level periods in many curves of satisfyingness. Furthermore, the collapse in productivity may occur after the individual has gone into a state of relative numbness during which "discomfort" is distinctly less marked than in earlier stages of the work. Such considerations again lead one to question the simple notion expressed by Thorndike as to the influence of satisfyingness upon production. The empirical study of discomforts incident to continuous work remains highly important and much more needs to be done along the lines marked out by Thorndike and Poffenberger; the clean-cut differences between decrement in satisfyingness and in output proves that point; but we are hardly in a position to explain all or nearly all decrements in output as due to decrements in satisfyingness simply because the latter are steeper in the earlier stages of the work.

THE CAUSES OF WORK DECREMENT

We have already introduced one explanation for that decrement in efficiency which is so frequently associated with highly continuous work, namely, Thorndike's claim that such small decrements as occur in so-called mental work are largely to be explained in terms of the apparently simple fact that the individual tends to relax his effort on any task the performance of which has become too uncomfortable. But we have suggested that this explanation, while true to a degree, is an oversimplification of the facts.   We shall now proceed to an examination of what seems to us to be the actual intricacies of the matter.

In the first place, there occur during the performance of continuous work certain events that can be treated as chemical phenomena.   Where and to the degree to which there is muscular movement, there is oxidation of the energy-producing material, the glycogen, of the muscles involved. There must also be a consumption of material of the active nerve cells. Earlier students naturally surmised that such depletions of combustible materials were prominent factors in the work decrement; and in certain severe cases of exhaustion there is actual evidence of serious depletion of these materials.   It now seems improbable, however, that the consumption of energy supplies to a point where these are insufficient to support further work is an important element in those decrements which appear in the laboratory performances of the intact organism.   Even such heavy muscular work as that involved in arm ergography ordinarily develops a complete decrement before there has been anything approaching an exhaustion of the glycogen necessary for the performance of such work.   This is shown by the fact that a relatively slight increase in incentive will ordinarily permit the subject to continue far beyond the point at which he ordinarily suffers from complete decrement.

The reasons why exhaustion of glycogen in the muscles does not readily take place are well understood.   During work there is a characteristic increase in the rate of adrenal secretion, and the endocrine product thus deposited in the blood stream stimulates the liver to increase its deposition of energy-producing materials that are conveyed to the muscles and compensate for the accelerated catabolism going on there.   Such a mechanism, of course, merely prolongs the interval before exhaustion, but before such eventual exhaustion can take place there are ordinarily other factors that bring about a cessation of activity.   We shall speak of those other factors shortly.

The exhaustion of the energy-producing materials of the neurons is an even rarer causal factor in work decrements.   That refractory phase which occurs both for the single neuron and for systems of neurons apparently provides inactivity of sufficient duration to allow for an almost completely rehabilitating anabolism.   It is possible that something like a true exhaustion of the nerve cells may be brought about by prolonged pathological conditions such as disease, enforced insomnia, or extreme emotional excitement, but the contribution of such exhaustion to experimental decrements is almost certainly very slight.

While it is now generally agreed that ordinary work decrements are brought about mainly by factors other than depletion of energy supplies, at least one of those other factors is susceptible to chemical description. We refer to the action of fatigue products.   To quote Ernest L. Scott (1918):

> In 1865 Johannes Ranke, then lecturer in the Physiological Institute at Munich, published a book of nearly 500 pages in which he gave the results which he had obtained from his studies on the

physiology of muscle. In many ways this book has never been super-ceded. Among other things he here developed the idea of fatigue substances. At that time Ranke brought out the fact that fatigue is due, at least to a great extent, to something which arises within the organ rather than to the absence of anything used up by the process of muscular contraction. That is, fatigue is to be explained on the basis of a full ash pit rather than an empty coal bin. His principal evidence consisted of the fact that when a fatigued muscle was irrigated with an indifferent fluid, as salt solution, it resumed its power of contraction. Now, it was argued, since the irrigating fluid could not have supplied anything necessary to the muscle, it must have removed something detrimental to it. The substances supposed to have been removed are the fatigue substances.

Obviously the next point is their isolation and identification. Their identification has been attempted both by chemical comparison of fatigued material with resting material and by the injection into the nonfatigued preparation of substances which are suspected of being fatigue substances. . . .

The story of the development of our knowledge of the chemical nature of the fatigue products is an interesting one. It would be outside our present purpose, however, to follow it in detail. Instead we shall simply present Scott's summary of the situation at the time his paper was written (p. 7):[2]

1. Substances carrying hydrogen ions, as lactic, B oxy-butyric acids, potassium, dihydrogen phosphate and carbon dioxide, stand as causal agents of fatigue.

2. Certain products of protein disintegration, as indol, skatol, and phenol may produce fatigue symptoms and may be active agents in producing normal fatigue.

3. There is some evidence that the negative ion of lactic and B oxy-butyric acids and that certain positive ions, especially that of potassium, are capable of producing certain fatigue phenomena.

4. There is no evidence that the negative ions of carbonic, phosphoric or sulphuric acids are fatigue substances.

5. There is no evidence at present for the existence of specific fatigue substances as proposed by Weichardt.

6. There is very little probability that creatin or creatinine have any relation to fatigue or to muscle work in general.

7. There are no doubt numerous bodies, as purine bases, uric acid, etc., which may be increased by work, but which have no causal bearing on fatigue.

There are two ways in which the fatigue products may act to diminish efficiency. In the first place, they undoubtedly have a direct and depressing influence upon muscular and nervous tissue. Evidence for this is especially good in regard to striped muscles. Muscle preparation when irrigated with solutions containing lactic acid or its salts will first show augmented contractions and then an abnormally early decrement (Lee, 1907). In the second place, these toxic substances undoubtedly act as stimuli to the receptors terminating in the striped muscles of the intact organism. As a result, sensations of fatigue are aroused which tend to instigate

[2]It should be kept in mind that this analysis is based upon results from *excised* nerve-muscle preparations.

relaxational behavior. It seems possible also that there are stimulus-response connections of this general type in which there is no awareness of definite fatigue sensations.

It is safe to say that, in work decrements secured in the laboratory, the presence of fatigue products is almost always a more important cause of decrement than is exhaustion of energy-producing materials of the active tissues. There is considerable uncertainty, however, as to the degree to which these toxins operate directly upon muscle and nerve and the degree to which they operate indirectly as sensory stimuli. There is reason to believe, further, that fatigue products have a larger part in producing decrements in weight-lifting, running, and other activities involving the vigorous operation of large muscles than in such work as mental multiplication, though there is no ground for concluding that they are totally ineffective in the latter case. Such a correlation is natural in light of what is known about the relative amounts of oxygen consumed in work of various types.

Over and above the chemical facts of exhaustion and toxicity, there are a number of fundamental principles of neuromuscular action which we may be quite sure are involved in the production of the work decrement. These principles are not to be thought of as independent of chemical action or as insusceptible to the application of chemical hypothesis. At present, however, our formulation of them is safer if carried out in terms of the gross reactions of neuromuscular systems.

Many writers have been aware of the fact that the causes of decrement run beyond the relatively simple factors of exhaustion and toxicity. An outstanding attempt to formulate these factors was made in 1917 by Dodge. Thorndike, it is true, had stressed the importance of discomfort, but, as we have already pointed out, his treatment of the problem was not very penetrating. In 1926 the writer felt that, by taking the general analytic attitude defined by Dodge's paper, it would be possible to elaborate his description of the factors presumably involved in the work decrement in such a manner as to give greater logical coherence to this whole field. The outcome of this opinion was the statement of seven factors or principles of work decrement over and above exhaustion and toxicity. These seven factors all seemed highly probable at the time of their formulation, though they differed considerably in the substantiality and definiteness of their experimental bases. Since the writing of that paper, new experimental results have come to hand which have important bearings upon those principles and these we shall introduce in connection with the following statement of the principles.

The terminology of the ensuing discussion is, like Dodge's, that of *stimulation* and *response*. There may be objection that such terminology imposes unnecessary limitations upon the conception of work decrement, unless *stimulation* be carelessly taken to mean any antecedent psychological activity and *response* any psychological consequent. It is possible (though hardly proved) that there may be chains of cortical activity each setting off a successor without specific determination coming in through sensory channels and that, if this is the case, there are other than stimulus-response relations capable of undergoing decrement. This possibility is hardly of sufficient importance, however, in connection with objectively measurable activities to warrant an avoidance of the useful *stimulation-response* conception.

Principle 1: The work decrement of a given S-R (stimulation-response) connection is relative to the recency of the previous functioning of that connection. This is simply the familiar law of refractory phase. Its isolation is well exemplified by such an experiment as that of Dodge (1913) on the protective wink reflex. In this study it was shown that, as in the case of the simpler laboratory preparations, a reaction of the intact organism is resistant to early repetition. It was also shown that the refractory phase is not absolute as had been claimed by Zwaardemaker and Lans. On the contrary, as the time interval between stimulation and restimulation increases, there is a *gradual* increase in the probability of occurrence and in the completeness of the repeated response.

Dodge has suggested that the relative refractory phase which is readily demonstrable in nerve and muscle tissue may be present in the more elaborate mental processes as well as in reflexes. He (1917, p. 103) points out that:

> Repetitions of all sorts tend to be avoided whenever practicable. The repetition of questions, courses, lectures, phrases, and even words is possible enough, but except for special re-enforcing circumstances, it is postponed until the effect of the initial case is somewhat worn off.

In this connection one might cite the experiments, such as that on reversible perspective, where the perceptual process tends toward variety rather than repetition. Another relevant experiment is that in which the subject concentrates for a period on a word, whereupon the word seems to lose or change its meaning. Binocular rivalry offers still another illustration of the general resistance to repetition.

In an investigation of associative process Thorndike (1927) obtained results which seem to be a reflection at a high level of something much like refractory phase, if, indeed, it is not the same phenomenon. Subjects were required to write a number between 0 and 9 every time a word was heard. A word was given every 2½ seconds. The subjects were given no directions either to vary the numbers used or to keep them constant. An effort was made to avoid suggestion along these lines by telling the subjects that the experiment was one on "thought-transference and other problems." The theoretical chance for a repetition like 00, 11, 22, etc., was 1 in 10, but the actual repetitions given were much fewer than would be secured by chance distribution. In only one of six subjects were the repetitions more than half the chance expectancy. In another experiment, in which the time interval between the stimulus words was increased to 5 seconds, there was still a resistance to repetition but not as strong a resistance as when the time interval was shorter. Thorndike is very conservative in considering the possibility that we here have a demonstration of the influence of refractory phase upon higher processes.   He suggests that the subjects may, after all, have considered it improper to repeat too frequently.   He cites the fact that the avoidance of sequences increased from day to day, which is difficult to interpret in terms of what is now known about refractory phase.   He also points out that the tendency to avoid repetition was almost as strong with the 5-second interval as with that half as long.   The first point ought to be decided with a group of competent introspectors as subjects.   The second point is not necessarily decisive.   Whereas refractory phase for the nerve trunk is short, it is longer for the reflex arc, and it is altogether likely that it becomes much longer as we get to the more highly integrated systems.

That Thorndike's results were due to the operation of refractory phase at the level of associative response is given support by an experiment performed by Telford (1931).   His subjects were directed to write down the first of the numbers from 1 to 10 which came to mind when they heard a nonsense syllable.   Syllables were read off at varying intervals.   One ex-

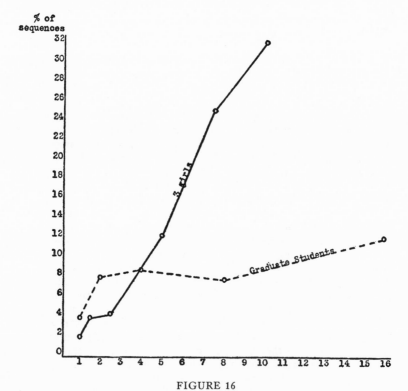

FIGURE 16

PERCENTAGE OF SEQUENCES WITH DIFFERENT TIME INTERVALS BETWEEN STIMULI
(From C. W. Telford's "The Refractory Phase of Voluntary and Associative
Responses," *J. Exper. Psychol.*, 1931.)

periment was performed with three young girls, aged 8, 10, and 11 years. Another was performed with 31 graduate students. The number of repeated responses was calculated for each of the several time intervals. In Figure 16 we have the relationship between percentage of repetition and time interval (seconds) between stimuli. The fact that the tendency against repetition varies with the time interval would favor some more fundamental explanation than the thought on the part of the subjects that they ought not to repeat. This is especially true in the case of the younger subjects. It seems probable that the use of greater time intervals would ultimately have resulted in a decrease in the number of repetitions.

In another experiment Telford studied serial reactions to simple auditory stimuli, the stimuli occurring at intervals of ½, 1, 2, and 4 seconds. Figure 17 gives the relationship between stimulus intervals and reaction-

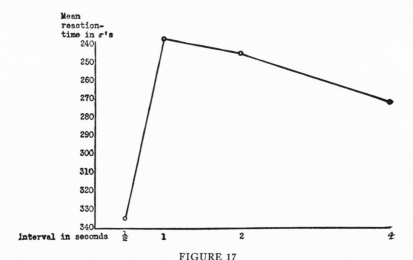

FIGURE 17

MEAN REACTION-TIME WITH VARYING TIME INTERVALS BETWEEN STIMULI
(From C. W. Telford's "The Refractory Phase of Voluntary and Associative Responses," *J. Exper. Psychol.*, 1931.)

time from the pooled results of 29 graduate students. The ½-second period falls within the relative refractory phase, while there is a facilitative effect at the intervals just above.

Garrett (1922) had found that in lifting weights and in judging linear magnitudes and handwriting specimens accuracy is greatest when the judgments are made at a 2-second rate. From 2 seconds down, accuracy falls off rapidly; from 2 seconds up, it falls off more gradually. Thus, a rate of something below 2 seconds would seem to bring the process of judgment within a refractory phase. At 2 seconds we presumably have facilitation and beyond that a slow return to normal efficiency. Telford had 25 members of a class in general psychology make continuous judgments of linear magnitudes, the standard line always being 30 mm. and the comparison lines being 33, 31, 29, and 27 mm.

Figure 18 gives the relationship between intervals between judgments

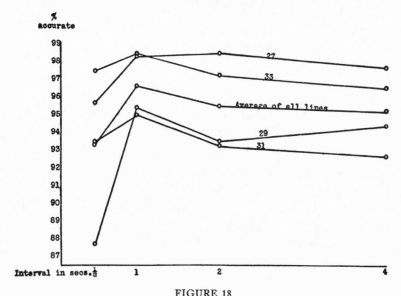

FIGURE 18

ACCURACY CURVES FOR JUDGING LENGTHS OF LINES WITH VARYING TIME INTERVALS
BETWEEN JUDGMENTS

(From C. W. Telford's "The Refractory Phase of Voluntary and Associative Response," *J. Exper. Psychol.*, 1931.)

and percentage of judgments accurate for the various comparison lines. The general drift of the results is clear. The shortest interval seems to bring the judgment within the refractory phase established by the preceding judgment. There is also evidence of an intermediate interval at which there is a facilitative effect.

Whatever be the accurate interpretation of these experiments, it is clear that there are barriers to repetition even at intellectual levels. The only serious question seems to be whether it is legitimate to identify such resistance with refractory phase in general. This is largely a matter of definition. Historically, according to Verworn (1913), the phenomenon was first noted for heart muscle. Since then, as we have pointed out, it has been found in nerve trunk and reflex arc as well. And, in spite of the fact that these several instances of refractory phase have shown marked differences in duration, there has been no hesitancy in grouping them together. There is no implication that their chemical basis is absolutely identical. It has simply been convenient to emphasize the general functional fact that reactive tissue and systems of tissue are resistant to early restimulation.

Under these circumstances of customary usage there would seem to be little reason to exclude from the conception of refractory phase the plain fact that the higher processes have an analogous resistance to repetition. So far as the writer is aware, no one has suggested that simple or accumulative[3] refractory phase is the "sole explanatory principle" of mental fatigue, a theory subjected to criticism by M. F. Robinson (1931).

It is important to note that refractory phase is both a work decrement and a mechanism that minimizes work decrement. We have already noticed that the prompt resistance to repeated action offered by nerve tissue renders exceedingly difficult the attainment of a true nervous exhaustion. In a similar manner the refractory phase manifested by all tissue and systems of tissue is a protection against a more serious decrement that would develop if the drain upon energy-supplies were continuous.

Principle 2: The work decrement of a given S-R connection is relative to the frequency of the previous functioning of that connection. The work curves of psychology and physiology do not represent the resistance to repetition brought about by a single act. They thus give little information about refractory phase as formulated in our first principle. Instead these curves represent the development of decrement as a consequence of an accumulation of repeated reactions. It is easily conceivable that an S-R connection having a pronounced resistance to repetition would show no accumulative decrement. Such a case would simply be an extreme illustration of the protective function of an immediate decrement against a more permanent, accumulative effect. On the other hand, since many work curves do show a decrement, it is clear that the resistance offered to each successive repetition of an act is by no means a complete protection against an accumulated resistance. Indeed, there is reason to believe that this accumulative decrement may be more important than most work curve studies would indicate. The favorite activity utilized by psychologists in such investigations has been some form of arithmetical operation, but such work does not consist of a series of repetitions of essentially the same acts. It consists rather in the performance of a class of acts called *adding* or *multiplying* within which class there may be a wide variety of specific acts. For example, in mental multiplication, one multiplies 7 by 6, then 5 by 3, then 9 by 8. There is usually a considerable period before one returns to a genuine case of repeated response. It is no wonder then that an investigator like Arai (1912), doing 4-place by 4-place mental multiplications, found only a relatively moderate accumulative decrement. The tacit assumption of her study and that of many others was that the work ought to show marked decrement simply because it was difficult, but she might equally well have guessed that it would show little decrement since actual repetitions are so widely spaced temporally as to allow for an extraordinary amount of recovery during work.

At the beginning of an investigation reported in 1926, Bills and the

---

[3]See our Principle 2.

present writer sought a psychological activity in which the factor of actual repetition could be made more prominent than it had been in most of the previous experiments. We selected the writings of groups of alphabetical sequences like *ababab,* or *abcabc,* or *abcdefabcdef.* Here we had not only work of a high degree of homogeneity (repetitiveness), but also other cases where the homogeneity was measurably less. If our hypothesis that a fundamental condition of accumulative decrement is amount of actual repetition, then we should find that this decrement shows a regular decrease as the work done contains more different elements or letters.

We shall not go into the detailed arrangements of this experiment. These are described completely in the paper cited. Suffice it to say that 24 adult subjects went through three cycles of experimentation during each of which every subject performed at least once under every experimental condition. The individual work periods were 20 minutes in length, a mark being made at the end of each minute of writing. Efficiency was measured in terms of letters per minute.

The differences in efficiency between the first and tenth minute of work were determined for three degrees of heterogeneity, i.e., for the 2-letter, 3-letter, and 6-letter sequences. These differences can be considered as measures of decrement magnitude. After inspecting our work curves, we selected the tenth minute as representative of the maximal decrement. Beyond the neighborhood of that point, the curves either continue at about the same level or show an actual rise. Almost the same results were obtained, however, by determining the decrement in terms of the difference between the first and poorest minute of work in a given curve.

In Figure 19 there are plotted for the three cycles of the experiment the relationship between the homogeneity of the work, as measured in terms of the number of letters involved, and the magnitude of the decrement, as measured by the difference between the production of the first minute and that of the tenth. All cycles agree in showing decelerated functions representative of the relationship between the heterogeneity of the work and its resistance to accumulative decrement. The experiment thus confirms the expectation.

While the writing of letter sequences develops a decrement in speed, another important change is also taking place. The writing is increasing in size. Work curves were constructed in terms of these size changes and they are shown in Figure 11 of the original paper. For the present purpose, the most important point about them is that their decrements are about the same for the three conditions of experimentation. So we may eliminate the size change as an important complicating factor in the interpretation of the results on speed.

In the investigation now under discussion, an effort was made to test the generality of the above findings regarding homogeneity and work decrement by setting up another set of tasks which, while differing considerably from letter-writing, should, like letter-writing, present a continuous series in respect to some definite meaning of homogeneity. We were limited in the work that might be studied because of this purpose

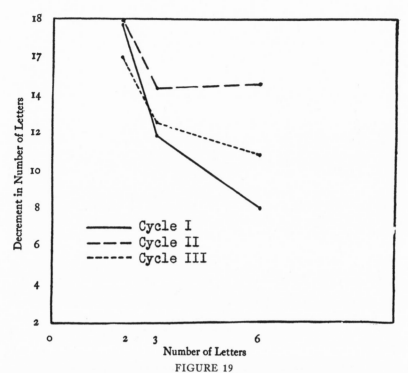

FIGURE 19

<small>RELATIONSHIPS BETWEEN DEGREES OF HETEROGENEITY AND THE WORK DECREMENTS</small>
Horizontal axis represents degrees of heterogeneity in terms of number of letters involved. Vertical axis represents decrements in terms of difference between number of letters written in first minute and number of letters written in tenth minute.
(From E. S. Robinson and A. G. Bills's "Two Factors in the Work Decrement,"
J. Exper. Psychol., 1926.)

to be definite. The activity finally decided upon was suggested by the familiar color-naming test. As mentioned in another connection, we found it desirable to use letters on the card instead of colors in order that we might work with more elements; there are so few colors having well-established names. The 5 types of cards in our experiment represented 5 degrees of homogeneity-heterogeneity. One type contained 2 different letters; another, 4; another, 8; another, 16; and another, 24. Twenty successive readings of a given card took place at an experimental sitting. The set was for speed. Errors were rare and were, therefore, not recorded. Inefficiency appeared almost always simply as an inability to call a letter by name. Eighteen subjects went through all conditions of experimentation four times and the results are the pooled performances of this group.

We determined the decrements for the different tasks by securing the difference between the rate of the first reading and that of the last, or twentieth. The decrements were determined in respect to the relation of these end-points because, in those curves which showed the decrement most markedly, there was no indication that the decrement tended to cease before the completion of the 20 readings. In Figure 20 we have plotted

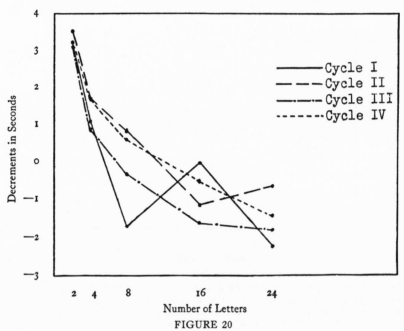

FIGURE 20

CURVES SHOWING RELATIONSHIPS BETWEEN THE DEGREES OF HETEROGENEITY AND THE WORK DECREMENT

Horizontal axis represents degrees of heterogeneity in terms of number of letters involved. Vertical axis represents decrement in terms of difference in time required for first reading of card and for twentieth reading.

(From E. S. Robinson and A. G. Bills's "Two Factors in the Work Decrement," *J. Exper. Psychol.*, 1926.)

for the 4 cycles of experimentation the relationships between the work decrements and the homogeneity-heterogeneity of the work. The functions secured are unequivocal. There is in general a decelerated relationship between heterogeneity and resistance to decrement. In each of the first two cycles there occurs a first-order inversion of this relationship, but even in these cases the general trend of the functions is as stated.

Thus, in an experiment involving a new type of activity and a wider range of homogeneity-heterogeneity, we were able to confirm the essential results obtained with letter-writing.

The point might be made that, even though we have been able experimentally to demonstrate that accumulative decrement is a function of the amount of actual repetition, i.e., of the homogeneity of the work, it was necessary to arrange tasks of highly artificial character in order to do this. In other words, while the decrements in the above laboratory tasks were related to homogeneity, it is possible that this apparently fundamental variable is ineffective in work of less artificial character.   Important evidence upon this question is supplied by Poffenberger (1927).   He used four types of work; (1) *continuous addition,* (2) *judgment of compositions,* (3) *completion of sentences,* and (4) *intelligence tests.*   Sufficient uniform material was provided for about 5 hours of continuous work. The work curves secured from these several tasks are plotted in Figure 21.

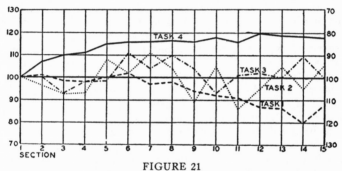

FIGURE 21

WORK CURVES FOR SUCCESSIVE SECTIONS OF WORK EXPRESSED IN TERMS OF PERCENTAGE
OF SCORE IN SECTION 1

Task 1 is continuous addition; Task 2 is in terms of errors in addition; Task 3
is completion of sentences; and Task 4 is intelligence tests.

(From A. T. Poffenberger's "The Effects of Continuous Mental Work," *Amer.
J. Psychol.,* 1927.)

The only curve showing a definite decrement is that for addition, the activity presumably having the greatest homogeneity.   Work on the intelligence tests, which was heterogeneous in nature, did not produce sufficient decrement to compensate for a pronounced practice effect.   The other two activities would seem from superficial examination to have an intermediate degree of homogeneity and they are approximately horizontal. Poffenberger raises the question as to whether the differences he obtained might not be explained in terms of the more frequent opportunities for a "let down" or rest in the most varied work.   In the intelligence tests "one has to turn pages, pass from one problem to another, and from one kind of work to another" (p. 296).   This possibility would lend itself to experimental test.   In the meantime, in light of the results obtained with letter-writing and letter-reading, it seems somewhat more likely that the Poffenberger experiment is another illustration of what is, perhaps, the most fundamental factor in accumulative decrement, namely, homogeneity or repetitiveness.

Before passing on to our third principle of the work decrement, there is an interesting point about the work curve which is customarily neglected by students of this subject. The work curve is plotted in the same coordinate system as the learning or practice curve. One axis in each case represents efficiency and the other frequency of repetition. Several writers have recently taken the pains to point out that greater frequency does not always strengthen an associative connection, that even the reverse may be true [as, for example, Dunlap (1928), Köhler (1929), Thorndike (1931)]. The very existence of the work curve with its typical accumulative decrement not only proves that this is the case, but also proves that it should have been recognized by experimentalists as a commonplace.

Principle 3: The work decrement of a given S-R connection is relative to the connections existing between that S and other R's. This is the principle of competition. Let us assume that a given S has acquired the capacity to instigate either of two responses, R_1 and R_2, but that the connection with R_1 is slightly the stronger. Now suppose that there is a frequent occurrence of S. At first the response instigated will be R_1, but, as repetition increases, R_1 will be less and less likely to be aroused (see principle 2). As a result, the connection between S and R_2 will have gained in *relative* strength, so that R_2, if inconsistent with R_1, will tend to block it or perhaps to occur in its stead.

It is to be noted that the principle of competition would not produce decrement without such principles as those of refractory phase and accumulative frequency, but, since refractory phase and accumulative frequency may be important factors in decrement without being associated with competition and since the results of refractory phase and accumulative frequency are different when competition is present, we need this separate formulation of a principle of competition.

In the investigation previously cited, Bills and the writer (1926) sought to secure an experimental test of the independent importance of competition. We asked ourselves whether there might not be situations in which more heterogeneous work, because of the greater possibility of competition introduced by heterogeneity, would show a greater decrement than less heterogeneous work, notwithstanding the larger amount of repetition present in the latter. We thought that this might be true if a comparison were made of the decrements in repeated movements of one finger and in alternating movements of two or three fingers. Such tasks were performed on the typewriter. The same fingers were, in the course of the experiment, represented in the three varieties of work, so that the fundamental variable was the number of fingers involved in a given reaction-system.

The work curves secured for the three types of work are given in Figure 7 (p. 586). The slightly greater irregularity of the 3-finger work is purely a statistical matter; for technical reasons described in our original report fewer samplings were taken of this particular task. It is plain from an inspection of these curves that the decrement is at least as great for the more heterogeneous tasks as it is for the more homogeneous.

From the first to the twentieth line there is a decrement of about 1.1 seconds in speed of the 1-finger work, of about 1.6 seconds in the 2-finger work, and of about 1.3 seconds in the 3-letter work. While these results do not show a markedly greater decrement for the more heterogeneous tasks, they clearly indicate that in work of this type the homogeneity-heterogeneity factor does not operate as it did in the earlier experiments. It looks as though the decrement produced in the 1-finger work by virtue of its homogeneity were at least equalled by the decrement which hetero-geneity, presumably by increasing the competition factor, produced in the 2- and 3-finger work.

Thus far we have dealt with the influence of this factor of com-petition upon decrements in speed. Competition is even more important, however, in connection with accuracy. In Figure 22 we have plotted the work curves in terms of accuracy for our three varieties of finger move-ments. The errors consisted of wrong letters struck and of failures to

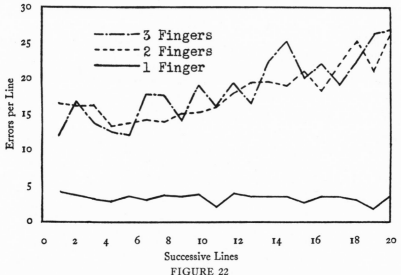

FIGURE 22

WORK CURVES—FIRST TRIALS

Horizontal axis represents successive lines written. Vertical axis represents total number of errors per line. Curves are totals for 21 subjects.

(From E. S. Robinson and A. G. Bills's "Two Factors in the Work Decrement," *J. Exper. Psychol.,* 1926.)

carry the key down to actual impression. In this case, it is clear that the presence of competing responses affects not only the average level of accuracy but also the magnitude of the decrement in accuracy.

Freeman and Lindley (1931) have found increasing muscle tone and increasing restlessness with continuous muscular work of the finger and with continuous addition of 4-place numbers. They interpret restlessness as the manifestation of increasing competition and tonus as the mechanism by means of which the decrement that might result from this competition is offset. In so far as their interpretation is correct, it further emphasizes the place of competition as a factor tending to produce or to augment the work decrement.

Principle 4: The work decrement of a given S-R connection is relative to the strength of that specific connection. We should expect this to be true from what we know about competition. If an S-R connection were weak, we should expect it to suffer interference upon the occurrence of the slightest hesitancy in the operation of the connection itself. On the other hand, if the connection were strong, we should expect that there might be some considerable diminution in its underlying efficiency before competing responses could block it or replace it.

The commonest factor in increasing the strength of an S-R connection is practice. If the above principle is valid, there should thus be a general decrease in susceptibility to decrement with increasing practice. So far as we know, this proposition has not been put to an experimental test for a simple, relatively isolated S-R connection. Results are nevertheless available for a reasonably simple form of behavior, namely, the continuous writing of *ababab*, etc. In a recent paper by Glaze (1930) it was shown that the decrement for such an activity does decrease with practice. One of his subjects performed at this task 20 minutes a day for 36 consecutive days, another for 32 days, and a third every other day for 23 days. In the case of all three subjects the decrement was much more pronounced during the first 5 days than it was later. Florence R. Robinson and the writer (1932) have also studied this matter. In our experiment 10 subjects each wrote *ababab*, etc., 20 minutes a day, 5 days a week, for 3 weeks. In Figure 23 we have plotted practice curves for the first, tenth, and twentieth minutes of work. The decrement on any given day

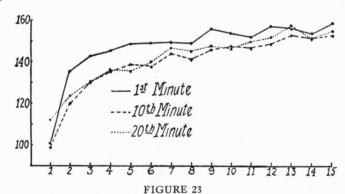

FIGURE 23

PRACTICE CURVES FOR THE FIRST, TENTH, AND TWENTIETH MINUTES OF WORK IN TERMS OF SPEED OF WRITING

(From E. S. Robinson and F. R. Robinson's "Practice and the Work Decrement," *Amer. J. Psychol.*, 1932.)

is equal to the distance at that day between the curve for the first minute and those for the tenth and twentieth minutes. The greatest decrement is in the early days of experimentation, after which the curves converge. An exception occurs in the case of the first day, but that can readily be explained as due to the fact that practice was at that time causing such a rapid increase in efficiency that the decrement which might otherwise have appeared during the first day was largely obscured.

Principle 5: The work decrement of a given S-R connection is relative to the qualitative integrity of the S throughout the work period during which the decrement develops. In the first two principles the assumption was made that we were dealing with simple *S-R* connections or connections whose complicating features are functionally insignificant. In the third principle, with its reference to the rôle of competition, we assumed that a given *S* might actually be connected with a number of *R*'s. In this fifth principle we assume that *S* is not, or at least need not be, identical throughout the period represented by a single work curve. It is generally acknowledged that, during practically all work of the intact and integrated organism, the work itself produces qualitative changes in the stimulational circumstances under which the work is done and that such changes may be important factors in decrement. Perhaps the most obvious example is that of heavy muscular work, such as ergography. Kinaesthetic stimulation begins to change in character in the earliest stages of the work period.

The influence of changing conditions of stimulation is, of course, frequently in the direction of increasing the decrement. This is likely to be true where the new elements among the operative stimuli act to arouse pain. It will be remembered from our earlier discussion that Thorndike has emphasized occurrences of this type to the point of claiming that they are the chief causal factors in the work decrement. While we need not go to such extremes, it is certainly true that the introduction of such a factor as sensory pain can and often does accelerate the appearance of a decrement.

This fifth principle is not quite so simple, however, as its superficial examination might indicate. There is reason to believe that such alterations in stimulation as the work itself produces may actually operate to postpone or to diminish decrement. Evidence is available that the sensory processes accompanying tiredness may have such a facilitative effect that decrements which we should naturally expect fail to appear. To put the matter very simply, the subject seems to realize that he must step up his effort in proportion to the discomforts present in the work.

Although it is not to be deduced from the third or fourth principles, the detailed operation of the fifth may reveal the simultaneous and closely related operation of the former two. The alteration of the *S* which is produced by continuous work may influence the efficiency of action because:

1. The new condition of stimulation may mean the addition of some competing responses and the elimination of others, or,

2. The new condition of stimulation may mean a change in the strength

of the connection between stimulation and the desired response. For example, the tendency to lift a weight upon the signal of a metronome might be weaker if the total stimulational situation were such as to introduce muscular pain.

Principle 6: The work decrement of a given S-R connection is relative to the quantitative constancy of the S throughout the work period during which the decrement develops. The continuous operation of an S-R connection may produce a decrement of a certain magnitude so long as that S remains at the same intensity. But the decrement may be diminished or augmented if there is an alteration in the intensity of S. It is possible to conceive of such an alteration in intensity as merely a special case under the wider, qualitative, fifth principle. Nevertheless, there is an element of safety in the formulation of separate qualitative and quantitative principles. The sixth principle is presumably related to the third and fourth principles as is the fifth. (See 1 and 2 above.)

Such experimental acquaintance as we have with the fifth and sixth principles comes largely from the fact that, although we seek to keep stimulational conditions constant during investigations of work, we know that they do not actually remain constant, and, especially from the subject's reports, we know some of the changes that take place. But we have few instances in which stimulational conditions have been purposely changed in order that the effect of such changes upon decrement could be measured. Crawley (1926) found that subjects who know how well they are performing on the ergograph will do more work, i.e., will be more resistant to decrement, than subjects who are not aware of the level of their performance. Yochelson (1930) found that the presence or absence of an audience influences the ergographic worker in similar fashion. Both investigators found that such resistance is at the expense of prompt recuperation after the work period. Studies of this type need to be extended. It should be profitable also to study the influence upon decrement of systematic and well-defined changes in the stimulational conditions of work. In the case of continuous letter-naming or color-naming it would be easy during the progress of the work to alter the simple physical characteristics of the stimuli in an attempt to retard or to hasten the appearance of the decrement.

Principle 7: The work decrement of a given S-R connection is relative to the decrements that have developed in other S-R connections. This principle is an expression of the well-established fact that there may be transfer of decrement from one connection to an essentially different one. It is also well established that, if the decrement in one connection is profound enough, the transfer will be very wide. In extreme cases we have general exhaustion.

Concerning the more specific determiners of transfer of decrement we are still largely in ignorance. We do have, it is true, the theory that the transfer of "fatigue" depends upon the presence of common elements in otherwise different functions. But this theory has a discouraging circularity since the final test of the presence of common elements in two activities seems to hinge upon whether and to what extent there is a transfer of decrement between them. Another theory of transfer of decrement, which is still taken seriously by some writers, holds that the difficulty of the first task rather than its qualitative nature is responsible for such decremental influence as it may have upon the subsequent task. At first glance this theory would seem to be susceptible to experimental investigation. But the haziness of the conception "difficult" renders it actually elusive. Perhaps supporters of such a theory, if pressed, would be forced to admit that the only sure criterion of difficulty in their sense is the amount of transfer of decrement from the activity under question to other activities. In such an event this theory would become as tautological as the common-element theory. But, in spite of all of these ambiguities, the fact of transfer of decrement still remains a fact and more precise knowledge about it awaits only a sharper conception of the problem. Most experimental studies of transfer of decrement have been so set up that, no matter what the results, they could not be understood. So long as we study and argue about the influence of basketball practice upon multiplication or of multiplication upon translating German, we shall have to be content with findings which may confirm the principle of transfer (which no longer needs confirming) but which add practically nothing to our systematic knowledge about it.

Real progress on this general problem has recently been made by Bills and McTeer (1932). Without accepting the common-element theory as a single principle underlying all transfer, they have taken the theory as setting a definite empirical problem. If two tasks are so made up that something which they may have in common can be experimentally controlled, will there then be any relationship between amount in common and amount of transfer of work decrement? These investigators utilized the method of writing alphabetical sequences. The conditions of experimentation were as follows:

		Constant task	Alternate task
Condition I	—*All* elements in common	—Write *abcabc*, etc.	Write *abcabc*, etc.
Condition II	—*Two* elements in common	—Write *abcabc*, etc.	Write *abdabd*, etc.
Condition III	—*One* element in common	—Write *abcabc*, etc.	Write *afeafe*, etc.
Condition IV	—No element in common	—Write *abcabc*, etc.	Write *defdef*, etc.
Condition V	—Control condition	—Write *abcabc*, etc.	Rest

Instead of having the subject work for a long period at the constant task and then for a long period at the alternate task, the two tasks were alternated every minute for 16 minutes. Twenty graduate students in psychology went through all five of the conditions five separate times.

The results were treated in two ways. In one case there was computed the total amount of the constant or standard work done under each of the experimental conditions. In the other case work curves were constructed for the alternate minutes of the standard task under each of the experimental conditions. In Table 5 are presented results obtained by the first method.

TABLE 5
TOTAL *abc* UNITS WRITTEN

Common elements	All	Two	One	None	Rest
Cycle I	6508	7280	7516	7934	8138
Cycle II	8304	8360	8552	8782	8855
Cycle III	8922	9115	9142	9110	9275
Average	7911	8252	8403	8609	8756

It is clear that the more elements there are common to constant and alternate task the more deleterious is the influence of the latter on the former. What we actually have here is not the transfer from one performance of one task to one performance of another but an average transfer from many performances of the alternate task to many performances of the standard *abc* task. There is no reason, however, to question the results on that account. What holds good in this experiment would probably hold good also if single alternations were made of long unbroken periods of two tasks.

Results from the second method of calculation appear in Table 6. The actual work curves are not given, but their decrements are given in terms of the drop in efficiency from the first four performances at the constant *abc* task to the last four performances of that task.

TABLE 6
RELATION OF LAST FOUR MINUTES OF *abc* TO FIRST FOUR MINUTES OF SAME TASK—
Minus MEANS DECREMENT, *Plus* MEANS INCREMENT

Common elements	All	Two	One	None	Rest
Cycle I	—176	— 66	—31	+23	+75
Cycle II	—152	—140	—61	—39	+40
Cycle III	—225	—100	—65	—55	+75
Average	—185	—102	—52	—24	+63

Again the results are clear. There is a direct and consistent relation between the number of elements common to the two tasks and the amount of decrement transferred from the variable to the standard.

One might accept this experiment of Bills and McTeer as a proof of the general theory that transfer of decrement is caused by the involvement in the second task of part-activities which had already undergone a decrement in the first. On the other hand, one might accept the results as demonstration of the fact that, among other things, decrement transfer is a function of the particular type of partial identity which was here under experimental control. This would leave the question quite open as to whether there are not other factors than partial identity which influence transfer of decrement. It would also leave open the question as to whether there are not other kinds of partial identity which influence transfer of decrement. Whereas a conventional form of the common-element theory assumes that all types of partial identity reduce to number-of-neurons-in-common, it is not at all necessary to make this assumption and it is safer not to do so. As far as the controllable features of the situation are concerned, there are various respects in which two activities can be partially identical, and the scientifically profitable program should be that of instituting just such controlled variations as Bills and McTeer have done in order to discover which of the possible varieties of partial identity are effective. For example, it would be possible in the letter-naming experiment to alter the letters with respect to color, size, and arrangement as well as with respect to the letters themselves.

While we have rejected the general common-element theory in favor of a program of investigating the actual influence of the several varieties of partial identity, it is clear that the older theory suggested the empirical program. It is likewise possible that a valuable experimental cue may be secured from the "difficulty" theory. It seems probable that the amount of decrement transfer is under certain circumstances related to the energy transformation involved in the first task. This is certainly the case where that first task has been carried on to a point approaching the actual exhaustion of the organism. It would seem to us that the needed experiment is one in which a task involving greater oxygen consumption shows a greater decrement transfer to a standard task than that obtained from the earlier performance of that standard task itself. This would demonstrate that a general factor like oxygen consumption *may* be more important than a specific factor such as letters-in-common. Of course there should be an equal interest in positive findings in regard to any other general factor in decrement transfer. We might, for example, expect severe sensory pain sometimes to have such a general influence.

WARMING-UP

In addition to the decrement, there are three other features that are frequently mentioned as characterizing the curve of continuous work. One of these is *initial spurt,* which is simply a high level of efficiency at the beginning of the work from which there is an almost immediate drop. It seems to us, however, that this is a misnomer. What we need to explain in curves having this feature is not so much the early high point, or spurt, as the sharp initial drop. And, if we seek to explain the latter, we shall have simply a case of early decrement which in all probability will be best interpreted in terms of such principles of decrement as have been discussed above. Another of these features of the work curve is *end-spurt,* a higher level of efficiency attained toward the end of the work period. Since there is nothing absolute about when such a period shall end, we should expect to find end-spurt only in those cases in which the subject knows when the end is coming. And in such a case, the end-spurt is simply to be classed as an effect of incentive. We do, as a matter of fact, find a spurt in just such cases and, while it is interesting, it does not have the general significance of the decrement. A third more important and interesting feature of the work curve is *warming-up.*

The warming-up effect is usually mentioned in discussions of the work curve, but little or nothing is said about the conditions that determine its appearance. Thorndike (1914) seems to feel that the importance of this characteristic of the work curve has been exaggerated, and that the evidence for it is mostly indirect. He points out that in most of the data bearing upon this subject it is almost impossible to separate warming-up (by definition a very temporary effect) from "the more permanent improvement that comes from the exercise of the function in general" that would ordinarily be called the *practice effect*. Watson (1919) states that experimental confirmation of the warming-up effect is not at hand either for vocal or manual functions. He does say, however, that "in baseball, track and crew work a process of limbering up or preliminary practice is universally indulged in and is apparently necessary."

We believe that something more definite can be said about warming-up, at least in so far as the speed curve is concerned. This feature of the work curve represents a rise in efficiency which is steeper and more temporary than the rise that can be seen in successive daily performances. Now it has frequently been pointed out that there is another feature of the work curve, the decrement or "fatigue" effect, which by its very nature tends to obscure any such opposite effect as warming-up. Since these two effects are opposite, it would be desirable to obtain controllable conditions that would give relative favor to one or the other. This, we believe, can be done. We believe it can be demonstrated that warming-up may fail to appear as a feature of the work curve simply because the work is highly continuous, a condition which gives maximum advantage to the decrement, and that warming-up can be made apparent by introducing a degree of discontinuity into the work.

The first evidence is from a well-known study of tapping by Wells (1908). Five 30-second periods of tapping were separated from each other by intervals of 2½ minutes. Considering the total number of taps made by the right hand in the successive 30-second periods, there is a consistent improvement or warming-up effect. But if we consider the 6 successive 5-second periods within each 30-second period of continuous tapping, we find the usual decrement in efficiency. In other words, the curve of work possessing a certain discontinuity (in this case where there is a 2½-minute rest every 30 seconds) may show a definite warming-up effect, while the curve for more continuous work (in this case 30 seconds of continuous tapping) shows a decrement. It is possible, from Wells' results, to estimate the amount of improvement going on from day to day, and the evidence is clear that this warming-up effect is much greater than "the more permanent improvement which comes from the exercise of the function in general."

Under different detailed conditions Heron and the present writer (1924) have decisively confirmed Wells's findings. We also studied the question in respect to the rapid backward recitation of the alphabet by five practiced subjects. Four tests were made for each subject under each of three conditions, as follows:

Condition   I—Recite continuously for 20 minutes
Condition   II—Recite for 30 seconds, rest 15 seconds, recite 30 sec-
    onds, rest 15 seconds, etc., until actual recitation totals 20
    minutes
Condition III—Like II except that rests were 30 seconds

A sharp rise or warming-up effect, more marked than subsequent irregularities, was found in all of the curves for two subjects, in the
Condition-III curve for one subject, and in the Condition-II and Condition-III curves for two subjects. These rises which we accepted as
instances of warming-up were not only greater than the chance irregularities
of the curves, but were also much greater than any general practice improvement could have been. These results, like those from the tapping
experiment, tend to show that warming-up is somewhat more likely to
occur where the work is not so continuous as greatly to favor the decrement. Those two subjects who showed warming-up even in the condition
of most continuous work did not show any of the usual decrement under
that condition, which again emphasizes the antagonistic characteristics
of the decrement and warming-up effects. We are presenting below
the work curves for Subject 2 and those for Subject 4.

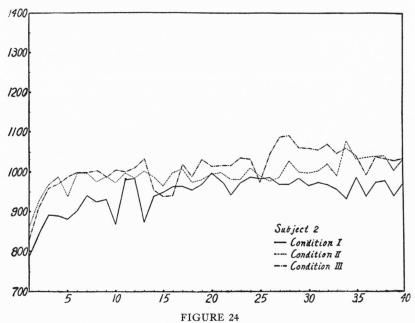

FIGURE 24

Horizontal axis represents the successive 30-second periods making up the total
20 minutes of recitation. Vertical axis represents the sums of the letters recited
during each of the 30-second periods for four complete recitations.

(From E. S. Robinson and W. T. Heron's "The Warming-Up Effect," *J. Exper.
Psychol.*, 1924.)

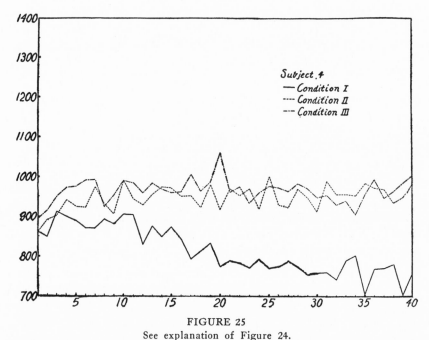

FIGURE 25
See explanation of Figure 24.
(From E. S. Robinson and W. T. Heron's "The Warming-Up Effect," *J. Exper.*
Psychol., 1924.)

The conclusion to be drawn from the above results is that the warming-up effect is certainly more than a statistical accident. We have also a clue as to why this effect does not appear more often in laboratory work curves. Further studies are needed to bring out other conditions favoring the occurrence of this phenomenon.

In the isolated muscle there is a preliminary augmentation of contrac-‘ tions, called the *treppe,* which reminds one of the warming-up effect in the work curves of such integrated performances as those we have been discussing. It is an interesting question whether all warming-up rests upon the same fundamental basis as the treppe. In our judgment this is hardly the case. The chemical basis of treppe seems to be understood. According to Lee (1907), this phenomenon is caused by small concentrations of that same lactic acid which in larger concentrations acts as a depressant and consequently as a factor in the work decrement. In such a muscular task as tapping, it is quite possible that warming-up, when present, is due partly to the presence of some optimal concentration of lactic acid. Recently, however, Heron (1928) has shown the presence of warming-up in the learning of lists of nonsense syllables. There are, of course, in such a task so many possible mechanisms by means of which a temporarily improved set for the task could be obtained that it does not seem safe to ascribe this improvement to the presence of lactic acid. Rather it would seem reasonable to entertain the idea that we are here dealing with short-lived habits, formed during the experimental sitting and lost before the next sitting. These might consist largely of a mental attitude or they might involve also the attainment of favorable muscular posture.

General Exhaustion

If we could combine all of the activities of living into a single general work curve, the equivalent of the decrement would be exhaustion affecting the individual's total efficiency. The outstanding fact about such exhaustion is its rarity. The regime of customary life protects against it. Furthermore, the prompt decrements that develop in specialized activities, if they are carried on too continuously, operate to prevent general exhaustion. Indeed, so rare is this highly generalized decrement that it is ordinarily thought of, when it does occur, as pathological. When such a condition is present, it almost never arises from "overwork" alone; at its basis there are likely to be grave somatic affections. Among these latter are the puerperal state, infectious disease, profuse hemorrhages, and inanition. The state of exhaustion itself emphasizes the complex integrative character of normal behavior. Manic tendencies, delusions, hallucinations, and general disorganization frequently precede stupor and coma.

The major explanations of *true exhaustion psychoses* introduce conceptions that we met in our consideration of more specialized decrement. One of these holds that there is a depletion of the energy resources of the organism, particularly of those involved in cerebral activity. The second stresses the possibility of an accumulation of fatigue products that act as intoxicating agents.

Psychiatrists distinguish between those breakdowns that have their basis in the fundamental metabolic processes and those that represent disorganization at a more complicated level. The former are the *exhaustion psychoses;* the latter are the psychoneuroses or neuroses grouped under *neurasthenia.* But the line between these two varieties of breakdown is not sharp. The official classification of the American Psychiatric Association says of the neurasthenic type of psychoneuroses (see Rosanoff *et al.,* 1927, p. 637) :

> This should designate the fatigue neuroses in which physical as well as mental causes evidently figure; characterized essentially by mental and motor fatigability and irritability; also various hyperaethesias, paraesthesias, hypochrondriasis and varying degrees of depression.

What we seem to have is a series of conditions running all the way from *true physiological exhaustion* to states of psychological frustration uncomplicated by any detectable somatic disorder. Between these two extremes, and this is where most actual cases lie, we have a mixture of somatic disorder and psychological maladjustment. Frequently it is difficult to say which side of the picture is fundamental. One of the frequent causes of psychological frustration is the malaise, weakness, and inadequacy incident upon somatic disturbances, but it is also true that an organism struggling with some emotional conflict is subject to bodily disturbance.   Thus we have the possibility of the vicious circle that so frequently characterizes neurasthenia.

In those general breakdowns that are relatively free of known somatic basis there is much to remind us of the disorganization that occurs as a result of the overly continuous operation of a special function involving a nice balance between competing factors.   The breakdown that comes in the case of the coordinated eye movements studied by Dodge (1917) or in the alternate finger movements of our investigation (Robinson and Bills, 1926) is a breakdown in balance, and it comes not because of excess demands upon energy supplies or because of too great concentration of fatigue products.   It comes rather because of the existence of undesired, competing responses that are of nearly equal strength with those responses that are desired.   As a result, an otherwise insignificant alteration in the strength of the desired responses may create a psychological chaos.   So in the case of the neurasthenic.   The individual may be living a life well adjusted to his environment, but this favorable adjustment may be prevailing by an exceedingly narrow margin.   Under the surface there may be emotional tendencies temporarily repressed which would cause havoc if the prevailing behavior of the individual were slightly weakened.

An interesting question arises as to what types of impulses or tendencies are likely to offer such strong competition with effective behavior as to threaten its maintenance.   The Freudians naturally emphasize sexual factors, and there can be no serious argument over the importance of the sexual undercurrent in present-day living.   As Malinowski (1927) has suggested, this may be as much an accident of our particular culture as it is an essential characteristic of our biological make-up, but, as life is now being lived by civilized people, repressed sexual forces are certainly competing with the even course of adjusted integrations.   That there are other competing elements constantly threatening the general level of efficiency there can be no doubt.   Of these, balked desires for recognition in one form or another are perhaps the most important.

In the array of breakdowns to which the integrated organism is subject, there is another distinction that is worth noting.   The disorganization and prostration of severe neurasthenia may not be susceptible to any conscious control on the part of the sufferer.   On the other hand, there are certainly many instances of *hysteroneurasthenia* in which the simulated exhaustion, by the use of adequate incentive, can be brought within conscious control.   We have parallels of such facts in the far simpler situation of the ergographic experiment.   When, after continuous work, a complete decrement occurs, the subject feels "completely exhausted."   Introduce an audience or some other incentive and he will suddenly realize that he was not exhausted at all, but that he had simply reached a point where he preferred to be exhausted.   The line, of course, is not sharp between exhaustion with conscious preference for that state and exhaustion which, while it is not actually a state of incapacity, seems definitely to be that to the subject's own observation.

The fundamental protection against true exhaustion and near exhaustion is sleep. The largest body of experimental researches on the course and consequences of exhaustion have, therefore, dealt with enforced wakefulness. The more recent literature has been fully and competently reviewed by Kleitman (1929) and by Johnson, Swan, and Weigand (1926).

Animals have been kept awake until complete collapse or death. Marie de Manaceïne (1897) found that there were definite pathological changes in the cerebral tissues of puppies that had been kept awake for from 96 to 100 hours. She concluded that conscious animals break down more quickly under enforced insomnia than under starvation. In starvation the brain seems to maintain something like its normal weight and constitution after other tissues have shown considerable wasting. In prolonged wakefulness, on the other hand, the brain shows early deterioration. More recently Piéron (1913) studied the central nervous systems of dogs kept awake for long periods. He found changes in the frontal areas of the cerebral cortex, but none in the occipital cortex, cerebellum, medulla, or spinal cord. Bast and his collaborators (1927) found changes even in the spinal cords of rabbits that had been kept awake in revolving cages for 8 to 31 days.

In 1896 Patrick and Gilbert reported an investigation of the effects of enforced insomnia on human subjects. Since that time there have been many studies of this problem. Although there have been exceptional cases here and there, it has been an outstanding finding that even difficult psychological work such as mental multiplication is very resistant to the influence of loss of sleep. For example, Hermann and the writer (1922) found no change in ability to do mental 2-place by 2-place multiplications after from 60 to 65 hours without sleep. Herz (1923) obtained similar results in regard to the effect of an 80-hour insomnia upon reaction-time and ability to repeat numbers. Richardson-Robinson and the writer (1922) have suggested that these results have been due to the fact that the subject when put in a test situation will exert effort to make up for any lack of fitness. Statistical results from estimates of tiredness and effort on the part of subjects would seem to bear out this suggestion. Some of the exceptions to the above findings are interesting. Smith (1915-17) found that a short abstinence from sleep had a stimulating effect upon the subject. This is not out of line with what we know of "fatigue" in general, though it has not been found by other investigators. Lee and Kleitman (1923) found that a prolonged and monotonous test (going through the customary color-naming test 12 times in succession) detects effects of sleeplessness not brought out by the usual short and varied performances for which the subject can, apparently, pull himself together and in some way compensate by extra effort for his depleted psychological resources. Most reflexes were found unaffected by Lee and Kleitman, though they found a pronounced impairment of postural control, a result later confirmed by Laslett (1928).

It is when the subject is not set for a test performance that the disintegrative effects of prolonged sleeplessness are most apparent. Slips of speech, time distortions, and even hallucinations have been observed. Subjects have sometimes reported dazed feelings similar to mild intoxication. As the experiment proceeds it becomes increasingly difficult to keep the subjects awake. Kleitman (1929) found it necessary to watch his subjects continually. If not watched they would fall asleep. When awakened they sometimes showed considerable irritation and denied that they had been asleep.

There is fairly general agreement that the period of sleep following prolonged wakefulness is not correspondingly long. As a rule 8 to 10 hours is sufficient to restore the subject's feeling of well-being. This may be due to the unusual depth of sleep following prolonged insomnia. Patrick and Gilbert found that, under these circumstances, an electric shock which would ordinarily bring forth a cry of pain would fail to arouse the sleeper.

OTHER FUNDAMENTAL FACTORS IN EFFICIENCY

For the psychologist there are two basic types of variation in efficiency— that which is called *learning* or *practice effect* and that which is called *fatigue* or *work decrement*. The former of these is treated in another chapter of this book. The latter we have considered in the preceding pages. We shall now turn our attention to some additional factors in efficiency, which, though they are not as general in implications as are practice effects and the work decrement, are nevertheless more than mere incidents of behavior.

The first group of conditions with which we shall deal are brought out by the classical method of simple reaction-time. The history of this method is so widely known and so well described (Johnson, 1923, and Ladd and Woodworth, 1911) that we shall not attempt to deal with it here. It is sufficient if we define *simple reaction* as a single response of a definite muscle group (usually the hand or finger) to a simple, unequivocal stimulus. Although the qualitative aspects of such movements may be studied, the directions ordinarily give the subject a set merely for speed and ordinarily speed is the criterion of efficiency.

The speed of the simple reaction varies with the sense stimulated. Ladd and Woodworth (1911) have gathered together in the following table the measurements of a number of the earlier students of this question. These results are in essential agreement with later findings.

TABLE 7

Observer	Optical stimulus	Acoustic stimulus	Touch stimulus
Hirsch	0.200 secs.	0.149	0.182 (hand)
Hankel	0.225	0.151	0.155
Donders	0.188	0.180	0.154 (neck)
Von Wittich	0.194	0.182	0.130 (forehead)
Wundt	0.175	0.128	0.188
Exner	0.1506	0.136	0.1276 (hand)
Auerbach	0.191	0.122	0.146
Von Kries	0.193	0.120	0.117

There is no clear-cut, consistent difference between reactions to touch and those to sound, but the visual reactions are definitely slowest. From a teleological point of view this is comprehensible. The visual reactions are rarely in direct relation to the impinging light, but are rather in relation to a distant object from which the light emanates or is reflected. While the ear is also a distance receptor, the action of sound upon that organ is, physically, more akin to the mechanical impact arousing the cutaneous receptors. And where reaction is to mechanical impact, the need for high speed is obvious. It can also be pointed out that touch is, from an evolutionary point of view, the most primitive of these three senses. In regard to the direct physical basis of the differences, it has been suggested that if equally intense stimuli were employed the reaction-times of the senses would be the same. Another suggestion is that visual reaction-time is longer because of the greater number of synapses crossed by the afferent optic impulse. Ladd and Woodworth, however, conclude, after a consideration of such explanations, that the differences are most likely due to differences in the latent time or inertia of the different sense-organs (p. 479).

The part of the sense-organ stimulated also influences reaction-time. Taking foveal reaction-time as a norm, Poffenberger (1912) got the following delays by moving the stimulus toward the periphery (Table 8).

TABLE 8

Degrees	Temporal	Nasal
3	4 sigma	4 sigma
10	9	6
30	14	10
45	24	15

This result is in harmony with the fact that the capacity to perceive form is greatest near the fovea, but it is out of accord with the greater sensitivity for faint light of the extra-foveal retina. Apparently, reacting quickly is more closely related neurologically to the process of perception than it is to the mere noting of the presence or absence of stimulation. The factor of habit may also be involved; we are more accustomed to reacting to foveal stimuli. In the case of peripheral stimulation, if we do react, we ordinarily do so first merely by moving the eyes so as to secure foveal stimulation.

In general, simple reaction-time decreases with increasing amounts of stimulation. Illustrative results on this point have been brought together from Froeberg (1907) by Woodworth and Poffenberger (1920, p. 187). Visual stimuli were used which varied in respect to intensity, area, and duration; and sound stimuli were used which varied in intensity.

The results given in Table 9 are, perhaps, more interesting in a negative way than they are positively. While increasing amounts of stimulation are accompanied by decreasing reaction-time, the latter does not decrease in proportion to the former. This fact is another illustration of the large

TABLE 9

Relative intensity of light	100	56	25	16	10	7	3	2	0.7
Reaction-time (sigma)	191	194	197	202	208	210	215	220	226
Area in square mm.	48	24	12	6	3				
Reaction-time (sigma)	179	182	184	188	195				
Duration of light stimulus (sigma)	48	24	12	6	3				
Reaction-time (sigma)	191	194	196	199	201				
Intensity of sound stimulus (height of fall in mm.)	1024	625	324	121	16				
Reaction-time (sigma)	131	134	141	152	192				

degree of internal determination in the reactions of the intact, integrated organism.

Miles (1931) has recently administered a battery of reaction-time tests to a group of 100 unselected adults in order to study the influence of age upon this type of performance.   His subjects ranged from 26 to 87 years old.   For five types of reaction the correlations between time and age are all positive—greater ages going with slower reactions—and the coefficients range from .25 to .55.

> The twelve oldest persons (average age 79 years) in the group of 100 adults reported registered means that were from 20 to 30 per cent slower than the comparable general means for the group as a whole.   However, one fourth of these oldest subjects were as quick or quicker than the average for the total group.

We may now turn to the attitude of the subject toward the reaction. As early as 1888, Lange noticed that the reaction-time was shorter if the subject, prior to the occurrence of the stimulus, fixed his attention upon the coming reaction rather than upon the coming stimulus.   The difference obtained by Lange was marked.   Time for the muscular reaction to sound was 123 sigma, while the *sensorial* reaction to the same stimulus was .227 sigma (see Ladd and Woodworth, 1911, p. 486).   Later investigators have failed to find such a large difference and in a few cases subjects have been found capable of reacting as quickly in the sensorial attitude. Within 10 years after the appearance of Lange's results, a large controversial literature grew up around this point.   But the present conclusions regarding the entire matter are simple.   It is recognized that the reaction-time of most subjects is shorter if, during the preparatory period, the coming movement is actually begun by heightening the tone of the muscles that are to move.   Unless the subject has had long practice, he is more likely to make this preliminary preparation if he is instructed to concentrate upon the coming movement than if told to concentrate upon the coming stimulus.

In the usual simple-reaction experiment the subject is given a ready signal shortly before the presentation of the stimulus.   When this signal occurs the subject goes into a relatively tense and expectant state which is maintained until the reaction is made.   That this preparatory set is effective is shown by the fact that the omission of the ready signal brings about an increase in reaction-time. Wundt got an increase from 76 to 253 sigma when the ready signal was omitted prior to stimulation by a fairly loud noise. In the case of a weaker noise the increase incident upon the omission of the signal was from 175 to 266 sigma (see Ladd and Woodworth, 1911, p. 481). When a ready signal is given, the effectiveness of the preparatory set depends upon its duration. The most favorable duration of this set has been found by Breitweiser (1911) and by Woodrow (1914) to vary from 2 to 4 seconds. Thus it seems to require 2 seconds to enable the individual to gather himself together, while periods longer than 4 seconds are likely to find him letting down.

A wide variety of interesting experiments have been made in which complexities have been introduced into the reaction. The simplest case is that in which either of two stimuli is used, the subject being instructed to react if one of these occurs and not to react if the other occurs. The situation has been further complicated by introducing more than one reaction. For example, the subject may be instructed to react with the right hand to red and with the left hand to green. In a well-known experiment by Merkel (see Ladd and Woodworth, 1911, p. 489) the stimuli consisted of the numerals 1, 2, 3, 4, 5, and I, II, III, IV, V. These were assigned to the ten fingers. The results from ten degrees of complication are given in Table 10.

TABLE 10
From Ladd and Woodworth (p. 489) after Merkel

One movement (simple reaction)	.186 secs.
Two movements, with two stimuli	.276
Three movements, three stimuli	.330
Four movements, four stimuli	.394
Five movements, five stimuli	.445
Six movements, six stimuli	.489
Seven movements, seven stimuli	.526
Eight movements, eight stimuli	.562
Nine movements, nine stimuli	.581
Ten movements, ten stimuli	.588

Another important form of elaboration of the reaction experiment is that found in the study of association times. The subject may be presented with German words to which he must respond with the English equivalent or he may be given words to which he must respond with the first word that occurs to him (free association).

In the early days of the reaction experiment, it was felt that the time of various cerebral processes, such as that for simple sensory discrimination, could be calculated by subtracting from the time for a simple reaction that for a discrimination or choice or association. This *subtraction* method was soon abandoned, however, because it was realized that the more complex experiments deal with something other than a summation of simpler processes. The fact still remains that, by means of the several degrees of complexity represented by the reaction experiments, we can sample the operations of several levels of neuromuscular elaboration.

Lanier (1931) has recently resumed the attack on this general problem. A wide variety of reactions was studied and the results handled in terms of statistical correlation. Among other results he found the intercorrelation among simple reactions to be very high (0.866). Discrimination times also had high intercorrelations between themselves, and the same was true of association times. Simple reactions and discrimination re actions showed a correlation of 0.44, but there was no correlation between associative reactions and the other groups. Low and unreliable correlations were found among simple reaction-time (cortical level), lid reflex time (cerebrospinal reflex), and psychogalvanic reaction-time (autonomic reflex). There was no correlation between any of these last three variables and Army Alpha scores.

We are simply not in a position to mark off the internal mechanisms of reaction by an inspection of the objective conditions. We may be sure that the simple auditory reaction to a tone is neurologically simpler than a reaction of right hand to 250 and of left hand to 260 vibrations, but we cannot say how much simpler.

FACILITATION AND DISTRACTION

Because each individual is equipped with a multiplicity of receptors and because the internal and external environment is constantly providing new stimuli, there are always present at the time of any given reaction many stimuli that are not the essential cues for that reaction. Popular thought has long recognized that stimuli which are not essential cues for a reaction may actually bring about, through the arousal of conflicting attitudes or reactions, a decrease in efficiency. Indeed, the popular disposition has been to assume that all stimuli not actually required to set off an act are at least potential distractors. If their intensity is insufficient they may have no noticeably deleterious influence, but if it is sufficient the distractive effect will be marked. When an individual is found who can work better in the presence of irrelevant but customary noises, there is a certain tendency to regard him simply as eccentric.

But scientific men have realized for many years that extraneous, or unessential, stimuli can facilitate a given reaction as well as interfere with it. Mitchell and Lewis, in 1886, observed that the knee-jerk could be augmented by visual stimulation or by painful stimulation of the skin, when that stimulation was followed by a voluntary muscular reaction. They also noted that the voluntary reaction, in order to reinforce the knee-jerk, must precede the tap on the knee (the adequate stimulus for the knee-jerk). This latter observation suggested to Bowditch and Warren (1890) the desirability of making a definite, quantitative study of the influence of various time relations between the reinforcing act or stimulus and the specific stimulation of the patellar tendon. The reinforcing agency most often used in their experiments was the clenching of the right hand in response to a bell. In Figure 26 we have the facilitation or distraction (inhibition) in its relationship to the interval between

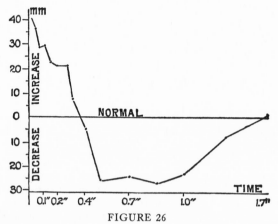

FIGURE 26

SHOWING IN MILLIMETERS THE AMOUNT BY WHICH THE "REINFORCED" KNEE-KICK
VARIED FROM THE NORMAL, THE LEVEL OF WHICH IS REPRESENTED BY
THE HORIZONTAL LINE AT 0, "NORMAL"

The time intervals elapsing between the clenching of the hands (which constituted the reinforcement) and the tap on the tendon are marked below. The
reinforcement is greatest when the two events are nearly simultaneous. At an
interval of 0.4 second it amounts to nothing; during the next 0.6 second the height
of the kick is actually diminished, while after an interval of 1 second the
negative reinforcement tends to disappear; and when 1.7 seconds is allowed to
elapse the height of the kick ceases to be affected by the clenching of the hands—
Bowditch and Warren.

(From W. H. Howell's *A Textbook of Physiology*, 11th ed., 1930, by permission
of the publishers, W. B. Saunders Co., Philadelphia.)

the clenching of the hand and the tap on the knee. The chief importance
of this curve is its illustration of the fact that the same extraneous stimulus
may have either a facilitating or distracting effect according to its temporal
relation to the normal stimulus for the reaction in question. In this case
it would seem that reinforcement is greatest where there is a degree of
actual overlapping of the two muscular acts, while distraction or inhibition is present if the normal stimulus occurs just after the completion of
the reaction to the extraneous stimulus. It is probable that this particular distractive effect is a refractory-phase phenomenon. Fearing
(1931) has raised the interesting question as to exactly what phase of
the total activity of clenching the hand to the bell was the reinforcing
factor in the Bowditch and Warren experiment. Inasmuch as a large
proportion of the knee-jerk probably occurred before the hand-clenching,
though of course after the bell stimulus, Fearing believes it unwarranted
to assume that such augmentation as occurred was due to the muscular
act of clenching the hand. He feels it more reasonable to assume that the
facilitation was effected by some factor prior to the act, such as the accompaniments of what is usually called *attention*. This is not impossible.
There is evidence that the application of a stimulus arousing no definite

response can function as a facilitator, and this suggests that the early stages of a muscular act, before the act has emerged into recordable form, may also function as a facilitator. A recent investigation relevant to this discussion is that of Peak (1931). Her subjects were presented with a sound stimulus adequate to instigate an involuntary wink. The establishment of a set to wink voluntarily or to move a finger introduced a certain irregularity into the reflex wink and also tended to increase its amplitude. But such considerations certainly do not mean that in general or on the average the preparatory phases of action have a stronger facilitative influence than have acts which have reached the overt form of muscular movement.

Results in substantial agreement with those of Bowditch and Warren have been obtained by Yerkes (1904, 1905), using the frog as subject. His experimental arrangement permitted him to measure the amplitude of a reflex kick made by the frog when it was struck on the head back of and between the ears by a rubber cone. The extraneous stimulus was produced by a bell or a sound hammer. Maximum augmentation occurred when the stimuli were coincident or close together in time. In one experiment the condition for inhibition was that in which a momentary auditory stimulus preceded the tactual by from 45 seconds to slightly less than 90 seconds. Here again we have an inhibition which suggests the refractory-phase phenomenon. In another experiment Yerkes studied as response the frog's jumping from an electrified grill. In this case reaction-time was measured. One of the extraneous stimuli used was the sight of a vibrating disk. This stimulus produced facilitation when introduced 0.1 second prior to the shock and inhibition when introduced 0.5 second prior to the shock.

The classic refractory-phase experiment is itself a demonstration of certain of the conditions of facilitation-distraction. According to Zwaardemaker and Lans (1900) a visual stimulus adequate to arouse a reflex wink will fail to arouse that reflex if it is preceded, 250 sigma to 500 sigma before, by an identical visual stimulus. Dodge (1913) used pairs of sound stimuli adequate for the same reflex. He found no absolute inhibition of response to the repeated stimulus but rather a diminution in the response to the second stimulus for as long as a 3-second interval.

Dodge (1931) has raised the interesting question as to whether inhibiting stimuli need to be of sufficient strength to arouse a conscious or overt muscular response. Upon the basis of experimental studies of the knee-jerk, the lid reflex, the perception of rotation, and the perception of color, he finds support for "the physiological presumption that faint stimuli are in the main inhibiting rather than stimulating in human reaction, and that inhibition may be produced without preliminary reactions" (p. 82). Whether the first of these propositions will be upheld by further experimentation is not so important as the further establishment of the fact that stimuli unessential or extraneous to the usual operation of a response may have a decided effect upon that response even though they are too weak to bring about any observable conscious or muscular results.

Hilgard (1931) has recently studied the reflex response of the eyelid to two unlike stimuli—sound and light:

> A faint stimulus, itself eliciting only minimal reflex responses, may greatly exaggerate or depress the responses to a more adequate stimulus which follows it. This is demonstrated in certain experiments on the human eyelid reflex, in which a faint light preceded a loud sound. The light alone evoked winking responses averaging 4 mm in extent, while the sound evoked winking responses averaging 20 mm. When the light preceded the sound by appropriate intervals (of from 0 to .050 sec.) the response to the sound was increased to a maximum average extent of 31 mm, an increase of 11 mm above the normal. This increase of 11 mm is due to the prior occurrence of a light which alone evoked a response of but 4 mm. On the other hand, the response to sound may be greatly decreased in extent if the light precedes the sound by a slightly lengthened time interval (interval of .075 sec. or greater). This inhibitory effect is even more pronounced than the reinforcement just described. The reaction to sound may fall as low as 1 mm in extent from the normal of 20 mm, a drop of 19 mm.

The facilitation-inhibition effects of extraneous stimuli have also been investigated for the simple voluntary reaction. In 1893 Bliss reported that reaction-time was shortened when the sound stimulus was presented to both ears instead of to one. More recently Poffenberger (1927; see also Woodworth and Poffenberger, 1920) has shown that the presentation of a light stimulus to both eyes gives a shorter reaction-time than monocular presentation. Results for three subjects are shown in Table 11.

TABLE 11

Subject	One eye	Two eyes
T	201 sigma	185 sigma
P	175	160
A	191	178

Results of great interest have been obtained where there has been simultaneous presentation of stimuli to different senses. Todd (1912), for example, employed light, sound, and electric shock. Reaction-times were obtained for these individually and in various combinations. It is not strange that the presentation of sound with light should have given a faster reaction than light alone, because light normally gives a slow reaction and the faster reaction to sound might simply mean that the subject was reacting to the sound instead of to the light. But light and sound in combination give a faster reaction than sound alone, which means that a stimulus the reaction to which is normally slow can act to quicken a normally fast reaction. The shortest reaction-times obtained by Todd were those to light, sound, and shock combined. Thus, whether a stimulus acts as facilitator or distractor does not seem to depend upon whether the simple reaction-time to that stimulus alone is slower or faster than the stimulus to which it is added.

Jenkins (1926) has shown that the introduction of quiet into a situation in which there has been a continuous noise is capable of acting facilitatively, though, under the conditions of his experiment, the onset of quiet was not as strong a facilitator as the onset of noise. That the onset of quiet may occasionally act as a distractor is, of course, well known from common experience. Some people find it difficult at first to go to sleep in the country. This positive functional value of the withdrawal of physical energy is another excellent illustration of the fundamental principle that the organism tends to respond to *changes in stimulation* rather than to the mere presence of stimuli.

In an experiment using a light stimulus preceded at varying intervals by electric shock, Todd obtained results somewhat like those of Bowditch and Warren for the knee-jerk. When the shock preceded the light by 45 or 90 sigma, there was a normal reaction-time. When the two were separated by 180 sigma there was a definite retardation of the reaction to light. There was slight evidence that with an interval of 360 sigma the inhibitory influence of the shock began to wane.

While such experiments as those we have been describing offer excellent opportunities for studying some of the fundamental factors in the facilitation-distraction situation, it is clear that in practical life the majority of the extraneous stimuli that have an important effect upon behavior are stimuli of considerable physical complexity to which we react emotionally or intellectually. For this reason it has been desirable to conduct experiments with situations somewhat more complicated and somewhat more difficult to define than those involving simple combinations of relatively neutral stimuli.

In an investigation reported by Burtt and Tuttle (1925) the subject was presented with pleasant, unpleasant, and indifferent words to each of which he gave a free-association response. The knee-jerk was depressed by an average amount of 16 per cent by the association processes involving unpleasant words. There was a slight but less regular depression also in the case of the pleasant words. Correlations were calculated between association reaction-time and the extent of the reflex. The values were not high, but there was some tendency toward greater reflex depression for those words having the longer reaction-times. The importance of this experiment is mainly its demonstration that an intellectual process can have a decided influence upon such a reflex as the knee-jerk. The fact that the influence was in this case depressive is not so important. With different time relations between the word stimuli and the stimulus for the knee-jerk there might have been facilitation instead of depression. In fact, an earlier paper by Tuttle (1924) does show a facilitative influence of intellectual activity upon the knee-jerk. The latter reaction was elicited while the subject was engaged in such tasks as mental arithmetic, conversation, and intelligence tests, and the results show that such activities augment the reflex.

Travis (1926) has reported an instance of facilitation of a relatively simple function by intellectual work. The function measured was the threshold for sound. The subject engaged in arithmetical calculation or in reading of prose or poetry.   His finger was placed upon a key and he was directed to react whenever he heard any tones.   The majority of the subjects showed a decrease in threshold during all four of the mental tasks.   There are at least two possible explanations of this result.   The mental activity may have increased the general level of excitability of the nervous system.   Or the mental activity may have been sufficiently definite to prevent the subject from thinking about matters foreign to the experimental situation and yet not so engrossing as to interfere with the simple auditory reaction.

Real-life conditions of facilitation-distraction are more nearly approached by experiments in which there is a high degree of complexity in both the extraneous stimulus or activity and the activity whose efficiency is under consideration.   Morgan's investigation (1916) is the one most frequently cited from among the many in this general field.   The standard task at which Morgan's subjects worked was a kind of substitution test in which letters were translated into numbers or numbers into letters according to a code. Extraneous noises were provided by a variety of bells, buzzers, and phonograph records.   Periods of quiet were alternated with periods of noise.   Efficiency was measured in terms of both speed and accuracy, but only the former proved important.   In Figure 27 there are given the

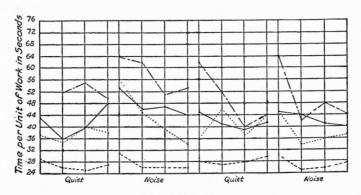

FIGURE 27

THE EFFECT OF NOISE UPON OUTPUT

[After J. J. B. Morgan (1916) and taken from A. T. Poffenberger's *Applied Psychology,* 1927, by permission of the publishers, D. Appleton & Co., New York.]

speed records of four subjects under the alternate conditions of quiet and noise.   There is a tendency upon the part of these subjects to slow their translations upon the onset of the noise.   Recovery from this retardation is rapid, however, and in the majority of instances speed at the end of a noise period is greater than that at the end of the preceding period of quiet.   Upon the introduction of the second period of quiet there is a marked distraction effect in the case of one subject and slight retardation in the others.   Jenkins has shown that quiet can act facilitatively and here is experimental evidence that quiet can also act to disrupt or retard activity.

Besides production records, Morgan obtained information about the "effort" exerted by his subjects. He did this by means of records of breathing, of pressure on the reaction keys utilized in making the substitutions, and by observations of tendencies toward articulation. He concludes from these facts that, though such an extraneous stimulation as noise may lead a subject to a higher level of productive efficiency, this is achieved only because, in overcoming the distraction in its early stages, the subject increases the intensity of his muscular reactions and indulges in articulation with consequent disturbances in breathing. All this would indicate that such facilitation as is brought about by an extraneous stimulus like noise is likely to be brought about at the cost of an increase in organic expenditure. In other words, we have here something a good deal more complicated than the simple type of facilitation that we obtain in reflex and simple voluntary reaction experiments where we add to the normal signal stimulus some other intellectually and emotionally neutral stimulus. The physiological costs of resistance to distraction have recently been examined by F. L. Harmon (1933). When noise was introduced into a period of mental work the energy expenditure was increased sometimes as much as 60 per cent or more. Harmon states, however, that because of the small energy normally expended in mental work even such an increase hardly has any far-reaching effects upon the general bodily economy.

That noises which we should expect to have a depressing effect on general efficiency do not always do so is further supported by the recent findings of Hovey (1928). Two groups of college students were used as subjects, an experimental group numbering 171 and a control group numbering 123. Six tests of Army Intelligence Examination Alpha, Form 8, were given both groups under normal conditions. The corresponding 6 tests of Form 7 were given under distraction to the experimental group and under normal conditions to the control group. The distractors were 7 bells and 5 buzzers, a 550-watt spotlight, a 90,000-volt rotary spark gap, phonograph, 2 adjustable organ pipes and 3 metal whistles, a 55-pound circular saw mounted on a wooden frame, a camera operated by a well-known photographer, and four students performing stunts. Several of these distractors were often used simultaneously, sometimes but one or two were used, and sometimes there were intervals of quiet. Subjects working in the presence of this medley of stimuli improved slightly less in going from Form 8 to Form 7 than did the students who worked at the latter without distraction. The difference was quite small, however, and it is Hovey's conclusion that "higher mental processes are comparatively unimpeded by a distraction." Obviously such a conclusion cannot be extended to higher mental processes in general and to distraction in general, but it certainly is interesting that such spectacular extraneous stimuli as these had such a small influence. An additional finding of Hovey was that the distractions had no more marked effect upon more intelligent workers than upon those of less intelligence. This, of course, runs counter to the frequently expressed opinion that highly intelligent individuals are un-usually susceptible to such disturbances as irrelevant noises. But perhaps Hovey would have obtained different results on this point if he had not worked with subjects who, being college students, were fairly homogeneous in intellect.

As another example of the influence of complex extraneous stimuli upon complex intellectual processes we shall cite the recent study by Ford (1929). The test activity was a combination of number perception and addition. The distracting stimulus was a loud phonograph giving a sup-posedly humorous monologue in a male voice or a Klaxon automobile horn placed about two feet from the subject's ear. Conditions of quiet and noise were alternated. The most conspicuous result obtained was an initial slowing of reaction-time at the beginning of the noise period and at the beginning of the quiet period. Thus, both noise and quiet acted as dis-tractors. The initial retardation is more marked at the beginning of the noise period. All this is quite in line with the results secured by Morgan. But Ford does not agree with Morgan in his interpretation of the recovery in efficiency which took place during the period of quiet or noise. Like Morgan, he found a disturbed condition marked by heightened muscle tone at the beginning of an altered stimulational setting, but he claims that the following improvement in efficiency is accompanied by a diminution of these symptoms of effort. If such is the case, the improvement in efficiency is hardly due to increased effort. It would, perhaps, be nearer the truth to say that the increased muscle tone or "effort" is simply a symptom of the fact that the individual is temporarily disorganized.

As indicators of general muscle tone or of neural diffusion, Ford used blood volume, breathing, and pressure of writing answers to the test problems. His method of recording the last is especially interesting:

> The strip of paper on which the answers were written was drawn on a spindle so as to run over a large tambour on which very stiff rubber had been stretched and then covered with a wooden plaque. The tambour thus constituted an indicator of writing pressure. The amount of deflection of the tambour was imperceptible to the Ss, only four of whom knew that the writing-pressure was being recorded. A tube extended through the wall from the writing-pressure board to the tambour recorder on the kymograph. The tension of the writ-ing-pressure board was calibrated by placing weights on the paper and noting the amount of deflection of the recording needle.

EFFORT

In the more complex experiments on facilitation-distraction which we have had under review we have come into repeated contact with the concept of effort. Altered stimulational setting has usually increased the amount of effort required to perform a certain task. It would, of course, be possible to define effort in such a way that no direct or objective ap-proach could be made to it, but experimentalists have recently been inclined to mean by effort the amount of neural and muscular activity going on during the performance of a given task. Thus, if one subject presses down hard in writing the answers to a problem he is solving, it is assumed that he is doing the work with comparatively great effort. If his breathing is disturbed or if he engages in an unusual amount of articulation, it may again be said that he is exerting considerable effort. For obvious reasons practically all of the symptoms of effort are muscular rather than neural, but because of the close correlation between the two types of activity it seems reasonable to consider effort a neuromuscular conception.

Fundamentally there are two experimental approaches to the general problem of effort. (1) We can set the subject to working under conditions which will presumably bring about alterations in effort and we can record such alterations as actually do occur. (2) We can attempt to control the amount of effort expended by the subject in order to note the influence of effort upon efficiency in a given task.

Such studies as those by Morgan and by Ford illustrate the first approach. The condition which it is assumed will alter effort is in this case some change in the stimulational setting of the work. We shall in this connection also cite the recent study by G. L. Freeman (1931). Freeman was not concerned with the introduction of such extraneous stimuli as noises. He was concerned rather with a comparison of the effort involved in work and rest, and during continuous work and interrupted work. A wide variety of tasks was used in the course of the research; there were arithmetical problems of several types, puzzle solving, opposites tests, writing numbers backward, and a number of other forms of mental activity. His conclusions are in essential agreement with those of Ford.

> Mental work involves an initial increase in muscular tension which decreases as the performance progresses toward completion . . . . A comparison of the tonus change during equivalent periods of interrupted and uninterrupted mental work showed a regular and notable increase in tension during the periods of interruption. . . .(p. 332)

Freeman employed a unique indicator of muscle tone, neural spread, or effort:

> The recording devise was, in essential, a lever serving to depress the patellar tendon. This lever was connected with an optical lever which magnified changes in tendon deformation approximately 500 times. A thread attached to the depressor lever at its point of contact with the tendon encircled a small cylinder (radius 2 mm.) carrying a convex mirror of suitable curvature (the optical lever). The thread was held under constant tension by a rubber band. The center of a 180 degree screen made of cardboard was placed 50 cm. away from the axis of the cylinder. The surface of this curved screen was covered with cross-section paper. After the depressor lever had been placed against the subject's tendon at the point of greatest deformability, the beam of light reflected by the optical lever was brought by a suitable adjustment to the center of the millimeter-scale. The experimenter simply read the level of muscular tension from the scale at stated intervals. [p. 311; see more fully Freeman (1931)]

There are a number of instances in the literature where an attempt has been made to record the results upon efficiency of various conditions of effort. Such studies as those of McDougall (1906) and of Newhall (1921, 1923) have shown that increased attention is capable of increasing the intensity of sensory processes. While attention and effort are not necessarily synonomous, they are certainly closely related. This seems especially likely in light of studies by Jacobson (1929) and Miller (1926) in which the enhancement of sensory intensity was clearly a function of muscular tension.

In 1927 Bills reported a systematic study of this problem utilizing better controls of effort than had hitherto been used. His subjects, during the performance of a variety of mental tasks, grasped a dynamometer in each hand. During the early stages of his investigation the dynamometer springs were stiff and the subjects were able to keep the grip only partially closed. Not only this, but the subject's grip varied during the course of an experimental sitting. These variations in muscular tension were recorded. Later it was found more feasible to weaken the dynamometers by about two-thirds. It was then possible for the subject to keep the grip closed throughout a work period. While this was not a guarantee of absolutely constant muscular tension, it did insure the maintenance of that tension at above a definite minimum. Since the experimental comparisons were between the conditions of work with tension and work without tension, this arrangement was quite satisfactory.

In his first two experiments Bills studied the influence of tension upon memorization and practice in memorization. Both nonsense and sense materials were employed. He found in general that tension was an aid to memorizing whether efficiency was measured in terms of learning time, savings, or recall. In the experiment with nonsense syllables he found that after the subject had practiced to the extent of learning 5 or 6 lists, the difference, as measured by recall or savings, was largely obliterated. In the second experiment, which utilized paired words, there was, however, an approximately constant difference in favor of tension throughout the experiment. There is evidence that learning time, in the first experiment, is aided more by tension after practice than in the early stages of the work.

Bills's later experiments which dealt with arithmetical work and letter-reading are somewhat more pertinent to the interests of the present chapter. In Experiment III the subjects added columns of 20 digits. Figure 28 gives work curves obtained under normal conditions and under tension, the criterion of efficiency being speed. It will be seen that the facilitative influence of tension is greater as the work proceeds. This suggests that the spread of muscular tension during the "fatigue" of everyday life may serve to protect against a more marked decrement. On the other hand, it might be said that the increase in muscular tension during continuous work is simply a sign of inexpertness at the task in question. Bills has interesting results on this point. The general level of efficiency under the two experimental conditions can be followed throughout 10 days of experimentation. From Figure 29 we see that, so far as speed

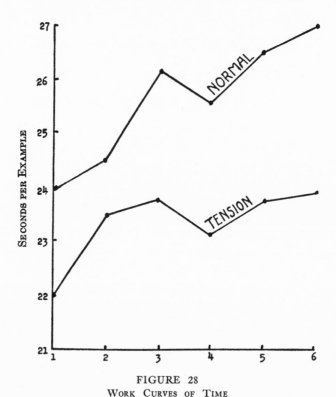

FIGURE 28
WORK CURVES OF TIME
Average number of seconds per example.
(From A. G. Bills's "The Influence of Muscular Tension on the Efficiency of
Mental Work," *Amer. J. Psychol.*, 1927.)

of work is concerned, the benefits of tension become greater with practice.
In the case of accuracy, the story is slightly different.   Tension has a
beneficial influence upon the amount of work done correctly, but the
difference between the tension and the normal condition in this regard is
not altered by practice or by "fatigue."

The findings of Experiment III receive some confirmation by those of
Experiment IV.   In the latter the work employed was letter-naming.
Five types of cards were employed, which contained combinations of 2,
4, 8, 16, and 24 letters.   Continuous reading of only the 2-letter type
was marked by pronounced decrement.   For that reason work curves for
that condition are given alone in Figure 30.   Here again we see not only
a superiority for tension but a superiority that grows more marked with
the continuation of the work.   In the reading involving more than two
letters there was a warming-up rather than a decrement in the work curves.
In Figure 31 we have work curves representing all of these latter types

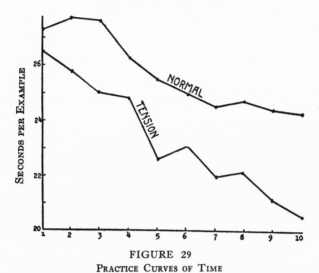

FIGURE 29

PRACTICE CURVES OF TIME

Average number of seconds per example.

(From A. G. Bills's "The Influence of Muscular Tension on the Efficiency of Mental Work," *Amer. J. Psychol.*, 1927.)

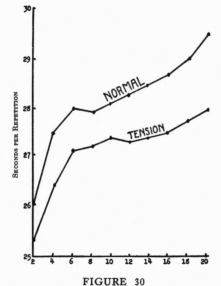

FIGURE 30

WORK CURVES OF TIME—TWO-LETTER COMBINATION

Average number of seconds per repetition.

(From A. G. Bills's "The Influence of Muscular Tension on the Efficiency of Mental Work," *Amer. J. Psychol.*, 1927.)

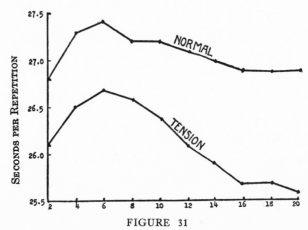

FIGURE 31

WORK CURVES OF TIME—AVERAGE OF ALL LETTER COMBINATIONS
(From A. G. Bills's "The Influence of Muscular Tension on the Efficiency of
Mental Work," *Amer. J. Psychol.*, 1927.)

of work. Again we find superiority for tension and again that superiority
increases with the progress of the work period. Thus there is the suggestion that the continuation of work gives an advantage to tension for
other reasons than simply because it is a protection against decrement.
If this is true we may assume that the advantage of tension has some
very general and fundamental basis.

In the present state of knowledge we are in a position to offer no more
than tentative interpretations of such findings as those of Bills. We must,
of course, be struck with a similarity between his findings and those in
connection with the facilitation of reflexes and simple voluntary reactions.
His condition of tension or effort was really one in which a proprioceptive
stimulation accompanied the performance of the essential task. If that
task had been a reflex or simple voluntary reaction we could have predicted directly from earlier results that there would be an increase in
speed and amplitude of movement. However, the performance in the
Bills experiment was intellectual. While this does not mean that no
movements were involved, it does mean that the reactions represented
highly complicated neural organizations. And, further, the organizations
were not stereotyped as might have been true if the tasks had been acts
of muscular skill. Indeed, the behavior was of distinctly a problem-solv-
ing order. Under these circumstances one feels a good deal of hesitation
about interpreting Bills's results in the fairly simple terms applicable to
reflexes and simple voluntary movements. In the latter cases, all that is
required is to show why we should expect an act performed under tension
or effort to be more highly energized than the same act performed under
normal conditions. But where the organization represented by an act is
complex and relatively fluid we should expect its efficiency to be less

affected by the sheer *amount* of cortical and muscular activity present at the time of action.

One explanation of Bills's results is in terms of the possibility that the higher the general level of excitement in the cortex, at least within the limits of this experiment, the more quickly and accurately will be the operation even of its more complex and fluid response patterns. Obviously this theory runs counter to the old doctrine of "drainage," but that need not trouble us too seriously.

Possibly a modification of the above hypothesis would be more relevant. Since all of the work studied by Bills involved some muscular movement, perhaps the general readiness for movement on the part of the subjects was relatively more important than one might suppose. And it may be supposed that the presence of a constant proprioceptive stimulation furnished by the squeeze of the hands on the dynamometers would bring about a fairly widespread increase in tension and, therefore, in readiness to act of the other muscle groups. This hypothesis is rendered somewhat more credible by the fact that the advantage of tension was greater when the criterion of efficiency was speed rather than accuracy.

A third hypothesis can be constructed along different lines. An outstanding characteristic of complex activities is that they are constantly open to conflict. They are more nicely balanced and are therefore more easily unbalanced. Now anything which would hold constant the world of extraneous stimuli while a subject is performing complicated intellectual work ought to prove an advantage to that work. Simple music might operate in this way (Diserens, 1926) and so might an established proprioceptive set. It may be that the main difference between the tension and the normal condition is not due so much to the higher level of neuromuscular activity represented by the tension as to the greater constancy of the proprioceptive afferency during work under fixed tension.

BIBLIOGRAPHY

ARAI, T. 1912. Mental fatigue. *Teach. Coll. Contrib. Educ.*, No. 54. Pp. 115.

ASH, I. E. 1914. Fatigue and its effects upon control. *Arch. Psychol.*, **4**, No. 31. Pp. 61.

BASS, M. J. 1931. Differentiation of the hypnotic trance from normal sleep. *J. Exper. Psychol.*, **14**, 382-399.

BAST, T. H., & LOEVENHART, A. S. 1927. Studies in exhaustion due to lack of sleep. *Amer. J. Physiol.*, **82**, 121-126.

BECKER, F. C., & OLSEN, O. 1914. Metabolism during mental work. *Skand. Arch. f. Physiol.*, **31**, 81-197.

BENEDICT, F. G., & BENEDICT, C. G. 1930. The energy requirements of intense mental effort. *Proc. Nat. Acad. Sci.*, **16**, 438-443.

BENEDICT, F. G., & CARPENTER, T. M. 1909. The influence of muscular and mental work on metabolism and the efficiency of the human body as a machine. Washington, D. C.: Govt. Print. Office. Pp. 100.

BENEDICT, F. G., & CATHCART, E. P. 1913. Muscular work: a metabolic study with special reference to the efficiency of the human body as a machine. Washington, D. C.: Carnegie Instit. Washington. Pp. vii+176.

BENEDICT, F. G., & MURSCHHAUSER, H. 1915. Physiology: energy transformations during horizontal walking. *Proc. Nat. Acad. Sci.,* **1**, 597-600.

BILLS, A. G. 1927. The influence of muscular tension on the efficiency of mental work. *Amer. J. Psychol.,* **38**, 227-251.

————. 1931a. Blocking: a new principle of mental fatigue. *Psychol. Bull.,* **28**, 208-209.

————. 1931b. Blocking: a new principle of mental fatigue. *Amer. J. Psychol.,* **43**, 230-245.

BILLS, A. G., & BROWN, C. 1929. The quantitative set. *J. Exper. Psychol.,* **12**, 301-323.

BILLS, A. G., & MCTEER, W. 1932. Transfer of fatigue and identical elements. *J. Exper. Psychol.,* **15**, 23-36.

BLISS, C. B. 1893. Investigations in reaction time and attention. *Stud. Yale Psychol. Lab.,* **1**, 1-55.

BOWDITCH, H. P., & WARREN, J. W. 1890. The kneejerk and its physiological modifications. *J. Physiol.,* **11**, 25-64.

BREITWEISER, J. V. 1911. Attention and movement in reaction times. *Arch. Psychol.,* **2**, No. 18. Pp. 49.

BURTT, H. E., & TUTTLE, W. W. 1925. The patellar tendon reflex and affective tone. *Amer. J. Psychol.,* **36**, 553-561.

CHAPMAN, J. C., & NOLAN, W. J. 1916. Spurt in a simple mental function. *Amer. J. Psychol.,* **27**, 256-260.

CRAWLEY, S. L. 1926. An experimental investigation of recovery from work. *Arch. Psychol.,* **13**, No. 85. Pp. 66.

DISERENS, C. M. 1926. The influence of music on behavior. Princeton, N. J.: Princeton Univ. Press. Pp. 224.

DODGE, R. 1913a. The protective wink reflex. *Amer. J. Psychol.,* **24**, 1-7.

————. 1913b. Mental work. A study in psychodynamics. *Psychol. Rev.,* **20**, 1-42.

————. 1917. The laws of relative fatigue. *Psychol. Rev.,* **24**, 89-113.

————. 1923. Habituation to rotation. *J. Exper. Psychol.,* **6**, 1-34.

————. 1927. A note on Professor Thorndike's experiment. *Psychol. Rev.,* **34**, 237-240.

————. 1931. Conditions and consequences of human variability. New Haven, Conn.: Yale Univ. Press. Pp. 162.

DUNLAP, K. 1928. A revision of the fundamental law of habit formation. *Science,* **67**, 360-362.

FEARING, F. S. 1931. Reflex action. Baltimore, Md.: Williams & Wilkins. Pp. 350.

FLÜGEL, J. C. 1928. Practice, fatigue, and oscillation. *Brit. J. Psychol., Monog. Suppl.,* **13**, 1-20.

FORD, A. 1929. Attention-automatization: an investigation of the transitional nature of mind. *Amer. J. Psychol.,* **41**, 1-32.

FREEMAN, G. L. 1930. Changes in tonus during interrupted and completed mental work. *J. Gen. Psychol.,* **4**, 309-334.

————. 1931. The spread of neuromuscular activity during mental work. *J. Gen. Psychol.,* **5**, 479-493.

FREEMAN, G. L., & LINDLEY, S. B. 1931. Two neuro-muscular indices of mental fatigue. *J. Exper. Psychol.,* **14**, 567-605.

FROEBERG, S. 1907. The relation between magnitude of stimulus and the time of reaction. *Arch. Psychol.,* **1**, No. 8. Pp. 38.

GARRETT, H. E. 1922. A study of the relation of accuracy to speed. *Arch. Psychol.,* **8**, No. 58. Pp. 104.

GLAZE, J. A. 1930. The effect of practice on fatigue. *Amer. J. Psychol.,* **42,** 628-630.

HARMON, F. L. 1933. The effects of noise upon certain psychological and physiological processes. *Arch. Psychol.,* **23,** No. 147. Pp. 81.

HERON, W. T. 1928. The warming-up effect in learning nonsense syllables. *J. Genet. Psychol.,* **35,** 219-227.

HERZ, F. 1923. Selbstbeobachtung über freiwillige Schlafentziehung. *Pflüg. Arch. f. d. ges. Physiol.,* **200,** 429-442.

HILGARD, E. R. 1931. Reinforcement and inhibition of eyelid reflexes to light and sound. *Science,* **74,** 638.

HILL, A. V. 1927. Living machinery. New York: Harcourt, Brace. Pp. 327.

HOVEY, H. B. 1928. Effects of general distraction on the higher thought processes. *Amer. J. Psychol.,* **40,** 585-591.

HOWELL, W. H. 1930. A textbook of physiology. (11th ed.) Philadelphia: Saunders. Pp. 1099.

JACOBSON, E. 1929. Progressive relaxation. Chicago: Univ. Chicago Press. Pp. xiii + 429.

JENKINS, T. N. 1926. Faciliation and inhibition. *Arch. Psychol.,* **14,** No. 86. Pp. 56.

JOHNSON, H. M. 1923. Reaction time measurements. *Psychol. Bull.,* **20,** 562-589.

JOHNSON, H. M., SWAN, T. H., & WEIGAND, G. E. 1926. Sleep. *Psychol. Bull.,* **23,** 482-502.

KLEITMAN, N. 1923. Studies on the physiology of sleep: effects of prolonged sleeplessness in man. *Amer. J. Physiol.,* **66,** 67-92.

―――. 1929. Sleep. *Physiol. Revs.,* **9,** 624-665.

KÖHLER, W. 1929. Gestalt psychology. New York: Liveright. Pp. x+403. London: Bell. Pp. 312.

LADD, G. T., & WOODWORTH, R. S. 1911. Elements of physiological psychology. (Rev. ed.) New York: Scribner's. Pp. xiv + 704.

LANIER, L. H. 1931. Speed of reaction at different neural levels. *Psychol. Bull.,* **38,** 597-598.

LASLETT, H. R. 1928. Experiments on the effects of loss of sleep. *J. Exper. Psychol.,* **11,** 370-396.

LEE, F. S. 1907. The cause of treppe. *Amer. J. Physiol.,* **18,** 267-282.

LEE, M. A. M., & KLEITMAN, N. 1923. Studies in the physiology of sleep. *Amer. J. Physiol.,* **67,** 141-151.

LOMBARD, W. P. 1887. The variations of the normal kneejerk and their relation to the activity of the central nervous system. *Amer. J. Psychol.,* **1,** 2-71.

MAGGIORA, A. 1890. Les lois de la fatigue étudiées dans les muscles de l'homme. *Arch. ital. de biol.,* **13,** 187-241.

MALINOWSKI, B. 1927. Sex and repression in savage society. New York: Harcourt, Brace. Pp. xiv+285.

MANACEÏNE, M. DE. 1897. Sleep, its physiology, pathology, hygiene, and psychology. (Trans. by E. Jaubert.) London: Scott. Pp. vii + 341.

MANZER, C. W. 1927. An experimental investigation of rest pauses. *Arch. Psychol.,* **14,** No. 90. Pp. 84.

McDOUGALL, W. 1906. Physiological factors of the attention process. *Mind,* **15,** 329-359.

MILES, W. R. 1931. Correlation of reaction and coordination speed with age in adults. *Amer. J. Psychol.,* **43,** 377-391.

MILLER, M. 1926. Changes in the response to electric shock by varying muscular conditions. *J. Exper. Psychol.,* **9,** 26-44.

MITCHELL, S. W., & LEWIS, M. J. 1886. Physiological studies of the knee-jerk and of the reactions of muscles under mechanical and other excitants. *Philadelphia Med. News,* **48,** 169-173.

MORGAN, J. J. B. 1916. The overcoming of distractions and other resistances. *Arch. Psychol.,* **5,** No. 35. Pp. 84.

MOSSO, A. 1904. Fatigue. (Trans. by M. Drummond and W. B. Drummond.) New York: Putnam. Pp. xiv + 334.

MUSCIO, B. 1921. Is a fatigue test possible? *Brit. J. Psychol.,* **12,** 31-46.

NEWHALL, S. M. 1921. The modification of intensity of sensation by attention. *J. Exper. Psychol.,* **4,** 222-243.

————. 1923. Effects of attention on the intensity of cutaneous pressure and on visual brightness. *Arch. Psychol.,* **9,** No. 61. Pp. 75.

PAINTER, W. S. 1916. Efficiency in mental multiplication under extreme fatigue. *J. Educ. Psychol.,* **7,** 23-51.

PATRICK, G. T. W., & GILBERT, J. A. 1896. On the effect of loss of sleep. *Psychol. Rev.,* **3,** 469-483.

PEAK, H. 1931. Modification of the lid-reflex by voluntarily induced sets. *Psychol. Monog.,* **42,** No. 188. Pp. 68.

PIÉRON, H. 1913. Le problème physiologique du sommeil. Paris: Masson. Pp. xv + 520.

POFFENBERGER, A. T. 1912. Reaction time to retinal stimulation. *Arch. Psychol.,* **3,** No. 23. Pp. iii+73.

————. 1927a. Applied psychology. New York: Appleton. Pp. 575.

————. 1927b. The effects of continuous mental work. *Amer. J. Psychol.,* **39,** 283-296.

————. 1928. The effects of continuous work upon output and feelings. *J. Appl. Psychol.,* **12,** 459-467.

RANKE, J. 1865. Tetanus. Leipzig: Engelmann. Pp. viii + 468.

ROBINSON, E. S. 1926. Principles of work decrement. *Psychol. Rev.,* **33,** 123-134.

ROBINSON, E. S., & BILLS, A. G. 1926. Two factors in the work decrement. *J. Exper. Psychol.,* **9,** 415-443.

ROBINSON, E. S., & HERMANN, S. O. 1922. Effects of loss of sleep. *J. Exper. Psychol.,* **5,** 19-32.

ROBINSON, E. S., & HERON, W. T. 1924. The warming-up effect. *J. Exper. Psychol.,* **7,** 81-97.

ROBINSON, E. S., & ROBINSON, F. R. 1922. Effects of loss of sleep: II. *J. Exper. Psychol.,* **5,** 93-100.

————. 1932. Practice and the work decrement. *Amer. J. Psychol.,* **44,** 547-551.

ROBINSON, M. F. 1931. Is the refractory phase theory adequate to explain mental fatigue? *Psychol. Rev.,* **38,** 229-241.

ROSANOFF, A. J., *et al.* 1927. Manual of psychiatry. (6th ed.) New York: Wiley. Pp. xvi + 697.

ROUNDS, G. H., & POFFENBERGER, A. T. 1931. The measurement of implicit speech reactions. *Amer. J. Psychol.,* **43,** 606-612.

SCHUBERT, H. J. P. 1932. Energy cost measurements on the curve of work. *Arch. Psychol.,* **21,** No. 139. Pp. 62.

SCOTT, E. L. 1918. The present status of our knowledge of fatigue products. *Pub. Health Reps.,* **33,** 605-611. (Reprint No. 465.)

SMITH, M. 1915-17. A contribution to the study of sleep. *Brit. J. Psychol.,* **8,** 327-350.

TELFORD, C. W. 1931. The refractory phase of voluntary and associative responses. *J. Exper. Psychol.,* **14,** 1-36.

THORNDIKE, E. L. 1914. Educational psychology: Vol. 3. Mental work and fatigue and individual differences and their causes. New York: Teach. Coll., Columbia Univ. Pp. xii + 442.

———. 1917. The curve of work and the curve of satisfyingness. *J. Appl. Psychol.*, 1, 265-267.

———. 1927. The refractory period in associative processes. *Psychol. Rev.*, 34, 234-236.

———. 1931. Human learning. New York: Century. Pp. 200.

TODD, J. W. 1912. Reaction to multiple stimuli. *Arch. Psychol.*, 3, No. 25. Pp. iii + 65.

TRAVIS, L. E. 1926. Changes in auditory acuity during the performance of certain mental tasks. *Amer. J. Psychol.*, 37, 139-142.

TRAVIS, L. E., & TUTTLE, W. W. 1928. Periodic fluctuations in the extent of the kneejerk and the achilles jerk. *J. Exper. Psychol.*, 11, 252-257.

TUTTLE, W. W. 1924. The effect of attention or mental activity on the patellar tendon reflex. *J. Exper. Psychol.*, 7, 401-419.

VERWORN, M. 1913. Irritability; a physiological analysis of the general effect of stimuli in living substances. New Haven, Conn.: Yale Univ. Press. Pp. xii + 264.

WATSON, J. B. 1919. Psychology from the standpoint of a behaviorist. Philadelphia: Lippincott. Pp. ix + 429.

WEINLAND, J. D. 1927. Variability of performance in the curve of work. *Arch. Psychol.*, 14, No. 87. Pp. 68.

WELLS, F. L. 1908. Normal performance in the tapping test. *Amer. J. Psychol.*, 19, 437-483.

WOODROW, H. 1914. The measurement of attention. *Psychol. Monog.*, 17, No. 76. Pp. 158.

WOODWORTH, R. S., & POFFENBERGER, A. T. 1920. Textbook of experimental psychology. (Mimeographed ed.)

WUNDT, W. 1903. Physiological psychology. (5th ed.) Leipzig: Engelmann. Pp. ix + 796.

YERKES, R. M. 1904. Inhibition and reinforcement of reaction in the frog *Rana clamitans*. *J. Comp. Neur. & Psychol.*, 14, 124-137.

———. 1905. Bahnung und Hemmung der Reactionen auf tactile Reize durch akustische Reize beim Frosche. *Pflüg. Arch. f. d. ges. Physiol.*, 107, 207-237.

YOCHELSON, S. 1930. Effects of rest-pauses on work decrement. Ph.D. thesis, Yale Univ.

ZWAARDEMAKER, H., & LANS, L. J. 1900. Ueber ein Studium relativer Unerregbarkeit als Ursache des intermitterenden Charakters des Lidschlagreflexes. *Zentbl. f. Physiol.*, 13, 325-329.

BIBLIOGRAPHIES

ARAI, T. 1912. Mental fatigue. *Teach. Coll. Contrib. Educ.*, No. 54. Pp. 115. (55 references)

ASH, I. E. 1914. Fatigue and its effects upon control. *Arch. Psychol.*, 4, No. 31. Pp. 61. (37 references)

BILLS, A. G. 1927. Inhibition and facilitation. *Psychol. Bull.*, 24, 473-487. (57 references)

———. 1929. Mental work. *Psychol. Bull.*, 26, 499-526. (94 references)

DOCKERAY, F. C. 1915. The effects of physical fatigue on mental efficiency. *Kans. Univ. Sci. Bull.*, 9, 197-243. (50 references)

———. 1920. Work, fatigue, and inhibition. *Psychol. Bull.*, 17, 322-330. (44 references)

GILLESPIE, R. D. 1924. The present day physiological basis of the clinical study of fatigue. *J. Neur. & Psychopath.*, **5**, 103-114. (42 references)

JOHNSON, H. M. 1923. Reaction time measurements. *Psychol. Bull.*, **20**, 562-589. (46 references)

JOHNSON, H. M., SWAN, T. H., & WEIGAND, G. E. 1926. Sleep. *Psychol. Bull.*, **23**, 482-503. (26 references)

KLEITMAN, N. 1929. Sleep. *Physiol. Revs.*, **9**, 624-665. (137 references.)

OFFNER, M. 1911. Mental fatigue. Baltimore, Md.: Warwick & York. Pp. viii + 133. (References, pp. 122-129)

ROBINSON, E. S. 1921. Mental work. *Psychol. Bull.*, **18**, 456-482. (108 references)

SPENCER, L. T. 1927. The curve of continuous work and related phenomena. *Psychol. Bull.*, **24**, 467-472. (38 references)

STRONG, E. K., JR. 1913. Fatigue, work, and inhibition. *Psychol. Bull.*, **10**, 444-450. (26 references)

————. 1914. Fatigue, work, and inhibition. *Psychol. Bull.*, **11**, 412-417. (42 references)

————. 1915. Fatigue, work, and inhibition. *Psychol. Bull.*, **12**, 416-419. (17 references)

————. 1916. Fatigue, work, and inhibition. *Psychol. Bull.*, **13**, 430-433. (12 references)

THORNDIKE, E. L. 1914. Educational psychology: Vol. 3. Mental work and fatigue and individual differences and their causes. New York: Teach. Coll., Columbia Univ. Pp. xii + 442. (References, pp. 434-442)

WELLS, F. L. 1913. Practice and the work curve. *Amer. J. Psychol.*, **24**, 35-51. (14 references)

YOAKUM, C. S. 1909. An experimental study of fatigue. *Psychol. Rev., Monog. Suppl.*, **11**, No. 46. Pp. vi + 131. (108 references)